Elementary Algebra

with Basic Mathematics

Elementary Algebra

with Basic Mathematics

Richard N. Aufmann
Palomar College, California

Vernon C. Barker
Palomar College, California

Joanne S. Lockwood
Plymouth State College, New Hampshire

Houghton Mifflin Company   Boston

Dallas   Geneva, Illinois   Palo Alto   Princeton, New Jersey

Cover image created and photographed by Montes DeOza/Light Images.

IBM is a registered trademark of International Business Machines Corporation. Apple is a registered trademark of Apple Computer, Inc.

Printed in the U.S.A.

Library of Congress Catalog Card Number: 88-83265

ISBN Numbers:
Text: 0-395-48633-5
Instructor's Annotated Edition: 0-395-48634-3
Solutions Manual: 0-395-48635-1
Instructor's Manual with Testing Program: 0-395-48636-X
Instructor's Computerized Test Generator (IBM): 0-395-51035-X
Instructor's Computerized Test Generator (Apple): 0-395-51034-1
Computer Tutor™ (IBM & Apple): 0-395-50745-6
Student Disk (IBM & Apple): 0-395-50747-2

ABCDEFGHIJ-B-9543210-898

Contents

x Contents

Preface

Elementary Algebra with Basic Mathematics provides mathematically sound and comprehensive coverage of the basic computational skills and an introduction to algebra. Chapters 1 and 2 provide a solid review of basic mathematics. Chapters 3–11 cover all the essential topics of a typical introductory algebra course. Chapter 12, *Applied Geometry*, uses the skills covered in Chapters 1–11 to solve problems in geometry. The text has been specifically developed not only for the traditional college student who needs to review basic mathematical competencies, but also for the non-traditional student whose mathematical proficiency may have declined during years away from formal schooling.

Features

REINFORCEMENT OF SKILLS

Instructors have long recognized the need for a text that requires the student to use a skill as it is being taught. *Elementary Algebra with Basic Mathematics* uses an interactive technique that meets this need. Each chapter is divided into sections, each section is divided into objectives, and every objective contains one or more sets of matched-pair examples. The first example in each set is worked out; the second example is not. By solving this second problem, the student gains immediate practice of newly learned skills and concepts. The complete worked-out solutions to these examples are provided in the answer section at the end of the book, so students can immediately check their answers. In addition, skills are reinforced through the exercise sets, Review/Tests, and Cumulative Review/Tests at the end of each chapter. A final exam is a test of the major skills presented in the text.

PROBLEM-SOLVING STRATEGIES

Elementary Algebra with Basic Mathematics features a carefully developed approach to problem solving that emphasizes developing strategies to solve problems. For each type of word problem contained in the text, the student is prompted to use a "strategy step" before performing the actual manipulation of numbers and variables. By developing problem-solving strategies, the student will know better how to analyze and solve word problems.

OBJECTIVE REFERENCED

Each chapter begins with a list of the learning objectives included within the sections of that chapter. Sections, exercises, Review/Tests, Cumulative Review/Tests, and the final exam are all objective referenced.

CALCULATOR AND COMPUTER ENRICHMENT TOPICS

Each chapter also contains optional calculator or computer enrichment topics. Calculator topics provide the student with valuable key-stroking instructions and practice in using a hand-held calculator. Computer topics correspond directly to the programs on the student disk.

Supplements for the Student

Two computerized study aids, the Computer Tutor and the Student Disk, accompany *Elementary Algebra with Basic Mathematics*.

THE COMPUTER TUTOR™

The Computer Tutor™ is an interactive instructional microcomputer program for student use. Each learning objective in the text is supported by a lesson on the Computer Tutor™. As a reminder of this, a reference appears at the start of each objective. Lessons on the tutor provide additional instruction and practice and can be used in several ways: (1) to cover material the student missed because of absence from class; (2) to repeat instruction on the skill or concept that the student has not yet mastered; or (3) to review material in preparation for examinations. This tutorial program is available for both the Apple II family of computers and the IBM PC or compatible computers.

STUDENT DISK

The Student Disk contains a number of computational and drill-and-practice programs that correspond to selected Calculator and Computer Enrichment Topics in the text. These programs are available for both the Apple II family of computers and the IBM PC or compatible computers.

Supplements for the Instructor

Elementary Algebra with Basic Mathematics has an unusually complete set of teaching aids for the instructor.

INSTRUCTOR'S ANNOTATED EDITION

The Instructor's Annotated Edition is an exact replica of the student text except that the answers to all of the exercises are printed in color next to the problems.

SOLUTIONS MANUAL

The Solutions Manual contains worked-out solutions for all end-of-section exercise sets, review tests, cumulative reviews, and the final exam.

INSTRUCTOR'S MANUAL WITH TESTING PROGRAM

The Instructor's Manual contains the printed testing program, which is the first of three sources of testing material available to users of *Elementary Algebra with Basic Mathematics*. Two printed tests, one free response and one multiple choice, are provided for each chapter, as are cumulative and final exams. In addition, the Instructor's Manual includes documentation for all the software ancillaries—the Student Disk, Computer Tutor™, and Instructor's Computerized Test Generator.

INSTRUCTOR'S COMPUTERIZED TEST GENERATOR

The Instructor's Computerized Test Generator is the second source of testing material for use with *Elementary Algebra with Basic Mathematics*. The database contains more than 1,500 test items. These questions are unique to the test generator and do not repeat items provided in the Instructor's Manual testing program. Organized according to the keyed objectives in the text, the Test Generator is designed to produce an unlimited number of tests for each chapter of the text, including cumulative tests and final exams. It is available for both the Apple II family of computers and the IBM PC or compatible computers.

PRINTED TEST BANK

The Printed Test Bank, the third component of the testing material, is a printout of all items in the Instructor's Computerized Test Generator. Instructors using the Test Generator can use the test bank to select specific items from the database. Instructors who do not have access to a computer can use the test bank to select items to be included on a test being prepared by hand.

GPA: GRADE PERFORMANCE ANALYZER

GPA is a microcomputer grading and record-keeping program available for use on the IBM PC and Apple II.

Acknowledgments

The authors would like to thank the people who have reviewed this manuscript and provided many valuable suggestions:

Patricia Confort
Roger Williams College

Bob Denton
Orange Coast College

Thomas Fournelle
University of Wisconsin–Parkside

Frank Gunnip
Macomb Community College

Miriam Keesey
San Diego State University

William Lapowsky
Laney College

Edward Leinse
Olive-Harvey City College of Chicago

Jean Millen
DeKalb Community College

Sylvester Roebuck
Olive-Harvey City College of Chicago

Elementary Algebra

with Basic Mathematics

chapter 1 Whole Numbers

Objectives

1.1A   To identify the order relation between two numbers

1.1B   To write whole numbers in expanded form

1.1C   To round a whole number to a given place value

1.2A   To add whole numbers

1.2B   To subtract whole numbers

1.3A   To multiply whole numbers

1.3B   To simplify expressions containing exponents

1.3C   To divide whole numbers

1.3D   To factor numbers

1.3E   To solve application problems

1.4A   To find the prime factorization of a number

1.4B   To find the least common multiple (LCM)

1.4C   To find the greatest common factor (GCF)

1.4D   To use the Order of Operations Agreement to simplify expressions

Section 1 Introduction to Whole Numbers

Objective A To identify the order relation between two numbers

Reference for Computer Tutor™

The **whole numbers** are 0, 1, 2, 3, 4, 5, 6, 7, 8, 9, 10, 11, 12, 13, 14, . . .

The three dots mean that the list continues on and on, and that there is no largest whole number.

Just as distances are associated with the markings on the edge of a ruler, the whole numbers can be associated with points on a line. This line is called the **number line.**

The Number Line

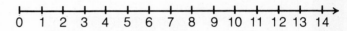

The **graph** of a whole number is shown by placing a heavy dot on the number line directly above the number.

The graph of 7 on the number line

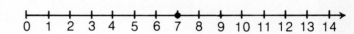

The number line can be used to order whole numbers. A number that appears to the left of a given number is **less than** the given number. The symbol for "is less than" is <. A number that appears to the right of a given number is **greater than** the given number. The symbol for "is greater than" is >.

Four is less than seven.
4 < 7

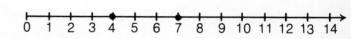

Twelve is greater than seven.
12 > 7

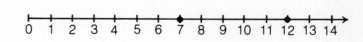

Copyright © 1989 HMCo

Example 1	Graph 11 on the number line.	**Example 2**	Graph 9 on the number line.
Solution		**Your solution**	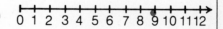

Example 3 Place the correct symbol, < or >, between the two numbers.
a. 39   24
b. 0   51

Solution a. 39 > 24
b. 0 < 51

Example 4 Place the correct symbol, < or >, between the two numbers.
a. 45   29
b. 27   0

Your solution a. 45 > 29
b. 27 > 0

Solution on p. A9

| Objective B | To write whole numbers in expanded form |

Reference for
Computer
Tutor™

When a whole number is written using the digits 0, 1, 2, 3, 4, 5, 6, 7, 8, and 9, it is said to be in **standard form.** The position of each digit in the number determines the digit's **place value.** The diagram below shows a **place-value chart** naming the first twelve place values. The number 37,462 is in standard form and has been entered in the chart.

In the number 37,462, the position of the digit "3" determines that its place value is ten-thousands.

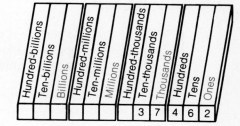

The whole number 37,462 can be written in **expanded form** as

30,000 + 7000 + 400 + 60 + 2

The place-value chart can be used to find the expanded form of a number.

3 Ten-thousands	+	7 Thousands	+	4 Hundreds	+	6 Tens	+	2 Ones
30,000	+	7000	+	400	+	60	+	2

Write the number 420,806 in expanded form.

Notice the effect of having zeros in the number.

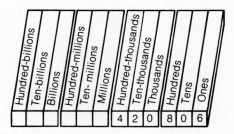

4 Hundred-thousands	+	2 Ten-thousands	+	0 Thousands	+	8 Hundreds	+	0 Tens	+	6 Ones
400,000	+	20,000	+	0	+	800	+	0	+	6

or simply 400,000 + 20,000 + 800 + 6

Example 5	Write 709,542 in expanded form.	**Example 6**	Write 109,207 in expanded form.
Solution	700,000 + 9000 + 500 + 40 + 2	**Your solution**	100,000 + 9000 + 200 + 7

Objective C

To round a whole number to a given place value

Reference for Computer Tutor™

When the distance to the moon is given as 240,000 miles, the number represents an approximation to the true distance. Giving an approximate value for an exact number is called **rounding.** A number is always rounded to a given place value.

37 is closer to 40 than it is to 30. 37 rounded to the nearest ten is 40.

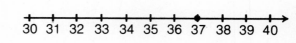

3673 rounded to the nearest ten is 3670. 3673 rounded to the nearest hundred is 3700.

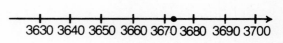

A whole number is rounded to a given place value without using the number line by looking at the first digit to the right of the given place value.

If the digit to the right of the given place value is less than 5, that digit and all digits to the right are replaced by zeros.

Round 13,834 to the nearest hundred.

```
        ┌── Given place value
13,834
          └── 3 < 5
```

13,834 rounded to the nearest hundred is 13,800.

If the digit to the right of the given place value is greater than or equal to 5, increase the digit in the given place value by 1 and replace all other digits to the right by zeros.

Round 386,217 to the nearest ten-thousand.

```
        ┌── Given place value
386,217
         └── 6 > 5
```

386,217 rounded to the nearest ten-thousand is 390,000.

Example 7	Round 525,453 to the nearest ten-thousand.	**Example 8**	Round 368,492 to the nearest ten-thousand.
Solution	┌── Given place value 525,453 └── 5 = 5 525,453 rounded to the nearest ten-thousand is 530,000.	**Your solution**	370,000

1.1A Exercises

Graph the number on the number line.

1. 3

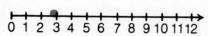

2. 5

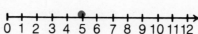

3. 8

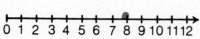

4. 10

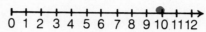

5. 1

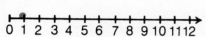

6. 4

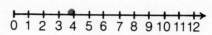

7. 6

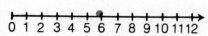

8. 0

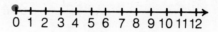

Place the correct symbol, < or >, between the two numbers.

9. 37 < 49

10. 58 > 21

11. 101 > 87

12. 16 > 5

13. 245 > 158

14. 2701 > 2071

15. 3521 > 3512

16. 4067 < 4076

17. 0 < 45

18. 107 > 0

19. 815 < 928

20. 297 > 229

21. 2400 < 24,000

22. 4650 < 46,000

23. 7003 < 7020

24. 36,010 > 36,001

25. 18,020 > 18,002

26. 55,900 < 59,500

1.1B Exercises

Write the number in expanded form.

27. 5287
$5000 + 200 + 80 + 7$

28. 6295
$6000 + 200 + 90 + 5$

29. 58,943
$50,000 + 8000 + 900 + 40 + 3$

30. 453,921
$400,000 + 50,000 + 3000 + 900 + 20 + 1$

31. 217,586
$200,000 + 10,000 + 7000 + 500 + 80 + 6$

32. 4053
$4000 + 50 + 3$

33. 50,943
$50,000 + 900 + 40 + 3$

34. 80,492
$80,000 + 400 + 90 + 2$

35. 200,583
$200,000 + 500 + 80 + 3$

36. 301,809
$300,000 + 1000 + 800 + 9$

37. 403,705
$400,000 + 3000 + 700 + 5$

38. 3,000,642
$3,000,000 + 600 + 40 + 2$

39. 93,277
$90,000 + 3000 + 200 + 70 + 7$

40. 8040
$8000 + 40$

41. 35,006
$30,000 + 5000 + 6$

42. 8,650,000
$8,000,000 + 600,000 + 50,000$

1.1C Exercises

Round the number to the given place value.

43. 926   Tens
930

44. 845   Tens
850

45. 1439   Hundreds
1400

46. 3973   Hundreds
4000

47. 35,682   Hundreds
35,700

48. 61,590   Hundreds
61,600

49. 7238   Thousands
7000

50. 7609   Thousands
8000

51. 43,607   Thousands
44,000

52. 52,715   Thousands
53,000

53. 647,989   Ten-thousands
650,000

54. 253,678   Ten-thousands
250,000

Section 2   Addition and Subtraction of Whole Numbers

Objective A   To add whole numbers

Reference for
Computer
Tutor™

Addition is the process of finding the total of two or more numbers.

By counting, we see that the total of $3 and $4 is $7.

$3   + $4   = $7

Addend   Addend   Sum

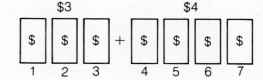

Addition can be illustrated on the number line by using arrows to represent the addends. The size or magnitude of a number can be represented on the number line by an arrow.

The number 3 can be represented anywhere on the number line by an arrow that is 3 units in length.

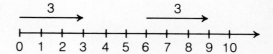

To add on the number line, place the arrows representing the addends head to tail, with the first arrow starting at zero. The sum is represented by an arrow starting at zero and stopping at the tip of the last arrow.

7 (sum)

3(addend) 4(addend)

```
+---+---+---+---+---+---+---+---+---+---+--->
0   1   2   3   4   5   6   7   8   9  10
```

3 + 4 = 7

More than two numbers can be added on the number line.

9

3   2   4

```
+---+---+---+---+---+---+---+---+---+---+--->
0   1   2   3   4   5   6   7   8   9  10
```

3 + 2 + 4 = 9

Some special properties of addition which are used frequently are given below.

Addition Property of Zero Zero added to a number does not change the number.	4 + 0 = 4 0 + 7 = 7

Commutative Property of Addition Two numbers can be added in either order. The sum will be the same.	4 + 8 = 8 + 4 12 = 12

Associative Property of Addition Grouping the addition in any order gives the same result. The parentheses are grouping symbols and have the meaning "do the operations inside the parentheses first."	(4 + 2) + 3 = 4 + (2 + 3) 6 + 3 = 4 + 5 9 = 9

The number line is not useful for adding large numbers. The basic addition facts for adding one digit to one digit are listed on page A2 in the Appendix for your review. Addition of larger numbers requires the repeated use of the basic addition facts.

To add large numbers, begin by arranging the numbers vertically, keeping the digits of the same place value in the same column.

Add: 321 + 6472

Add the digits in each column.

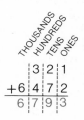

When the sum of the digits in a column exceeds 9, the addition will involve "carrying."

Add: 487 + 369

Add the ones' column.
7 + 9 = 16 (1 ten + 6 ones).
Write the 6 in the ones' column and
carry the 1 ten to the tens' column.

```
    HUNDREDS
      TENS
       ONES
    1
  4 8 7
 +3 6 9
      6
```

Add the tens' column.
1 + 8 + 6 = 15 (1 hundred + 5 tens).
Write the 5 in the tens' column and
carry the 1 hundred to the hundreds' column.

```
  1 1
  4 8 7
 +3 6 9
    5 6
```

Add the hundreds' column.
1 + 4 + 3 = 8 (8 hundreds).
Write the 8 in the hundreds' column.

```
  1 1
  4 8 7
 +3 6 9
  8 5 6
```

Example 1   Add: 4205 + 72,103

Solution
```
  4 2 0 5
+7 2 1 0 3
  7 6 3 0 8
```

Example 2   Add: 3508 + 92,170

Your solution   95,678

Example 3   Add: 131 + 2135 + 3123 + 510

Solution
```
    1 3 1
    2 1 3 5
    3 1 2 3
+     5 1 0
    5 8 9 9
```

Example 4   Add: 102 + 7351 + 1024 + 410

Your solution   8887

Example 5   Add: 89 + 36 + 98

Solution
```
   2
  89
  36
+ 98
 223
```

Example 6   Add: 95 + 88 + 67

Your solution   250

Example 7   Add: 41,395
                         4,327
                       497,625
                     + 32,991

Solution
```
  1 1 2  2 1
  41,395
   4,327
 497,625
+ 32,991
 576,338
```

Example 8   Add: 392
                          4,079
                         89,035
                       + 4,992

Your solution   98,498

Objective B

To subtract whole numbers

Subtraction is the process of finding the difference between two numbers.

By counting, we see that the difference between $8 and $5 is $3.

$8   — $5   = $3

Minuend   Subtrahend   Difference

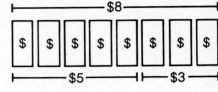

The difference $8 − $5 can be shown on the number line.

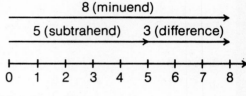

Note from the number line that addition and subtraction are related.

	Subtrahend	$5
+	Difference	+$3
=	Minuend	$8

The fact that the sum of the subtrahend and difference equals the minuend can be used to check subtraction.

To subtract large numbers, begin by arranging the numbers vertically, keeping the digits of the same place value in the same column. Then subtract the digits in each column.

Subtract 8955 − 2432 and check.

```
THOUSANDS HUNDREDS TENS ONES
  8 | 9 | 5 | 5
 −2 | 4 | 3 | 2
  6 | 5 | 2 | 3
```

Check:
	Subtrahend	2432
+	Difference	+6523
=	Minuend	8955

When the lower digit in a column is larger than the upper digit, subtraction will involve "borrowing."

Subtract: 692 − 378

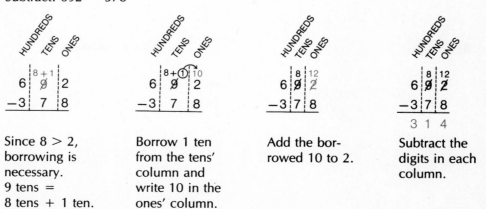

Since 8 > 2, borrowing is necessary. 9 tens = 8 tens + 1 ten.

Borrow 1 ten from the tens' column and write 10 in the ones' column.

Add the borrowed 10 to 2.

Subtract the digits in each column.

Subtract 751 − 234 and check.

Step 1
$$\begin{array}{r} 7\ \overset{4}{\cancel{5}}\ \overset{11}{\cancel{1}} \\ -2\ 3\ 4 \\ \hline \end{array}$$

Step 2
$$\begin{array}{r} 7\ \overset{4}{\cancel{5}}\ \overset{11}{\cancel{1}} \\ -2\ 3\ 4 \\ \hline 5\ 1\ 7 \end{array}$$

Check:
$$\begin{array}{r} \overset{1}{}234 \\ +517 \\ \hline 751 \end{array}$$

There may be more than one column in which borrowing is necessary.

Subtract 1234 − 485 and check.

Step 1
$$\begin{array}{r} 1\ 2\ \overset{2}{\cancel{3}}\ \overset{14}{\cancel{4}} \\ -\ \ 4\ 8\ 5 \\ \hline 9 \end{array}$$

Step 2
$$\begin{array}{r} 1\ \overset{1}{\cancel{2}}\ \overset{12}{\cancel{3}}\ \overset{14}{\cancel{4}} \\ -\ \ 4\ 8\ 5 \\ \hline 4\ 9 \end{array}$$

Step 3
$$\begin{array}{r} \overset{0}{\cancel{1}}\ \overset{11}{\cancel{2}}\ \overset{12}{\cancel{3}}\ \overset{14}{\cancel{4}} \\ -\ \ 4\ 8\ 5 \\ \hline 7\ 4\ 9 \end{array}$$

Check:
$$\begin{array}{r} \overset{1\ 1}{}485 \\ +749 \\ \hline 1234 \end{array}$$

Subtraction with a zero in the minuend involves repeated borrowing.

Subtract: 3904 − 1775

$$\begin{array}{r} 3\ \overset{8}{\cancel{9}}\ \overset{10}{\cancel{0}}\ 4 \\ -1\ 7\ 7\ 5 \\ \hline \end{array}$$

5 > 4
There is a 0 in the tens'
column. Borrow 1
hundred from the
hundreds' column and
write 10 in the tens'
column.

$$\begin{array}{r} 3\ \overset{8}{\cancel{9}}\ \overset{\overset{9}{\cancel{10}}}{\cancel{0}}\ \overset{14}{\cancel{4}} \\ -1\ 7\ 7\ 5 \\ \hline \end{array}$$

Borrow 1 ten from the
tens' column and add
10 to the 4 in the ones'
column.

$$\begin{array}{r} 3\ \overset{8}{\cancel{9}}\ \overset{\overset{9}{\cancel{10}}}{\cancel{0}}\ \overset{14}{\cancel{4}} \\ -1\ 7\ 7\ 5 \\ \hline 2\ 1\ 2\ 9 \end{array}$$

Subtract the digits in
each column.

Example 9

Subtract 6594 − 3271 and check.

Solution

$$\begin{array}{r} 6594 \\ -3271 \\ \hline 3323 \end{array}$$
Check:
$$\begin{array}{r} 3271 \\ +3323 \\ \hline 6594 \end{array}$$

Example 10

Subtract 8925 − 6413 and check.

Your solution

2512

Example 11

Subtract 15,762 − 7541 and check.

Solution

$$\begin{array}{r} 15,762 \\ -\ 7,541 \\ \hline 8,221 \end{array}$$
Check:
$$\begin{array}{r} 7541 \\ +8221 \\ \hline 15,762 \end{array}$$

Example 12

Subtract 17,504 − 9302 and check.

Your solution

8202

Solutions on p. A9

Example 13   Subtract 4392 − 678 and check

Solution
$$\overset{3\ \ 13\ \ 8\ \ 12}{\cancel{4}\ \cancel{3}\ \cancel{9}\ \cancel{2}}$$
$$-\ \ \ 6\ 7\ 8$$
$$\overline{\ \ \ 3\ 7\ 1\ 4\ }$$

Check: 678
             +3714
         $\overline{\ \ \ \ 4392\ }$

Example 14   Subtract 3481 − 865 and check.

Your solution   2616

Example 15   Subtract 63,221 − 23,954 and check.

Solution
$$\overset{5\ \ 12\ \ 11\ \ 11\ \ 11}{\cancel{6}\ \cancel{3},\cancel{2}\ \cancel{2}\ \cancel{1}}$$
$$-\ 2\ 3,9\ 5\ 4$$
$$\overline{\ \ 3\ 9,2\ 6\ 7\ }$$

Check: 23,954
        +39,267
      $\overline{\ \ \ 63,221\ }$

Example 16   Subtract 54,562 − 14,485 and check.

Your solution   40,077

Example 17   Subtract 3604 − 1275 and check.

Solution
$$\overset{\ \ \ \ 9}{\overset{5\ \ \cancel{10}\ \ 14}{3\ \cancel{6}\ \cancel{0}\ \cancel{4}}}$$
$$-1\ 2\ 7\ 5$$
$$\overline{\ \ 2\ 3\ 2\ 9\ }$$

Check: 1275
        +2329
      $\overline{\ \ \ 3604\ }$

Example 18   Subtract 5904 − 2357 and check.

Your solution   3547

Example 19   Subtract 46,005 − 32,167 and check.

Solution
$$\overset{5\ \ 10}{4\ \cancel{6},\cancel{0}\ 0\ 5}$$
$$-3\ 2,1\ 6\ 7$$
$$\overline{}$$

There are two zeros in the minuend. Borrow 1 thousand from the thousands' column and write 10 in the hundreds' column.

$$\overset{\ \ \ \ 9}{\overset{\cancel{10}\ 10}{4\ \cancel{6},\cancel{0}\ \cancel{0}\ 5}}$$
$$-3\ 2,1\ 6\ 7$$
$$\overline{}$$

Borrow 1 hundred from the hundreds' column and write 10 in the tens' column.

$$\overset{\ \ \ \ \ 9\ \ 9}{\overset{5\ \ \cancel{10}\ \cancel{10}\ 15}{4\ \cancel{6},\cancel{0}\ \cancel{0}\ \cancel{5}}}$$
$$-3\ 2,1\ 6\ 7$$
$$\overline{\ 1\ 3,8\ 3\ 8\ }$$

Borrow 1 ten from the tens' column and add 10 to the 5 in the ones' column.

Check: 32,167
        +13,838
      $\overline{\ \ \ 46,005\ }$

Example 20   Subtract 64,003 − 54,936 and check.

Your solution   9067

Solutions on p. A9

1.2A Exercises

Add.

1. 421
+308
 729

2. 202
+725
 927

3. 658
+831
 1489

4. 842
+936
 1778

5. 8092
+6307
 14,399

6. 5024
+7902
 12,926

7. 6721
+9144
 15,865

8. 6503
+9285
 15,788

9. 71,092
+85,407
 156,499

10. 62,304
+94,093
 156,397

11. 8004
+6391
 14,395

12. 6002
+7297
 13,299

13. 923,571
+863,117
 1,786,688

14. 580,236
+516,643
 1,096,879

15. 823,453
+571,346
 1,394,799

16. 3911 + 4045
 7956

17. 9144 + 7632
 16,776

18. 6648 + 9221
 15,869

19. 67,453 + 82,546
 149,999

20. 73,581 + 66,418
 139,999

21. 88,123 + 80,451
 168,574

22. 44,765 + 82,033
 126,798

23. 86,332 + 43,511
 129,843

24. 94,531 + 91,346
 185,877

25. 859
+725
 1584

26. 637
+829
 1466

27. 470
+749
 1219

28. 427
+690
 1117

29. 6016
+5050
 11,066

30. 4505
+6009
 10,514

31. 1897
+3246
 5143

32. 8975
+2146
 11,121

33. 36,925
+65,392
 102,317

34. 56,772
+51,239
 108,011

35. 50,873
+28,453
 79,326

36. 34,872
+46,079
 80,951

37. 878
737
+189
 1804

38. 768
461
+669
 1898

39. 319
348
+912
 1579

40. 292
579
+315
 1186

41. 482
309
+551
 1342

42. 366
901
+132
 1399

43. 648
219
+196
 1063

44. 592
374
+311
 1277

Add.

45.　　9409
　　　 3253
　　　+7078
　　　19,740

46.　　8188
　　　 8020
　　　+7104
　　　23,312

47.　　2038
　　　 2243
　　　+3139
　　　7420

48.　　4252
　　　 6882
　　　+5235
　　　16,369

49.　 67,428
　　　32,171
　　　+20,971
　　　120,570

50.　52,801
　　　11,664
　　　+89,638
　　　154,103

51.　76,290
　　　43,761
　　　+87,402
　　　207,453

52.　43,901
　　　98,301
　　　+67,943
　　　210,145

53.　　439
　　　 332
　　　 589
　　　+528
　　　1888

54.　　847
　　　 769
　　　 114
　　　+319
　　　2049

55.　　563
　　　 336
　　　 761
　　　+109
　　　1769

56.　　209
　　　 776
　　　 772
　　　+125
　　　1882

57.　45,098
　　　44,532
　　　98,123
　　　44,109
　　　+77,310
　　　309,172

58.　32,087
　　　33,687
　　　66,301
　　　63,442
　　　+91,842
　　　287,359

59.　56,035
　　　66,321
　　　66,281
　　　99,517
　　　+55,109
　　　343,263

60. 20,958 + 3218 + 42
24,218

61. 80,973 + 5168 + 29
86,170

62. 79 + 302 + 9546 + 37
9964

63. 92 + 907 + 2943 + 62
4004

64. 392 + 37 + 10,924 + 621
11,974

65. 694 + 62 + 70,129 + 217
71,102

66. 294 + 1029 + 7935 + 65
9323

67. 692 + 2107 + 3196 + 92
6087

68. 97 + 7234 + 69,532 + 276
77,139

69. 87 + 1698 + 27,317 + 727
29,829

70. 62 + 329 + 8954 + 1072
10,417

71. 87 + 946 + 6571 + 2103
9707

72. 654 + 7293 + 237 + 33
8217

73. 994 + 91,764 + 872 + 65
93,695

1.2B Exercises

Subtract.

74. 55
    − 4
    51

75. 68
    − 8
    60

76. 77
    − 3
    74

77. 89
    −23
    66

78. 68
    −43
    25

79. 54
    −21
    33

80. 88
    −57
    31

81. 1202
    − 701
    501

82. 1305
    − 404
    901

83. 1763
    − 801
    962

84. 1497
    − 706
    791

85. 8974
    −3972
    5002

86. 2836
    −1711
    1125

87. 8976
    −7463
    1513

88. 9273
    −6142
    3131

89. 1347 − 103
    1244

90. 4865 − 304
    4561

91. 1525 − 702
    823

92. 9999 − 6794
    3205

93. 7806 − 3405
    4401

94. 8843 − 7621
    1222

95. 8713 − 6512
    2201

96. 5672 − 4361
    1311

97. 2900 − 1900
    1000

98. 7727 − 4326
    3401

99. 5988 − 1713
    4275

100. 2904 − 1403
    1501

101. 71
    −18
    53

102. 93
    −28
    65

103. 47
    −18
    29

104. 44
    −27
    17

105. 71
    −67
    4

106. 37
    −29
    8

107. 50
    −27
    23

108. 70
    −33
    37

109. 88
    −79
    9

110. 65
    −57
    8

111. 67
    −49
    18

112. 93
    −32
    61

113. 993
    −537
    456

114. 681
    −328
    353

115. 250
    −192
    58

116. 840
    −783
    57

117. 768
    −194
    574

118. 679
    −519
    160

119. 770
    −395
    375

120. 630
    −475
    155

121. 893
    −874
    19

122. 673
    −649
    24

123. 508
    −299
    209

124. 704
    −157
    547

125. 401
    −288
    113

Subtract.

126. 5933 − 3754
2179

127. 7293 − 3748
3545

128. 8143 − 2417
5726

129. 7236 − 1978
5258

130. 5714 − 2367
3347

131. 8462 − 3575
4887

132. 9407 − 2918
6489

133. 3517 − 946
2571

134. 3706 − 2957
749

135. 8605 − 7716
889

136. 8502 − 2709
5793

137. 80,305 − 9176
71,129

138. 70,702 − 4239
66,463

139. 10,024 − 9306
718

140. 80,529 − 63,419
17,110

141. 70,618 − 41,213
29,405

142. 80,053 − 27,649
52,404

143. 70,700 − 21,076
49,624

144. 80,800 − 42,023
38,777

145. 95,432 − 87,857
7575

146. 13,806 − 9439
4367

147.   3129
        − 1785
        1344

148.   6356
        − 2975
        3381

149.   7407
        − 2359
        5048

150.   9703
        − 2347
        7356

151.   3907
        − 629
        3278

152.   7403
        − 294
        7109

153.   1305
        − 826
        479

154.   1203
        − 429
        774

155.   2600
        − 1972
        628

156.   8400
        − 3762
        4638

157.   9003
        − 2471
        6532

158.   6004
        − 2392
        3612

159.   8202
        − 3916
        4286

160.   7050
        − 4137
        2913

161.   7015
        − 2973
        4042

162.   4207
        − 1624
        2583

163.   7005
        − 1796
        5209

164.   8003
        − 2735
        5268

165.   27,005
        − 9,627
        17,378

166.   86,004
        − 8,237
        77,767

Section **3** # Multiplication and Division of Whole Numbers

| Objective A | To multiply whole numbers |

Reference for Computer Tutor™

Six boxes of toasters are ordered. Each box contains eight toasters. How many toasters are ordered?

This problem can be solved by adding six 8's.

$8 + 8 + 8 + 8 + 8 + 8 = 48$

This problem involves repeated addition of the same number and can be solved by a shorter process called **multiplication.**

Multiplication is the repeated addition of the same number.

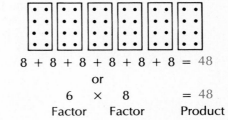

$8 + 8 + 8 + 8 + 8 + 8 = 48$

or

$6 \quad \times \quad 8 \qquad = 48$

Factor   Factor   Product

The numbers that are multiplied are called **factors.** The answer is called the **product.**

The product of 6×8 can be represented on the number line. The arrow representing the whole number 8 is repeated 6 times. The result is the arrow representing 48.

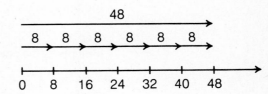

The times sign "×" is one symbol that is used to mean multiplication. Another common symbol used is a dot placed between the numbers. Parentheses also indicate multiplication.

$$7 \times 8 = 56 \qquad 7 \cdot 8 = 56 \qquad 7(8) = 56$$

As with addition, there are some useful properties of multiplication.

Multiplication Property of Zero The product of a number and zero is zero.	$0 \times 4 = 0$ $7 \times 0 = 0$
Multiplication Property of One The product of a number and one is the number.	$1 \times 6 = 6$ $8 \times 1 = 8$
Commutative Property of Multiplication Two numbers can be multiplied in either order. The product will be the same.	$4 \times 3 = 3 \times 4$ $12 = 12$
Associative Property of Multiplication Grouping the multiplication in any order gives the same result. Do the multiplication inside the parentheses first.	$(4 \times 2) \times 3 = 4 \times (2 \times 3)$ $8 \quad \times 3 = 4 \times \quad 6$ $24 = 24$

The basic facts for multiplying one digit numbers are listed on page A2 in the Appendix for your review. Multiplication of larger numbers requires the repeated use of the basic multiplication facts.

Multiply: 37 × 4

Multiply 4 × 7.   4 × 7 = 28 (2 tens + 8 ones).
Write the 8 in the ones' column and
carry the 2 to the tens' column.

$$\overset{2}{3}\!\mid\!7$$
$$\times\quad\mid\!4$$
$$\overline{\qquad\mid\!8}$$

The 3 in 37 is 3 tens.
Multiply 4 × 3 tens. 4 × 3 tens =   12 tens
                Add the carry digit.   + 2 tens
                                        —————
                                        14 tens

$$\overset{2}{3}\!\mid\!7$$
$$\times\quad\mid\!4$$
$$\overline{14\!\mid\!8}$$

Write the 14.

Multiply: 47 × 23

Step 1
Multiply by the ones' digit.

```
  47
×23
———
141
```

Step 2
Multiply by the tens' digit.

```
  47
×23
———
141
 94
———
```

Step 3
Add.

```
  47
×23
———
141
 94
————
1081
```

The last digit in the product is written in the ones' column.

The last digit in the product is written in the tens' column.

The place-value chart illustrates the placement of the products.

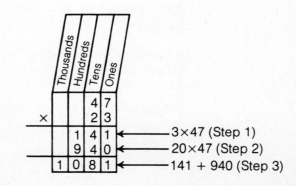

3×47 (Step 1)
20×47 (Step 2)
141 + 940 (Step 3)

Note the placement of the products when multiplying by a factor that contains a zero.

Multiply: 439 × 206

```
    439
  × 206
   2634
    000      0 × 439
   878
  90,434
```

When working the problem, usually only one zero is written. Writing this zero insures the proper placement of the products.

```
    439
  × 206
   2634
   8780
  90,434
```

Example 1   Multiply: 64 × 8

Solution

```
     ³
    64
  ×  8
   512
```

Example 2   Multiply: 78 × 6

Your solution

468

Example 3   Multiply: 735 × 9

Solution

```
    ³ ⁴
   735
  ×  9
  6615
```

Example 4   Multiply: 648 × 7

Your solution

4536

Example 5   Multiply: 58 × 47

Solution

```
    58
  × 47
   406
   232
  2726
```

Example 6   Multiply: 97 × 38

Your solution

3686

Example 7   Multiply: 829 × 603

Solution

```
     829
   × 603
    2487
   49740
  499,887
```

Example 8   Multiply: 756 × 305

Your solution

230,580

Solutions on p. A10

Objective B

Reference for
Computer
Tutor™

To simplify expressions containing exponents

Repeated multiplication of the same factor can be written two ways.

$$3 \cdot 3 \cdot 3 \cdot 3 \cdot 3 \qquad \text{or} \qquad 3^5 \leftarrow \textbf{exponent}$$

The exponent indicates how many times the factor occurs in the multiplication. The expression 3^5 is in **exponential notation.**

It is important to be able to read numbers written in exponential notation.

$6 = 6^1$	read "six to the first power" or just "six." Usually the exponent 1 is not written.
$6 \cdot 6 = 6^2$	read "six squared" or "six to the second power."
$6 \cdot 6 \cdot 6 = 6^3$	read "six cubed" or "six to the third power."
$6 \cdot 6 \cdot 6 \cdot 6 = 6^4$	read "six to the fourth power."
$6 \cdot 6 \cdot 6 \cdot 6 \cdot 6 = 6^5$	read "six to the fifth power."

Each place value in the place-value chart can be expressed as a power of 10.

Ten =	10	=	10		$= 10^1$
Hundred =	100	=	$10 \cdot 10$		$= 10^2$
Thousand =	1000	=	$10 \cdot 10 \cdot 10$		$= 10^3$
Ten-Thousand =	10,000	=	$10 \cdot 10 \cdot 10 \cdot 10$		$= 10^4$
Hundred-Thousand =	100,000	=	$10 \cdot 10 \cdot 10 \cdot 10 \cdot 10$		$= 10^5$
Million =	1,000,000	=	$10 \cdot 10 \cdot 10 \cdot 10 \cdot 10 \cdot 10$		$= 10^6$

To simplify a number expression containing exponents, write each factor as many times as indicated by the exponent and carry out the indicated multiplication.

$$4^3 = 4 \cdot 4 \cdot 4 = 64$$
$$2^2 \cdot 3^4 = (2 \cdot 2) \cdot (3 \cdot 3 \cdot 3 \cdot 3) = 4 \cdot 81 = 324$$

Example 9 Write $3 \cdot 3 \cdot 3 \cdot 5 \cdot 5$ in exponential notation.

Solution $3 \cdot 3 \cdot 3 \cdot 5 \cdot 5 = 3^3 \cdot 5^2$

Example 10 Write $2 \cdot 2 \cdot 2 \cdot 2 \cdot 3 \cdot 3 \cdot 3$ in exponential notation.

Your solution $2^4 \cdot 3^3$

Example 11 Write $10 \cdot 10 \cdot 10 \cdot 10$ as a power of 10.

Solution $10 \cdot 10 \cdot 10 \cdot 10 = 10^4$

Example 12 Write $10 \cdot 10 \cdot 10 \cdot 10 \cdot 10 \cdot 10 \cdot 10$ as a power of 10.

Your solution 10^7

Example 13 Simplify $3^2 \cdot 5^3$.

Solution $3^2 \cdot 5^3 = (3 \cdot 3) \cdot (5 \cdot 5 \cdot 5) = 9 \cdot 125 = 1125$

Example 14 Simplify $2^3 \cdot 5^2$.

Your solution $2^3 \cdot 5^2 = 8 \cdot 25 = 200$

Solutions on p. A10

Reference for
Computer
Tutor™

Objective C

To divide whole numbers

Division is used to separate objects into equal groups.

A store manager wants to distribute 24 new objects equally on 4 shelves. From the diagram, we see that the manager would place 6 objects on each shelf.

The manager's division problem would be written:

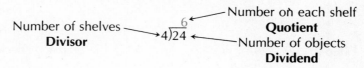

Number of shelves ⟶ Number on each shelf
Divisor **Quotient**
$4\overline{)24}$
Number of objects
Dividend

Notice that the quotient multiplied by the divisor equals the dividend.

$$4\overline{)24}^{\,6}$$

because

6	×	4	=	24
Quotient		Divisor		Dividend

$$9\overline{)54}^{\,6}$$ because $6 \times 9 = 54$

$$8\overline{)40}^{\,5}$$ because $5 \times 8 = 40$

Here are some important quotients and the properties of 0 in division.

Important Quotients
Any whole number, except zero, divided by itself is 1.

$$8\overline{)8}^{\,1} \qquad 14\overline{)14}^{\,1} \qquad 10\overline{)10}^{\,1}$$

Any whole number divided by 1 is the whole number.

$$1\overline{)9}^{\,9} \qquad 1\overline{)27}^{\,27} \qquad 1\overline{)10}^{\,10}$$

Properties of 0 in Division
Zero divided by any other whole number is zero.

$$7\overline{)0}^{\,0} \qquad 13\overline{)0}^{\,0} \qquad 10\overline{)0}^{\,0}$$

Division by zero is not allowed.

$$0\overline{)8}^{\,?}$$

There is no number whose product with 0 is 8.

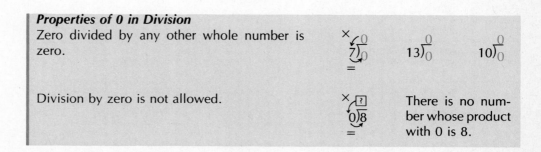

When the dividend is a larger whole number, the digits in the quotient are found in steps.

Divide $4\overline{)3192}$ and check.

Step 1

$$
\begin{array}{r}
7 \\
4\overline{)\,3192} \\
-28 \\
\hline
39
\end{array}
$$

Think $4\overline{)31}$.
Subtract 7×4.
Bring down the 9.

Step 2

$$
\begin{array}{r}
79 \\
4\overline{)\,3192} \\
-28 \\
\hline
39 \\
-36 \\
\hline
32
\end{array}
$$

Think $4\overline{)39}$.
Subtract 9×4.
Bring down the 2.

Step 3

$$
\begin{array}{r}
798 \\
4\overline{)\,3192} \\
-28 \\
\hline
39 \\
-36 \\
\hline
32 \\
-32 \\
\hline
0
\end{array}
$$

Think $4\overline{)32}$.
Subtract 8×4.

Step 4   Check:

$$
\begin{array}{r}
798 \\
\times\ \ 4 \\
\hline
3192
\end{array}
$$

The place-value chart can be used to show why this method works.

$$
\begin{array}{r}
\text{HUNDREDS} \quad \text{TENS} \quad \text{ONES} \\
7 \quad 9 \quad 8 \\
4\overline{)\ 3 \quad 1 \quad 9 \quad 2} \\
-2\ 8\ 0\ 0 \\
\hline
3\ 9\ 2 \\
-3\ 6\ 0 \\
\hline
3\ 2 \\
-3\ 2 \\
\hline
0
\end{array}
$$

7 hundreds × 4   **(Step 1)**

9 tens × 4   **(Step 2)**

8 ones × 4   **(Step 3)**

Division is also expressed by using the symbols "÷" or "—", which are read "divided by."

· 54 divided by 9 equals 6.

54   ÷   9 equals 6.

$\dfrac{54}{9}$ equals 6.

It is not always possible to separate objects into a whole number of equal groups.

A warehouse clerk must place 14 objects into 3 boxes. From the diagram, we see that the clerk would place 4 objects in each box and have 2 objects left over. The 2 is called the **remainder.**

The clerk's division problem could be written:

$$
\begin{array}{r}
\text{Number in each box} \\
4 \swarrow \quad \text{Quotient} \\
\text{Number of boxes} \rightarrow 3)\overline{14} \leftarrow \text{Total number of objects} \\
\text{Divisor} \qquad -12 \qquad \text{Dividend} \\
\hline
2 \leftarrow \text{Number left over} \\
\text{Remainder}
\end{array}
$$

The answer to a division problem with a remainder is frequently written:

$$
3)\overline{14}^{\ 4\ r2}
$$

Notice that
4 Quotient	×	3 Divisor	+	2 Remainder	=	14 Dividend

When the divisor has more than one digit, estimate at each step by using the first digit of the divisor. If that guess does not work, lower the guess by 1 and try again.

Divide $34)\overline{1598}$ and check.

Step 1
$$
\begin{array}{r}
5 \\
34)\overline{1598} \\
-170 \\
\end{array}
$$
Think $3)\overline{15}$. Subtract 5×34.

170 is too large. Lower guess by 1 and try again.

Step 2
$$
\begin{array}{r}
4 \\
34)\overline{1598} \\
-136 \\
\hline
238 \\
\end{array}
$$
Subtract 4×34.

Step 3
$$
\begin{array}{r}
47 \\
34)\overline{1598} \\
-136 \\
\hline
238 \\
-238 \\
\hline
0 \\
\end{array}
$$
Think $3)\overline{23}$. Subtract 7×34.

Step 4 Check:
$$
\begin{array}{r}
47 \\
\times 34 \\
\hline
188 \\
141 \\
\hline
1598 \\
\end{array}
$$

Example 15 Divide $7)\overline{56}$ and check.

Solution
$$
7)\overline{56}^{\ 8}
$$
Check: $8 \times 7 = 56$

Example 16 Divide $9)\overline{63}$ and check.

Your solution
7

Solution on p. A10

Example 17   Divide 7)2856 and check.

Solution

```
        408
   7) 2856
      −28
        05     Think 7)5.
      − 0      Place 0 in quotient.
        56     Subtract 0 × 7.
      −56      Bring down the 6.
        0
```

Check: 408 × 7 = 2856

Example 18   Divide 9)6345 and check.

Your solution

705

Example 19   Divide 4)2522 and check.

Solution

```
       630 r2
   4) 2522
      −24
        12
      −12
        02     Think 4)2.
      − 0      Place 0 in quotient.
        2      Subtract 0 × 4.
```

Check: (630 × 4) + 2 =
        2520   + 2 = 2522

Example 20   Divide 6)5225 and check.

Your solution

870 r 5

Example 21   Divide 21,312 ÷ 56 and check.

Solution

```
        380 r32
   56) 21,312       Think 5)21.
      −16 8         4 × 56 is too
        4 51        large.  Try 3.
      −4 48
          32
        − 0
          32
```

Check: (380 × 56) + 32 =
        21,280   + 32 = 21,312

Example 22   Divide 18,359 ÷ 39 and check.

Your solution

470 r 29

Example 23   Divide 427)24,782 and check.

Solution

```
           58 r16
   427) 24,782
       −21 35
         3 432
       −3 416
           16
```

Check: (58 × 427) + 16 =
        24,766   + 16 = 24,782

Example 24   Divide 534)33,219 and check.

Your solution

62 r III

Solutions on p. A10

| Objective D | # To factor numbers |

**Reference for
Computer
Tutor™**

Whole number factors of a number divide that number evenly (there is no remainder).

1, 2, 3, and 6 are whole number factors of 6 since they divide 6 evenly.

$$1\overline{)6}^{\,6} \qquad 2\overline{)6}^{\,3}$$

Notice that both the divisor and the quotient are factors of the dividend.

$$3\overline{)6}^{\,2} \qquad 6\overline{)6}^{\,1}$$

To find the factors of a number, try dividing the number by the numbers 1, 2, 3, 4, 5, ... Those that divide the number evenly are its factors. Continue this process until the factors start to repeat.

Find all the factors of 42.

$42 \div 1 = 42$ 1 and 42 are factors
$42 \div 2 = 21$ 2 and 21 are factors
$42 \div 3 = 14$ 3 and 14 are factors
$42 \div 4$ Will not divide evenly
$42 \div 5$ Will not divide evenly
$42 \div 6 = 7$ 6 and 7 are factors ⎫ Factors are repeating; all the factors of 42
$42 \div 7 = 6$ 7 and 6 are factors ⎭ have been found.

1, 2, 3, 6, 7, 14, 21, and 42 are factors of 42.

The following rules are helpful in finding the factors of a number.

A number is divisible by 2 if the last digit is 0, 2, 4, 6, or 8.

436 ends in 6; therefore, 436 is divisible by 2. ($436 \div 2 = 218$)

A number is divisible by 3 if the sum of the digits is divisible by 3.

The sum of the digits of 489 is $4 + 8 + 9 = 21$. 21 is divisible by 3. Therefore, 489 is divisible by 3. ($489 \div 3 = 163$)

A number is divisible by 5 if the last digit is 0 or 5.

520 ends in 0; therefore, 520 is divisible by 5. ($520 \div 5 = 104$)

Example 25   Find all the factors of 30.

Solution

$30 \div 1 = 30$
$30 \div 2 = 15$
$30 \div 3 = 10$
$30 \div 4$ Will not divide evenly
$30 \div 5 = 6$
$30 \div 6 = 5$

1, 2, 3, 5, 6, 10, 15, and 30 are factors of 30.

Example 26   Find all the factors of 40.

Your solution

1, 2, 4, 5, 8, 10, 20, 40
are factors of 40.

Solution on p. A10

Objective E   To solve application problems

To solve an application problem, first read the problem carefully. The **strategy** involves identifying the quantity to be found and planning the necessary steps to find that quantity. The **solution** involves performing each operation stated in the strategy and writing the answer.

Example 27   You had $1054 in your checking account before you made a deposit of $870. Find the amount in your checking account after the deposit.

Strategy   To find the amount in the checking account after the deposit, add the amount deposited ($870) to the amount in the checking account before the deposit ($1054).

Solution
$1054
+ 870
——————
$1924

The amount in your checking account after the deposit is $1924.

Example 28   The down payment on a car costing $3250 is $675. Find the amount that remains to be paid.

Your strategy

Your solution

$ 2575

Example 29   A press operator earns $320 for working a 40-hour week. This week the press operator also worked 7 hours of overtime at $13 an hour. Find the press operator's total pay for the week.

Strategy   To find the press operator's income for the week:
▷ Find the overtime pay by multiplying the hours of overtime (7) by the overtime rate of pay ($13).
▷ Add the weekly salary ($320) to the overtime pay.

Solution
$13 $320
× 7   + 91
——————   ——————
$91 overtime pay $411

The press operator earned $411 this week.

Example 30   A soft-drink manufacturer produces 12,600 cans of soft drink each hour. Cans are packed 24 to a case. How many cases of soft drink are produced in 8 hours?

Your strategy

Your solution

4200 cases

Solutions on p. A11

1.3A Exercises

Multiply.

1. 6
×9
54

2. 8
×5
40

3. 82
× 4
328

4. 79
× 3
237

5. 55
× 4
220

6. 72
× 2
144

7. 89
× 7
623

8. 96
× 5
480

9. 79
× 9
711

10. 67
× 7
469

11. 45
× 9
405

12. 66
× 3
198

13. 70
× 4
280

14. 67
× 5
335

15. 127
× 9
1143

16. 623
× 4
2492

17. 802
× 5
4010

18. 607
× 9
5463

19. 300
× 5
1500

20. 600
× 7
4200

21. 906
× 8
7248

22. 703
× 9
6327

23. 127
× 5
635

24. 632
× 3
1896

25. 559
× 4
2236

26. 632
× 8
5056

27. 780
× 7
5460

28. 690
× 5
3450

29. 465
× 4
1860

30. 382
× 7
2674

31. 367
× 3
1101

32. 524
× 4
2096

33. 337
× 5
1685

34. 841
× 6
5046

35. 6709
× 7
46,963

36. 3608
× 5
18,040

37. 8568
× 7
59,976

38. 5495
× 4
21,980

39. 4780
× 4
19,120

40. 3690
× 5
18,450

41. 9895
× 2
19,790

42. 4697
× 3
14,091

43. 48,253
× 3
144,759

44. 69,587
× 8
556,696

45. 80,057
× 7
560,399

46. 90,032
× 7
630,224

47. 93,000
× 7
651,000

48. 87,000
× 9
783,000

49. 93,257
× 6
559,542

50. 88,524
× 7
619,668

51. 16
×21
336

52. 18
×24
432

53. 35
×26
910

54. 27
×72
1944

55. 20
×32
640

Multiply.

56. 30
    ×47
    1410

57. 40
    ×20
    800

58. 30
    ×70
    2100

59. 39
    ×46
    1794

60. 37
    ×25
    925

61. 67
    ×23
    1541

62. 95
    ×33
    3135

63. 693
    × 91
    63,063

64. 581
    × 72
    41,832

65. 419
    × 80
    33,520

66. 727
    × 60
    43,620

67. 998
    × 67
    66,866

68. 659
    × 43
    28,337

69. 588
    × 75
    44,100

70. 499
    × 47
    23,453

71. 8279
    × 46
    380,834

72. 9577
    × 35
    335,195

73. 6938
    × 78
    541,164

74. 8875
    × 67
    594,625

75. 7035
    × 57
    400,995

76. 6702
    × 48
    321,696

77. 3009
    × 35
    105,315

78. 6003
    × 57
    342,171

79. 3300
    × 20
    66,000

80. 5400
    × 60
    324,000

81. 3987
    × 29
    115,623

82. 4765
    × 37
    176,305

83. 3574
    × 37
    132,238

84. 4372
    × 84
    367,248

85. 5673
    × 97
    550,281

86. 5769
    × 58
    334,602

87. 809
    ×530
    428,770

88. 607
    ×460
    279,220

89. 800
    ×325
    260,000

90. 700
    ×274
    191,800

91. 987
    ×349
    344,463

92. 688
    ×674
    463,712

93. 312
    ×134
    41,808

94. 423
    ×427
    180,621

95. 379
    ×500
    189,500

96. 684
    ×700
    478,800

97. 985
    ×408
    401,880

98. 758
    ×209
    158,422

99. 684
    ×329
    225,036

100. 292
    ×927
    270,684

101. 386
    ×759
    292,974

102. 386
    ×573
    221,178

103. 3407
    × 309
    1,052,763

104. 5207
    × 902
    4,696,714

105. 4258
    × 986
    4,198,388

106. 6327
    × 876
    5,542,452

107. 8800
    × 140
    1,232,000

108. 9900
    × 320
    3,168,000

109. 2675
    × 487
    1,302,725

110. 3985
    × 364
    1,450,540

1.3B Exercises

Write the number in exponential notation.

111. $2 \cdot 2 \cdot 2$ 2^3

112. $7 \cdot 7 \cdot 7 \cdot 7 \cdot 7$ 7^5

113. $6 \cdot 6 \cdot 6 \cdot 7 \cdot 7 \cdot 7 \cdot 7$ $6^3 \cdot 7^4$

114. $3 \cdot 3 \cdot 3 \cdot 5 \cdot 5 \cdot 5 \cdot 5$ $3^3 \cdot 5^4$

115. $6 \cdot 6 \cdot 6 \cdot 11 \cdot 11 \cdot 11 \cdot 11$ $6^3 \cdot 11^4$

116. $2 \cdot 2 \cdot 2 \cdot 2 \cdot 2 \cdot 2 \cdot 3 \cdot 3 \cdot 3$ $2^6 \cdot 3^3$

117. $3 \cdot 10 \cdot 10 \cdot 10 \cdot 10$ $3 \cdot 10^4$

118. $7 \cdot 10 \cdot 10 \cdot 10 \cdot 10 \cdot 10$ $7 \cdot 10^5$

119. $2 \cdot 2 \cdot 3 \cdot 3 \cdot 3 \cdot 5 \cdot 5 \cdot 5 \cdot 5$ $2^2 \cdot 3^3 \cdot 5^4$

120. $2 \cdot 3 \cdot 3 \cdot 7 \cdot 7 \cdot 11$ $2 \cdot 3^2 \cdot 7^2 \cdot 11$

121. $5 \cdot 7 \cdot 7 \cdot 9 \cdot 9 \cdot 11$ $5 \cdot 7^2 \cdot 9^2 \cdot 11$

122. $2 \cdot 2 \cdot 7 \cdot 7 \cdot 7 \cdot 7 \cdot 11 \cdot 11 \cdot 11$ $2^2 \cdot 7^4 \cdot 11^3$

Simplify.

123. $2^3 \cdot 5^2$
200

124. $2^6 \cdot 3^2$
576

125. $3^2(10^2)$
900

126. $2^3(10^4)$
80,000

127. $6^2 \cdot 3^3$
972

128. $4^3 \cdot 5^2$
1600

129. $5 \cdot 2^3 \cdot 3$
120

130. $6 \cdot 3^2 \cdot 4$
216

131. $2^2 \cdot 3^2 \cdot 10$
360

132. $3^2 \cdot 5^2 \cdot 10$
2250

133. $0^2(4^3)$
0

134. $6^2(0^3)$
0

135. $3^2 \cdot 10^4$
90,000

136. $5^3 \cdot 10^3$
125,000

137. $2^2 \cdot 3^3 \cdot 5$
540

138. $5^2 \cdot 7^3 \cdot 2$
17,150

139. $3^4(2^6)(5)$
25,920

140. $4^3(6^3)(7)$
96,768

141. $4^2 \cdot 3^3 \cdot 10^4$
4,320,000

142. $5^2 \cdot 2^3 \cdot 10^3$
200,000

1.3C Exercises

Divide.

143. $5\overline{)25}$ 5

144. $7\overline{)49}$ 7

145. $5\overline{)80}$ 16

146. $6\overline{)96}$ 16

147. $6\overline{)480}$ 80

148. $9\overline{)630}$ 70

149. $4\overline{)840}$ 210

150. $3\overline{)690}$ 230

151. $7\overline{)308}$ 44

152. $7\overline{)203}$ 29

153. $7\overline{)1442}$ 206

154. $9\overline{)6327}$ 703

155. $4\overline{)2120}$ 530

156. $8\overline{)7280}$ 910

157. $9\overline{)8118}$ 902

158. $8\overline{)7264}$ 908

159. $9\overline{)3510}$ 390

160. $7\overline{)6020}$ 860

161. $5\overline{)5280}$ 1056

162. $6\overline{)7218}$ 1203

Divide.

163. $\overset{2607}{6)15,642}$ 164. $\overset{3209}{6)19,254}$ 165. $\overset{9800}{4)39,200}$ 166. $\overset{5400}{3)16,200}$ 167. $\overset{21,560}{3)64,680}$

168. $\overset{12,690}{4)50,760}$ 169. $\overset{3580}{6)21,480}$ 170. $\overset{3610}{5)18,050}$ 171. $\overset{2\ r1}{4)9}$ 172. $\overset{3\ r1}{2)7}$

173. $\overset{5\ r2}{5)27}$ 174. $\overset{9\ r7}{9)88}$ 175. $\overset{13\ r1}{3)40}$ 176. $\overset{16\ r1}{6)97}$ 177. $\overset{10\ r3}{8)83}$

178. $\overset{10\ r4}{5)54}$ 179. $\overset{90\ r2}{7)632}$ 180. $\overset{90\ r3}{4)363}$ 181. $\overset{230\ r1}{4)921}$ 182. $\overset{120\ r5}{7)845}$

183. $\overset{204\ r3}{8)1635}$ 184. $\overset{309\ r3}{5)1548}$ 185. $\overset{1347\ r3}{7)9432}$ 186. $\overset{1058\ r4}{6)6352}$ 187. $\overset{778\ r2}{9)7004}$

188. $\overset{857\ r2}{7)6001}$ 189. $\overset{391\ r4}{6)2350}$ 190. $\overset{796\ r2}{8)6370}$ 191. $\overset{2417\ r1}{3)7252}$ 192. $\overset{1634\ r2}{4)6538}$

193. $\overset{461\ r8}{9)4157}$ 194. $\overset{881\ r5}{7)6172}$ 195. $\overset{1160\ r4}{7)8124}$ 196. $\overset{1720\ r2}{3)5162}$ 197. $\overset{708\ r2}{5)3542}$

198. $\overset{409\ r2}{8)3274}$ 199. $\overset{3825}{4)15,300}$ 200. $\overset{6214\ r2}{7)43,500}$ 201. $\overset{9044\ r2}{8)72,354}$ 202. $\overset{8708\ r3}{5)43,543}$

203. $\overset{3\ r15}{27)96}$ 204. $\overset{1\ r38}{44)82}$ 205. $\overset{2\ r3}{42)87}$ 206. $\overset{1\ r26}{67)93}$ 207. $\overset{21\ r36}{41)897}$

208. $\overset{21\ r21}{32)693}$ 209. $\overset{34\ r2}{23)784}$ 210. $\overset{30\ r22}{25)772}$ 211. $\overset{19\ r20}{23)457}$ 212. $\overset{40\ r5}{17)685}$

213. $\overset{21\ r12}{33)705}$ 214. $\overset{13\ r36}{67)907}$ 215. $\overset{8\ r8}{74)600}$ 216. $\overset{5\ r40}{92)500}$ 217. $\overset{4\ r49}{70)329}$

Divide.

218. $\overset{9\ r17}{50\overline{)467}}$ 219. $\overset{200\ r25}{36\overline{)7225}}$ 220. $\overset{200\ r21}{44\overline{)8821}}$ 221. $\overset{203\ r2}{19\overline{)3859}}$ 222. $\overset{303\ r1}{32\overline{)9697}}$

223. $\overset{33\ r33}{93\overline{)3102}}$ 224. $\overset{73\ r31}{82\overline{)6017}}$ 225. $\overset{810\ r3}{11\overline{)8913}}$ 226. $\overset{209\ r7}{15\overline{)3142}}$ 227. $\overset{185\ r2}{23\overline{)4257}}$

228. $\overset{147\ r29}{62\overline{)9143}}$ 229. $\overset{67\ r70}{92\overline{)6234}}$ 230. $\overset{56\ r39}{87\overline{)4911}}$ 231. $\overset{601\ r8}{14\overline{)8422}}$ 232. $\overset{107\ r3}{42\overline{)4497}}$

233. $\overset{200\ r9}{26\overline{)5209}}$ 234. $\overset{200\ r3}{37\overline{)7403}}$ 235. $\overset{35\ r47}{88\overline{)3127}}$ 236. $\overset{67\ r13}{92\overline{)6177}}$ 237. $\overset{271}{33\overline{)8943}}$

238. $\overset{176\ r13}{27\overline{)4765}}$ 239. $\overset{4484\ r6}{22\overline{)98,654}}$ 240. $\overset{1086\ r7}{77\overline{)83,629}}$ 241. $\overset{608}{64\overline{)38,912}}$ 242. $\overset{403}{78\overline{)31,434}}$

243. $\overset{708}{19\overline{)13,452}}$ 244. $\overset{505}{42\overline{)21,210}}$ 245. $\overset{468\ r60}{67\overline{)31,416}}$ 246. $\overset{390\ r15}{29\overline{)11,325}}$ 247. $\overset{15\ r7}{206\overline{)3097}}$

248. $\overset{12\ r456}{504\overline{)6504}}$ 249. $\overset{1\ r563}{654\overline{)1217}}$ 250. $\overset{4\ r160}{546\overline{)2344}}$ 251. $\overset{50\ r92}{169\overline{)8542}}$ 252. $\overset{16\ r427}{456\overline{)7723}}$

1.3D Exercises

Find all the factors of each number.

253. 10
1, 2, 5, 10

254. 20
1, 2, 4, 5, 10, 20

255. 5
1, 5

256. 7
1, 7

257. 12
1, 2, 3, 4, 6, 12

258. 9
1, 3, 9

259. 8
1, 2, 4, 8

260. 16
1, 2, 4, 8, 16

261. 13
1, 13

262. 17
1, 17

263. 18
1, 2, 3, 6, 9, 18

264. 24
1, 2, 3, 4, 6, 8, 12, 24

265. 28
1, 2, 4, 7, 14, 28

266. 32
1, 2, 4, 8, 16, 32

267. 29
1, 29

268. 33
1, 3, 11, 33

269. 22
1, 2, 11, 22

270. 26
1, 2, 13, 26

271. 44
1, 2, 4, 11, 22, 44

272. 52
1, 2, 4, 13, 26, 52

273. 49
1, 7, 49

274. 82
1, 2, 41, 82

275. 57
1, 3, 19, 57

276. 69
1, 3, 23, 69

277. 48
1, 2, 3, 4, 6, 8, 12, 16, 24, 48

278. 64
1, 2, 4, 8, 16, 32, 64

279. 87
1, 3, 29, 87

280. 95
1, 5, 19, 95

281. 46
1, 2, 23, 46

282. 54
1, 2, 3, 6, 9, 18, 27, 54

1.3E Exercises

Solve.

283. Your bank balance is $542. You then write checks for $122, $89, and $16. Find the new bank balance.

$ 315

284. A librarian receives a total salary of $1840 per month. Deductions from the check are $428 for taxes, $118 for social security, and $37 for insurance. Find the librarian's take-home pay.

$ 1257

285. A sales executive has an expense account of $400. The amount already spent includes $132 for transportation, $82 for food, and $112 for lodging. Find the balance remaining in the expense account.

$ 74

286. Your monthly budget for household expenses is $500. After $132 is spent for food, $89 for clothes, and $65 for entertainment, how much is left in the budget?

$ 214

287. The Environmental Protection Agency (EPA) estimates that a compact car gets 27 mi on one gallon of gas. How many miles could such a car travel on 16 gal of gas?

432 mi

288. A tooling machine produces 365 bearings in one hour. How many bearings does the machine produce in 40 hours?

14,600 bearings

289. A gasoline storage tank contains 75,000 gal of gasoline. A valve is opened that lets out 37 gal each minute. How many gallons remain in the tank after the valve has been open for 28 minutes?

73,964 gal

290. A clerk earns $265 for working a 40-hour week. Last week the clerk worked an additional 9 hours at $11 an hour. Find the clerk's total pay for last week's work.

$ 364

291. A donation of $147,980 is divided equally among four hospital projects. What amount does each project receive?

$ 36,995

292. The total cost of a car, including finance charges, is $8544. This amount is to be repaid in 48 equal payments. What is the amount of each payment?

$ 178

293. A lettuce farmer harvested 39,544 heads of lettuce from one plot of land and 38,456 from a second plot. The lettuce is packed in boxes with 24 heads in each box. How many boxes were needed to pack the lettuce from the two plots?

3250 boxes

294. A consumer makes a down payment of $1591 on a large-screen television costing $3595. The balance is to be paid in 12 equal monthly payments. What is the payment for one month?

$ 167

295. A clothing manufacturer produces and boxes 240 pairs of slacks each hour. Four pairs of slacks are put in each box for shipment. How many boxes of slacks can be produced in 12 hours?

720 boxes

296. A charity organization collected $352,765 in a recent fund-raising drive. Of the amount collected, $35,000 was used to pay expenses. The remaining money was divided equally among five charities. What amount did each charity receive?

$63,553

Section 4 Prime Factorization and the Order of Operations Agreement

Objective A To find the prime factorization of a number

Reference for
Computer
Tutor™

A number is **prime** if its only whole number factors are 1 and itself. Therefore, 7 is prime, since its only factors are 1 and 7. If a number is not prime, it is called a **composite** number. Thus, 6 is composite since 6 has factors of 2 and 3. The number 1 is not considered a prime number. Therefore, it is not included in the following list of prime numbers less than 50.

2, 3, 5, 7, 11, 13, 17, 19, 23, 29, 31, 37, 41, 43, 47

The **prime factorization** of a number is the expression of the number as a product of its prime factors. To find the prime factors of 60, begin with the smallest prime number as a trial divisor and continue with prime numbers as trial divisors until the final quotient is prime.

$$
\begin{array}{cc}
& 15 \\
& 2\overline{)30} \\
30 & 2\overline{)60} \\
2\overline{)60} &
\end{array}
\qquad
\begin{array}{ll}
& \quad\quad 5 \;\;\text{Prime}\\
\text{Prime} & 3\overline{)15} \\
\text{Divisors} & 2\overline{)30} \\
& 2\overline{)60}
\end{array}
$$

The prime factorization of 60 is $2 \cdot 2 \cdot 3 \cdot 5$.

Finding the prime factorization of larger numbers can be more difficult. Try each prime number as a trial divisor. Stop when the square of the trial divisor is greater than the number being factored.

Find the prime factorization of 106.

$$
\begin{array}{c}
53 \\
2\overline{)106}
\end{array}
$$
53 cannot be divided evenly by 2, 3, 5, 7, or 11. Prime numbers greater than 11 need not be tested since 11^2 is greater than 53.

The prime factorization of 106 is $2 \cdot 53$.

Example 1　Find the prime factorization of 84.

Solution
$$
\begin{array}{c}
7 \\
3\overline{)21} \\
2\overline{)42} \\
2\overline{)84}
\end{array}
$$
$84 = 2 \cdot 2 \cdot 3 \cdot 7$

Example 2　Find the prime factorization of 44.

Your solution

$44 = 2 \cdot 2 \cdot 11$

Example 3　Find the prime factorization of 201.

Solution
$$
\begin{array}{c}
67 \\
3\overline{)201}
\end{array}
$$
Try only 2, 3, 5, 7, and 11 since $11^2 > 67$.

$201 = 3 \cdot 67$

Example 4　Find the prime factorization of 177.

Your solution

$177 = 3 \cdot 59$

Solutions on p. A11

Reference for
Computer
Tutor™

| Objective B | To find the least common multiple (LCM) |

The **multiples** of a number are the products of that number and the numbers 1, 2, 3, 4, 5, ...

$3 \times 1 = 3$
$3 \times 2 = 6$
$3 \times 3 = 9$ The multiples of 3 are 3, 6, 9, 12, 15, ...
$3 \times 4 = 12$
$3 \times 5 = 15$

A number that is a multiple of two or more numbers is a **common multiple** of those numbers.

The multiples of 4 are 4, 8, 12, 16, 20, 24, 28, 32, 36, ...
The multiples of 6 are 6, 12, 18, 24, 30, 36, 42, ...
Some common multiples of 4 and 6 are 12, 24, and 36.

The **least common multiple** (LCM) is the smallest common multiple of two or more numbers.

The least common multiple of 4 and 6 is 12.

Listing the multiples of each number is one way to find the LCM. Another way to find the LCM uses the prime factorization of each number.

To find the LCM of 450 and 600, find the prime factorization of each number and write the factorization of each number in a table. Circle the largest product in each column. The LCM is the product of the circled numbers.

	2	3	5
450 =	2	(3 · 3)	5 · 5
600 =	(2 · 2 · 2)	3	(5 · 5)

In the column headed by 5, the products are equal. Circle just one product.

The LCM is the product of the circled numbers.
The LCM = $2 \cdot 2 \cdot 2 \cdot 3 \cdot 3 \cdot 5 \cdot 5 = 1800$.

Example 5   Find the LCM of 24, 36, and 50.

Solution

	2	3	5
24 =	(2 · 2 · 2)	3	
36 =	2 · 2	(3 · 3)	
50 =	2		(5 · 5)

The LCM =
$2 \cdot 2 \cdot 2 \cdot 3 \cdot 3 \cdot 5 \cdot 5 = 1800$.

Example 6   Find the LCM of 50, 84, and 135.

Your solution

18,900

Solution on p. A12

Objective C

To find the greatest common factor (GCF)

Recall that a number that divides another number evenly is a factor of that number. Since 64 can be evenly divided by 1, 2, 4, 8, 16, 32, and 64, the numbers 1, 2, 4, 8, 16, 32, and 64 are factors of 64.

A number that is a factor of two or more numbers is a **common factor** of those numbers.

The factors of 30 are 1, 2, 3, 5, 6, 10, 15, 30.
The factors of 105 are 1, 3, 5, 7, 15, 21, 35, 105.
The common factors of 30 and 105 are 1, 3, 5, and 15.

The **greatest common factor** (GCF) is the largest common factor of two or more numbers.

The greatest common factor of 30 and 105 is 15.

Listing the factors of each number is one way of finding the GCF. Another way to find the GCF uses the prime factorization of each number.

To find the GCF of 126 and 180, find the prime factorization of each number and write the factorization of each number in a table. Circle the smallest product in each column that does not have a blank. The GCF is the product of the circled numbers.

	2	3	5	7
126 =	(2)	(3 · 3)		7
180 =	2 · 2	3 · 3	5	

In the column headed by 3, the products are equal. Circle just one product.
Columns 5 and 7 have a blank. So 5 and 7 are not common factors of 126 and 180. Do not circle any number in these columns.

The GCF is the product of the circled numbers.
The GCF = 2 · 3 · 3 = 18.

Example 7   Find the GCF of 90, 168, and 420.

Solution

	2	3	5	7
90 =	(2)	3 · 3	5	
168 =	2 · 2 · 2	(3)		7
420 =	2 · 2	3	5	7

The GCF = 2 · 3 = 6.

Example 8   Find the GCF of 36, 60, and 72.

Your solution

12

Example 9   Find the GCF of 7, 12, and 20.

Solution

	2	3	5	7
7 =				7
12 =	2 · 2	3		
20 =	2 · 2		5	

Since no numbers are circled, the GCF = 1.

Example 10   Find the GCF of 11, 24, and 30.

Your solution

GCF = 1

| Objective D | To use the order of operations agreement to simplify expressions |

More than one operation may occur in arithmetic problems. The answer will be different, depending on the order in which the operations are performed. An Order of Operations Agreement is used so that only one answer will be possible.

> **The Order of Operations Agreement**
> Step 1   Do all operations inside parentheses.
> Step 2   Simplify any number expressions containing exponents.
> Step 3   Do multiplication and division as they occur from left to right.
> Step 4   Do addition and subtraction as they occur from left to right.

Simplify $3 \times (2 + 1) - 2^2 + 4 \div 2$ by using the Order of Operations Agreement.

$3 \times \underline{(2 + 1)} - 2^2 + 4 \div 2$ 1.   Perform operations in parentheses.

$3 \times 3 - \underline{2^2} + 4 \div 2$ 2.   Simplify expressions with exponents.

$\underline{3 \times 3} - 4 + 4 \div 2$ 3.   Do multiplications and divisions as they occur from left to right.

$9 - 4 + \underline{4 \div 2}$

$\underline{9 - 4} + 2$ 4.   Do additions and subtractions as they occur from left to right.

$\underline{5 + 2}$

7

One or more of the above steps may not be needed to simplify an expression. In that case, proceed to the next step in the Order of Operations Agreement.

Simplify $5 + 8 \div 2$.   No parentheses or exponents. Proceed to Step 3 of the agreement.

$5 + \underline{8 \div 2}$ 3.   Do multiplication or division.

$\underline{5 + 4}$ 4.   Do addition or subraction.

9

Example 11   Simplify
$16 \div (8 - 4) \cdot 9 - 5^2$.

Solution $16 \div (8 - 4) \cdot 9 - 5^2$
$16 \div 4 \cdot 9 - 5^2$
$16 \div 4 \cdot 9 - 25$
$4 \cdot 9 - 25$
$36 - 25$
11

Example 12   Simplify
$5 \cdot (8 - 4) \div 4 - 2$.

Your solution

3

Solution on p. A12

1.4A Exercises

Find the prime factorization.

1. 6
   2·3

2. 14
   2·7

3. 17
   17 is prime

4. 37
   37 is prime

5. 16
   2·2·2·2

6. 24
   2·2·2·3

7. 12
   2·2·3

8. 27
   3·3·3

9. 9
   3·3

10. 15
    3·5

11. 36
    2·2·3·3

12. 40
    2·2·2·5

13. 65
    5·13

14. 115
    5·23

15. 80
    2·2·2·2·5

16. 87
    3·29

17. 18
    2·3·3

18. 26
    2·13

19. 28
    2·2·7

20. 49
    7·7

21. 29
    29 is prime

22. 31
    31 is prime

23. 42
    2·3·7

24. 62
    2·31

25. 81
    3·3·3·3

26. 51
    3·17

27. 95
    5·19

28. 105
    3·5·7

29. 120
    2·2·2·3·5

30. 144
    2·2·2·
    2·3·3

31. 50
    2·5·5

32. 90
    2·3·3·5

33. 22
    2·11

34. 39
    3·13

35. 70
    2·5·7

36. 66
    2·3·11

37. 74
    2·37

38. 78
    2·3·13

39. 67
    67 is prime

40. 89
    89 is prime

41. 122
    2·61

42. 130
    2·5·13

1.4B Exercises

Find the LCM.

43. 5, 8
    40

44. 3, 6
    6

45. 3, 8
    24

46. 2, 5
    10

47. 5, 6
    30

48. 5, 7
    35

49. 4, 6
    12

50. 6, 8
    24

51. 8, 12
    24

52. 12, 16
    48

53. 5, 12
    60

54. 3, 16
    48

55. 6, 18
    18

56. 3, 9
    9

57. 4, 10
    20

Find the LCM.

58. 8, 32
32

59. 14, 42
42

60. 44, 60
660

61. 7, 21
21

62. 8, 14
56

63. 4, 8, 12
24

64. 3, 5, 10
30

65. 2, 5, 8
40

66. 3, 8, 12
24

67. 5, 12, 18
180

68. 9, 36, 64
576

69. 12, 18, 24
72

70. 5, 10, 15
30

71. 9, 12, 15
180

72. 6, 9, 15
90

73. 8, 18, 24
72

74. 12, 15, 25
300

75. 10, 15, 40
120

76. 12, 48, 72
144

77. 30, 60, 80
240

1.4C Exercises

Find the GCF.

78. 3, 5
1

79. 5, 7
1

80. 6, 9
3

81. 18, 24
6

82. 15, 25
5

83. 14, 49
7

84. 16, 80
16

85. 25, 100
25

86. 40, 68
4

87. 32, 51
1

88. 21, 44
1

89. 12, 80
4

90. 8, 36
4

91. 12, 76
4

92. 8, 14
2

93. 24, 30
6

94. 48, 144
48

95. 44, 96
4

96. 18, 32
2

97. 16, 30
2

98. 40, 64
8

99. 60, 82
2

100. 24, 140
4

101. 2, 5, 7
1

102. 3, 5, 11
1

103. 6, 8, 10
2

104. 7, 14, 49
7

105. 6, 15, 36
3

106. 8, 12, 16
4

107. 10, 15, 20
5

108. 24, 40, 72
8

109. 14, 42, 84
14

110. 12, 68, 92
4

111. 28, 35, 70
7

112. 24, 36, 48
12

1.4D Exercises

Simplify by using the Order of Operations Agreement.

113. $4 - 2 + 3$
5

114. $6 - 3 + 2$
5

115. $6 \div 3 + 2$
4

116. $4 - 8 \div 2$
0

117. $6 + 9 \div 3$
9

118. $12 \div 2 - 4$
2

119. $8 \div 4 + 8$
10

120. $6 \cdot 3 + 5$
23

121. $5(9) + 2$
47

122. $3^2 - 4$
5

123. $5^2 - 17$
8

124. $4(5 - 3) + 2$
10

125. $3 + (4 + 2) \div 3$
5

126. $5 + (8 + 4) \div 6$
7

127. $8 - 2^2 + 4$
8

128. $2^2 + 8 \div 2$
8

129. $5^2 + 12 \div 6$
27

130. $4 \cdot 3 \div 6 + 5$
7

131. $6 + (2 + 7) \div 3$
9

132. $18 - (3 + 5) \div 4$
16

133. $14 + (9 - 4) \div 5$
15

134. $2^2 \cdot 3 - 3$
9

135. $32 - 16 \div 2^3$
30

136. $24 - 18 \div 3 + 2$
20

137. $16 + 15 \div 5 - 2$
17

138. $14 - 2^2 - (7 - 4)$
7

139. $18 \div (9 - 2^3)$
18

140. $16(3 + 2) \div 10$
8

141. $12(1 + 5) \div 12$
6

142. $10 - 2^3 + 4$
6

Simplify using the Order of Operations Agreement.

143. $5(3^3) + 8$
143

144. $16 + 4 \cdot 3^2$
52

145. $12 + 4 \cdot 2^3$
44

146. $16 + (8 - 3) \cdot 2$
26

147. $7 + (9 - 5) \cdot 3$
19

148. $2^2 + 3(6 - 2)$
16

149. $3^2 \cdot 5(4 - 1)$
135

150. $6(3 + 2) \cdot 2^3$
240

151. $4^2 \div (9 - 1)$
2

152. $3^3 + 5(8 - 6)$
37

153. $2^2(3^2) + 2 \cdot 3$
42

154. $4(6) + 3^2 \cdot 4^2$
168

155. $16 - 2 \cdot 4$
8

156. $12 + 3 \cdot 5$
27

157. $3 \cdot (6 - 2) + 4$
16

158. $5 \cdot (8 - 4) - 6$
14

159. $8 - (8 - 2) \div 3$
6

160. $12 - (12 - 4) \div 4$
10

161. $8 + 2 - 3 \cdot 2 \div 3$
8

162. $10 + 1 - 5 \cdot 2 \div 5$
9

163. $3 \cdot (4 + 2) \div 6$
3

164. $8 \cdot 2 + 4 - 3$
17

165. $3(4 - 1) + 3^2$
18

166. $5(7 - 2) - 2^3$
17

167. $9 + 3 - 4 \cdot 2 \div 8$
11

168. $12 + 5 - 4 \cdot 3 \div 6$
15

169. $4(3 + 7) \div 5$
8

170. $18(3) \div 9 + 4$
10

171. $24 \div 6(3) - 8$
4

172. $36 \div 9(4) + 7$
23

Calculators and Computers

Does your calculator use the Order of Operations Agreement? To find out, try this problem:

$$2 + 4 \cdot 7$$

If your answer is 30, then the calculator uses the Order of Operations Agreement. If your answer is 42, it does not use that agreement.

Even if your calculator does not use the Order of Operations Agreement, you can still correctly evaluate numerical expressions. The parentheses keys, ⊏(and ⊐), are used for this purpose.

Remember that $2 + 4 \cdot 7$ means $2 + (4 \cdot 7)$ since the multiplication is completed before addition. To evaluate this expression enter the following:

Enter	Display	Comments
2	2.	
+	2.	
(	(	Not all scientific calculators display the "(" when it is entered.
4	4.	
×	4.	
7	7.	
)	28.	The product inside the parentheses is 28.
=	30.	The answer to $2 + (4 \times 7)$ is 30.

When using your calculator to evaluate numerical expressions, insert parentheses around multiplications or divisions. This has the effect of forcing the calculator to do the operations in the order you want rather than in the order the calculator wants.

Evaluate $3 \cdot (15 - 2 \cdot 3) - 36 \div 3$.

Press the keys shown in the box.

$$3 \times (15 - (2 \times 3)) - (36 \div 3) =$$

The answer 15 should be in the display.

Notice that parentheses were used around $15 - 2 \cdot 3$ and around $2 \cdot 3$. This is important to insure that multiplication is performed before additions or subtractions from the innermost grouping symbols to the outermost grouping symbols.

Simplify by using the Order of Operations Agreement.

1. $2^2 + 8 \div 2$

2. $5^2 + 12 \div 6$

3. $4 \cdot 3 \div 6 + 5$

4. $8 \cdot 2 \div 4 - 3$

5. $3 \cdot (4 - 1) + 3^2$

6. $5 \cdot (7 - 2) - 2^3$

ANSWERS: **1.** 8   **2.** 27   **3.** 7   **4.** 1   **5.** 18   **6.** 17

Chapter Summary

KEY WORDS

The **whole numbers** are
       0, 1, 2, 3, 4, 5, 6, 7, 8, 9, 10, . . .

The symbol for **"is less than"** is <. The symbol for **"is greater than"** is >.

The position of a digit in a number determines its **place value.**

Giving an approximate value for an exact number is called **rounding.**

An expression of the form 4^2 is in **exponential notation.** The 2 is the **exponent.**

A number is **prime** if its only whole number factors are 1 and itself. The **prime factorization** of a number is the expression of the number as a product of prime factors.

The **multiples** of a number are the products of that number and the numbers 1, 2, 3, 4, 5, ... A number that is a multiple of two or more numbers is a **common multiple** of those numbers. The **least common multiple** (LCM) is the smallest common multiple of two or more numbers.

A number that is a factor of two or more numbers is a **common factor** of those numbers. The **greatest common factor** (GCF) is the largest common factor of two or more numbers.

ESSENTIAL RULES

The Addition Property of Zero	Zero added to a number does not change the number. **5 + 0 = 0 + 5 = 5**
The Commutative Property of Addition	Two numbers can be added in either order. **6 + 5 = 5 + 6 = 11**
The Associative Property of Addition	Grouping the addition in any order gives the same result. **(2 + 3) + 5 = 2 + (3 + 5) = 10**
The Multiplication Property of Zero	The product of a number and zero is zero. **0 × 3 = 3 × 0 = 0**
The Multiplication Property of One	The product of a number and one is the number. **1 × 8 = 8 × 1 = 8**
The Commutative Property of Multiplication	Two numbers can be multiplied in any order. **5 × 2 = 2 × 5 = 10**
The Associative Property of Multiplication	Grouping multiplication in any order gives the same result. **(3 × 2) × 5 = 3 × (2 × 5) = 30**
The Properties of Zero in Division	Zero divided by any other number is zero. Division by zero is not allowed.
The Order of Operations Agreement	**Step 1** Perform operations inside grouping symbols. **Step 2** Simplify expressions with exponents. **Step 3** Do multiplications and divisions as they occur from left to right. **Step 4** Do additions and subtractions as they occur from left to right.

Review/Test

1. Graph 2 on the number line.

    0 1 2 3 4 5 6 7 8 9 10 11 12

2. Place the correct symbol, < or >, between the two numbers.
   21 > 19

3. Write 906,378 in expanded form.
   900,000 + 6000 + 300 + 70 + 8

4. Round 74,965 to the nearest hundred.
   75,000

5. Add: 25,492 + 71,306
   96,798

6. Add: 89,756 + 9094 + 37,065
   135,915

7. Subtract: 17,495 − 8162
   9333

8. Subtract: 20,736 − 9854
   10,882

9. Multiply: 90,763 × 8
   726,104

10. Multiply: 9736 × 704
    6,854,144

11. Write $3 \cdot 3 \cdot 3 \cdot 7 \cdot 7$ in exponential form.
    $3^3 \cdot 7^2$

12. Simplify $3^3 \cdot 4^2$.
    432

13. Divide: $8\overline{)5624}$
    703

14. Divide: 60,972 ÷ 7
    8710 r2

15. Divide: $97\overline{)108,764}$
    1121 r27

16. Find all the factors of 36.
    1, 2, 3, 4, 6, 9, 12, 18, 36

17. Find the prime factorization of 84.
    $2 \cdot 2 \cdot 3 \cdot 7$

18. Find the LCM of 30 and 42.
    210

19. Find the GCF of 60 and 80.
    20

20. Simplify $4^2 \cdot (4 - 2) \div 8 + 5$.
    9

21. Bluff College has an enrollment of 1249 freshmen, 1167 sophomores, 967 juniors, and 1047 seniors. Find the total enrollment of Bluff College.
    4430 students

22. A bank manager receives a total salary of $2136 per month. Deductions from the check are $479 for taxes, $99 for social security, and $56 for insurance. Find the bank manager's take-home pay.
    $1502

23. The manager of a clothing store can buy 80 men's suits for $4800. Each sports jacket will cost the store $23. The manager orders 80 men's suits and 25 sports jackets. What is the total cost of the order?
    $5375

24. A farmer harvested 48,290 lb of avocados from one grove and 23,710 lb of avocados from another grove. The avocados were packed in boxes with 24 lb in each box. How many boxes were needed to pack the avocados?
    3000 boxes

Cumulative Review/Test

1. Add: 87,256 + 3095 + 9981
   100,332

2. Multiply: 687 × 6
   4122

3. Divide: 907)30,297
   33 r366

4. Find the prime factorization of 220.
   2 · 2 · 5 · 11

5. Write 60,705 in expanded form.
   60,000 + 700 + 5

6. Subtract: 9504 − 7819
   1685

7. Divide: 6)2415
   402 r3

8. Simplify 2 · (4 + 2) ÷ 3 − 2.
   2

9. Place the correct symbol, < or >, between the two numbers.
   37 > 16

10. Add: 692,079 + 37,576 + 9,069,757
    9,799,412

11. Multiply: 5879 × 208
    1,222,832

12. Write 5 · 5 · 5 · 7 · 7 in exponential notation.
    $5^3 \cdot 7^2$

13. Round 789,487 to the nearest thousand.
    789,000

14. Subtract: 92,003 − 9479
    82,524

15. Divide: 36)7535
    209 r11

16. Find all the factors of 18.
    1, 2, 3, 6, 9, 18

17. Find the LCM of 9 and 36.
    36

18. Find the GCF of 16 and 140.
    4

19. You had a balance of $549 in your checking account before making deposits of $52, $102, $17, and $279. What is your new checking account balance?
    $999

20. The down payment on a motorcycle costing $1105 is $185. Find the amount that remains to be paid.
    $920

21. A manufacturer of calculators now has 3280 calculators in stock. The company manufactures 140 calculators each hour. How many calculators will be in stock 8 hours from now?
    4400 calculators

22. A mechanic earns $560 for working 40 hours during the week. This week the mechanic worked an additional 12 hours at $19 per hour. Find the mechanic's total pay for the week.
    $788

23. A teacher receives $24,780 for teaching 12 months. How much does the teacher receive each month?
    $2065

24. The total cost of a computer system is $4758. A down payment of $1500 is made and the balance is paid in 18 equal monthly payments. Find the monthly payment.
    $181

chapter 2

Fractions and Decimals

Objectives

2.1A To write an improper fraction as a mixed number or a whole number and a mixed number as an improper fraction

2.1B To find equivalent fractions by raising to higher terms

2.1C To reduce a fraction to simplest form

2.1D To identify the order relation between two fractions

2.2A To add fractions

2.2B To subtract fractions

2.3A To multiply fractions

2.3B To divide fractions

2.3C To solve application problems

2.4A To round a decimal to a given place value

2.4B To add and subtract decimals

2.4C To multiply decimals

2.4D To divide decimals

2.4E To find the average of a set of numbers

2.5A To convert fractions to decimals and decimals to fractions

2.5B To identify the order relation between two decimals or between a decimal and fraction

Section **1**

Introduction to Fractions

Objective A

To write an improper fraction as a mixed number or a whole number and a mixed number as an improper fraction

Reference for
Computer
Tutor™

A **fraction** can represent the number of equal parts of a whole.

The shaded portion of the circle is represented by the fraction $\frac{4}{7}$.

Four-sevenths of the circle is shaded.

Each part of a fraction has a name.

Fraction bar $\rightarrow \frac{4}{7}$ $\leftarrow$ **Numerator**
$\phantom{Fraction bar \rightarrow \frac{4}{7}}\leftarrow$ **Denominator**

A **proper fraction** is a fraction less than 1. The numerator of a proper fraction is smaller than the denominator. The shaded portion of the circle can be represented by the proper fraction $\frac{3}{4}$.

$\frac{3}{4}$

A **mixed number** is a number greater than 1 with a whole number part and a fractional part. The shaded portion of the circles can be represented by the mixed number $2\frac{1}{4}$.

$2\frac{1}{4}$

An **improper fraction** is a fraction greater than or equal to one. The numerator of an improper fraction is greater than or equal to the denominator. The shaded portion of the circles can be represented by the improper fraction $\frac{9}{4}$. The shaded portion of the square can be represented by $\frac{4}{4}$.

$\frac{9}{4}$

$\frac{4}{4}$

Note from the diagram that the mixed number $2\frac{3}{5}$ and the improper fraction $\frac{13}{5}$ represent the shaded portion of the circles.

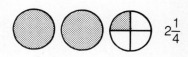

$2\frac{3}{5}$

$\frac{13}{5}$

$2\frac{3}{5} = \frac{13}{5}$

An improper fraction can be written as a mixed number.

Write $\frac{13}{5}$ as a mixed number.

Step 1
Divide the numerator by the denominator.

$$\begin{array}{r} 2 \\ 5{\overline{\smash{\big)}\,13}} \\ \underline{-10} \\ 3 \end{array}$$

Step 2
To write the fractional part of the mixed number, write the remainder over the divisor.

$$\begin{array}{r} 2\frac{3}{5} \\ 5{\overline{\smash{\big)}\,13}} \\ \underline{-10} \\ 3 \end{array}$$

Step 3
Write the answer.

$$\frac{13}{5} = 2\frac{3}{5}$$

To write a mixed number as an improper fraction, multiply the denominator of the fractional part by the whole number part. The sum of this product and the numerator of the fractional part is the numerator of the improper fraction. The denominator remains the same.

Write $7\frac{3}{8}$ as an improper fraction.

$$7\frac{3}{8} = \frac{(8 \times 7) + 3}{8} = \frac{56 + 3}{8} = \frac{59}{8} \qquad\qquad 7\frac{3}{8} = \frac{59}{8}$$

Example 1
Express the shaded portion of the circles as an improper fraction and as a mixed number.

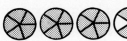

Solution
$\frac{17}{5}$; $3\frac{2}{5}$

Example 2
Express the shaded portion of the circles as an improper fraction and as a mixed number.

Your solution
$\frac{17}{4}$; $4\frac{1}{4}$

Example 3
Write $\frac{21}{4}$ as a mixed number.

Solution

$$\begin{array}{r} 5 \\ 4{\overline{\smash{\big)}\,21}} \\ \underline{-20} \\ 1 \end{array} \qquad \frac{21}{4} = 5\frac{1}{4}$$

Example 4
Write $\frac{22}{5}$ as a mixed number.

Your solution
$4\frac{2}{5}$

Example 5
Write $\frac{18}{6}$ as a whole number.

Solution

$$\begin{array}{r} 3 \\ 6{\overline{\smash{\big)}\,18}} \\ \underline{-18} \\ 0 \end{array}$$ Note: the remainder is zero. $\qquad \frac{18}{6} = 3$

Example 6
Write $\frac{28}{7}$ as a whole number.

Your solution
4

Example 7
Write $21\frac{3}{4}$ as an improper fraction.

Solution

$$21\frac{3}{4} = \frac{84 + 3}{4} = \frac{87}{4}$$

Example 8
Write $14\frac{5}{8}$ as an improper fraction.

Your solution
$\frac{117}{8}$

Solutions on p. A13

Objective B

2
DISK
TWO

Reference for
Computer
Tutor™

To find equivalent fractions by raising to higher terms

Equal fractions with different denominators are called **equivalent fractions.**

$\frac{4}{6}$ is equivalent to $\frac{2}{3}$.

$\frac{2}{3}$ was built to the equivalent fraction $\frac{4}{6}$.

Note from the diagram that an equivalent fraction can be built by multiplying the numerator and denominator by the same number.

$$\frac{2}{3} = \frac{2 \cdot 2}{3 \cdot 2} = \frac{4}{6}$$

Remember that the Multiplication Property of One stated that the product of a number and one is the number. This is true for fractions as well as for whole numbers. This property can be used to write equivalent fractions.

$$\frac{2}{3} \times 1 = \frac{2}{3} \times \frac{1}{1} = \frac{2 \cdot 1}{3 \cdot 1} = \frac{2}{3}$$

$$\frac{2}{3} \times 1 = \frac{2}{3} \times \boxed{\frac{2}{2}} = \frac{2 \cdot 2}{3 \cdot 2} = \frac{4}{6} \qquad \frac{4}{6} \text{ is equivalent to } \frac{2}{3}.$$

$$\frac{2}{3} \times 1 = \frac{2}{3} \times \boxed{\frac{4}{4}} = \frac{2 \cdot 4}{3 \cdot 4} = \frac{8}{12} \qquad \frac{8}{12} \text{ is equivalent to } \frac{2}{3}.$$

$\frac{2}{3}$ was built to the equivalent fractions $\frac{4}{6}$ and $\frac{8}{12}$.

Build a fraction that is equivalent to $\frac{5}{8}$ and has a denominator of 32.

Step 1 Divide the larger denominator by the smaller. $32 \div 8 = 4$

Step 2 Multiply the numerator and denominator of the given fraction by the quotient (4). $\frac{5 \cdot 4}{8 \cdot 4} = \frac{20}{32}$

$\frac{20}{32}$ is equivalent to $\frac{5}{8}$.

Example 9	Build a fraction that is equivalent to $\frac{2}{3}$ and has a denominator of 42.	**Example 10**	Build a fraction that is equivalent to $\frac{3}{5}$ and has a denominator of 45.
Solution	$42 \div 3 = 14 \qquad \frac{2 \cdot 14}{3 \cdot 14} = \frac{28}{42}$ $\frac{28}{42}$ is equivalent to $\frac{2}{3}$.	**Your solution**	$\frac{27}{45}$
Example 11	Build a fraction that is equivalent to 4 and has a denominator of 12.	**Example 12**	Build a fraction that is equivalent to 6 and has a denominator of 18.
Solution	Write 4 as $\frac{4}{1}$. $12 \div 1 = 12 \qquad \frac{4 \cdot 12}{1 \cdot 12} = \frac{48}{12}$ $\frac{48}{12}$ is equivalent to 4.	**Your solution**	$\frac{108}{18}$

Solutions on p. A13

| Objective C | To reduce a fraction to simplest form |

The fractions $\frac{4}{6}$ and $\frac{2}{3}$ are equivalent fractions.

$\frac{4}{6}$ has been reduced to $\frac{2}{3}$.

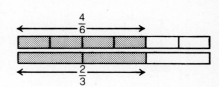

The Multiplication Property of One can be used to reduce fractions. Write the numerator and denominator of the given fraction as a product of factors. Write factors common to both the numerator and denominator as an improper fraction equivalent to 1.

$$\frac{4}{6} = \frac{2 \cdot 2}{2 \cdot 3} = \frac{2 \cdot 2}{2 \cdot 3} = \frac{2}{2} \cdot \frac{2}{3} = 1 \cdot \frac{2}{3} = \frac{2}{3}$$

The process of eliminating common factors is usually written as shown at the right. This method is called **canceling.**

$$\frac{4}{6} = \frac{\overset{1}{\cancel{2}} \cdot 2}{\underset{1}{\cancel{2}} \cdot 3} = \frac{2}{3}$$

A fraction should always be reduced to *simplest form*. A fraction is in **simplest form** when there are no common factors in the numerator and the denominator. To reduce a fraction to simplest form, write the prime factorizations of the numerator and denominator and cancel the common factors.

$$\frac{18}{30} = \frac{\overset{1}{\cancel{2}} \cdot \overset{1}{\cancel{3}} \cdot 3}{\underset{1}{\cancel{2}} \cdot \underset{1}{\cancel{3}} \cdot 5} = \frac{3}{5}$$

An improper fraction should be changed to a mixed number.

$$\frac{22}{6} = \frac{\overset{1}{\cancel{2}} \cdot 11}{\underset{1}{\cancel{2}} \cdot 3} = \frac{11}{3} = 3\frac{2}{3}$$

Example 13   Reduce $\frac{15}{40}$ to simplest form.

Solution $\frac{15}{40} = \frac{3 \cdot \overset{1}{\cancel{5}}}{2 \cdot 2 \cdot 2 \cdot \underset{1}{\cancel{5}}} = \frac{3}{8}$

Example 14   Reduce $\frac{16}{24}$ to simplest form.

Your solution $\frac{2}{3}$

Example 15   Reduce $\frac{6}{42}$ to simplest form.

Solution $\frac{6}{42} = \frac{\overset{1}{\cancel{2}} \cdot \overset{1}{\cancel{3}}}{\underset{1}{\cancel{2}} \cdot \underset{1}{\cancel{3}} \cdot 7} = \frac{1}{7}$

Example 16   Reduce $\frac{8}{56}$ to simplest form.

Your solution $\frac{1}{7}$

Example 17   Reduce $\frac{8}{9}$ to simplest form.

Solution $\frac{8}{9} = \frac{2 \cdot 2 \cdot 2}{3 \cdot 3} = \frac{8}{9}$

$\frac{8}{9}$ cannot be reduced, as there are no common factors in the numerator and denominator.

Example 18   Reduce $\frac{15}{32}$ to simplest form.

Your solution $\frac{15}{32}$

Example 19   Reduce $\frac{30}{12}$ to simplest form.

Solution $\frac{30}{12} = \frac{\overset{1}{\cancel{2}} \cdot \overset{1}{\cancel{3}} \cdot 5}{\underset{1}{\cancel{2}} \cdot 2 \cdot \underset{1}{\cancel{3}}} = \frac{5}{2} = 2\frac{1}{2}$

Example 20   Reduce $\frac{48}{36}$ to simplest form.

Your solution $1\frac{1}{3}$

Solutions on p. A13

Reference for
Computer
Tutor™

Objective D   To identify the order relation between two fractions

Recall that whole numbers can be associated with points on the number line. Fractions can also be associated with points on the number line.

The graph of $\frac{3}{4}$ on
the number line

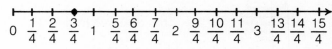

The number line can be used to determine the order relation between two fractions. A fraction that appears to the left of a given fraction is less than the given fraction. A fraction that appears to the right of a given fraction is greater than the given fraction.

$\frac{1}{8} < \frac{3}{8}$ $\frac{6}{8} > \frac{3}{8}$

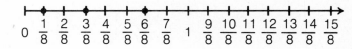

To find the order relation between two fractions with the same denominator, compare numerators. The fraction that has the smaller numerator is the smaller fraction. When the denominators are different, begin by building equivalent fractions with a common denominator; then compare numerators.

Find the order relation between $\frac{11}{18}$ and $\frac{5}{8}$.

The LCM of 18 and 8 is 72.

$\frac{11}{18} = \frac{44}{72}$ ← Smaller Numerator

$\frac{5}{8} = \frac{45}{72}$ ← Larger Numerator

$\frac{11}{18} < \frac{5}{8}$ or $\frac{5}{8} > \frac{11}{18}$

Example 21   Place the correct symbol, $<$ or $>$, between the numbers.

$$\frac{5}{17} \quad \frac{9}{17}$$

Solution $\frac{5}{17} < \frac{9}{17}$

Example 22   Place the correct symbol, $<$ or $>$, between the numbers.

$$\frac{4}{15} \quad \frac{11}{15}$$

Your solution $\frac{4}{15} < \frac{11}{15}$

Example 23   Place the correct symbol, $<$ or $>$, between the numbers.

$$\frac{5}{12} \quad \frac{7}{18}$$

Solution $\frac{5}{12} = \frac{15}{36}$

$\frac{7}{18} = \frac{14}{36}$

$\frac{5}{12} > \frac{7}{18}$

Example 24   Place the correct symbol, $<$ or $>$, between the numbers.

$$\frac{9}{14} \quad \frac{13}{21}$$

Your solution $\frac{9}{14} > \frac{13}{21}$

Solutions on p. A13

2.1A Exercises

Express the shaded portion of the circles as an improper fraction and as a mixed number.

1. 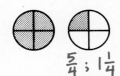 $\frac{5}{4}$; $1\frac{1}{4}$

2. 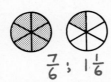 $\frac{7}{6}$; $1\frac{1}{6}$

3. 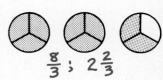 $\frac{8}{3}$; $2\frac{2}{3}$

4. 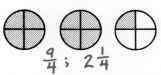 $\frac{9}{4}$; $2\frac{1}{4}$

5. 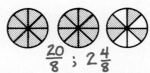 $\frac{20}{8}$; $2\frac{4}{8}$

6. 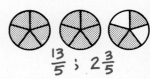 $\frac{13}{5}$; $2\frac{3}{5}$

Write the improper fraction as a mixed number or a whole number.

7. $\frac{11}{4}$

$2\frac{3}{4}$

8. $\frac{16}{3}$

$5\frac{1}{3}$

9. $\frac{20}{4}$

5

10. $\frac{18}{9}$

2

11. $\frac{9}{8}$

$1\frac{1}{8}$

12. $\frac{13}{4}$

$3\frac{1}{4}$

13. $\frac{23}{10}$

$2\frac{3}{10}$

14. $\frac{29}{2}$

$14\frac{1}{2}$

15. $\frac{48}{16}$

3

16. $\frac{51}{3}$

17

17. $\frac{8}{7}$

$1\frac{1}{7}$

18. $\frac{16}{9}$

$1\frac{7}{9}$

19. $\frac{7}{3}$

$2\frac{1}{3}$

20. $\frac{9}{5}$

$1\frac{4}{5}$

21. $\frac{16}{1}$

16

22. $\frac{23}{1}$

23

23. $\frac{17}{8}$

$2\frac{1}{8}$

24. $\frac{12}{5}$

$2\frac{2}{5}$

25. $\frac{9}{9}$

1

26. $\frac{3}{3}$

1

Write the mixed number as an improper fraction.

27. $2\frac{1}{3}$

$\frac{7}{3}$

28. $4\frac{2}{3}$

$\frac{14}{3}$

29. $6\frac{1}{2}$

$\frac{13}{2}$

30. $8\frac{2}{3}$

$\frac{26}{3}$

31. $6\frac{5}{6}$

$\frac{41}{6}$

32. $7\frac{3}{8}$

$\frac{59}{8}$

33. $9\frac{1}{4}$

$\frac{37}{4}$

34. $6\frac{1}{4}$

$\frac{25}{4}$

35. $10\frac{1}{2}$

$\frac{21}{2}$

36. $15\frac{1}{8}$

$\frac{121}{8}$

37. $8\frac{1}{9}$

$\frac{73}{9}$

38. $3\frac{5}{12}$

$\frac{41}{12}$

39. $5\frac{3}{11}$

$\frac{58}{11}$

40. $3\frac{7}{9}$

$\frac{34}{9}$

41. $2\frac{5}{8}$

$\frac{21}{8}$

42. $12\frac{2}{3}$

$\frac{38}{3}$

43. $1\frac{5}{8}$

$\frac{13}{8}$

44. $5\frac{3}{7}$

$\frac{38}{7}$

45. $11\frac{1}{9}$

$\frac{100}{9}$

46. $12\frac{3}{5}$

$\frac{63}{5}$

2.1B Exercises

Build an equivalent fraction with the given denominator.

47. $\dfrac{3}{16} = \dfrac{9}{48}$ 48. $\dfrac{5}{9} = \dfrac{45}{81}$ 49. $\dfrac{3}{8} = \dfrac{12}{32}$ 50. $\dfrac{7}{11} = \dfrac{21}{33}$ 51. $\dfrac{3}{17} = \dfrac{9}{51}$

52. $\dfrac{7}{10} = \dfrac{63}{90}$ 53. $\dfrac{3}{4} = \dfrac{12}{16}$ 54. $\dfrac{5}{8} = \dfrac{20}{32}$ 55. $3 = \dfrac{27}{9}$ 56. $5 = \dfrac{125}{25}$

57. $\dfrac{1}{16} = \dfrac{3}{48}$ 58. $\dfrac{11}{15} = \dfrac{44}{60}$ 59. $\dfrac{2}{3} = \dfrac{12}{18}$ 60. $\dfrac{5}{9} = \dfrac{20}{36}$ 61. $\dfrac{7}{8} = \dfrac{28}{32}$

62. $\dfrac{5}{9} = \dfrac{10}{18}$ 63. $\dfrac{7}{9} = \dfrac{35}{45}$ 64. $\dfrac{5}{6} = \dfrac{35}{42}$ 65. $\dfrac{15}{16} = \dfrac{60}{64}$ 66. $\dfrac{5}{8} = \dfrac{30}{48}$

2.1C Exercises

Reduce the fraction to simplest form.

67. $\dfrac{4}{12}$ $\dfrac{1}{3}$ 68. $\dfrac{8}{22}$ $\dfrac{4}{11}$ 69. $\dfrac{22}{44}$ $\dfrac{1}{2}$ 70. $\dfrac{2}{14}$ $\dfrac{1}{7}$ 71. $\dfrac{2}{12}$ $\dfrac{1}{6}$

72. $\dfrac{6}{25}$ $\dfrac{6}{25}$ 73. $\dfrac{50}{75}$ $\dfrac{2}{3}$ 74. $\dfrac{40}{36}$ $1\dfrac{1}{9}$ 75. $\dfrac{12}{8}$ $1\dfrac{1}{2}$ 76. $\dfrac{36}{9}$ 4

77. $\dfrac{14}{35}$ $\dfrac{2}{5}$ 78. $\dfrac{75}{25}$ 3 79. $\dfrac{8}{60}$ $\dfrac{2}{15}$ 80. $\dfrac{16}{84}$ $\dfrac{4}{21}$ 81. $\dfrac{14}{45}$ $\dfrac{14}{45}$

82. $\dfrac{20}{44}$ $\dfrac{5}{11}$ 83. $\dfrac{12}{35}$ $\dfrac{12}{35}$ 84. $\dfrac{8}{36}$ $\dfrac{2}{9}$ 85. $\dfrac{28}{44}$ $\dfrac{7}{11}$ 86. $\dfrac{12}{16}$ $\dfrac{3}{4}$

2.1D Exercises

Place the correct symbol, $<$ or $>$, between the two numbers.

87. $\dfrac{11}{40} < \dfrac{19}{40}$ 88. $\dfrac{92}{103} > \dfrac{19}{103}$ 89. $\dfrac{2}{3} < \dfrac{5}{7}$ 90. $\dfrac{2}{5} > \dfrac{3}{8}$

91. $\dfrac{5}{8} > \dfrac{7}{12}$ 92. $\dfrac{11}{16} < \dfrac{17}{24}$ 93. $\dfrac{7}{9} < \dfrac{11}{12}$ 94. $\dfrac{5}{12} < \dfrac{7}{15}$

95. $\dfrac{13}{14} > \dfrac{19}{21}$ 96. $\dfrac{13}{18} > \dfrac{7}{12}$ 97. $\dfrac{7}{24} < \dfrac{11}{30}$ 98. $\dfrac{13}{36} < \dfrac{19}{48}$

Section 2   # Addition and Subtraction of Fractions

Objective A   ## To add fractions

Reference for
Computer
Tutor™

Fractions with the same denominator are added by adding the numerators and placing the sum over the common denominator. After adding, reduce the fraction to simplest form.

Add: $\frac{2}{7} + \frac{4}{7}$

$$\begin{array}{r} \frac{2}{7} \\ +\frac{4}{7} \\ \hline \frac{6}{7} \end{array}$$

Add the numerators and place the sum over the common denominator.

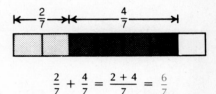

$$\frac{2}{7} + \frac{4}{7} = \frac{2+4}{7} = \frac{6}{7}$$

To add fractions with unlike denominators, first rewrite the fractions as equivalent fractions with a common denominator.

Add: $\frac{1}{2} + \frac{1}{3}$

Step 1
Find the LCM of the denominators 2 and 3. LCM = 6. The LCM of denominators is sometimes called the **least common denominator** (LCD).

Step 2
Built equivalent fractions using the LCM.

$$\frac{1}{2} = \frac{3}{6}$$
$$+\frac{1}{3} = \frac{2}{6}$$

Step 3
Add the fractions.

$$\frac{1}{2} = \frac{3}{6}$$
$$+\frac{1}{3} = \frac{2}{6}$$
$$\overline{\qquad \frac{5}{6}}$$

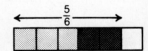

To add a whole number and a mixed number, write the fraction, then add the whole numbers.

Add: $7\frac{2}{5} + 4$

Step 1 Write the fraction.

$$\begin{array}{r} 7\frac{2}{5} \\ +4 \\ \hline \frac{2}{5} \end{array}$$

Step 2 Add the whole numbers.

$$\begin{array}{r} 7\frac{2}{5} \\ +4 \\ \hline 11\frac{2}{5} \end{array}$$

To add two mixed numbers, add the fractional parts and then add the whole numbers. Remember to reduce the sum to simplest form.

Add: $5\frac{4}{9} + 6\frac{14}{15}$

Step 1   Add the fractional parts.

$$5\frac{4}{9} = 5\frac{20}{45}$$
$$+6\frac{14}{15} = 6\frac{42}{45}$$
$$\frac{62}{45}$$

The LCM of 9 and 15 is 45.

Step 2   Add the whole numbers.

$$5\frac{4}{9} = 5\frac{20}{45}$$
$$+6\frac{14}{15} = 6\frac{42}{45}$$
$$11\frac{62}{45} = 11 + 1\frac{17}{45} = 12\frac{17}{45}$$

Example 1   Add: $\frac{5}{8} + \frac{7}{9}$

Solution

$$\frac{5}{8} = \frac{45}{72}$$
$$+\frac{7}{9} = \frac{56}{72}$$
$$\frac{101}{72} = 1\frac{29}{72}$$

The LCM of 8 and 9 is 72.

Example 2   Add: $\frac{7}{8} + \frac{11}{15}$

Your solution

$$1\frac{73}{120}$$

Example 3   Add: $\frac{2}{3} + \frac{3}{5} + \frac{5}{6}$

Solution

$$\frac{2}{3} = \frac{20}{30}$$
$$\frac{3}{5} = \frac{18}{30}$$
$$+\frac{5}{6} = \frac{25}{30}$$
$$\frac{63}{30} = 2\frac{3}{30} = 2\frac{1}{10}$$

The LCM of 3, 5, and 6 is 30.

Example 4   Add: $\frac{3}{4} + \frac{4}{5} + \frac{5}{8}$

Your solution

$$2\frac{7}{40}$$

Example 5   Add: $5\frac{2}{3} + 11\frac{5}{6} + 12\frac{7}{9}$

Solution

$$5\frac{2}{3} = 5\frac{12}{18}$$
$$11\frac{5}{6} = 11\frac{15}{18}$$
$$+12\frac{7}{9} = 12\frac{14}{18}$$
$$28\frac{41}{18} = 30\frac{5}{18}$$

The LCM of 3, 6, and 9 is 18.

Example 6   Add: $7\frac{4}{5} + 6\frac{7}{10} + 13\frac{11}{15}$

Your solution

$$28\frac{7}{30}$$

Solutions on p. A14

Objective B

Reference for
Computer
Tutor™

To subtract fractions

Fractions with the same denominator are subtracted by subtracting the numerators and placing the difference over the common denominator. After subtracting, reduce the fraction to simplest form.

Subtract: $\frac{5}{7} - \frac{3}{7}$

$\frac{5}{7}$
$-\frac{3}{7}$
$\frac{2}{7}$

Subtract the numerators and place the difference over the common denominator.

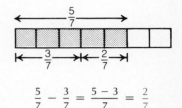

$$\frac{5}{7} - \frac{3}{7} = \frac{5-3}{7} = \frac{2}{7}$$

To subtract fractions with unlike denominators, first rewrite the fractions as equivalent fractions with a common denominator.

Subtract: $\frac{5}{6} - \frac{1}{4}$

Step 1
Find the LCM of the denominators 6 and 4. LCM = 12. The LCM of denominators is sometimes called the **least common denominator** (LCD).

Step 2
Build equivalent fractions using the LCM.

$\frac{5}{6} = \frac{10}{12}$
$-\frac{1}{4} = \frac{3}{12}$

Step 3
Subtract the fractions.

$\frac{5}{6} = \frac{10}{12}$
$-\frac{1}{4} = \frac{3}{12}$
$\frac{7}{12}$

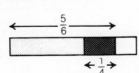 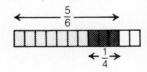 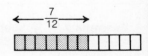

To subtract mixed numbers, subtract the fractional parts and then subtract the whole numbers.

Subtract: $5\frac{5}{6} - 2\frac{3}{4}$

Step 1 Subtract the fractional parts.

$5\frac{5}{6} = 5\frac{10}{12}$
$-2\frac{3}{4} = 2\frac{9}{12}$
$\frac{1}{12}$

The LCM of 6 and 4 is 12.

Step 2 Subtract the whole numbers.

$5\frac{5}{6} = 5\frac{10}{12}$
$-2\frac{3}{4} = 2\frac{9}{12}$
$3\frac{1}{12}$

As with whole numbers, subtraction of mixed numbers sometimes involves borrowing.

Subtract: $5 - 2\frac{5}{8}$

Step 1
Borrow 1 from 5.

$$5 = \overset{4}{\cancel{5}}1$$

$$-2\frac{5}{8} = 2\frac{5}{8}$$

Step 2
Write 1 as a fraction so that the fractions have the same denominators.

$$5 = 4\frac{8}{8}$$

$$-2\frac{5}{8} = 2\frac{5}{8}$$

Step 3
Subtract the mixed numbers.

$$5 = 4\frac{8}{8}$$

$$-2\frac{5}{8} = 2\frac{5}{8}$$

$$2\frac{3}{8}$$

Subtract: $7\frac{1}{6} - 2\frac{5}{8}$

Step 1
Build equivalent fractions using the LCM.

$$7\frac{1}{6} = 7\frac{4}{24}$$

$$-2\frac{5}{8} = 2\frac{15}{24}$$

Step 2
Borrow 1 from 7 and add it to $\frac{4}{24}$. Write as an improper fraction.

$$7\frac{1}{6} = 7\overset{6}{1}\frac{4}{24} = 6\frac{28}{24}$$

$$-2\frac{5}{8} = \quad 2\frac{15}{24} = 2\frac{15}{24}$$

Step 3
Subtract the mixed numbers.

$$7\frac{1}{6} = 6\frac{28}{24}$$

$$-2\frac{5}{8} = 2\frac{15}{24}$$

$$4\frac{13}{24}$$

Example 7   Subtract: $15\frac{7}{8} - 12\frac{2}{3}$

Solution

$$15\frac{7}{8} = 15\frac{21}{24}$$ The LCM of 8 and 3 is 24.

$$-12\frac{2}{3} = 12\frac{16}{24}$$

$$3\frac{5}{24}$$

Example 8   Subtract: $17\frac{5}{9} - 11\frac{5}{12}$

Your solution

$6\frac{5}{36}$

Example 9   Subtract: $11\frac{5}{12} - 2\frac{11}{16}$

Solution

The LCM of 12 and 16 is 48.

$$11\frac{5}{12} = 11\frac{20}{48} = 10\frac{68}{48}$$

$$-\ 2\frac{11}{16} = \ 2\frac{33}{48} = \ \ 2\frac{33}{48}$$

$$8\frac{35}{48}$$

Example 10   Subtract: $21\frac{7}{9} - 7\frac{11}{12}$

Your solution

$13\frac{31}{36}$

Solutions on p. A14

2.2A Exercises

Add.

1. $\frac{1}{2} + \frac{1}{2}$
1

2. $\frac{1}{3} + \frac{2}{3}$
1

3. $\frac{8}{11} + \frac{7}{11}$
$1\frac{4}{11}$

4. $\frac{9}{13} + \frac{7}{13}$
$1\frac{3}{13}$

5. $\frac{3}{5} + \frac{8}{5} + \frac{3}{5}$
$2\frac{4}{5}$

6. $\frac{3}{8} + \frac{5}{8} + \frac{7}{8}$
$1\frac{7}{8}$

7. $\frac{3}{4} + \frac{1}{4} + \frac{5}{4}$
$2\frac{1}{4}$

8. $\frac{2}{7} + \frac{4}{7} + \frac{5}{7}$
$1\frac{4}{7}$

9. $\frac{1}{2} + \frac{2}{3}$
$1\frac{1}{6}$

10. $\frac{2}{3} + \frac{1}{4}$
$\frac{11}{12}$

11. $\frac{3}{14} + \frac{5}{7}$
$\frac{13}{14}$

12. $\frac{3}{5} + \frac{7}{10}$
$1\frac{3}{10}$

13. $\frac{5}{9} + \frac{7}{15}$
$1\frac{1}{45}$

14. $\frac{8}{15} + \frac{7}{20}$
$\frac{53}{60}$

15. $\frac{1}{6} + \frac{7}{9}$
$\frac{17}{18}$

16. $\frac{3}{8} + \frac{9}{14}$
$1\frac{1}{56}$

17. $\frac{5}{12} + \frac{5}{16}$
$\frac{35}{48}$

18. $\frac{13}{40} + \frac{12}{25}$
$\frac{161}{200}$

19. $\frac{3}{20} + \frac{7}{30}$
$\frac{23}{60}$

20. $\frac{5}{12} + \frac{7}{30}$
$\frac{13}{20}$

21. $\frac{3}{7} + \frac{4}{21}$
$\frac{13}{21}$

22. $\frac{3}{10} + \frac{7}{45}$
$\frac{41}{90}$

23. $\frac{2}{7} + \frac{3}{8}$
$\frac{37}{56}$

24. $\frac{5}{8} + \frac{4}{9}$
$1\frac{5}{72}$

25. $\frac{3}{14} + \frac{6}{49}$
$\frac{33}{98}$

26. $1\frac{1}{2}$
$+2\frac{1}{6}$
$3\frac{2}{3}$

27. $2\frac{2}{5}$
$+3\frac{3}{10}$
$5\frac{7}{10}$

28. $4\frac{1}{2}$
$+5\frac{7}{12}$
$10\frac{1}{12}$

29. $3\frac{3}{8}$
$+2\frac{5}{16}$
$5\frac{11}{16}$

30. $2\frac{7}{9}$
$+3\frac{5}{12}$
$6\frac{7}{36}$

31. $4\frac{7}{15}$
$+3\frac{11}{12}$
$8\frac{23}{60}$

32. 4
$+5\frac{2}{7}$
$9\frac{2}{7}$

33. $6\frac{8}{9}$
$+12$
$18\frac{8}{9}$

34. $3\frac{5}{8}$
$+2\frac{11}{20}$
$6\frac{7}{40}$

35. $4\frac{5}{12}$
$+6\frac{11}{18}$
$11\frac{1}{36}$

36. $10\frac{2}{7}$
$+7\frac{21}{35}$
$17\frac{31}{35}$

37. $16\frac{2}{3}$
$+8\frac{1}{4}$
$24\frac{11}{12}$

38. $7\frac{5}{12}$
$+2\frac{9}{16}$
$9\frac{47}{48}$

39. $9\frac{1}{2}$
$+3\frac{3}{11}$
$12\frac{17}{22}$

40. $6\frac{1}{3}$
$+2\frac{3}{13}$
$8\frac{22}{39}$

Add.

41. $\dfrac{1}{3} + \dfrac{5}{6} + \dfrac{7}{9}$

42. $\dfrac{2}{3} + \dfrac{5}{6} + \dfrac{7}{12}$

43. $\dfrac{5}{6} + \dfrac{1}{12} + \dfrac{5}{16}$

44. $\dfrac{2}{9} + \dfrac{7}{15} + \dfrac{4}{21}$

45. $\dfrac{2}{3} + \dfrac{1}{5} + \dfrac{7}{12}$

46. $\dfrac{3}{4} + \dfrac{4}{5} + \dfrac{7}{12}$

47. $\dfrac{1}{4} + \dfrac{4}{5} + \dfrac{5}{9}$

48. $\dfrac{2}{3} + \dfrac{3}{5} + \dfrac{7}{8}$

49. $\dfrac{5}{16} + \dfrac{11}{18} + \dfrac{17}{24}$

50. $\dfrac{3}{10} + \dfrac{14}{15} + \dfrac{9}{25}$

51. $\dfrac{2}{3} + \dfrac{5}{8} + \dfrac{7}{9}$

52. $\dfrac{1}{3} + \dfrac{2}{9} + \dfrac{7}{8}$

53. $\dfrac{5}{6} + \dfrac{1}{2} + \dfrac{3}{11}$

54. $\dfrac{9}{11} + \dfrac{1}{2} + \dfrac{1}{6}$

55. $\dfrac{3}{4} + \dfrac{5}{6} + \dfrac{7}{8}$

56. $16\dfrac{5}{8} + 3\dfrac{7}{20}$

57. $2\dfrac{3}{8} + 4\dfrac{9}{20}$

58. $2\dfrac{7}{10} + 7\dfrac{11}{15}$

59. $3\dfrac{3}{8} + 8\dfrac{5}{12}$

60. $8\dfrac{21}{40} + 6\dfrac{21}{32}$

61. $8\dfrac{29}{30} + 7\dfrac{11}{40}$

62. $17\dfrac{5}{16} + 3\dfrac{11}{24}$

63. $17\dfrac{3}{8} + 7\dfrac{7}{20}$

64. $14\dfrac{7}{12} + 29\dfrac{13}{21}$

65. $5\dfrac{7}{8} + 27\dfrac{5}{12}$

66. $7\dfrac{5}{6} + 3\dfrac{5}{9}$

67. $7\dfrac{5}{9} + 2\dfrac{7}{12}$

68. $3\dfrac{1}{2} + 2\dfrac{3}{4} + 1\dfrac{5}{6}$

69. $2\dfrac{1}{2} + 3\dfrac{2}{3} + 4\dfrac{1}{4}$

70. $3\dfrac{1}{3} + 7\dfrac{1}{5} + 2\dfrac{1}{7}$

71. $3\dfrac{1}{2} + 3\dfrac{1}{5} + 8\dfrac{1}{9}$

72. $6\dfrac{5}{9} + 6\dfrac{5}{12} + 2\dfrac{5}{18}$

73. $2\dfrac{3}{8} + 4\dfrac{7}{12} + 3\dfrac{5}{16}$

74. $2\dfrac{1}{8} + 4\dfrac{2}{9} + 5\dfrac{17}{18}$

75. $3\dfrac{5}{6} + 7\dfrac{7}{8} + 3\dfrac{1}{12}$

76. $7\dfrac{2}{5} + 3\dfrac{7}{10} + 5\dfrac{11}{15}$

2.2B Exercises

Subtract.

77. $\dfrac{11}{24}$
$-\dfrac{5}{24}$
$\dfrac{1}{4}$

78. $\dfrac{23}{30}$
$-\dfrac{13}{30}$
$\dfrac{1}{3}$

79. $\dfrac{17}{42}$
$-\dfrac{5}{42}$
$\dfrac{2}{7}$

80. $\dfrac{29}{48}$
$-\dfrac{13}{48}$
$\dfrac{1}{3}$

81. $\dfrac{2}{3}$
$-\dfrac{1}{6}$
$\dfrac{1}{2}$

82. $\dfrac{7}{8}$
$-\dfrac{5}{16}$
$\dfrac{9}{16}$

83. $\dfrac{5}{8}$
$-\dfrac{2}{7}$
$\dfrac{19}{56}$

84. $\dfrac{5}{6}$
$-\dfrac{3}{7}$
$\dfrac{17}{42}$

85. $\dfrac{5}{7}$
$-\dfrac{3}{14}$
$\dfrac{1}{2}$

86. $\dfrac{7}{10}$
$-\dfrac{3}{5}$
$\dfrac{1}{10}$

87. $\dfrac{5}{9}$
$-\dfrac{7}{15}$
$\dfrac{4}{45}$

88. $\dfrac{8}{15}$
$-\dfrac{7}{20}$
$\dfrac{11}{60}$

89. $\dfrac{7}{9}$
$-\dfrac{1}{6}$
$\dfrac{11}{18}$

90. $\dfrac{9}{14}$
$-\dfrac{3}{8}$
$\dfrac{15}{56}$

91. $\dfrac{5}{12}$
$-\dfrac{5}{16}$
$\dfrac{5}{48}$

92. $\dfrac{12}{25}$
$-\dfrac{13}{40}$
$\dfrac{31}{200}$

93. $\dfrac{7}{30}$
$-\dfrac{3}{20}$
$\dfrac{1}{12}$

94. $\dfrac{5}{12}$
$-\dfrac{7}{30}$
$\dfrac{11}{60}$

95. $\dfrac{2}{3}$
$-\dfrac{6}{19}$
$\dfrac{20}{57}$

96. $\dfrac{1}{2}$
$-\dfrac{3}{29}$
$\dfrac{23}{58}$

97. $\dfrac{5}{9}$
$-\dfrac{1}{12}$
$\dfrac{17}{36}$

98. $\dfrac{11}{16}$
$-\dfrac{5}{12}$
$\dfrac{13}{48}$

99. $\dfrac{46}{51}$
$-\dfrac{3}{17}$
$\dfrac{37}{51}$

100. $\dfrac{9}{16}$
$-\dfrac{17}{32}$
$\dfrac{1}{32}$

101. $\dfrac{21}{35}$
$-\dfrac{5}{14}$
$\dfrac{17}{70}$

102. $\dfrac{19}{40}$
$-\dfrac{3}{16}$
$\dfrac{23}{80}$

103. $\dfrac{29}{60}$
$-\dfrac{3}{40}$
$\dfrac{49}{120}$

104. $\dfrac{53}{70}$
$-\dfrac{13}{35}$
$\dfrac{27}{70}$

105. $\dfrac{2}{9}$
$-\dfrac{1}{42}$
$\dfrac{25}{126}$

106. $\dfrac{11}{15}$
$-\dfrac{5}{27}$
$\dfrac{74}{135}$

107. $\dfrac{7}{16}$
$-\dfrac{5}{24}$
$\dfrac{11}{48}$

108. $\dfrac{11}{18}$
$-\dfrac{7}{24}$
$\dfrac{23}{72}$

109. $\dfrac{7}{8}$
$-\dfrac{5}{9}$
$\dfrac{23}{72}$

110. $\dfrac{5}{6}$
$-\dfrac{3}{5}$
$\dfrac{7}{30}$

111. $\dfrac{21}{29}$
$-\dfrac{3}{8}$
$\dfrac{81}{232}$

112. $\dfrac{17}{31}$
$-\dfrac{4}{9}$
$\dfrac{29}{279}$

113. $5\dfrac{7}{12}$
$-2\dfrac{5}{12}$
$3\dfrac{1}{6}$

114. $16\dfrac{11}{15}$
$-11\dfrac{8}{15}$
$5\dfrac{1}{5}$

115. $72\dfrac{21}{23}$
$-16\dfrac{17}{23}$
$56\dfrac{4}{23}$

116. $19\dfrac{16}{17}$
$-9\dfrac{7}{17}$
$10\dfrac{9}{17}$

Subtract.

117. $6\frac{1}{3}$
-2
$4\frac{1}{3}$

118. $5\frac{7}{8}$
-1
$4\frac{7}{8}$

119. 10
$-6\frac{1}{3}$
$3\frac{2}{3}$

120. 3
$-2\frac{5}{21}$
$\frac{16}{21}$

121. $6\frac{2}{5}$
$-4\frac{4}{5}$
$1\frac{3}{5}$

122. $16\frac{3}{8}$
$-10\frac{7}{8}$
$5\frac{1}{2}$

123. $25\frac{4}{9}$
$-16\frac{7}{9}$
$8\frac{2}{3}$

124. $8\frac{3}{7}$
$-2\frac{6}{7}$
$5\frac{4}{7}$

125. $16\frac{2}{5}$
$-8\frac{4}{9}$
$7\frac{43}{45}$

126. $23\frac{7}{8}$
$-16\frac{2}{3}$
$7\frac{5}{24}$

127. 6
$-4\frac{3}{5}$
$1\frac{2}{5}$

128. 12
$-2\frac{7}{9}$
$9\frac{2}{9}$

129. $16\frac{3}{20}$
$-1\frac{7}{20}$
$14\frac{4}{5}$

130. $16\frac{3}{10}$
$-7\frac{9}{10}$
$8\frac{2}{5}$

131. $25\frac{5}{12}$
$-4\frac{17}{24}$
$20\frac{17}{24}$

132. $16\frac{5}{8}$
$-13\frac{11}{12}$
$2\frac{17}{24}$

133. $6\frac{1}{8}$
-3
$3\frac{1}{8}$

134. $32\frac{4}{15}$
-17
$15\frac{4}{15}$

135. 32
$-6\frac{7}{15}$
$25\frac{8}{15}$

136. 47
$-9\frac{7}{20}$
$37\frac{13}{20}$

137. $14\frac{3}{5}$
$-7\frac{8}{9}$
$6\frac{32}{45}$

138. $17\frac{3}{4}$
$-8\frac{10}{11}$
$8\frac{37}{44}$

139. $3\frac{9}{32}$
$-1\frac{11}{40}$
$2\frac{1}{160}$

140. $7\frac{11}{30}$
$-5\frac{13}{36}$
$2\frac{1}{180}$

141. $9\frac{13}{40}$
$-7\frac{12}{25}$
$1\frac{169}{200}$

142. $13\frac{27}{50}$
$-5\frac{39}{40}$
$7\frac{113}{200}$

143. $65\frac{8}{35}$
$-16\frac{11}{14}$
$48\frac{31}{70}$

144. $82\frac{4}{33}$
$-16\frac{5}{22}$
$65\frac{59}{66}$

145. $101\frac{2}{9}$
-16
$85\frac{2}{9}$

146. $77\frac{5}{18}$
-61
$16\frac{5}{18}$

147. 17
$-7\frac{8}{13}$
$9\frac{5}{13}$

148. 7
$-3\frac{22}{45}$
$3\frac{23}{45}$

149. $25\frac{7}{15}$
$-14\frac{19}{36}$
$10\frac{169}{180}$

150. $14\frac{17}{24}$
$-10\frac{31}{36}$
$3\frac{61}{72}$

151. $61\frac{5}{21}$
$-28\frac{5}{9}$
$32\frac{43}{63}$

152. $26\frac{7}{20}$
$-13\frac{11}{14}$
$12\frac{79}{140}$

153. $137\frac{3}{5}$
$-69\frac{7}{12}$
$68\frac{1}{60}$

154. $267\frac{4}{7}$
$-129\frac{2}{9}$
$138\frac{22}{63}$

155. $13\frac{7}{25}$
$-6\frac{9}{20}$
$6\frac{83}{100}$

156. $68\frac{5}{18}$
$-13\frac{17}{24}$
$54\frac{41}{72}$

Section 3 Multiplication and Division of Fractions

Reference for
Computer
Tutor™

Objective A To multiply fractions

The product of two fractions is the product of the numerators over the product of the denominators.

Multiply: $\frac{2}{3} \times \frac{4}{5}$

Multiply the numerators.
Multiply the denominators.

$$\frac{2}{3} \times \frac{4}{5} = \frac{2 \cdot 4}{3 \cdot 5} = \frac{8}{15}$$

The product $\frac{2}{3} \times \frac{4}{5}$ can be read "$\frac{2}{3}$ times $\frac{4}{5}$" or "$\frac{2}{3}$ of $\frac{4}{5}$."

Reading the times sign as "of" is useful in application problems involving fractions and in diagramming the product of fractions.

$\frac{4}{5}$ of the bar is shaded.

Shade $\frac{2}{3}$ of the $\frac{4}{5}$ already shaded.

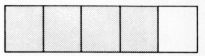

$\frac{8}{15}$ of the bar is then shaded.

$\frac{2}{3}$ of $\frac{4}{5}$ = $\frac{8}{15}$

After multiplying two fractions, reduce the product to simplest form.

Multiply: $\frac{3}{4} \times \frac{14}{15}$

Step 1
Multiply the fractions.

Step 2
Write the prime factorization of each number.

Step 3
Cancel the common factors.

Step 4
Multiply the numbers remaining in the numerator. Multiply the numbers remaining in the denominator.

$$\frac{3}{4} \times \frac{14}{15} = \frac{3 \cdot 14}{4 \cdot 15} \qquad = \frac{3 \cdot 2 \cdot 7}{2 \cdot 2 \cdot 3 \cdot 5} \qquad = \frac{\overset{1}{\cancel{3}} \cdot \overset{1}{\cancel{2}} \cdot 7}{\cancel{2} \cdot 2 \cdot \underset{1}{\cancel{3}} \cdot 5} \qquad = \frac{7}{10}$$

To multiply a whole number by a fraction or mixed number, first write the whole number as a fraction with a denominator of 1.

Multiply: $4 \times \frac{3}{7}$

Write 4 with a denominator of 1; then multiply the fractions.

$$\boxed{4} \times \frac{3}{7} = \boxed{\frac{4}{1}} \times \frac{3}{7} = \frac{4 \cdot 3}{1 \cdot 7} = \frac{2 \cdot 2 \cdot 3}{7} = \frac{12}{7} = 1\frac{5}{7}$$

When one of the factors in a product is a mixed number, write the mixed number as an improper fraction before multiplying.

Multiply: $2\frac{1}{3} \times \frac{3}{14}$

Write $2\frac{1}{3}$ as an improper fraction; then multiply the fractions.

$$\boxed{2\frac{1}{3}} \times \frac{3}{14} = \boxed{\frac{7}{3}} \times \frac{3}{14} = \frac{7 \cdot 3}{3 \cdot 14} = \frac{\overset{1}{7} \cdot \overset{1}{\cancel{3}}}{\cancel{3} \cdot 2 \cdot \underset{1}{\cancel{7}}} = \frac{1}{2}$$

Multiply: $5\frac{3}{5} \times 4\frac{2}{3}$

Write the mixed numbers as improper fractions; then multiply the fractions.

$$5\frac{3}{5} \times 4\frac{2}{3} = \frac{28}{5} \times \frac{14}{3} = \frac{28 \cdot 14}{5 \cdot 3} = \frac{2 \cdot 2 \cdot 7 \cdot 2 \cdot 7}{5 \cdot 3} = \frac{392}{15} = 26\frac{2}{15}$$

Example 1   Multiply: $4\frac{5}{6} \times \frac{12}{13}$

Solution $4\frac{5}{6} \times \frac{12}{13} = \frac{29}{6} \times \frac{12}{13} =$

$\frac{29 \cdot 12}{6 \cdot 13} = \frac{29 \cdot \overset{1}{\cancel{2}} \cdot 2 \cdot \overset{1}{\cancel{3}}}{\underset{1}{\cancel{2}} \cdot \underset{1}{\cancel{3}} \cdot 13} =$

$\frac{58}{13} = 4\frac{6}{13}$

Example 2   Multiply: $5\frac{2}{5} \times \frac{5}{9}$

Your solution

3

Example 3   Multiply: $5\frac{2}{3} \times 4\frac{1}{2}$

Solution $5\frac{2}{3} \times 4\frac{1}{2} = \frac{17}{3} \times \frac{9}{2} = \frac{17 \cdot 9}{3 \cdot 2} =$

$\frac{17 \cdot \overset{1}{\cancel{3}} \cdot 3}{\underset{1}{\cancel{3}} \cdot 2} = \frac{51}{2} = 25\frac{1}{2}$

Example 4   Multiply: $3\frac{2}{5} \times 6\frac{1}{4}$

Your solution

$21\frac{1}{4}$

Example 5   Multiply: $4\frac{2}{5} \times 7$

Solution $4\frac{2}{5} \times 7 = \frac{22}{5} \times \frac{7}{1} = \frac{22 \cdot 7}{5 \cdot 1} =$
$\frac{2 \cdot 11 \cdot 7}{5} = \frac{154}{5} = 30\frac{4}{5}$

Example 6   Multiply: $3\frac{2}{7} \times 6$

Your solution

$19\frac{5}{7}$

Solutions on p. A15

Objective B	# To divide fractions

**Reference for
Computer
Tutor™**

The **reciprocal** of a fraction is the fraction with the numerator and denominator interchanged. The process of interchanging the numerator and denominator of a fraction is called **inverting.**

The reciprocal of $\frac{2}{3}$ is $\frac{3}{2}$.

To find the reciprocal of a whole number, first write the whole number as a fraction with a denominator of 1; then find the reciprocal of that fraction.

The reciprocal of 5 is $\frac{1}{5}$. $\qquad \left(\text{Think } 5 = \frac{5}{1} \right)$

Reciprocals are used to rewrite division problems as related multiplication problems. Look at the following two problems.

$$8 \div 2 = 4 \qquad\qquad\qquad 8 \times \frac{1}{2} = 4$$

8 divided by 2 is **4.** $\qquad$ 8 times the reciprocal of 2 is **4.**

"Divided by" means the same thing as "times the reciprocal of." So "÷ 2" can be replaced with "$\times \frac{1}{2}$," and the answer will be the same. Fractions are divided by making this replacement.

Divide: $\quad \frac{2}{3} \div \frac{3}{4}$

$$\frac{2}{3} \div \frac{3}{4} = \frac{2}{3} \times \frac{4}{3} = \frac{2 \cdot 4}{3 \cdot 3} = \frac{2 \cdot 2 \cdot 2}{3 \cdot 3} = \frac{8}{9}$$

To divide a fraction and a whole number, first write the whole number as a fraction with a denominator of 1.

Divide: $\quad \frac{3}{7} \div 5$

Write 5 with a denominator of 1. Then divide the fractions.

$$\frac{3}{7} \div \boxed{5} = \frac{3}{7} \div \boxed{\frac{5}{1}} = \frac{3}{7} \times \frac{1}{5} = \frac{3 \cdot 1}{7 \cdot 5} = \frac{3}{35}$$

When one of the numbers in a quotient is a mixed number, write the mixed number as an improper fraction before dividing.

Divide: $4\frac{2}{3} \div \frac{8}{15}$

Write $4\frac{2}{3}$ as an improper fraction; then divide the fractions.

$$\boxed{4\frac{2}{3}} \div \frac{8}{15} = \boxed{\frac{14}{3}} \div \frac{8}{15} = \frac{14}{3} \times \frac{15}{8} = \frac{14 \cdot 15}{3 \cdot 8} = \frac{\overset{1}{\cancel{2}} \cdot 7 \cdot \overset{1}{\cancel{3}} \cdot 5}{\cancel{3} \cdot 2 \cdot \cancel{2} \cdot 2} = \frac{35}{4} = 8\frac{3}{4}$$

Divide: $1\frac{13}{15} \div 4\frac{4}{5}$

Write the mixed numbers as improper fractions; then divide the fractions.

$$1\frac{13}{15} \div 4\frac{4}{5} = \frac{28}{15} \div \frac{24}{5} = \frac{28}{15} \times \frac{5}{24} = \frac{28 \cdot 5}{15 \cdot 24} = \frac{\overset{1}{\cancel{2}} \cdot \overset{1}{\cancel{2}} \cdot 7 \cdot \overset{1}{\cancel{5}}}{3 \cdot \cancel{5} \cdot \underset{1}{\cancel{2}} \cdot \underset{1}{\cancel{2}} \cdot 2 \cdot 3} = \frac{7}{18}$$

Example 7   Divide: $\frac{3}{8} \div 2\frac{1}{10}$

Solution $\frac{3}{8} \div 2\frac{1}{10} = \frac{3}{8} \div \frac{21}{10} = \frac{3}{8} \times \frac{10}{21} =$

$\frac{3 \cdot 10}{8 \cdot 21} = \frac{\overset{1}{\cancel{3}} \cdot \overset{1}{\cancel{2}} \cdot 5}{\cancel{2} \cdot 2 \cdot 2 \cdot \cancel{3} \cdot 7} = \frac{5}{28}$

Example 8   Divide: $12\frac{3}{5} \div 7$

Your solution

$1\frac{4}{5}$

Example 9   Divide: $1\frac{13}{15} \div 4\frac{1}{5}$

Solution $1\frac{13}{15} \div 4\frac{1}{5} = \frac{28}{15} \div \frac{21}{5} =$

$\frac{28}{15} \times \frac{5}{21} = \frac{28 \cdot 5}{15 \cdot 21} =$

$\frac{2 \cdot 2 \cdot \overset{1}{\cancel{7}} \cdot \overset{1}{\cancel{5}}}{3 \cdot \underset{1}{\cancel{5}} \cdot 3 \cdot \underset{1}{\cancel{7}}} = \frac{4}{9}$

Example 10   Divide: $2\frac{5}{6} \div 8\frac{1}{2}$

Your solution

$\frac{1}{3}$

Example 11   Divide: $4\frac{3}{8} \div 7$

Solution $4\frac{3}{8} \div 7 = \frac{35}{8} \div \frac{7}{1} = \frac{35}{8} \times \frac{1}{7} =$

$\frac{35 \cdot 1}{8 \cdot 7} = \frac{5 \cdot \overset{1}{\cancel{7}}}{2 \cdot 2 \cdot 2 \cdot \underset{1}{\cancel{7}}} = \frac{5}{8}$

Example 12   Divide: $6\frac{2}{5} \div 4$

Your solution

$1\frac{3}{5}$

Solutions on p. A15

Objective C To solve application problems

Example 13

A $2\frac{2}{3}$-foot piece is cut from a $6\frac{5}{8}$-foot board. How much of the board is left?

Strategy

To find the length remaining, subtract the length of the piece from the total length of the board.

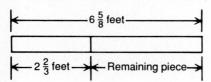

Solution

$$6\frac{5}{8} = 6\frac{15}{24} = 5\frac{39}{24}$$
$$-2\frac{2}{3} = 2\frac{16}{24} = 2\frac{16}{24}$$
$$\overline{\phantom{-2\frac{2}{3} = 2\frac{16}{24} = \;}3\frac{23}{24}}$$

$3\frac{23}{24}$ ft of the board are left.

Example 14

An investor purchased a $2\frac{1}{2}$-ounce gold coin for $1275. What was the price for 1 oz?

Your strategy

Your solution

$ 510

Example 15

A student worked $5\frac{2}{3}$ hours, $2\frac{1}{3}$ hours, and 4 hours this week on a part-time job. The student is paid $5 an hour. How much did the student earn this week?

Strategy

To find how much the student earned:
▷ Find the total number of hours worked.
▷ Multiply the total number of hours worked by the hourly wage ($5).

Solution

$$5\frac{2}{3}$$
$$2\frac{1}{3}$$
$$+4$$
$$\overline{11\frac{3}{3}} = 12 \text{ hours worked}$$

$$\begin{array}{r} 12 \\ \times\; 5 \\ \hline 60 \end{array}$$

The student earned $60 this week.

Example 16

The value of a small office building and the land on which it is built is $120,000. The value of the land is $\frac{1}{4}$ of the total value. What is the value of the building (in dollars)?

Your strategy

Your solution

$ 90,000

Solutions on p. A15

Example 17

A 12-foot board is cut into pieces $2\frac{1}{4}$ ft long for use as bookshelves. What is the length of the remaining piece after as many shelves as possible are cut?

Example 18

Two painters are staining a house. In one day one painter stains $\frac{1}{3}$ of the house while the other stains $\frac{1}{4}$ of the house. How much of the job remains to be done?

Strategy

To find the length of the remaining piece:
▷ Divide the total length by the length of each shelf $\left(12 \div 2\frac{1}{4}\right)$. The answer is the number of shelves cut with a certain fraction of a shelf left over.
▷ Multiply the fraction left over by the length of a shelf to determine the length of the piece remaining.

Your strategy

Solution

$12 \div 2\frac{1}{4} = \frac{12}{1} \div \frac{9}{4} = \frac{12}{1} \times \frac{4}{9} = \frac{12 \cdot 4}{1 \cdot 9} = \frac{16}{3} = 5\frac{1}{3}$

5 pieces, each $2\frac{1}{4}$ ft long, were cut from the board.

1 piece, $\frac{1}{3}$ of $2\frac{1}{4}$ ft long, remains.

$\frac{1}{3} \times 2\frac{1}{4} = \frac{1}{3} \times \frac{9}{4} = \frac{1 \cdot 9}{3 \cdot 4} = \frac{3}{4}$

The length of the piece remaining is $\frac{3}{4}$ ft.

Your solution

$\frac{5}{12}$

Solution on p. A15

2.3A Exercises

Multiply.

1. $\frac{2}{3} \times \frac{7}{8}$

$\frac{7}{12}$

2. $\frac{1}{2} \times \frac{2}{3}$

$\frac{1}{3}$

3. $\frac{5}{16} \times \frac{7}{15}$

$\frac{7}{48}$

4. $\frac{3}{8} \times \frac{6}{7}$

$\frac{9}{28}$

5. $\frac{1}{2} \times \frac{5}{6}$

$\frac{5}{12}$

6. $\frac{1}{6} \times \frac{1}{8}$

$\frac{1}{48}$

7. $\frac{2}{5} \times \frac{5}{6}$

$\frac{1}{3}$

8. $\frac{11}{12} \times \frac{6}{7}$

$\frac{11}{14}$

9. $\frac{11}{12} \times \frac{3}{5}$

$\frac{11}{20}$

10. $\frac{2}{5} \times \frac{4}{9}$

$\frac{8}{45}$

11. $\frac{1}{6} \times \frac{6}{7}$

$\frac{1}{7}$

12. $\frac{3}{5} \times \frac{10}{11}$

$\frac{6}{11}$

13. $\frac{1}{5} \times \frac{5}{8}$

$\frac{1}{8}$

14. $\frac{6}{7} \times \frac{14}{15}$

$\frac{4}{5}$

15. $\frac{4}{9} \times \frac{15}{16}$

$\frac{5}{12}$

16. $\frac{8}{9} \times \frac{27}{4}$

6

17. $\frac{3}{5} \times \frac{3}{10}$

$\frac{9}{50}$

18. $\frac{5}{6} \times \frac{1}{2}$

$\frac{5}{12}$

19. $\frac{3}{8} \times \frac{5}{12}$

$\frac{5}{32}$

20. $\frac{3}{10} \times \frac{6}{7}$

$\frac{9}{35}$

21. $\frac{16}{9} \times \frac{27}{8}$

6

22. $\frac{5}{8} \times \frac{16}{15}$

$\frac{2}{3}$

23. $\frac{3}{2} \times \frac{4}{9}$

$\frac{2}{3}$

24. $\frac{5}{3} \times \frac{3}{7}$

$\frac{5}{7}$

25. $\frac{5}{16} \times \frac{12}{11}$

$\frac{15}{44}$

26. $\frac{7}{8} \times \frac{3}{14}$

$\frac{3}{16}$

27. $\frac{5}{12} \times \frac{6}{7}$

$\frac{5}{14}$

28. $\frac{1}{3} \times \frac{9}{2}$

$1\frac{1}{2}$

29. $\frac{15}{8} \times \frac{16}{3}$

10

30. $\frac{5}{6} \times \frac{4}{15}$

$\frac{2}{9}$

31. $\frac{1}{2} \times \frac{2}{15}$

$\frac{1}{15}$

32. $\frac{5}{7} \times \frac{14}{15}$

$\frac{2}{3}$

33. $\frac{5}{12} \times \frac{42}{65}$

$\frac{7}{26}$

34. $\frac{16}{33} \times \frac{55}{72}$

$\frac{10}{27}$

35. $\frac{8}{3} \times \frac{21}{32}$

$1\frac{3}{4}$

36. $\frac{12}{5} \times \frac{5}{3}$

4

37. $\frac{17}{9} \times \frac{81}{17}$

9

38. $\frac{19}{64} \times \frac{48}{95}$

$\frac{3}{20}$

39. $4 \times \frac{3}{8}$

$1\frac{1}{2}$

40. $14 \times \frac{5}{7}$

10

41. $\frac{2}{3} \times 6$

4

42. $\frac{5}{12} \times 40$

$16\frac{2}{3}$

43. $\frac{1}{3} \times 1\frac{1}{3}$

$\frac{4}{9}$

44. $\frac{2}{5} \times 2\frac{1}{2}$

1

45. $1\frac{7}{8} \times \frac{4}{15}$

$\frac{1}{2}$

46. $2\frac{1}{5} \times \frac{5}{22}$

$\frac{1}{2}$

47. $4 \times 2\frac{1}{2}$

10

48. $9 \times 3\frac{1}{3}$

30

49. $2\frac{1}{7} \times 3$

$6\frac{3}{7}$

50. $5\frac{1}{4} \times 8$

42

Multiply.

51. $3\frac{2}{3} \times 5$
$18\frac{1}{3}$

52. $4\frac{2}{9} \times 3$
$12\frac{2}{3}$

53. $\frac{1}{2} \times 3\frac{3}{7}$
$1\frac{5}{7}$

54. $\frac{3}{8} \times 4\frac{4}{5}$
$1\frac{4}{5}$

55. $6\frac{1}{8} \times \frac{4}{7}$
$3\frac{1}{2}$

56. $5\frac{1}{3} \times \frac{5}{16}$
$1\frac{2}{3}$

57. $6 \times 2\frac{2}{3}$
16

58. $6\frac{1}{8} \times 0$
0

59. $1\frac{1}{2} \times 5\frac{1}{2}$
$8\frac{1}{4}$

60. $3\frac{1}{8} \times 2\frac{1}{4}$
$7\frac{1}{32}$

61. $6\frac{1}{2} \times 4\frac{3}{13}$
$27\frac{1}{2}$

62. $7\frac{3}{5} \times 4\frac{1}{6}$
$31\frac{2}{3}$

63. $5\frac{1}{2} \times 1\frac{3}{11}$
7

64. $2\frac{2}{5} \times 1\frac{7}{12}$
$3\frac{4}{5}$

65. $3\frac{1}{2} \times 7$
$24\frac{1}{2}$

66. $3\frac{1}{3} \times 6\frac{3}{5}$
22

67. $5\frac{3}{7} \times 3\frac{1}{2}$
19

68. $7\frac{5}{12} \times 3\frac{3}{7}$
$25\frac{3}{7}$

69. $5\frac{3}{16} \times 5\frac{1}{3}$
$27\frac{2}{3}$

70. $3\frac{1}{7} \times 2\frac{1}{8}$
$6\frac{19}{28}$

71. $2\frac{1}{3} \times 3\frac{1}{3}$
$7\frac{7}{9}$

72. $3\frac{2}{3} \times 5\frac{2}{11}$
19

73. $0 \times 5\frac{2}{3}$
0

74. $2\frac{2}{7} \times 3\frac{1}{2}$
8

75. $4\frac{1}{2} \times \frac{1}{3}$
$1\frac{1}{2}$

76. $2\frac{2}{3} \times 3\frac{1}{4}$
$8\frac{2}{3}$

77. $5\frac{1}{5} \times 3\frac{3}{4}$
$19\frac{1}{2}$

78. $4\frac{1}{7} \times 2\frac{1}{3}$
$9\frac{2}{3}$

79. $6\frac{1}{3} \times 1\frac{2}{19}$
7

80. $1\frac{1}{2} \times 1\frac{1}{3}$
2

81. $2\frac{2}{5} \times 3\frac{1}{12}$
$7\frac{2}{5}$

82. $2\frac{2}{3} \times \frac{3}{20}$
$\frac{2}{5}$

83. $5\frac{1}{5} \times 3\frac{1}{13}$
16

84. $3\frac{3}{4} \times 2\frac{3}{20}$
$8\frac{1}{16}$

85. $10\frac{1}{4} \times 3\frac{1}{5}$
$32\frac{4}{5}$

86. $12\frac{3}{5} \times 1\frac{3}{7}$
18

87. $5\frac{3}{7} \times 5\frac{1}{4}$
$28\frac{1}{2}$

88. $6\frac{1}{2} \times 1\frac{3}{13}$
8

89. $8\frac{2}{3} \times 2\frac{1}{13}$
18

90. $10\frac{2}{5} \times 3\frac{5}{26}$
$33\frac{1}{5}$

91. $3\frac{1}{5} \times 2\frac{2}{3}$
$8\frac{8}{15}$

92. $15\frac{1}{3} \times 6\frac{1}{2}$
$99\frac{2}{3}$

93. $5\frac{3}{8} \times 6\frac{2}{5}$
$34\frac{2}{5}$

94. $3\frac{1}{2} \times 2\frac{5}{14}$
$8\frac{1}{4}$

95. $21\frac{5}{8} \times 24$
519

96. $16 \times 3\frac{3}{4}$
60

97. $84 \times 3\frac{3}{14}$
270

98. $5\frac{1}{8} \times 41$
$210\frac{1}{8}$

99. $11\frac{1}{3} \times 7\frac{3}{34}$
$80\frac{1}{3}$

100. $8\frac{7}{9} \times 6\frac{6}{11}$
$57\frac{5}{11}$

2.3B Exercises

Divide.

101. $\frac{1}{3} \div \frac{2}{5}$
$\frac{5}{6}$

102. $\frac{3}{7} \div \frac{3}{7}$
1

103. $0 \div \frac{1}{2}$
0

104. $0 \div \frac{3}{4}$
0

105. $\frac{16}{33} \div \frac{4}{11}$
$1\frac{1}{3}$

106. $\frac{5}{24} \div \frac{15}{36}$
$\frac{1}{2}$

107. $\frac{11}{15} \div \frac{1}{12}$
$8\frac{4}{5}$

108. $\frac{2}{9} \div \frac{16}{19}$
$\frac{19}{72}$

109. $\frac{2}{15} \div \frac{3}{5}$
$\frac{2}{9}$

110. $\frac{8}{9} \div \frac{4}{5}$
$1\frac{1}{9}$

111. $\frac{11}{15} \div \frac{5}{22}$
$3\frac{17}{75}$

112. $\frac{12}{13} \div \frac{4}{9}$
$2\frac{1}{13}$

113. $\frac{1}{9} \div \frac{2}{3}$
$\frac{1}{6}$

114. $\frac{10}{21} \div \frac{5}{7}$
$\frac{2}{3}$

115. $\frac{2}{5} \div \frac{4}{7}$
$\frac{7}{10}$

116. $\frac{3}{8} \div \frac{5}{12}$
$\frac{9}{10}$

117. $\frac{5}{9} \div \frac{15}{32}$
$1\frac{5}{27}$

118. $\frac{1}{2} \div \frac{1}{4}$
2

119. $\frac{1}{3} \div \frac{1}{9}$
3

120. $\frac{4}{15} \div \frac{2}{5}$
$\frac{2}{3}$

121. $\frac{7}{15} \div \frac{14}{5}$
$\frac{1}{6}$

122. $\frac{5}{8} \div \frac{15}{2}$
$\frac{1}{12}$

123. $\frac{14}{3} \div \frac{7}{9}$
6

124. $\frac{7}{4} \div \frac{9}{2}$
$\frac{7}{18}$

125. $\frac{5}{9} \div \frac{25}{3}$
$\frac{1}{15}$

126. $\frac{5}{16} \div \frac{3}{8}$
$\frac{5}{6}$

127. $\frac{2}{3} \div \frac{1}{3}$
2

128. $\frac{4}{9} \div \frac{1}{9}$
4

129. $\frac{5}{7} \div \frac{2}{7}$
$2\frac{1}{2}$

130. $\frac{5}{6} \div \frac{1}{9}$
$7\frac{1}{2}$

131. $\frac{2}{3} \div \frac{2}{9}$
3

132. $\frac{5}{12} \div \frac{5}{6}$
$\frac{1}{2}$

133. $4 \div \frac{2}{3}$
6

134. $\frac{2}{3} \div 4$
$\frac{1}{6}$

135. $\frac{3}{2} \div 3$
$\frac{1}{2}$

136. $3 \div \frac{3}{2}$
2

137. $\frac{15}{8} \div \frac{5}{16}$
6

138. $\frac{15}{8} \div \frac{5}{32}$
12

139. $\frac{5}{6} \div 25$
$\frac{1}{30}$

140. $22 \div \frac{3}{11}$
$80\frac{2}{3}$

141. $6 \div 3\frac{1}{3}$
$1\frac{4}{5}$

142. $5\frac{1}{2} \div 11$
$\frac{1}{2}$

143. $3\frac{1}{3} \div \frac{3}{8}$
$8\frac{8}{9}$

144. $6\frac{1}{2} \div \frac{1}{2}$
13

145. $\frac{3}{8} \div 2\frac{1}{4}$
$\frac{1}{6}$

146. $\frac{5}{12} \div 4\frac{4}{5}$
$\frac{25}{288}$

147. $1\frac{1}{2} \div 1\frac{3}{8}$
$1\frac{1}{11}$

148. $2\frac{1}{4} \div 1\frac{3}{8}$
$1\frac{7}{11}$

149. $1\frac{3}{5} \div 2\frac{1}{10}$
$\frac{16}{21}$

150. $2\frac{5}{6} \div 1\frac{1}{9}$
$2\frac{11}{20}$

Divide.

151. $2\frac{1}{3} \div 3\frac{2}{3}$

$\frac{7}{11}$

152. $4\frac{1}{2} \div 2\frac{1}{6}$

$2\frac{1}{13}$

153. $7\frac{1}{2} \div 2\frac{2}{3}$

$2\frac{13}{16}$

154. $8\frac{1}{4} \div 2\frac{3}{4}$

3

155. $3\frac{5}{9} \div 32$

$\frac{1}{9}$

156. $4\frac{1}{5} \div 21$

$\frac{1}{5}$

157. $6\frac{8}{9} \div \frac{31}{36}$

8

158. $5\frac{3}{5} \div \frac{7}{10}$

8

159. $\frac{11}{12} \div 2\frac{1}{3}$

$\frac{11}{28}$

160. $\frac{7}{8} \div 3\frac{1}{4}$

$\frac{7}{26}$

161. $27 \div \frac{3}{8}$

72

162. $35 \div \frac{7}{24}$

120

163. $\frac{3}{8} \div 2\frac{3}{4}$

$\frac{3}{22}$

164. $\frac{11}{18} \div 2\frac{2}{9}$

$\frac{11}{40}$

165. $7\frac{3}{5} \div 1\frac{7}{12}$

$4\frac{4}{5}$

166. $1\frac{2}{3} \div \frac{3}{8}$

$4\frac{4}{9}$

167. $2\frac{1}{2} \div 3\frac{5}{14}$

$\frac{35}{47}$

168. $16 \div 1\frac{1}{2}$

$10\frac{2}{3}$

169. $16\frac{5}{8} \div 1\frac{2}{3}$

$9\frac{39}{40}$

170. $24\frac{4}{5} \div 2\frac{3}{5}$

$9\frac{7}{13}$

171. $1\frac{1}{3} \div 5\frac{8}{9}$

$\frac{12}{53}$

172. $13\frac{2}{3} \div 0$

undefined

173. $15\frac{1}{3} \div 7\frac{1}{6}$

$2\frac{6}{43}$

174. $0 \div 1\frac{1}{2}$

0

175. $3\frac{5}{12} \div 2\frac{1}{6}$

$1\frac{15}{26}$

176. $4\frac{5}{16} \div 2\frac{3}{8}$

$1\frac{31}{38}$

177. $6\frac{1}{3} \div 5$

$1\frac{4}{15}$

178. $15 \div \frac{1}{8}$

120

179. $\frac{1}{12} \div 12$

$\frac{1}{144}$

180. $3\frac{5}{11} \div 3\frac{4}{5}$

$\frac{10}{11}$

181. $19\frac{1}{2} \div \frac{1}{2}$

39

182. $\frac{1}{4} \div 2\frac{5}{6}$

$\frac{3}{34}$

183. $5\frac{3}{8} \div 2\frac{7}{16}$

$2\frac{8}{39}$

184. $7\frac{4}{13} \div 2\frac{3}{26}$

$3\frac{5}{11}$

185. $82\frac{3}{4} \div 6\frac{1}{8}$

$13\frac{25}{49}$

186. $19\frac{3}{7} \div 4\frac{5}{14}$

$4\frac{28}{61}$

187. $45\frac{3}{5} \div 15$

$3\frac{1}{25}$

188. $102 \div 1\frac{1}{2}$

68

189. $0 \div 3\frac{1}{2}$

0

190. $8\frac{2}{7} \div 1$

$8\frac{2}{7}$

191. $6\frac{9}{16} \div 1\frac{3}{32}$

6

192. $5\frac{5}{14} \div 3\frac{4}{7}$

$1\frac{1}{2}$

193. $8\frac{8}{9} \div 2\frac{13}{18}$

$3\frac{13}{49}$

194. $10\frac{1}{5} \div 1\frac{7}{10}$

6

195. $7\frac{3}{8} \div 1\frac{27}{32}$

4

196. $4\frac{5}{11} \div 2\frac{1}{3}$

$1\frac{10}{11}$

197. $15\frac{3}{8} \div 7\frac{3}{4}$

$1\frac{61}{62}$

198. $7\frac{2}{9} \div 1\frac{17}{18}$

$3\frac{5}{7}$

199. $3\frac{7}{8} \div 7\frac{3}{4}$

$\frac{1}{2}$

200. $9\frac{7}{12} \div \frac{5}{12}$

23

2.3C Exercises

Solve.

201. A wall that is $\frac{7}{8}$-inch thick is covered by a $\frac{3}{16}$-inch veneer. Find the total thickness after the veneer is installed.

$1\frac{1}{16}$ in.

202. A carpenter built a header by nailing a $1\frac{5}{8}$-inch board to a $3\frac{1}{2}$-inch beam. Find the total thickness of the header.

$5\frac{1}{8}$ in.

203. At the beginning of last week, Simplex Electric Company stock was selling at $37\frac{3}{8}$ $\left(\$37\frac{3}{8}\text{ per share}\right)$. During the week, the stock gained $5\frac{3}{4}$ $\left(\$5\frac{3}{4}\text{ per share}\right)$. Find the price of the stock at the end of the week.

$\$43\frac{1}{8}$

204. You bought stock in a microcomputer company for $17\frac{3}{8}$ $\left(\$17\frac{3}{8}\text{ per share}\right)$. The price of the stock gained $7\frac{3}{4}$ $\left(\$7\frac{3}{4}\text{ per share}\right)$ during a six-month period. Find the price of the stock at the end of the six months.

$\$25\frac{1}{8}$

205. A planer removes $\frac{1}{3}$ in. from a $\frac{7}{8}$-inch board. Find the resulting thickness of the board.

$\frac{13}{24}$ in.

206. A board $8\frac{2}{3}$ ft long is cut from a board 12 ft long. What is the length of the remaining piece of board?

$3\frac{1}{3}$ ft

207. A board is $2\frac{3}{4}$ ft long. One-third of the board is cut off. What is the length of the piece cut off?

$\frac{11}{12}$ ft

208. A compact car gets 24 mi on each gallon of gasoline. How many miles can the car travel on $5\frac{3}{4}$ gal of gasoline?

138 mi

209. A painter earns $88 for each day worked. What is the total of the painter's earnings for working $5\frac{1}{2}$ days?

$\$484$

210. A bank recommends that the maximum monthly payment for a home be $\frac{1}{4}$ of your total monthly income. Your monthly income is $2400. What would the bank recommend as your maximum monthly house payment?

$\$600$

211. An electrician works $2\frac{2}{3}$ hours of overtime on Monday, $1\frac{1}{4}$ hours on Wednesday, $1\frac{1}{3}$ hours on Friday, and $6\frac{3}{4}$ hours on Saturday. At a salary of $22 for each hour of overtime, how much overtime pay does the electrician receive?

$\$264$

212. You have a part-time job that pays $5 an hour. You worked 5, $3\frac{3}{4}$, $2\frac{1}{3}$, $1\frac{1}{4}$, and $7\frac{2}{3}$ hours during five days last week. Find your total salary for the week.

$\$100$

Solve.

213. A package contains 20 oz of cereal. How many $1\frac{1}{4}$-ounce portions can be served from this package?

     16 portions

214. A car used $18\frac{4}{10}$ gal of gasoline on a 460-mile trip. How many miles can this car travel on 1 gal of gasoline?

     25 mi

215. A home building contractor bought $4\frac{1}{2}$ acres of land for $63,000. What was the cost for each acre?

     $14,000

216. A jeweler purchased a $\frac{3}{4}$-carat diamond for $600. What would be the cost of a similar diamond weighing one carat?

     $800

217. You bought gas-and-electric stock for $26\frac{3}{16}$ $\left(\$26\frac{3}{16}\text{ per share}\right)$. Monthly gains for the first three months of ownership were $1\frac{1}{2}$, $\frac{5}{16}$, and $2\frac{5}{8}$. Find the value of the stock at the end of the three months.

     $30 $\frac{5}{8}$

218. You painted $\frac{2}{5}$ of your house today. How much of the paint job remains to be done?

     $\frac{3}{5}$

219. A 12-mile race has two checkpoints. The first checkpoint is $3\frac{3}{8}$ mi from the starting point. The second checkpoint is $4\frac{1}{3}$ mi from the first checkpoint. How many miles is it from the second checkpoint to the finish line?

     $4\frac{7}{24}$ mi

220. A patient is put on a diet to lose 38 lb in three months. The patient loses $12\frac{1}{2}$ lb the first month and $16\frac{3}{8}$ lb the second month. How much weight must be lost the third month to achieve the goal?

     $9\frac{1}{8}$ lbs

221. A family has an income of $2400 each month. The family spends $\frac{1}{10}$ of its income each month for food. How much of the family's income (in dollars) is left after spending $\frac{1}{10}$ for food?

     $2160

222. A chef purchased a roast that weighed $10\frac{3}{4}$ lb. After trimming the fat and removing the bone, the roast weighed $9\frac{1}{3}$ lb. How many $\frac{1}{3}$-pound servings can the chef cut from the roast?

     28

223. A land developer purchases $9\frac{3}{4}$ acres of land for a building project, of which $1\frac{1}{2}$ acres are set aside for a park. From the remaining land, how many $\frac{1}{4}$-acre parcels can be sold?

     33 parcels

224. A 15-foot board is cut into pieces $3\frac{1}{2}$ ft long for use as bookshelves. What is the length of the piece remaining after as many shelves as possible are cut?

     1 ft

Section 4   Addition, Subtraction, Multiplication, and Division of Decimals

Objective A   To round a decimal to a given place value

2
DISK
TWO

Reference for Computer Tutor™

The smallest human bone is found in the middle ear and measures 0.135 in. in length. The number 0.135 is in **decimal notation.**

Note the relationship between fractions and numbers written in decimal notation.

Three-tenths	Three-hundredths	Three-thousandths
$\frac{3}{10} = 0.\underline{3}$	$\frac{3}{100} = 0.0\underline{3}$	$\frac{3}{1000} = 0.00\underline{3}$
1 zero 1 decimal place	2 zeros 2 decimal places	3 zeros 3 decimal places

A number written in decimal notation has three parts.

351   .   7089

Whole number part   **Decimal point**   **Decimal part**

A number written in decimal notation is often called simply a **decimal.** The position of a digit in a decimal determines the digit's place value.

In the decimal 351.7089, the position of the digit "9" determines that its place value is ten-thousandths.

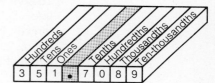

Rounding decimals is the same as rounding whole numbers except that the digits to the right of the given place value are dropped instead of being replaced by zeros.

If the digit to the right of the given place value is less than 5, that digit and all digits to the right are dropped. If the digit to the right of the given place value is greater than or equal to 5, increase the given place value by one and drop all digits to its right.

Round 26.3799 to the nearest hundredth.

┌──Given place value

26.37̲99

└──9 > 5   Increase 7 by one and drop all digits to the right of 7.

26.3799 rounded to the nearest hundredth is 26.38.

Example 1	Round 0.39275 to the nearest ten-thousandth.	**Example 2**	Round 4.349254 to the nearest hundredth.
Solution	┌──Given place value 0.3927̲5 └──5 = 5 0.3928	**Your solution**	4.35

Solution on p. A16

**Reference for
Computer
Tutor™**

| Objective B | To add and subtract decimals |

To add decimals, write the numbers so that the decimal points are on a vertical line. Add as for whole numbers and write the decimal point in the sum directly below the decimal points in the addends.

Add: 0.237 + 4.9 + 27.32

	Tens	Ones		Tenths	Hundredths	Thousandths
	¹	¹0	.	2	3	7
		4	.	9		
+	2	7	.	3	2	
	3	2	.	4	5	7

Note that by placing the decimal points on a vertical line, digits of the same place value are added.

To subtract decimals, write the numbers so that the decimal points are on a vertical line. Subtract as for whole numbers and write the decimal point in the difference directly below the decimal point in the subtrahend.

Subtract 21.532 − 9.875 and check.

	Tens	Ones		Tenths	Hundredths	Thousandths
	¹2̸	¹⁰1̸	.	¹⁴5̸	¹²3̸	¹²2̸
		9	.	8	7	5
	1	1	.	6	5	7

Note that by placing the decimal points on a vertical line, digits of the same place value are subtracted.

Check: Subtrahend $\overset{11\ 11}{9.875}$
         + Difference   +11.657
         = Minuend   21.532

Subtract 4.3 − 1.7942 and check.

Zeros must be inserted in the minuend before the subtrahend can be subtracted.

$$\overset{3\ 12\ 9\ 9\ 10}{4.3\ 0\ 0\ 0}$$
$$-1.7\ 9\ 4\ 2$$
$$2.5\ 0\ 5\ 8$$

Check: $\overset{1\ 111}{1.7942}$
        +2.5058
        4.3000

| **Example 3** | Add: 42.3 + 162.903 + 65.0729 | **Example 4** | Add: 4.62 + 27.9 + 0.62054 |

| **Solution** | $\overset{111}{42.3}$ 162.903 + 65.0729 270.2759 | **Your solution** | 33. 14054 |

Solution on p. A16

Example 5	Subtract 1.2 − 0.8235 and check.	**Example 6**	Subtract 3.7 − 1.9715 and check.

Solution

$$\begin{array}{r} \overset{0\ \ 11\ \ 9\ \ 9\ \ 10}{\cancel{1}.\cancel{2}\ \cancel{0}\ \cancel{0}\ \cancel{0}} \\ -0.8\ 2\ 3\ 5 \\ \hline 0.3\ 7\ 6\ 5 \end{array}$$
Check:
$$\begin{array}{r} \overset{1\ \ 1\ 1\ 1}{\ \ 0.8235} \\ +0.3765 \\ \hline 1.2000 \end{array}$$

Your solution

$$1.7285$$

Solution on p. A17

Objective C   # To multiply decimals

Reference for Computer Tutor™

Decimals are multiplied in the same way as whole numbers. The decimal point is then placed in the product. Writing the decimals as fractions shows where to write the decimal point in the product.

$$0.\underline{3} \times 5 = \frac{3}{10} \times \frac{5}{1} = \frac{15}{10} = 1.\underline{5}$$

1 decimal place   1 decimal place

$$0.\underline{3} \times 0.\underline{5} = \frac{3}{10} \times \frac{5}{10} = \frac{15}{100} = 0.\underline{15}$$

1 decimal place   1 decimal place   2 decimal places

$$0.\underline{3} \times 0.\underline{05} = \frac{3}{10} \times \frac{5}{100} = \frac{15}{1000} = 0.\underline{015}$$

1 decimal place   2 decimal places   3 decimal places

To multiply decimals, multiply the numbers as in whole numbers. Write the decimal point in the product so that the number of decimal places in the product is the sum of the decimal places in the factors.

Multiply: 21.4 × 0.36

$$\begin{array}{r} 21.4 \\ \times 0.36 \\ \hline 1284 \\ 642 \\ \hline 7.704 \end{array}$$
1 decimal place
2 decimal places

3 decimal places

Multiply: 357 × 0.29

$$\begin{array}{r} 357 \\ \times 0.29 \\ \hline 3213 \\ 714 \\ \hline 103.53 \end{array}$$
no decimal places
2 decimal places

2 decimal places

Multiply: 0.037×0.08

0.037	3 decimal places
× 0.08	2 decimal places
0.00296	5 decimal places

Two zeros must be inserted between the 2 and the decimal point so that there are 5 decimal places in the product.

To multiply a decimal by a power of 10 (10, 100, 1000, . . .), move the decimal point to the right the same number of places as there are zeros in the power of 10.

$3.8925 \times 1\underline{0}$ $= 38.925$

     1 zero   1 decimal place

$3.8925 \times 1\underline{00}$ $= 389.25$

     2 zeros   2 decimal places

$3.8925 \times 1\underline{000}$ $= 3892.5$

     3 zeros   3 decimal places

$3.8925 \times 1\underline{0,000}$ $= 38,925.$

       4 zeros   4 decimal places

$3.8925 \times 1\underline{00,000}$ $= 389,250.$

        5 zeros   5 decimal places

Note that a zero must be inserted before the decimal point.

Note that if the power of 10 is written in exponential notation, the exponent indicates how many places to move the decimal point.

$3.8925 \times 10^1 = 38.925$

              1 decimal place

$3.8925 \times 10^2 = 389.25$

              2 decimal places

$3.8925 \times 10^3 = 3892.5$

              3 decimal places

$3.8925 \times 10^4 = 38,925.$

              4 decimal places

$3.8925 \times 10^5 = 389,250.$

              5 decimal places

Example 7	Multiply: 3.69 × 2.07	**Example 8**	Multiply: 4.68 × 6.03

Example 7   Multiply: 3.69 × 2.07

Solution
$$\begin{array}{r} 3.69 \\ \times\, 2.07 \\ \hline 2583 \\ 7380 \\ \hline 7.6383 \end{array}$$

Example 8   Multiply: 4.68 × 6.03

Your solution

28.2204

Example 9   Multiply: 42.07 × 10,000

Solution   42.07 × 10,000 = 420,700

Example 10   Multiply: 6.9 × 1000

Your solution

6900

Example 11   Multiply: 3.01 × 10³

Solution   3.01 × 10³ = 3010

Example 12   Multiply: 4.0273 × 10²

Your solution

402.73

Solutions on p. A17

Objective D   # To divide decimals

Reference for Computer Tutor™

To divide decimals, move the decimal point in the divisor to make it a whole number. Move the decimal in the dividend the same number of places to the right. Place the decimal point in the quotient directly over the decimal point in the dividend. Then divide as in whole numbers.

Divide: $3.25)\overline{15.275}$

Step 1 $3.25)\overline{15.27.5}$

Move the decimal point 2 places to the right in the divisor and then in the dividend. Place the decimal point in the quotient.

Step 2
$$\begin{array}{r} 4.7 \\ 325.)\overline{1527.5} \\ -1300 \\ \hline 227\ 5 \\ -227\ 5 \\ \hline 0 \end{array}$$

Moving the decimal point the same number of decimal places in the divisor and dividend does not change the value of the quotient. The reason is that this process is the same as multiplying the numerator and denominator of a fraction by the same number. In the example above,

$$3.25)\overline{15.275} \;=\; \frac{15.275}{3.25} \;=\; \frac{15.275 \times 100}{3.25 \times 100} \;=\; \frac{1527.5}{325} \;=\; 325)\overline{1527.5}$$

When dividing decimals, the quotient is usually rounded off to a specified place value, rather than writing the quotient with a remainder. The symbol $\approx$ is used to indicate that the quotient is an approximate value after being rounded off.

Divide: 0.3)0.56
Round to the nearest hundredth.

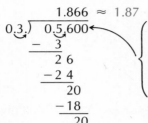

```
          1.866  ≈  1.87
  0.3,)  0.5,600
      − 3
        2 6
      −2 4
        20
       −18
         20
        −18
```

The division must be carried to the thousandths' place to round the quotient to the nearest hundredth. Therefore, zeros must be inserted in the dividend so the quotient has a digit in the thousandths' place.

Divide: 57.93 ÷ 3.24
Round to the nearest thousandth.

```
          17.8796  ≈  17.880
  3.24,)  57.93,0000
      −32 4
        25 53
       −22 68
         2 85 0
        −2 59 2
           25 80
          −22 68
            3 120
           −2 916
             2040
            −1944
```

Zeros must be inserted in the dividend so the quotient has a digit in the ten-thousandths' place.

To divide a decimal by a power of 10 (10, 100, 1000, . . .), move the decimal point to the left the same number of places as there are zeros in the power of 10.

34.65 ÷ 1<u>0</u>   = 3,465
      1 zero   1 decimal place

34.65 ÷ 1<u>00</u>   = 0,3465
      2 zeros   2 decimal places

34.65 ÷ 1<u>000</u> = 0,03465

      3 zeros   3 decimal places

Note that a zero must be inserted between the 3 and the decimal point.

34.65 ÷ 1<u>0,000</u> = 0,003465

      4 zeros   4 decimal places

Note that two zeros must be inserted between the 3 and the decimal point.

Note that if the power of 10 is written in exponential notation, the exponent indicates how many places to move the decimal point.

$34.65 \div 10^1 = 3.465$

1 decimal place

$34.65 \div 10^2 = 0.3465$

2 decimal places

$34.65 \div 10^3 = 0.03465$

3 decimal places

$34.65 \div 10^4 = 0.003465$

4 decimal places

Example 13 Divide: $0.1344 \div 0.032$

Solution

$$
\begin{array}{r}
4.2 \\
0.032\overline{)0.134.4} \\
-128 \\
\hline
6\,4 \\
-6\,4 \\
\hline
0
\end{array}
$$

Example 14 Divide: $0.1404 \div 0.052$

Your solution

2.7

Example 15 Divide: $420.9 \div 7.06$
Round to the nearest tenth.

Solution

$$
\begin{array}{r}
59.61 \approx 59.6 \\
7.06.\overline{)\ 420.90.00} \\
-353\,0 \\
\hline
67\,90 \\
-63\,54 \\
\hline
4\,36\,0 \\
-4\,23\,6 \\
\hline
12\,40 \\
-\ 7\,06
\end{array}
$$

Example 16 Divide: $370.2 \div 5.09$
Round to the nearest tenth.

Your solution

72.7

Example 17 Divide: $402.75 \div 1000$

Solution $402.75 \div 1000 = 0.40275$

Example 18 Divide: $309.21 \div 10,000$

Your solution

0.030921

Example 19 Divide: $0.625 \div 10^2$

Solution $0.625 \div 10^2 = 0.00625$

Example 20 Divide: $42.93 \div 10^4$

Your solution

0.004293

Solutions on p. A17

Objective E   ## To find the average of a set of numbers

Reference for
Computer
Tutor™

A student's test scores for five tests are listed below.

Test 1	Test 2	Test 3	Test 4	Test 5
86	95	94	87	93

The **average** or **mean** score is the sum of all the test scores divided by the number of tests.

$$\frac{\text{Sum of scores}}{\text{Number of tests}} = \frac{86 + 95 + 94 + 87 + 93}{5} = \frac{455}{5} = 91$$

Notice that a student who scored 91 on each of the five tests would have the same grade average as the student whose test scores are given in the example above.

Example 21   For a price comparison of six supermarkets, identical items were purchased in each store. The results are listed below.

Store	Cost	Store	Cost
1	$40.74	4	$39.05
2	$39.45	5	$38.86
3	$38.57	6	$39.25

Find the average cost of the items purchased.

Strategy   To find the mean cost of the items purchased:
▷ Find the sum of the costs.
▷ Divide the sum of the costs by the number of stores (6).

Solution
```
 $40.74          $39.32
  39.45        6)$235.92
  38.57
  39.05
  38.86
+ 39.25
 $235.92   sum of costs
```

The mean cost of the items purchased was $39.32.

Example 22   The amounts that a sales representative spent each month for gasoline are listed below.

Month	Cost
Jan	$118.50
Feb	$130.50
Mar	$109.50

Find the average monthly cost for gasoline.

Your strategy

Your solution

$ 119.50

Solution on p. A17

2.4A Exercises

Round each decimal to the given place value.

1. 7.359   Tenths
7.4

2. 6.405   Tenths
6.4

3. 23.009   Tenths
23.0

4. 89.19204   Tenths
89.2

5. 22.68259   Hundredths
22.68

6. 16.30963   Hundredths
16.31

7. 480.325   Hundredths
480.33

8. 670.974   Hundredths
670.97

9. 1.03925   Thousandths
1.039

10. 7.072854   Thousandths
7.073

11. 1946.3745   Thousandths
1946.375

12. 62.009435   Thousandths
62.009

2.4B Exercises

Add.

13. 0.29 + 0.4
0.69

14. 1.007 + 2.1
3.107

15. 7.3 + 9.005
16.305

16. 8.962 + 10.599
19.561

17. 11.957 + 9.374
21.331

18. 27.42 + 9.765
37.185

19. 7.85 + 29.762
37.612

20. 4.9257 + 27.05 + 9.0063
40.9820

21. 8.72 + 99.073 + 2.9736
110.7666

22. 8 + 89.43 + 7.0659
104.4959

23. 17.32 + 1.0579 + 16.5
34.8779

24. 1.792 + 67 + 27.0526
95.8446

25. 8.772 + 1.09 + 26.5027
36.3647

26. 3.02 + 62.7 + 3.924
69.644

27. 9.06 + 4.976 + 59.6
73.636

28. 82.006 + 9.95 + 0.927
92.883

29. 0.826 + 8.76 + 79.005
88.591

30. 2.9804 + 21.32 + 6.253
30.5534

31. 7.6507 + 7.259 + 72
86.9097

32. 4.307 + 99.82 + 3 + 9.078
116.205

33. 2.543 + 7.906 + 2.07 + 1.4092
13.9282

34. 82.907 + 76.2 + 0.0039 + 234.78308
393.89398

35. 0.0072 + 87.65 + 96 + 235.09873
418.75593

Subtract and check.

36. 0.675
    −0.32
    0.355

37. 0.924
    −0.91
    0.014

38. 3
    −1.296
    1.704

39. 7.507
    −3.419
    4.088

40. 27.09
    − 7.265
    19.825

41. 82.07
    − 7.354
    74.716

42. 18.314
    − 9.785
    8.529

43. 16.123
    − 7.457
    8.666

44. 0.32
    −0.0058
    0.3142

45. 0.78
    −0.0073
    0.7727

46. 3.005
    −1.982
    1.023

47. 6.007
    −2.734
    3.273

48. 352.16
    − 90.994
    261.166

49. 872
    − 80.753
    791.247

50. 625.46
    − 77.509
    547.951

51. 67.301
    − 9.9325
    57.3685

52. 55.607
    − 6.8191
    48.7879

53. 123.79
    − 92.456
    31.334

54. 279.37
    − 65.692
    213.678

55. 362.394
    − 19.4672
    342.9268

56. 24.037 − 18.41
    5.627

57. 26.029 − 19.31
    6.719

58. 123.07 − 9.4273
    113.6427

59. 214 − 7.143
    206.857

60. 16.5 − 9.7902
    6.7098

61. 13.2 − 8.6205
    4.5795

62. 235.79 − 20.093
    215.697

63. 463.27 − 40.095
    423.175

64. 63.005 − 9.1274
    53.8776

65. 23.004 − 7.2175
    15.7865

66. 92 − 19.2909
    72.7091

67. 41.2405 − 25.2709
    15.9696

68. 7.01 − 2.325
    4.685

69. 8.07 − 5.392
    2.678

70. 19.0035 − 8.967
    10.0365

2.4C Exercises

Multiply.

71. 7.7
    ×0.9
    6.93

72. 3.4
    ×0.4
    1.36

73. 9.2
    ×0.2
    1.84

74. 2.6
    ×0.7
    1.82

75. 7.9
    × 5
    39.5

76. 9.3
    × 7
    65.1

77. 0.68
    × 4
    2.72

78. 0.83
    × 9
    7.47

79. 0.67
    × 0.9
    0.603

80. 0.84
    × 0.3
    0.252

Copyright © 1989 HMCo

Multiply.

81.   2.5
     $\times 5.4$
     13.50

82.   3.9
     $\times 1.9$
     7.41

83.   8.4
     $\times 9.5$
     79.80

84.   7.6
     $\times 5.8$
     44.08

85.   0.83
     $\times 5.2$
     4.316

86.   0.24
     $\times 2.7$
     0.648

87.   0.46
     $\times 3.9$
     1.794

88.   0.78
     $\times 6.8$
     5.304

89.   0.24
     $\times 0.3$
     0.072

90.   0.17
     $\times 0.5$
     0.085

91.   1.47
     $\times 0.09$
     0.1323

92.   6.37
     $\times 0.05$
     0.3185

93.   8.92
     $\times 0.004$
     0.03568

94.   6.75
     $\times 0.007$
     0.04725

95.   0.49
     $\times 0.16$
     0.0784

96.   0.38
     $\times 0.21$
     0.0798

97.   7.6
     $\times 0.01$
     0.076

98.   5.1
     $\times 0.01$
     0.051

99.   5.41
     $\times 0.7$
     3.787

100.   6.97
     $\times 0.4$
     2.788

101.   8.62
     $\times 4$
     34.48

102.   5.83
     $\times 7$
     40.81

103.   2.19
     $\times 9.2$
     20.148

104.   1.25
     $\times 5.6$
     7.000

105.   1.85
     $\times 0.023$
     0.04255

106.   37.8
     $\times 0.052$
     1.9656

107.   0.478
     $\times 0.37$
     0.17686

108.   0.526
     $\times 0.22$
     0.11572

109.   48.3
     $\times 0.0041$
     0.19803

110.   67.2
     $\times 0.0086$
     0.57792

111.   51.36
     $\times 3.8$
     195.168

112.   47.76
     $\times 6.5$
     310.440

113.   2.437
     $\times 6.1$
     14.8657

114.   4.237
     $\times 0.54$
     2.28798

115.   94.73
     $\times 0.57$
     53.9961

116. 4.29×0.01
     0.0429

117. 5.29×0.4
     2.116

118. 1.4×0.73
     1.022

119. 6.3×0.37
     2.331

120. 5.2×7.3
     37.96

121. 7.4×2.9
     21.46

122. 0.32×10
     3.2

123. 6.93×10
     69.3

Multiply.

124. 0.065 × 100
 6.5

125. 0.039 × 100
 3.9

126. 6.2856 × 1000
 6285.6

127. 3.2954 × 1000
 3295.4

128. 0.006 × 10,000
 60

129. 3.57 × 10,000
 35,700

130. 8.52 × 10¹
 85.2

131. 0.63 × 10¹
 6.3

132. 82.9 × 10²
 8290

133. 0.039 × 10²
 3.9

134. 6.8 × 10³
 6800

135. 4.9 × 10⁴
 49,000

2.4D Exercises

Divide.

136. $3\overline{)2.46}$ 0.82
137. $7\overline{)3.71}$ 0.53
138. $0.8\overline{)3.84}$ 4.8
139. $0.9\overline{)6.93}$ 7.7

140. $0.7\overline{)62.3}$ 89
141. $0.4\overline{)52.8}$ 132
142. $0.4\overline{)24}$ 60
143. $0.5\overline{)65}$ 130

144. $7\overline{)0.42}$ 0.06
145. $3\overline{)0.12}$ 0.04
146. $0.4\overline{)27.88}$ 69.7
147. $0.8\overline{)3.312}$ 4.14

148. $0.7\overline{)59.01}$ 84.3
149. $0.9\overline{)8.721}$ 9.69
150. $6.3\overline{)8.19}$ 1.3
151. $3.2\overline{)7.04}$ 2.2

152. $3.6\overline{)0.396}$ 0.11
153. $2.7\overline{)0.648}$ 0.24
154. $6.9\overline{)26.22}$ 3.8
155. $1.7\overline{)84.66}$ 49.8

156. $3.9\overline{)8.034}$ 2.06
157. $0.41\overline{)2.501}$ 6.1
158. $0.59\overline{)1.003}$ 1.7
159. $0.04\overline{)27.2}$ 680

160. $0.06\overline{)44.4}$ 740
161. $0.08\overline{)23.2}$ 290
162. $0.018\overline{)0.1314}$ 7.3
163. $0.064\overline{)0.2304}$ 3.6

Divide. Round to the nearest tenth.

164. 55.62 ÷ 8.8
6.3

165. 25.43 ÷ 5.4
4.7

166. 5.427 ÷ 9.5
0.6

167. 1.837 ÷ 1.4
1.3

168. 18.4 ÷ 7.3
2.5

169. 52.9 ÷ 8.1
6.5

170. 0.183 ÷ 0.17
1.1

171. 0.381 ÷ 0.47
0.8

Divide. Round to the nearest hundredth.

172. 4.817 ÷ 16
0.30

173. 6.467 ÷ 8
0.81

174. 0.0418 ÷ 0.53
0.08

175. 0.0647 ÷ 0.72
0.09

176. 9 ÷ 0.48
18.75

177. 7 ÷ 0.55
12.73

178. 19.08 ÷ 0.45
42.40

179. 21.792 ÷ 0.96
22.70

Divide. Round to the nearest thousandth.

180. 1.028 ÷ 54
0.019

181. 6.729 ÷ 27
0.249

182. 0.0437 ÷ 0.5
0.087

183. 0.0915 ÷ 0.4
0.229

184. 0.2837 ÷ 2.7
0.105

185. 0.4268 ÷ 4.1
0.104

186. 75.469 ÷ 77.8
0.970

187. 34.31 ÷ 95.3
0.360

Divide. Round to the nearest whole number.

188. 16.5 ÷ 4
4

189. 89.76 ÷ 90
1

190. 1.94 ÷ 0.3
6

191. 6.72 ÷ 0.2
34

192. 0.1467 ÷ 0.12
1

193. 1.0478 ÷ 0.413
3

194. 2.148 ÷ 0.519
4

195. 392 ÷ 6.9
57

Divide.

196. 4.07 ÷ 10
0.407

197. 42.67 ÷ 10
4.267

198. 389.7 ÷ 100
3.897

199. 237.835 ÷ 100
2.37835

200. 82,547 ÷ 1000
82.547

201. 825.37 ÷ 1000
0.82537

202. 8.35 ÷ 10^1
0.835

203. 87.65 ÷ 10^1
8.765

204. 23.627 ÷ 10^2
0.23627

205. 2.954 ÷ 10^2
0.02954

206. 289.32 ÷ 10^3
0.28932

207. 1.8932 ÷ 10^3
0.0018932

2.4E Exercises

Solve.

208. A student received grades of 86, 91, 87, 93, and 95 on five history exams. Find the student's average grade on the history exams.

90.4

209. The closing prices of a stock for five days were $36.25, $35.75, $36.50, $36.00, and $36.50. Find the average closing price of the stock.

$36.20

210. The prices of one pound of steak at six different grocery stores were $3.08, $3.12, $2.99, $3.25, $3.16, and $3.18. Find the average price of steak at the six grocery stores.

$3.13

211. The number of hamburgers sold during five lunch hours at a fast-food restaurant was 252, 286, 245, 292, and 277. Find the average number of hamburgers sold at the restaurant per lunch hour. Round to the nearest whole number.

270 hamburgers

212. An appliance repair shop's records show the number of requests for service each day last week. Find the average number of requests for service. Round to the nearest whole number.

Mon	Tue	Wed	Thu	Fri	Sat
24	30	28	27	25	35

28

213. An accountant's pay checks for four months are given in the table below. Find the average monthly check.

Jan	Feb	Mar	Apr
$1225	$1385	$1195	$1220

$1256.25

214. A sales representative recorded the number of miles traveled for each of five days of a business trip. Find the average number of miles traveled each day.

Mon	Tue	Wed	Thu	Fri
128	213	188	231	189

189.8

215. A taxi driver's records show the number of gallons of gasoline purchased each day on the job last week. Find the average number of gallons of gasoline purchased.

Wed	Thu	Fri	Sat	Sun
9.4	9.3	11.8	10.3	9.7

10.1 gal

216. The prices of identical raincoats at each of five department stores were $68.75, $74.50, $72.95, $71.00, and $82.00. Find the average price of the raincoat.

$73.84

217. The monthly utility bills for eight homes are $86.48, $92.81, $48.92, $74.16, $112.53, $61.92, $87.48, and $97.92. Find the average utility bill. Round to the nearest cent.

$82.78

218. The number of hours of television watched by ten families during one day is recorded in the table below. Find the average number of hours of television watched by the ten families. Round to the nearest tenth.

Family	Hours	Family	Hours
1	3.4	6	3.8
2	2.5	7	4.1
3	3.0	8	2.7
4	2.6	9	5.0
5	4.2	10	2.8

3.4

219. The annual rainfall for each of six years is recorded in the table below. Find the average annual rainfall.

Year	Number of Inches
1	16.2
2	19.3
3	17.4
4	16.5
5	20.1
6	18.5

18 in.

Section 5   Comparing and Converting Fractions and Decimals

Objective A	To convert fractions to decimals and decimals to fractions

Reference for Computer Tutor™

Every fraction can be written as a decimal. To write a fraction as a decimal, divide the numerator of the fraction by the denominator.

Convert $\frac{3}{4}$ to a decimal.

$$\begin{array}{r} 0.75 \\ 4)\overline{3.00} \\ -2\,8 \\ \hline 20 \\ -20 \\ \hline 0 \end{array}$$ ← This is called a **terminating decimal.**

← The remainder is zero.

$\frac{3}{4} = 0.75$

Convert $\frac{4}{9}$ to a decimal.

$$\begin{array}{r} 0.44\ldots \\ 9)\overline{4.00} \\ -3\,6 \\ \hline 40 \\ -36 \\ \hline 4 \end{array}$$ ← This is called a **repeating decimal.**

← The remainder is never zero.

$\frac{4}{9}$ rounded to the nearest tenth is 0.4.

A number that can be written as a terminating or a repeating decimal is a **rational number.**

To convert a decimal to a fraction, remove the decimal point and place the decimal part over a denominator equal to the place value of the last digit in the decimal.

$0.4\overset{\longrightarrow\text{hundredths}}{7} = \frac{47}{100}$

$7.4\overset{\longrightarrow\text{hundredths}}{5} = 7\frac{45}{100} = 7\frac{9}{20}$

$0.27\overset{\longrightarrow\text{thousandths}}{5} = \frac{275}{1000} = \frac{11}{40}$

$0.16\overset{\longrightarrow\text{hundredths}}{\frac{2}{3}} = \frac{16\frac{2}{3}}{100} = 16\frac{2}{3} \div 100 = \frac{50}{3} \times \frac{1}{100} = \frac{1}{6}$

Example 1	Convert $\frac{3}{8}$ to a decimal. Round to the nearest hundredth.	**Example 2**	Convert $\frac{9}{16}$ to a decimal. Round to the nearest tenth.
Solution	$\begin{array}{r} 0.375 \\ 8)\overline{3.000} \end{array} \approx 0.38$	**Your solution**	0.6
Example 3	Convert $2\frac{3}{4}$ to a decimal. Round to the nearest tenth.	**Example 4**	Convert $4\frac{1}{6}$ to a decimal. Round to the nearest hundredth.
Solution	$2\frac{3}{4} = \frac{11}{4}$ $\begin{array}{r} 2.75 \\ 4)\overline{11.00} \end{array} \approx 2.8$	**Your solution**	4.17

Solutions on p. A18

Solutions on p. A18

Example 5	Convert 0.82 and 4.75 to fractions.	**Example 6**	Convert 0.56 and 5.35 to fractions.
Solution	$0.82 = \frac{82}{100} = \frac{41}{50}$ $4.75 = 4\frac{75}{100} = 4\frac{3}{4}$	**Your solution**	$\frac{14}{25}$ $5\frac{7}{20}$
Example 7	Convert $0.15\frac{2}{3}$ to a fraction.	**Example 8**	Convert $0.12\frac{7}{8}$ to a fraction.
Solution	$0.15\frac{2}{3} = \frac{15\frac{2}{3}}{100} = 15\frac{2}{3} \div 100 =$ $\frac{47}{3} \times \frac{1}{100} = \frac{47}{300}$	**Your solution**	$\frac{103}{800}$

Objective B   To identify the order relation between two decimals or between a decimal and a fraction

Reference for Computer Tutor™

Decimals, like whole numbers and fractions, can be associated with points on the number line. The number line can be used to order decimals. A decimal that appears to the right of a given number is greater than the given number. A decimal that appears to the left of a given number is less than the given number.

3.00 3.05 3.10 3.15 3.20 3.25 3.30 3.35 3.40

Note that 3, 3.0, and 3.00 represent the same number.

Find the order relation between $\frac{3}{8}$ and 0.38.

Write $\frac{3}{8}$ as a decimal.

$$\frac{3}{8} = 0.375$$
$$0.375 < 0.38$$
$$\frac{3}{8} < 0.38$$

Example 9	Place the correct symbol, $<$ or $>$, between the numbers. 17.005 17.050	**Example 10**	Place the correct symbol, $<$ or $>$, between the numbers. 64.009 64.99
Solution	$17.005 < 17.050$	**Your solution**	$64.009 < 64.99$
Example 11	Place the correct symbol, $<$ or $>$, between the numbers. $\frac{5}{16}$ 0.32	**Example 12**	Place the correct symbol, $<$ or $>$, between the numbers. 0.63 $\frac{5}{8}$
Solution	$\frac{5}{16} \approx 0.313$ $0.313 < 0.32$ $\frac{5}{16} < 0.32$	**Your solution**	$0.63 > \frac{5}{8}$

Solutions on p. A18

2.5A Exercises

Convert the fraction to a decimal. Round to the nearest thousandth.

1. $\frac{5}{8}$
0.625

2. $\frac{7}{12}$
0.583

3. $\frac{2}{3}$
0.667

4. $\frac{5}{6}$
0.833

5. $\frac{1}{6}$
0.167

6. $\frac{7}{8}$
0.875

7. $\frac{5}{12}$
0.417

8. $\frac{9}{16}$
0.563

9. $\frac{7}{4}$
1.75

10. $\frac{5}{3}$
1.667

11. $\frac{1}{12}$
0.083

12. $\frac{4}{3}$
1.333

13. $\frac{9}{4}$
2.25

14. $\frac{8}{3}$
2.667

15. $\frac{7}{9}$
0.778

16. $1\frac{1}{2}$
1.5

17. $2\frac{1}{3}$
2.333

18. $\frac{16}{4}$
4

19. $\frac{36}{9}$
4

20. $\frac{3}{1000}$
0.003

21. $\frac{5}{10}$
0.5

22. $7\frac{2}{25}$
7.080

23. $16\frac{7}{9}$
16.778

24. $37\frac{1}{2}$
37.5

25. $87\frac{1}{2}$
87.5

26. $\frac{3}{8}$
0.375

27. $\frac{11}{16}$
0.688

28. $\frac{5}{24}$
0.208

29. $\frac{4}{25}$
0.16

30. $3\frac{1}{3}$
3.333

31. $8\frac{2}{5}$
8.4

32. $5\frac{4}{9}$
5.444

33. $3\frac{1}{12}$
3.083

34. $\frac{5}{16}$
0.313

35. $\frac{11}{12}$
0.917

36. $2\frac{3}{14}$
2.214

37. $1\frac{7}{16}$
1.438

38. $3\frac{3}{24}$
3.125

39. $4\frac{2}{3}$
4.667

40. $9\frac{4}{5}$
9.8

Convert the decimal to a fraction.

41. 0.8
$\frac{4}{5}$

42. 0.4
$\frac{2}{5}$

43. 0.32
$\frac{8}{25}$

44. 0.48
$\frac{12}{25}$

45. 0.125
$\frac{1}{8}$

46. 0.485
$\frac{97}{200}$

47. 1.25
$1\frac{1}{4}$

48. 3.75
$3\frac{3}{4}$

49. 16.9
$16\frac{9}{10}$

50. 17.5
$17\frac{1}{2}$

51. 8.4
$8\frac{2}{5}$

52. 10.7
$10\frac{7}{10}$

53. 8.437
$8\frac{437}{1000}$

54. 9.279
$9\frac{279}{1000}$

55. 7.75
$7\frac{3}{4}$

56. 3.05
$3\frac{1}{20}$

57. 8.005
$8\frac{1}{200}$

58. 6.015
$6\frac{3}{200}$

59. 14.024
$14\frac{3}{125}$

60. 28.02
$28\frac{1}{50}$

Convert the decimal to a fraction.

61. 1.68
$1\frac{17}{25}$

62. 7.38
$7\frac{19}{50}$

63. 0.045
$\frac{9}{200}$

64. 0.085
$\frac{17}{200}$

65. 16.72
$16\frac{18}{25}$

66. 82.32
$82\frac{8}{25}$

67. 0.33
$\frac{33}{100}$

68. 0.57
$\frac{57}{100}$

69. 6.035
$6\frac{7}{200}$

70. 2.25
$2\frac{1}{4}$

71. $0.15\frac{1}{3}$
$\frac{23}{150}$

72. $0.17\frac{2}{3}$
$\frac{53}{300}$

73. $0.87\frac{7}{8}$
$\frac{703}{800}$

74. $0.12\frac{5}{9}$
$\frac{113}{900}$

75. $0.10\frac{5}{8}$
$\frac{17}{160}$

76. $0.33\frac{1}{3}$
$\frac{1}{3}$

77. $0.66\frac{2}{3}$
$\frac{2}{3}$

78. $0.27\frac{3}{7}$
$\frac{48}{175}$

79. $0.29\frac{4}{7}$
$\frac{207}{700}$

80. $0.25\frac{4}{9}$
$\frac{229}{900}$

2.5B Exercises

Place the correct symbol, < or >, between the numbers.

81. $0.15 < 0.5$

82. $0.6 > 0.45$

83. $6.65 > 6.56$

84. $3.89 < 3.98$

85. $2.504 > 2.054$

86. $0.025 < 0.105$

87. $8.304 > 8.034$

88. $7.821 > 7.812$

89. $\frac{3}{8} > 0.365$

90. $\frac{4}{5} < 0.802$

91. $\frac{2}{3} > 0.65$

92. $0.85 < \frac{7}{8}$

93. $\frac{5}{9} > 0.55$

94. $\frac{7}{12} > 0.58$

95. $0.62 > \frac{7}{15}$

96. $\frac{11}{12} < 0.92$

97. $0.161 > \frac{1}{7}$

98. $\frac{5}{24} > 0.202$

99. $\frac{7}{36} < 0.198$

100. $0.429 < \frac{4}{9}$

101. $0.623 > 0.6023$

102. $0.86 > 0.856$

103. $0.87 > 0.087$

104. $1.005 > 0.5$

105. $0.033 < 0.3$

106. $0.044 < 0.4$

107. $8.881 > 8.818$

108. $0.06 > 0.0499$

109. $0.835 > \frac{11}{16}$

110. $0.902 < \frac{10}{11}$

111. $\frac{4}{9} < 0.445$

112. $\frac{8}{25} < 0.33$

Calculators and Computers

The program to ADD OR SUBTRACT FRACTIONS on the Student Disk will provide you with practice on these operations. The program is designed to provide you with a problem. Then, using paper and pencil, you are to solve the problem. After you have solved the problem, press the RETURN key. The solution will be displayed. Compare this solution with your solution.

The $\boxed{\cdot}$ key on a calculator is used to enter a decimal point. To enter 36.43 on your calculator, enter 36, press the $\boxed{\cdot}$ key, and then enter 43.

Divide:　308.758 ÷ 48.7

Press the keys shown in the box.
　　　　　　　　$\boxed{308}\ \boxed{\cdot}\ \boxed{758}\ \boxed{÷}\ \boxed{48}\ \boxed{\cdot}\ \boxed{7}\ \boxed{=}$

The answer 6.34 should be displayed.

Multiply:　2.43478 × 3.2411

Press the keys shown in the box.
　　　　　　　　$\boxed{2}\ \boxed{\cdot}\ \boxed{43478}\ \boxed{×}\ \boxed{3}\ \boxed{\cdot}\ \boxed{2411}\ \boxed{=}$

The answer displayed will be 7.8913655 or 7.8913654, where the only difference is the last digit. The reason for this difference is that 2.43478 × 3.2411 is only approximately equal to the number in the calculator's display. The exact answer is 7.891365458. Because the display of most calculators contains only 8 digits, the engineer who designs a calculator decides on one of two methods for displaying an answer of more than 8 digits, either to round off the answer, as in

7.891365458 ≈ 7.8913655

or to truncate the answer, which means that the digits that cannot be displayed are discarded, as in

7.891365458 ≈ 7.8913654.

A calculator can also be used to convert a fraction to a decimal.

Convert $\frac{8}{17}$ to a decimal.

Press the keys shown in the box.
　　　　　　　　$\boxed{8}\ \boxed{÷}\ \boxed{17}\ \boxed{=}$

The decimal 0.4705882 should be displayed. This is an approximate answer; $\frac{8}{17}$ rounded to the nearest thousandth is 0.471.

Simplify. Round to the nearest hundredth.

1. 25.407 + 1.98 + 118.257　　　2. 93.079256 − 66.09249　　　3. 49.6854 × 39.0672

4. 2.00547 × 9.672　　　　　　5. 423.0925 ÷ 3.0927　　　　6. 0.03629 ÷ 0.00054

Convert the fraction to a decimal. Round to the nearest thousandth.

7. $\frac{6}{7}$　　　　　　　　　8. $\frac{5}{11}$　　　　　　　　　9. $\frac{9}{22}$

ANSWERS: **1.** 145.64　　**2.** 26.99　　**3.** 1941.07　　**4.** 19.40　　**5.** 136.80　　**6.** 67.20　　**7.** 0.857　　**8.** 0.455　　**9.** 0.409

Chapter Summary

KEY WORDS

A **fraction** can represent the number of equal parts of a whole.

Each part of a fraction has a name.

Fraction bar $\rightarrow \dfrac{3}{8}$ $\leftarrow$ **Numerator**
$\leftarrow$ **Denominator**

A **proper fraction** is a fraction less than one. A **mixed number** is a number greater than one with a whole number part and a fractional part. An **improper fraction** is a fraction greater than or equal to one. The numerator of an improper fraction is greater than or equal to the denominator.

Equal fractions with different denominators are called **equivalent fractions.**

A fraction is in **simplest form** when there are no common factors in the numerator and the denominator.

The **reciprocal** of a fraction is the fraction with the numerator and denominator interchanged.

The **average** or **mean** of a set of numbers is the sum of the numbers divided by the number of numbers in the set.

ESSENTIAL RULES

To **add fractions with like denominators,** add the numerators and place the sum over the common denominator. To **add fractions with unlike denominators,** rewrite the fractions as equivalent fractions with a common denominator. Then add the fractions.

To **subtract fractions with like denominators,** subtract the numerators and place the difference over the common denominator. To **subtract fractions with unlike denominators,** rewrite the fractions as equivalent fractions with a common denominator. Then subtract the fractions.

To **multiply fractions,** multiply the numerators and place the product over the product of the denominators. To **divide fractions,** replace the divisor by its reciprocal and proceed as in multiplication.

To **add decimals,** write the numbers so that the decimal points are on a vertical line. Add as for whole numbers and write the decimal point in the sum directly below the decimal point in the addends.

To **subtract decimals,** write the numbers so that the decimal points are on a vertical line. Subtract as for whole numbers and write the decimal point in the difference directly below the decimal point in the subtrahend.

To **multiply decimals,** multiply the numbers as for whole numbers. Write the decimal point in the product so that the number of decimal places in the product is the sum of the decimal places in the factors.

To **divide decimals,** move the decimal point in the divisor to make it a whole number. Move the decimal point in the dividend the same number of places to the right. Place the decimal point in the quotient directly over the decimal point in the dividend. Then divide as in whole numbers.

To **write a fraction as a decimal,** divide the numerator of the fraction by the denominator. To **convert a decimal to a fraction,** remove the decimal point and place the decimal part over the denominator equal to the place value of the last digit in the decimal.

Review/Test

1. Write $\frac{18}{5}$ as a mixed number.

    $3\frac{3}{5}$

2. Write $9\frac{4}{5}$ as an improper fraction.

    $\frac{49}{5}$

3. Build an equivalent fraction with the given denominator.

    $\frac{5}{8} = \frac{45}{72}$

4. Reduce $\frac{40}{64}$ to simplest form.

    $\frac{5}{8}$

5. Place the correct symbol, $<$ or $>$, between the two numbers.

    $\frac{3}{8} < \frac{5}{12}$

6. Add: $\frac{5}{6} + \frac{7}{9} + \frac{1}{15}$

    $1\frac{61}{90}$

7. Add: $12\frac{5}{12} + 9\frac{17}{20}$

    $22\frac{4}{15}$

8. Subtract: $\frac{9}{16} - \frac{5}{12}$

    $\frac{7}{48}$

9. Subtract: $23\frac{1}{8} - 9\frac{9}{44}$

    $13\frac{81}{88}$

10. Multiply: $\frac{9}{11} \times \frac{44}{81}$

    $\frac{4}{9}$

11. Multiply: $5\frac{2}{3} \times 1\frac{7}{17}$

    8

12. Divide: $\frac{5}{9} \div \frac{7}{18}$

    $1\frac{3}{7}$

13. Divide: $6\frac{2}{3} \div 3\frac{1}{6}$

    $2\frac{2}{19}$

14. Round 7.0954625 to the nearest thousandth.

    7.095

15. Add: $270.93 + 97 + 1.976 + 88.675$

    458.581

16. Subtract: $37.003 - 9.23674$

    27.76626

17. Multiply: 0.369×6.7

    2.4723

18. Divide: $0.037\overline{)0.0569}$
    Round to the nearest thousandth.

    1.538

19. Convert $\frac{9}{13}$ to a decimal. Round to the nearest thousandth.

    0.692

20. Convert 0.825 to a fraction.

    $\frac{33}{40}$

21. Place the correct symbol, $<$ or $>$, between the two numbers.

    $0.66 < 0.666$

22. Place the correct symbol, $<$ or $>$, between the two numbers.

    $\frac{3}{8} > 0.35$

23. A person can walk $3\frac{1}{3}$ mi in one hour. How many miles can the person walk in $2\frac{1}{2}$ hours?

    $8\frac{1}{3}$ mi

24. The hourly wage for four job classifications at a company are $9.25, $8.25, $7.25, and $6.75. Find the average hourly wage for the four job classifications. Round to the nearest cent.

    $7.88

Cumulative Review/Test

1. Add: $\frac{7}{12} + \frac{9}{16}$

   $1\frac{7}{48}$

2. Divide: $8.09\overline{)17.42963}$
   Round to the nearest thousandth.

   2.154

3. Multiply: $3\frac{1}{8} \times 2\frac{2}{5}$

   $7\frac{1}{2}$

4. Place the correct symbol, $<$ or $>$, between the two numbers.

   $\frac{8}{9} < 0.98$

5. Subtract: $390{,}047 - 98{,}769$

   $291{,}278$

6. Write $\frac{25}{4}$ as a mixed number.

   $6\frac{1}{4}$

7. Add: $379.006 + 27.523 + 9.8707$

   416.3997

8. Convert $\frac{11}{15}$ to a decimal.
   Round to the nearest thousandth.

   0.733

9. Divide: $6\frac{1}{8} \div 2\frac{1}{3}$

   $2\frac{5}{8}$

10. Multiply: 926×79

    $73{,}154$

11. Write $7\frac{2}{3}$ as an improper fraction.

    $\frac{23}{3}$

12. Subtract: $29.005 - 7.9286$

    21.0764

13. Convert $0.16\frac{2}{3}$ to a fraction.

    $\frac{1}{6}$

14. Multiply: 9.074×6.09

    55.26066

15. Simplify $4 \cdot (6 - 3) \div 6 - 1$.

    1

16. Build an equivalent fraction with the given denominator.

    $\frac{5}{16} = \frac{15}{48}$

17. Round $290{,}496$ to the nearest thousand.

    $290{,}000$

18. Subtract: $\frac{11}{12} - \frac{3}{8}$

    $\frac{13}{24}$

19. Reduce $\frac{24}{60}$ to simplest form.

    $\frac{2}{5}$

20. Find the prime factorization of 44.

    $2 \cdot 2 \cdot 11$

21. Round 0.05762 to the nearest hundredth.

    0.06

22. Place the correct symbol, $<$ or $>$, between the two numbers.

    $\frac{7}{9} < \frac{5}{6}$

23. A student received grades of 82, 76, 84, and 78 on four math exams. Find the student's average grade on the math exams.

    80

24. The prices of identical calculators at each of three stores were $38.80, $36.90, and $37.97. Find the average price of the calculator.

    $\$37.89$

chapter 3

Signed Numbers and Variable Expressions

Objectives

3.1A   To identify the order relation between two signed numbers

3.1B   To evaluate expressions containing the absolute value symbol

3.1C   To add and subtract signed numbers

3.1D   To multiply and divide signed numbers

3.1E   To use the Order of Operations Agreement to simplify expressions

3.2A   To evaluate a variable expression

3.2B   To simplify a variable expression using the Properties of Addition

3.2C   To simplify a variable expression using the Properties of Multiplication

3.2D   To simplify a variable expression using the Distributive Property

3.3A   To translate a verbal expression into a variable expression

Section 1 Signed Numbers

Objective A To identify the order relation between two signed numbers

Reference for
Computer
Tutor™

Thus far only zero and the numbers greater than zero have been encountered in this text. The numbers greater than zero are called **positive numbers.** However, the phrases "10° below zero," "$25 in debt," and "15 feet below sea level" refer to numbers less than zero. These numbers are called **negative numbers.**

The positive and negative numbers together are called **signed numbers.** A plus sign (+) in front of a number indicates a positive number. A negative sign (−) in front of a number indicates a negative number. A negative sign is always used with a negative number. However, the plus sign on a positive number is usually omitted. Therefore, +2 and 2 represent the same positive number.

Negative numbers are to the left of zero on the number line.

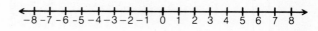

The graph of a signed number is shown by placing a heavy dot on the number line directly above the number.

The graphs of −3 and 1.5 on the number line

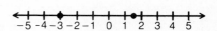

The number line can be used to order signed numbers. A number that appears to the left of a given number is less than (<) the given number. A number that appears to the right of a given number is greater than (>) the given number.

Negative 4 is less than negative 2.5.
$-4 < -2.5$

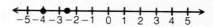

Example 1	A stock is down $2\frac{5}{8}$ points for the week. Represent this change by a signed number.	**Example 2**	The surface of the Salton Sea is 232 ft below sea level. Represent this depth by a signed number.
Solution	$-2\frac{5}{8}$	**Your solution**	-232
Example 3	Graph -2 on the number line.	**Example 4**	Graph -4 on the number line.
Solution		**Your solution**	

Example 5	Place the correct symbol, < or >, between the two numbers. **a.** -5 -7 **b.** $\frac{1}{2}$ -2	**Example 6**	Place the correct symbol, < or >, between the two numbers. **a.** -12 7 **b.** -4.5 0
Solution	**a.** $-5 > -7$ **b.** $\frac{1}{2} > -2$	**Your solution**	**a.** $-12 < 7$ **b.** $-4.5 < 0$

Solutions on p. A19

Copyright © 1989 HMCo

Objective B

To evaluate expressions containing the absolute value symbol

Reference for
Computer
Tutor™

Two numbers that are the same distance from zero on the number line but on opposite sides of zero are called **opposites.**

−4 is the opposite of 4
and
4 is the opposite of −4.

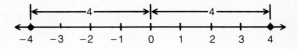

Note that a negative sign can be read as "the opposite of."
−(4) = −4   The opposite of 4 is negative 4.
−(−4) = 4   The opposite of negative 4 is 4.

The **absolute value** of a number is the distance between zero and the number on the number line. Therefore, the absolute value of a number is a positive number or zero. The symbol for absolute value is "| |."

The distance from 0 to 4 is 4
Thus |4| = 4 (the absolute value of 4 is 4).

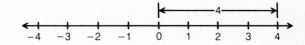

The distance from 0 to −4 is 4
Thus |−4| = 4 (the absolute value of −4 is 4).

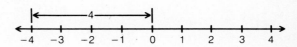

The absolute value of a positive number is the number itself. The absolute value of a negative number is the opposite of the negative number. The absolute value of zero is zero.

Example 7   Find the absolute value of 2 and −3.

Solution |2| = 2

|−3| = 3

Example 8   Find the absolute value of −7 and 3.4.

Your solution   7 , 3.4

Example 9   Evaluate |−34| and |17.5|.

Solution |−34| = 34

|17.5| = 17.5

Example 10   Evaluate $\left|2\frac{1}{2}\right|$ and |−9|.

Your solution $2\frac{1}{2}$, 9

Example 11   Evaluate $-\left|-4\frac{1}{2}\right|$.

Solution $-\left|-4\frac{1}{2}\right| = -4\frac{1}{2}$ The minus sign *in front of* the absolute value sign is not affected by the absolute value sign.

Example 12   Evaluate −|−12|.

Your solution   −12

Solutions on p. A19

Reference for
Computer
Tutor™

| Objective C | # To add and subtract signed numbers |

The size or magnitude of a number can be represented anywhere along the number line by an arrow. A positive number is represented by an arrow pointing to the right. A negative number is represented by an arrow pointing to the left.

Each arrow is 3 units long
and represents the number 3.

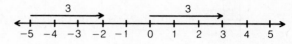

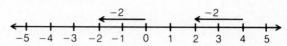

Each arrow is 2 units long
and represents the number −2.

Addition of signed numbers can be shown with arrows. The arrow representing the first addend starts at zero. The arrow representing the second addend starts at the head of the first arrow. The sum is represented by the arrow starting at zero and stopping at the head of the second arrow.

$5 + 2 = 7$

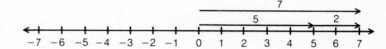

$(-5) + (-2) = -7$

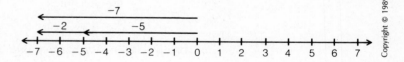

$5 + (-2) = 3$

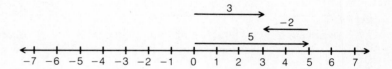

$(-5) + 2 = -3$

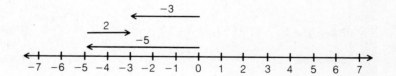

The rule used for adding two signed numbers depends on whether the signs of the addends are the same or different.

Like Signs   To add signed numbers with like signs, add the absolute values of the numbers. Then attach the sign of the addends.

$$5 + 2 = +7$$
$$-5 + (-2) = -7$$

Unlike Signs   To add signed numbers with unlike signs, find the difference between the absolute values of the addends. Then attach the sign of the addend with the larger absolute value.

$$5 + (-2) = +3$$
$$-5 + 2 = -3$$

When adding more than two signed numbers, start from the left and add the first two numbers. Then add the sum to the third number. Continue the process until all the numbers have been added.

Add: $4 + (-5) + 3 + (-7)$

$\underline{4 + (-5)} + 3 + (-7)$ Add the first two numbers.

$\quad \underline{-1 + 3} + (-7)$ Add the sum to the third number.

$\qquad \underline{2 + (-7)}$ Continue adding until all the numbers have been added.

$\qquad\quad -5$

Notice that the subtraction of a *whole number* is the same as the addition of the opposite number.

Subtraction		Addition of the Opposite	
$8 - 4$	$=$	$8 + (-4)$	$= 4$
$22 - 17$	$=$	$22 + (-17)$	$= 5$

Subtraction of *signed numbers* can also be written as the addition of the opposite number.

Subtraction		Addition of the Opposite	
$7 - (-3)$	$=$	$7 + 3$	$= 10$
$(-6) - 2$	$=$	$(-6) + (-2)$	$= -8$
$(-19) - (-14)$	$=$	$(-19) + 14$	$= -5$

To subtract signed numbers, rewrite the subtraction as the addition of the opposite, then add.

First number	$-$	second number	$=$	first number	$+$	the opposite of the second number	
5	$-$	2	$=$	5	$+$	(-2)	$= 3$
-5	$-$	(-2)	$=$	(-5)	$+$	2	$= -3$
5	$-$	(-2)	$=$	5	$+$	2	$= 7$
-5	$-$	2	$=$	(-5)	$+$	(-2)	$= -7$

When subtraction occurs several times in a problem, rewrite each subtraction as the addition of the opposite. Then proceed as in the addition of signed numbers.

Subtract: $-4 - (-2) - 3 - (-4) - 5$

$-4 - (-2) - 3 - (-4) - 5$

$-4 + 2 + (-3) + 4 + (-5)$ Each subtraction has been changed to addition. Each number being subtracted has been changed to its opposite.

$(-2) + (-3) + 4 + (-5)$

$(-5) + 4 + (-5)$

$(-1) + (-5)$

-6

Example 13   Add: $-4 + (-6)$

Solution $-4 + (-6) = -10$

Example 14   Add: $-3 + (-6)$

Your solution -9

Example 15   Add: $6.5 + (-8.35)$

Solution   Since signs are unlike, subtract absolute values.
$8.35 - 6.5 = 1.85$

Attach the negative sign.
$6.5 + (-8.35) = -1.85$

Example 16   Add: $10.37 + (-15.9)$

Your solution -5.53

Example 17   Add: $-4\frac{1}{2} + \left(-12\frac{1}{3}\right)$

Solution $-4\frac{1}{2} + \left(-12\frac{1}{3}\right) =$
$\left(-4\frac{3}{6}\right) + \left(-12\frac{2}{6}\right) =$
$-16\frac{5}{6}$

Example 18   Add: $-5\frac{3}{8} + 9\frac{5}{12}$

Your solution $4\frac{1}{24}$

Example 19   Add: $-4 + (-3) + (-10) + 6$

Solution $-4 + (-3) + (-10) + 6 =$
$(-7) + (-10) + 6 =$
$(-17) + 6 =$
-11

Example 20   Add: $-2 + 4 + (-8) + 7$

Your solution 1

Example 21   Subtract: $-10 - 12$

Solution $-10 - 12 = -10 + (-12)$
$\qquad\qquad = -22$

Example 22   Subtract: $12 - 15$

Your solution -3

Example 23   Subtract: $14.75 - 16.3$

Solution $14.75 - 16.3 =$
$14.75 + (-16.3)$

Since signs are unlike, subtract absolute values.
$16.3 - 14.75 = 1.55$

Attach the negative sign.
$14.75 + (-16.3) = -1.55$

Example 24   Subtract: $5.72 - 11.4$

Your solution -5.68

Solutions on p. A19

Example 25   Subtract: $12\frac{1}{2} - \left(-4\frac{3}{8}\right)$ **Example 26**   Subtract: $8\frac{1}{2} - \left(-2\frac{3}{4}\right)$

Solution $12\frac{1}{2} - \left(-4\frac{3}{8}\right) = 12\frac{1}{2} + 4\frac{3}{8}$ **Your solution** $11\frac{1}{4}$

$$= 12\frac{4}{8} + 4\frac{3}{8}$$

$$16\frac{7}{8}$$

Example 27   Subtract:
$-3.9 - 16.78 - (-3.2)$

Example 28   Subtract:
$-14.2 - (-7.3) - 7.89$

Solution $-3.9 - 16.78 - (-3.2) =$
$-3.9 + (-16.78) + 3.2 =$
$-20.68 + 3.2 =$
-17.48

Your solution -14.79

Solutions on p. A19

| Objective D |

To multiply and divide signed numbers

Reference for Computer Tutor™

When 2 is multiplied by a sequence of decreasing whole numbers, each product decreases by 2.

$2 \times 3 = 6$
$2 \times 2 = 4$
$2 \times 1 = 2$
$2 \times 0 = 0$

The pattern developed can be continued so that 2 is multiplied by a sequence of negative numbers. The resulting products must be negative in order to maintain the pattern of decreasing by 2.

$2 \times (-1) = -2$
$2 \times (-2) = -4$
$2 \times (-3) = -6$
$2 \times (-4) = -8$

Therefore, the product of a positive number and a negative number is negative.

When -2 is multiplied by a sequence of decreasing whole numbers, each product increases by 2.

$-2 \times 3 = -6$
$-2 \times 2 = -4$
$-2 \times 1 = -2$
$-2 \times 0 = 0$

The pattern developed can be continued so that -2 is multiplied by a sequence of negative numbers. The resulting products must be positive in order to maintain the pattern of increasing by 2.

$-2 \times (-1) = 2$
$-2 \times (-2) = 4$
$-2 \times (-3) = 6$
$-2 \times (-4) = 8$

Therefore, the product of two negative numbers is positive.

When multiplying signed numbers, multiply the absolute values of the factors.

If the signs of the factors are alike, the product is positive.

$$2 \times 3 = 6$$
$$-2 \times (-3) = 6$$

If the signs of the factors are different, the product is negative.

$$2 \times (-3) = -6$$
$$-2 \times 3 = -6$$

For every division problem there is a related multiplication problem.

Division: $\dfrac{10}{2} = 5$ Related multiplication: $5 \times 2 = 10$

This fact can be used to illustrate the rules for dividing signed numbers.

The quotient of two numbers with like signs is positive.

$$\frac{10}{2} = 5 \text{ because } 5 \times 2 = 10$$

$$\frac{-10}{-2} = 5 \text{ because } 5 \times (-2) = -10$$

The quotient of two numbers with unlike signs is negative.

$$\frac{10}{-2} = -5 \text{ because } -5 \times (-2) = 10$$

$$\frac{-10}{2} = -5 \text{ because } -5 \times 2 = -10$$

Note that $\dfrac{10}{-2} = -5$, $\dfrac{-10}{2} = -5$, and $-\dfrac{10}{2} = -5$.

Therefore, $\dfrac{10}{-2}$, $\dfrac{-10}{2}$, and $-\dfrac{10}{2}$ are equivalent.

Divide: $1\frac{1}{2} \div \left(-\frac{2}{3}\right)$

$1\frac{1}{2} \div \left(-\frac{2}{3}\right) = -\left(1\frac{1}{2} \div \frac{2}{3}\right)$ Since the signs are unlike, the answer will be negative.
Divide the absolute values of the numbers.

$$= -\left(\frac{3}{2} \div \frac{2}{3}\right)$$

$$= -\left(\frac{3}{2} \times \frac{3}{2}\right)$$

$$= -\frac{9}{4}$$

$$= -$$

Example 29   Multiply: $3 \times (-2.1)$

Solution $3 \times (-2.1) = -6.3$

Example 30   Multiply: -3.5×7

Your solution -24.5

Example 31   Multiply: $-2 \times (-3) \times (-4)$

Solution $-2 \times (-3) \times (-4) =$
                 $6 \times (-4) = -24$

Example 32   Multiply: $-3 \times (-6) \times \left(-\frac{1}{2}\right)$

Your solution -9

Example 33   Divide: $-12 \div 6$

Solution $\frac{-12}{6} = -2$

Example 34   Divide: $-15 \div 5$

Your solution -3

Example 35   Divide: $12 \div (-8)$

Solution $\frac{12}{-8} = -1.5$

Example 36   Divide: $18 \div (-4)$

Your solution -4.5

Example 37   Divide: $-3.27 \div (-1.12)$
Round to the nearest
hundredth.

Solution $\frac{-3.27}{-1.12} \approx 2.92$

Example 38   Divide: $-6.25 \div (-1.49)$
Round to the nearest
hundredth.

Your solution 4.19

Solutions on p. A19

Objective E

To use the order of operations agreement to simplify expressions

3 DISK THREE

Reference for Computer Tutor™

The Order of Operations Agreement was presented in Chapter 1. In simplifying expressions with signed numbers, Step 4 of the Order of Operations Agreement is modified so that subtraction of a number is rewritten as the addition of the opposite before adding from left to right.

> ***The Order of Operations Agreement***
> Step 1   Do all operations inside parentheses.
> Step 2   Simplify any expressions containing exponents.
> Step 3   Do multiplication and division as they occur from left to right.
> Step 4   Rewrite subtraction as the addition of the opposite. Then do additions as they occur from left to right.

Exponents may be confusing in expressions with signed numbers.

$(-3)^2 = (-3) \times (-3) = 9$
$-3^2 = -(3)^2 = -(3 \times 3) = -9$

Note that -3 is squared only when the negative sign is *inside* parentheses.

Simplify $(-3)^2 - 2 \times (8 - 3) + (-5)$.

$(-3)^2 - 2 \times \underline{(8 - 3)} + (-5) =$
$\underline{(-3)^2} - 2 \times 5 + (-5) =$
$9 \underline{- 2 \times 5} + (-5) =$
$9 \underline{- 10} + (-5) =$
$\underline{9 + (-10)} + (-5) =$
$\underline{(-1) + (-5)} =$
-6

1. Perform operations inside parentheses.

2. Simplify expressions with exponents.

3. Do multiplications and divisions as they occur from left to right.

4. Rewrite subtraction as the addition of the opposite. Then add from left to right.

Example 39   Simplify $8 - 4 \div (-2)$.

Solution
$8 - 4 \div (-2) =$
$8 - (-2) =$
$8 + 2 =$
10

Example 40   Simplify $9 - 9 \div (-3)$.

Your solution

12

Example 41   Simplify $12 \div (-2)^2 + 5$.

Solution
$12 \div (-2)^2 + 5 =$
$12 \div 4 + 5 =$
$3 + 5 =$
8

Example 42   Simplify $8 \div 4 \cdot 4 - (-2)^2$.

Your solution

4

Example 43   Simplify $12 - (-10) \div (8 - 3)$.

Solution
$12 - (-10) \div (8 - 3) =$
$12 - (-10) \div 5 =$
$12 - (-2) =$
$12 + 2 =$
14

Example 44   Simplify $8 - (-15) \div (2 - 7)$.

Your solution

5

Example 45   Simplify $\left(\frac{1}{4} - \frac{1}{2}\right)^2 + \frac{3}{8}$.

Solution
$\underline{\left(\frac{1}{4} - \frac{1}{2}\right)}^2 \div \frac{3}{8} =$
$\underline{\left(-\frac{1}{4}\right)}^2 \div \frac{3}{8} =$
$\frac{1}{16} \div \frac{3}{8} =$
$\frac{1}{16} \times \frac{8}{3} =$
$\frac{1}{6}$

Example 46   Simplify $7 \div \left(\frac{1}{7} - \frac{3}{14}\right) - 9$.

Your solution

-107

Solutions on p. A19

3.1A Exercises

Represent the quantity by a signed number.

1. A temperature 30° below zero
-30

2. A lake 120 ft below sea level
-120

3. A stock up $7\frac{1}{4}$ points
$+7\frac{1}{4}$

4. A loss of $324
-324

5. A mountain 12,382 ft above sea level
$+12,382$

6. A gain of $800
$+800$

Graph the numbers on the number line.

7. 4, −4
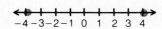

8. −1, 0
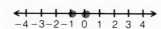

9. −3, 1
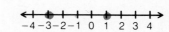

10. 3, −1
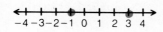

11. −0.5, 3.5

12. $-3\frac{1}{2}$, 2
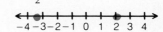

13. $\frac{1}{2}$, $2\frac{1}{2}$
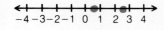

14. 0.5, −2.5

15. $-1\frac{1}{2}$, $-\frac{1}{2}$
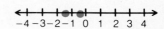

Place the correct symbol, < or >, between the two numbers.

16. 6 $<$ 10

17. 3 $<$ 5

18. −2 $>$ −7

19. −8 $<$ −3

20. −1 $<$ 0

21. 0 $<$ 10

22. −2 $<$ 1

23. −12 $<$ 3

24. 7 $>$ −2

25. 9 $>$ −1

26. −3 $<$ 2

27. 0 $<$ 5

28. 0 $>$ −5

29. 6 $>$ $4\frac{1}{2}$

30. −21 $<$ 3.5

31. −10 $<$ 40

32. $3\frac{1}{4}$ $>$ $3\frac{1}{8}$

33. $-3\frac{1}{2}$ $<$ $2\frac{1}{3}$

34. $-7\frac{1}{3}$ $>$ $-9\frac{2}{3}$

35. 5.3 $>$ −6.9

36. −17 $<$ 2.8

37. −8.5 $>$ −10.9

38. 12.7 $>$ −21.03

39. $-3\frac{1}{3}$ $<$ $2\frac{1}{8}$

3.1B Exercises

Evaluate.

40. |5|
5

41. |7|
7

42. |−2|
2

43. |−8|
8

44. |−1|
1

45. |−12|
12

46. |22|
22

47. |4|
4

48. |0|
0

49. |−0.1|
0.1

50. |−1|
1

51. |−4|
4

52. −|−2|
−2

53. −|−6|
−6

54. −|4|
−4

55. −|8|
−8

56. $\left|-\frac{3}{8}\right|$
$\frac{3}{8}$

57. $\left|\frac{1}{2}\right|$
$\frac{1}{2}$

58. |−40.6|
40.6

59. |−6.4|
6.4

60. $\left|-2\frac{1}{2}\right|$
$2\frac{1}{2}$

61. −|−1.7|
−1.7

62. $-\left|-3\frac{4}{5}\right|$
$-3\frac{4}{5}$

63. |−45.9|
45.9

64. |−2.5|
2.5

65. |3.4|
3.4

66. −|−4.9|
−4.9

67. $-\left|-1\frac{1}{2}\right|$
$-1\frac{1}{2}$

68. $\left|-6\frac{7}{8}\right|$
$6\frac{7}{8}$

69. |−13.08|
13.08

3.1C Exercises

Add.

70. 4 + (−2)
2

71. 6 + (−5)
1

72. −10 + 2
−8

73. −7 + 3
−4

74. −3 + (−2)
−5

75. −8 + (−5)
−13

76. 35 + (−64)
−29

77. −39 + (−42)
−81

78. −37 + 94
57

79. 75 + 92
167

80. 149 + (−239)
−90

81. −347 + 937
590

82. 6 + (−12) + 3
−3

83. 4 + 8 + (−16)
−4

84. 16 + (−23) + (−4)
−11

85. −4 + 34 + (−13)
17

86. −12 + (−8) + 9
−11

87. 4 + 56 + (−25)
35

88. 3.4 + (−6.8)
−3.4

89. −4.9 + 3.27
−1.63

90. −8.32 + (−6.09)
−14.41

91. −3.5 + 7
3.5

92. −4.8 + (−3.2)
−8.0

93. 6.2 + (−4.29)
1.91

Add.

94. $-4.6 + 3.92$
-0.68

95. $7.2 + (-8.42)$
-1.22

96. $3.09 + 6.025$
9.115

97. $-45.71 + (-135.8)$
-181.51

98. $124.09 + (-67.5)$
56.59

99. $-35.274 + 129.9$
94.626

100. $-6.8 + 4.2 + 5.3$
2.7

101. $-4.5 + 3.2 + 6.8$
5.5

102. $\frac{1}{2} + \left(-\frac{1}{3}\right)$
$\frac{1}{6}$

103. $-\frac{7}{12} + \frac{3}{8}$
$-\frac{5}{24}$

104. $-\frac{3}{8} + \left(-\frac{5}{12}\right)$
$-\frac{19}{24}$

105. $\frac{2}{5} + \left(-\frac{3}{10}\right)$
$\frac{1}{10}$

106. $-\frac{5}{6} + \left(-\frac{7}{9}\right)$
$-1\frac{11}{18}$

107. $-\frac{11}{12} + \frac{5}{9}$
$-\frac{13}{36}$

108. $2\frac{1}{4} + \left(-1\frac{1}{2}\right)$
$\frac{3}{4}$

109. $-3\frac{1}{3} + \left(-4\frac{1}{2}\right)$
$-7\frac{5}{6}$

110. $-5\frac{1}{8} + 3\frac{2}{3}$
$-1\frac{11}{24}$

111. $\frac{1}{2} + \left(-\frac{3}{8}\right) + \frac{5}{12}$
$\frac{13}{24}$

112. $-\frac{3}{8} + \frac{3}{4} + \left(-\frac{3}{16}\right)$
$\frac{3}{16}$

113. $\frac{1}{3} + 3\frac{1}{5} + \left(-1\frac{1}{9}\right)$
$2\frac{19}{45}$

Subtract.

114. $3 - 9$
-6

115. $5 - 12$
-7

116. $-3 - 8$
-11

117. $-12 - 4$
-16

118. $6 - (-3)$
9

119. $4 - (-9)$
13

120. $(-6) - (-3)$
-3

121. $-12 - (-30)$
18

122. $-35 - (-83)$
48

123. $82 - (-193)$
275

124. $37 - 68$
-31

125. $-129 - 49$
-178

126. $-185 - (-296)$
111

127. $3 - 12 - 7$
-16

128. $8 - 7 - 9$
-8

129. $4 - (-12) - 3$
13

130. $6 - (-3) - 7$
2

131. $-7 - (-3) - (-7)$
3

132. $1 - (-3) - (-5)$
9

133. $12 - (-7) - (-3)$
22

134. $6 - (-1) - (-2)$
9

135. $-4.9 - 13.6$
-18.5

136. $6.7 - (-14.023)$
20.723

137. $-3.02 - (-4.7)$
1.68

138. $-12.7 - (-15.32)$
2.62

139. $-3.4 - (-4.5)$
1.1

140. $6.8 - (-1.14)$
7.94

141. $4.72 - 8.09$
-3.37

Subtract.

142. $-4.7 - 6.3$
-11

143. $16.98 - 24.32$
-7.34

144. $16.23 - 9.45$
6.78

145. $75.9 - 93.87$
-17.97

146. $-6.05 - (-3.09)$
-2.96

147. $-7.82 - 1.65$
-9.47

148. $-\frac{3}{4} - \frac{5}{8}$
$-1\frac{3}{8}$

149. $-\frac{7}{12} - \left(-\frac{7}{8}\right)$
$\frac{7}{24}$

150. $\frac{5}{12} - \frac{11}{15}$
$-\frac{19}{60}$

151. $\frac{2}{5} - \frac{14}{15}$
$-\frac{8}{15}$

152. $-\frac{2}{3} - \frac{5}{8}$
$-1\frac{7}{24}$

153. $-\frac{3}{4} - \left(-\frac{2}{3}\right)$
$-\frac{1}{12}$

154. $\frac{3}{4} - \frac{3}{7}$
$\frac{9}{28}$

155. $-2\frac{11}{15} - \left(-3\frac{7}{20}\right)$
$\frac{37}{60}$

156. $-2\frac{1}{2} - \left(-3\frac{1}{4}\right)$
$\frac{3}{4}$

157. $4\frac{1}{2} - 2\frac{1}{4} - 7\frac{5}{8}$
$-5\frac{3}{8}$

3.1D Exercises

Multiply.

158. -2×3
-6

159. $8 \times (-7)$
-56

160. $-3 \times (-8)$
24

161. $-6 \times (-12)$
72

162. 4×9
36

163. 17×0
0

164. $-12(17)$
-204

165. $18(-32)$
-576

166. $-29 \times (-65)$
1885

167. $3 \times 6 \times (-4)$
-72

168. $-2 \times 7 \times 4$
-56

169. $-2 \times (-3) \times 6$
36

170. $8 \times (-3) \times (-7)$
168

171. $0 \times 6 \times (-2)$
0

172. $18 \times 0 \times (-14)$
0

173. $4 \times (-7) \times 6$
-168

174. 4.2×0.9
3.78

175. $-6.7 \times (-4.2)$
28.14

176. $-8.9 \times (-3.5)$
31.15

177. $-1.6(4.9)$
-7.84

178. $7.8(9.6)$
74.88

179. -14.3×7.9
-112.97

180. $-\frac{1}{3} \times \frac{5}{8}$
$-\frac{5}{24}$

181. $-\frac{3}{5} \times \left(-\frac{5}{20}\right)$
$\frac{3}{20}$

182. $\frac{4}{15} \times \left(-\frac{3}{22}\right)$
$-\frac{2}{55}$

183. $-2\frac{1}{2} \times \frac{1}{3}$
$-\frac{5}{6}$

184. $-1\frac{3}{5} \times \left(-2\frac{7}{9}\right)$
$4\frac{4}{9}$

185. $4\frac{1}{2} \times \left(-1\frac{1}{2}\right)$
$-6\frac{3}{4}$

Divide.

186. $\frac{1}{3} \div \left(-\frac{1}{2}\right)$
$-\frac{2}{3}$

187. $-\frac{3}{8} \div \frac{7}{8}$
$-\frac{3}{7}$

188. $-\frac{3}{4} \div \left(-\frac{7}{40}\right)$
$4\frac{2}{7}$

189. $-\frac{3}{11} \div 4\frac{1}{11}$
$-\frac{1}{15}$

Divide.

190. $2\frac{1}{3} \div \left(-1\frac{1}{4}\right)$

$-1\frac{13}{15}$

191. $-3\frac{1}{2} \div 2\frac{5}{8}$

$-1\frac{1}{3}$

192. $-1\frac{3}{8} \div \left(-2\frac{3}{5}\right)$

$\frac{55}{104}$

193. $-1\frac{1}{4} \div \left(-7\frac{5}{9}\right)$

$\frac{45}{272}$

Divide. Round to the nearest hundredth.

194. $18 \div (-2)$

-9

195. $-24 \div 8$

-3

196. $-64 \div (-8)$

8

197. $-49 \div (-7)$

7

198. $-12 \div 5$

-2.4

199. $16 \div (-9)$

-1.78

200. $-82 \div 0$

undefined

201. $95 \div 9$

10.56

202. $105 \div (-4)$

-26.25

203. $-162 \div 9$

-18

204. $184 \div (-16)$

-11.5

205. $-275 \div 21$

-13.10

206. $-621 \div (-14)$

44.36

207. $-882 \div (-65)$

13.57

208. $1.8 \div 4$

0.45

209. $0 \div (-8)$

0

210. $-1.42 \div 6$

-0.24

211. $-3.72 \div 7$

-0.53

212. $-9.01 \div 8$

-1.13

213. $-1.62 \div 17$

-0.10

3.1E Exercises

Simplify.

214. $8 \div 4 + 2$

4

215. $3 - 12 \div 2$

-3

216. $4 + (-7) + 3$

0

217. $-16 \div 2 + 8$

0

218. $4^2 - 4$

12

219. $6 - 2^2$

2

220. $2 \times (3 - 5) - 2$

-6

221. $2 - (8 - 10) \div 2$

3

222. $4 - (-3)^2$

-5

223. $(-2)^2 - 6$

-2

224. $4 - (-3) - 5$

2

225. $6 + (-8) - (-3)$

1

226. $16 \div 8 \times 4$

8

227. $4 \times 8 \div 16$

2

228. $3^2 + 2^2 + 5$

18

229. $(-3)^2 - (-2)^2 - 5$

0

230. $4 \times (2 - 4) - 4$

-12

231. $6 - 2 \times (1 - 3)$

10

232. $4 - (-2)^2 + (-3)$

-3

233. $-3 + (-6)^2 - 1$

32

Simplify.

234. $3^2 - 4 \times 2$
1

235. $9 \div 3 - (-3)^2$
−6

236. $3 \times (6 - 2) \div 6$
2

237. $4 \times (2 - 7) \div 5$
−4

238. $2^2 - (-3)^2 + 2$
−3

239. $3 \times (8 - 5) + 4$
13

240. $6 - 2 \times (1 - 5)$
14

241. $4 \times 2 \times (3 - 6)$
−24

242. $4^2 - 3^2 - 4$
3

243. $6 - (-3) \times (-3)^2$
33

244. $4 - (-5) \times (-2)^2$
24

245. $4 \times 2 - 3 \times 7$
−13

246. $16 \div 2 - 9 \div 3$
5

247. $4 - 2 \times 7 - 3^2$
−19

248. $(1.2)^2 - 4.1 \times 0.3$
0.21

249. $2.4 \times (-3) - 2.5$
−9.7

250. $1.6 - (1.6)^2$
−0.96

251. $4.1 \times 8 \div (-4.1)$
−8

252. $(4.1 - 3.9) - 0.7^2$
−0.29

253. $1.8 \times (-2.3) - 2$
−6.14

254. $(0.4)^2 \times 1.5 - 2$
−1.76

255. $(6.2 - 1.3) \times (-3)$
−14.7

256. $4.2 - (-3.9) - 6$
2.1

257. $-\frac{1}{2} + \frac{3}{8} \div \left(-\frac{3}{4}\right)$
−1

258. $\left(\frac{3}{4}\right)^2 - \frac{3}{8}$
$\frac{3}{16}$

259. $\left(\frac{1}{2}\right)^2 - \left(-\frac{1}{2}\right)^2$
0

260. $\frac{5}{16} - \frac{3}{8} + \frac{1}{2}$
$\frac{7}{16}$

261. $\frac{2}{7} \div \frac{5}{7} - \frac{3}{14}$
$\frac{13}{70}$

262. $\frac{1}{2} \times \frac{1}{4} \times \frac{1}{2} - \frac{3}{8}$
$-\frac{5}{16}$

263. $\frac{2}{3} \times \frac{5}{8} \div \frac{2}{7}$
$1\frac{11}{24}$

264. $\frac{1}{2} - \left(\frac{3}{4} - \frac{3}{8}\right) \div \frac{1}{3}$
$-\frac{5}{8}$

265. $\frac{3}{8} \div \left(-\frac{1}{2}\right)^2 + 2$
$3\frac{1}{2}$

266. $3 \times 2^2 + 5 \times (3 + 2) - 17$
20

267. $3 \times 4^2 - 16 - 4 + 3 - (1 - 2)^2$
30

268. $-12 \times (6 - 8) + 1^2 \times 3^2 \times 2 - 6 \times 2$
30

269. $-3 \times (-2)^2 \times 4 \div 8 - (-12)$
6

270. $3^2 \times (4 - 7) \div 9 + 6 - 3 - 4 \times 2$
−8

271. $16 - 4 \times 8 + 4^2 - (-18) \div (-9)$
−2

Section 2 Variable Expressions

Objective A To evaluate a variable expression

Reference for
Computer
Tutor™

Often we discuss a quantity without knowing its exact value, for example, the price of gold next month, the cost of a new automobile next year, or the tuition cost for next semester. In algebra, a letter of the alphabet is used to stand for a quantity that is unknown or that can change or *vary*. The letter is called a **variable.** An expression that contains one or more variables is called a **variable expression.**

A variable expression is shown at the right. The expression can be rewritten by writing subtraction as the addition of the opposite.

$$3x^2 - 5y + 2xy - x - 7$$

$$3x^2 + (-5y) + 2xy + (-x) + (-7)$$

Note that the expression has 5 addends. The **terms** of a variable expression are the addends of the expression. The expression has 5 terms.

5 terms

$$\underbrace{3x^2 \quad - \quad 5y \quad + \quad 2xy \quad - \quad x}_{\text{variable terms}} \quad \underbrace{- \quad 7}_{\substack{\text{constant} \\ \text{term}}}$$

The terms $3x^2$, $-5y$, $2xy$, and $-x$ are **variable terms.**

The term -7 is a **constant term** or simply a **constant.**

Each variable term is composed of a **numerical coefficient** and a **variable part** (the variable or variables and their exponents).

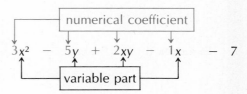

When the numerical coefficient is 1 or -1, the 1 is usually not written ($x = 1x$ and $-x = -1x$).

Variable expressions occur naturally in science. In a physics lab, a student may discover that a weight of one pound will stretch a spring $\frac{1}{2}$ in. Two pounds will stretch the spring 1 in. By experimenting, the student can discover that the distance the spring will stretch is found by multiplying the weight by $\frac{1}{2}$. By letting W represent the weight attached to the spring, the distance the spring stretches can be represented by the variable expression $\frac{1}{2}W$.

With a weight of W pounds, the spring will stretch $\frac{1}{2} \cdot W = \frac{1}{2}W$ in.

With a weight of 10 pounds, the spring will stretch $\frac{1}{2} \cdot 10 = 5$ in.

With a weight of 3 pounds, the spring will stretch $\frac{1}{2} \cdot 3 = 1\frac{1}{2}$ in.

Replacing the variable or variables in a variable expression and then simplifying the resulting numerical expression is called **evaluating the variable expression.**

Evaluate $ab - b^2$ when $a = 2$ and $b = -3$.

Step 1   Replace each variable in the expression with the number it stands for.

$$ab - b^2$$
$$2(-3) - (-3)^2$$

Step 2   Use the Order of Operations Agreement to simplify the resulting numerical expression.

$$-6 - 9$$
$$-15$$

Example 1   Name the variable terms of the expression $2a^2 - 5a + 7$.

Solution $2a^2$
$-5a$

Example 2   Name the constant term of the expression $6n^2 + 3n - 4$.

Your solution -4

Example 3   Evaluate $x^2 - 3xy$ when $x = 3$ and $y = -4$.

Solution
$$x^2 - 3xy$$
$$3^2 - 3(3)(-4)$$
$$9 - 3(3)(-4)$$
$$9 - 9(-4)$$
$$9 - (-36)$$
$$45$$

Example 4   Evaluate $2xy + y^2$ when $x = -4$ and $y = 2$.

Your solution -12

Example 5   Evaluate $\dfrac{a^2 - b^2}{a - b}$ when $a = 3$ and $b = -4$.

Solution
$$\frac{a^2 - b^2}{a - b}$$
$$\frac{3^2 - (-4)^2}{3 - (-4)}$$
$$\frac{9 - 16}{3 - (-4)}$$
$$\frac{-7}{7} = -1$$

Example 6   Evaluate $\dfrac{a^2 + b^2}{a + b}$ when $a = 5$ and $b = -3$.

Your solution 17

Example 7   Evaluate $x^2 - 3(x - y) - z^2$ when $x = 2$, $y = -1$, and $z = 3$.

Solution
$$x^2 - 3(x - y) - z^2$$
$$2^2 - 3[2 - (-1)] - 3^2$$
$$2^2 - 3(3) - 3^2$$
$$4 - 3(3) - 9$$
$$4 - 9 - 9$$
$$-5 - 9$$
$$-14$$

Example 8   Evaluate $x^3 - 2(x + y) + z^2$ when $x = 2$, $y = -4$, and $z = -3$.

Your solution 21

Solutions on p. A20

| **Objective B** | To simplify a variable expression using the Properties of Addition |

Reference for Computer Tutor™

Like terms of a variable expression are the terms with the same variable part. (Since $x^2 = x \cdot x$, x^2 and x are not like terms.)

Constant terms are like terms.
4 and 9 are like terms.

```
            ┌──────────→ like terms
            │      ┌────────┐
     3x  +  4  −  7x  +  9  −  x²
            └──→   like terms  ←──┘
```

To **simplify a variable expression,** add or **combine** like terms by adding the numerical coefficients. The variable part of the terms remains unchanged.

Simplify $2x + 3x$.

Add the numerical coefficients of the like variable terms.

$2x + 3x$
$(x + x) + (x + x + x)$
$5x$

Simplify $5x - 11x$.

Add the numerical coefficients of the like variable terms.

$5x - 11x$

$5x + (-11x)$ Do this step mentally.

$-6x$

In simplifying more complicated expressions, the following Properties of Addition are used.

The Associative Property of Addition
If a, b, and c are real numbers, then $a + b + c = (a + b) + c = a + (b + c)$.

When adding three or more terms, the terms can be grouped in any order. The sum is the same.

$3x + 5x + 9x = (3x + 5x) + 9x = 3x + (5x + 9x)$
$8x + 9x = 3x + 14x$
$17x = 17x$

The Commutative Property of Addition
If a and b are real numbers, then $a + b = b + a$.

When adding two like terms, the terms can be added in either order. The sum is the same.

$2x + (-4x) = -4x + 2x$
$-2x = -2x$

The Addition Property of Zero
If a is a real number, then $a + 0 = 0 + a = a$.

The sum of a term and zero is the term. $5x + 0 = 0 + 5x = 5x$

The Inverse Property of Addition
If a is a real number, then $a + (-a) = (-a) + a = 0$.

The sum of a term and its opposite is zero. The opposite of a number is called its **additive inverse.**

$7x + (-7x) = -7x + 7x = 0$

Simplify $8x + 3y - 8x$.

Use the Commutative and Associative Properties of Addition to rearrange and group like terms.

$8x + 3y - 8x$

$3y + (8x - 8x)$ Do these steps
$3y + 0$ mentally.

Combine like terms.

$3y$

Simplify $4x^2 + 5x - 6x^2 - 2x$.

Use the Commutative and Associative Properties of Addition to rearrange and group like terms.

$4x^2 + 5x - 6x^2 - 2x$

$(4x^2 - 6x^2) + (5x - 2x)$ Do this step
                                               mentally.

Combine like terms.

$-2x^2 + 3x$

Example 9   Simplify $3x + 4y - 10x + 7y$.

Solution $3x + 4y - 10x + 7y$
                 $-7x + 11y$

Example 10   Simplify $3a - 2b - 5a + 6b$.

Your solution
                  $-2a + 4b$

Example 11   Simplify $x^2 - 7 + 4x^2 - 16$.

Solution $x^2 - 7 + 4x^2 - 16$
                  $5x^2 - 23$

Example 12   Simplify $-3y^2 + 7 + 8y^2 - 14$.

Your solution
                  $5y^2 - 7$

Solutions on p. A20

Reference for
Computer
Tutor™

Objective C To simplify a variable expression using the Properties of Multiplication

In simplifying variable expressions, the following Properties of Multiplication are used.

The Associative Property of Multiplication
If a, b, and c are real numbers, then $a \cdot b \cdot c = (a \cdot b) \cdot c = a \cdot (b \cdot c)$.

When multiplying three or more factors, the factors can be grouped in any order. The product is the same.

$$2(3x) = (2 \cdot 3)x = 6x$$

The Commutative Property of Multiplication
If a and b are real numbers, then $a \cdot b = b \cdot a$.

When multiplying two factors, the factors can be multiplied in either order. The product is the same.

$$(2x) \cdot 3 = 3 \cdot (2x) = (3 \cdot 2)x = 6x$$

The Multiplication Property of One
If a is a real number, then $a \cdot 1 = 1 \cdot a = a$.

The product of a term and one is the term.

$$(8x)(1) = (1)(8x) = 8x$$

The Inverse Property of Multiplication
If a is a real number, and a is not equal to zero, then $a \cdot \frac{1}{a} = \frac{1}{a} \cdot a = 1$.

$\frac{1}{a}$ is called the **reciprocal** of a. $\frac{1}{a}$ is also called the **multiplicative inverse** of a.

The product of a number and its reciprocal is one.

$$7 \cdot \frac{1}{7} = \frac{1}{7} \cdot 7 = 1$$

Simplify $2(-x)$.

Use the Associative Property of Multiplication to group factors.

$$2(-x)$$
$$2(-1 \cdot x)$$
$$[2 \cdot (-1)]x$$
Do these steps mentally.
$$-2x$$

Simplify $\frac{3}{2}\left(\frac{2x}{3}\right)$.

Note that $\frac{2x}{3} = \frac{2}{3} \cdot \frac{x}{1} = \frac{2}{3}x$.

$$\frac{3}{2}\left(\frac{2x}{3}\right)$$
$$\frac{3}{2}\left(\frac{2}{3}x\right)$$

Use the Associative Property of Multiplication to group factors. Use the Inverse Property of Multiplication and the Multiplication Property of One.

$$\left(\frac{3}{2} \cdot \frac{2}{3}\right)x$$
$$1x$$
Do these steps mentally.
$$x$$

Simplify (16x)2.

Use the Commutative and Associative Properties
of Multiplication to rearrange and group
factors.

(16x)2

$$2(16x)$$
$$(2 \cdot 16)x$$

Do these steps
mentally.

32x

Example 13   Simplify $-2(3x^2)$.

Solution $-2(3x^2)$
         $6x^2$

Example 14   Simplify $-5(4y^2)$.

Your solution
$-20y^2$

Example 15   Simplify $-5(-10x)$.

Solution $-5(-10x)$
         $50x$

Example 16   Simplify $-7(-2a)$.

Your solution
$14a$

Example 17   Simplify $(6x)(-4)$.

Solution $(6x)(-4)$
         $-24x$

Example 18   Simplify $(-5x)(-2)$.

Your solution
$10x$

Objective D

To simplify a variable expression using the Distributive Property

Reference for
Computer
Tutor™

A student works 3 hours on Friday and 5 hours on Saturday. The hourly rate of pay is $4 an hour. Find the total wages received for the two days.

The total income can be found in two ways.

1. Multiply the hourly wage by the
   total number of hours worked.

   $4(3 + 5) = \$4 \cdot 8 = \$32$

2. Find the income for each day and
   add.

   $4(3) + \$4(5) = \$12 + \$20 = \$32$

Note that $(3 + 5) = 4(3) + 4(5)$. This is an example of the Distributive Property of Multiplication over Addition.

> **The Distributive Property**
> If a, b, and c are real numbers, then $a(b + c) = ab + ac$ or
> $$(b + c)a = ba + ca.$$

The Distributive Property is used to remove
parentheses from a variable expression.

$3(2x - 5)$

$$3(2x) + 3(-5)$$

Do this step
mentally.

$6x - 15$

Simplify $-3(5 + x)$.

Use the Distributive Property to remove parentheses from the variable expression.

$-3(5 + x)$

$\boxed{-3(5) + (-3)x}$ Do this step mentally.

$-15 - 3x$

Simplify $-(2x - 4)$.

Use the Distributive Property to remove parentheses from the variable expression.

$-(2x - 4)$

$\boxed{\begin{array}{l} -1(2x - 4) \\ -1(2x - (-1)(4) \end{array}}$ Do these steps mentally.

$-2x + 4$

Notice: When a negative sign immediately precedes the parentheses, the sign of *each* term inside the parentheses is changed.

When simplifying variable expressions, use the Distributive Property to remove parentheses and brackets used as grouping symbols.

Simplify $4(x - y) - 2(-3x + 6y)$.

Use the Distributive Property to remove parentheses.

$4(x - y) - 2(-3x + 6y)$
$4x - 4y + 6x - 12y$

Combine like terms.

$10x - 16y$

Example 19   Simplify $7(4 + 2x)$.

Solution $7(4 + 2x)$
$28 + 14x$

Example 20   Simplify $5(3 + 7b)$.

Your solution

$15 + 35b$

Example 21   Simplify $(2x - 6)2$.

Solution $(2x - 6)2$
$4x - 12$

Example 22   Simplify $(3a - 1)5$.

Your solution

$15a - 5$

Example 23   Simplify $-3(-5a + 7b)$.

Solution $-3(-5a + 7b)$
$15a - 21b$

Example 24   Simplify $-8(-2a + 7b)$.

Your solution

$16a - 56b$

Solutions on p. A20

Example 25   Simplify $-(3a - 2)$.

Solution $-(3a - 2)$
           $-3a + 2$

Example 26   Simplify $-(5x - 12)$.

Your solution
         $-5x + 12$

Example 27   Simplify $-2(x^2 + 5x - 4)$.

Solution $-2(x^2 + 5x - 4)$
           $-2x^2 - 10x + 8$

Example 28   Simplify $3(-a^2 - 6a + 7)$.

Your solution
         $-3a^2 - 18a + 21$

Example 29   Simplify $2x - 3(2x - 7y)$.

Solution $2x - 3(2x - 7y)$
           $2x - 6x + 21y$
           $-4x + 21y$

Example 30   Simplify $3y - 2(y - 7x)$.

Your solution
         $y + 14x$

Example 31   Simplify
         $7(x - 2y) - 3(-x - 2y)$.

Solution $7(x - 2y) - 3(-x - 2y)$
           $7x - 14y + 3x + 6y$
           $10x - 8y$

Example 32   Simplify
         $-2(x - 2y) + 4(x - 3y)$.

Your solution
         $2x - 8y$

Example 33   Simplify
         $-2(-3x + 7y) - 14x$.

Solution $-2(-3x + 7y) - 14x$
           $6x - 14y - 14x$
           $-8x - 14y$

Example 34   Simplify
         $-5(-2y - 3x) + 4y$.

Your solution
         $14y + 15x$

Example 35   Simplify
         $2x - 3[2x - 3(x + 7)]$.

Solution $2x - 3[2x - 3(x + 7)]$
           $2x - 3[2x - 3x - 21]$
           $2x - 3[-x - 21]$
           $2x + 3x + 63$
           $5x + 63$

Example 36   Simplify
         $3y - 2[x - 4(2 - 3y)]$.

Your solution
         $-21y - 2x + 16$

3.2A Exercises

Name the variable terms of the variable expression. Then underline the constant term.

1. $2x^2 + 5x - 8$

   $2x^2$; $5x$; $\underline{-8}$

2. $-3n^2 - 4n + 7$

   $-3n^2$; $-4n$; $\underline{7}$

3. $6 - a^4$

   $-a^4$; $\underline{6}$

4. $8x^4 - x^2 + 1$

   $8x^4$; $-x^2$; $\underline{1}$

Name the variable terms of the expression. Then underline the variable part of each term.

5. $9b^2 - 4ab + a^2$

   $9\underline{b^2}$; $-4\underline{ab}$; $\underline{a^2}$

6. $7x^2y + 6xy^2 + 10$

   $7\underline{x^2y}$; $6\underline{xy^2}$

7. $5 - 8n - 3n^2$

   $-8\underline{n}$; $-3\underline{n^2}$

8. $5x^2y^2 + 6xy + 5$

   $5\underline{x^2y^2}$; $6\underline{xy}$

Name the coefficients of the variable terms.

9. $x^2 - 9x + 2$

   $1, -9$

10. $12a^2 - 8ab - b^2$

    $12, -8, -1$

11. $n^3 - 4n^2 - n + 9$

    $1, -4, -1$

12. $3x^2y^2 - xy - 6$

    $3, -1$

Evaluate the variable expression when $a = 2$, $b = 3$, and $c = -4$.

13. $3a + 2b$

    12

14. $a - 2c$

    10

15. $-a^2$

    -4

16. $2c^2$

    32

17. $-3a + 4b$

    6

18. $3b - 3c$

    21

19. $16 \div (2c)$

    -2

20. $6b \div (-a)$

    -9

21. $a^2 - b^2$

    -5

22. $b^2 - c^2$

    -7

23. $(a + b)^2$

    25

24. $2a - (c + a)^2$

    0

25. $(b - a)^2 + 4c$

    -15

26. $(b - 2a)^2 + bc$

    -11

27. $b^2 - \frac{ac}{8}$

    10

28. $\frac{5ab}{6} - 3cb$

    41

Evaluate the variable expression when $a = -2$, $b = 4$, $c = -1$, and $d = 3$.

29. $\frac{b + c}{d}$

    1

30. $\frac{d - b}{c}$

    1

31. $\frac{2d + b}{-a}$

    5

32. $\frac{2c - d}{-ad}$

    $-\frac{5}{6}$

33. $(b + d)^2 - 4a$

    57

34. $(d - a)^2 - 3c$

    28

35. $(d - a)^2 \div 5$

    5

36. $(b - c)^2 \div 5$

    5

37. $\frac{bd}{a} \div c$

    6

38. $\frac{2ac}{b} \div (-c)$

    1

39. $2(b + c) - 2a$

    10

40. $3(b - a) - bc$

    22

Evaluate the variable expression when $a = -2$, $b = 4$, $c = -1$, and $d = 3$.

41. $\dfrac{b - 2a}{bc^2 - d}$

    8

42. $\dfrac{b^2 - a}{ad + 3c}$

    −2

43. $\frac{1}{3}d^2 - \frac{3}{8}b^2$

    −3

44. $\frac{5}{8}a^4 - c^2$

    9

45. $\dfrac{-4bc}{2a - b}$

    −2

46. $\dfrac{abc}{b - d}$

    8

47. $a^3 - 3a^2 + a$

    −22

48. $d^3 - 3d - 9$

    9

49. $-\frac{3}{4}b + \frac{1}{2}(ac + bd)$

    4

50. $-\frac{2}{3}d - \frac{1}{5}(bd - ac)$

    −4

51. $(b - a)^2 - (d - c)^2$

    20

52. $(b + c)^2 + (a + d)^2$

    10

3.2B Exercises

Simplify.

53. $6x + 8x$

    14x

54. $12x + 13x$

    25x

55. $9a - 4a$

    5a

56. $12a - 3a$

    9a

57. $4y + (-10y)$

    −6y

58. $8y + (-6y)$

    2y

59. $-3b - 7$

    −3b −7

60. $-12y - 3$

    −12y − 3

61. $-12a + 17a$

    5a

62. $-3a + 12a$

    9a

63. $5ab - 7ab$

    −2ab

64. $9ab - 3ab$

    6ab

65. $-12xy + 17xy$

    5xy

66. $-15xy + 3xy$

    −12xy

67. $-3ab + 3ab$

    0

68. $-7ab + 7ab$

    0

69. $-\frac{1}{2}x - \frac{1}{3}x$

    $-\frac{5}{6}x$

70. $-\frac{2}{5}y + \frac{3}{10}y$

    $-\frac{1}{10}y$

71. $\frac{3}{8}x^2 - \frac{5}{12}x^2$

    $-\frac{1}{24}x^2$

72. $\frac{2}{3}y^2 - \frac{4}{9}y^2$

    $\frac{2}{9}y^2$

73. $3x + 5x + 3x$

    11x

74. $8x + 5x + 7x$

    20x

75. $5a - 3a + 5a$

    7a

76. $10a - 17a + 3a$

    −4a

77. $-y^2 - 8y^2 + 7y^2$

    −2y²

78. $7x + (-8x) + 3y$

    −x + 3y

79. $7x - 3y + 10x$

    17x − 3y

80. $8y + 8x - 8y$

    8x

81. $3a + (-7b) - 5a + b$

    −2a − 6b

82. $-5b + 7a - 7b + 12a$

    −12b + 19a

83. $3x + (-8y) - 10x + 4x$

    −3x − 8y

84. $3y + (-12x) - 7y + 2y$

    −12x − 2y

85. $x^2 - 7x + (-5x^2) + 5x$

    −4x² − 2x

86. $3x^2 + 5x - 10x^2 - 10x$

    −7x² − 5x

3.2C Exercises

Simplify.

87. $4(3x)$
$12x$

88. $12(5x)$
$60x$

89. $-3(7a)$
$-21a$

90. $-2(5a)$
$-10a$

91. $-2(-3y)$
$6y$

92. $-5(-6y)$
$30y$

93. $(4x)2$
$8x$

94. $(6x)12$
$72x$

95. $(3a)(-2)$
$-6a$

96. $(7a)(-4)$
$-28a$

97. $(-3b)(-4)$
$12b$

98. $(-12b)(-9)$
$108b$

99. $-5(3x^2)$
$-15x^2$

100. $-8(7x^2)$
$-56x^2$

101. $\frac{1}{3}(3x^2)$
x^2

102. $\frac{1}{6}(6x^2)$
x^2

103. $\frac{1}{5}(5a)$
a

104. $\frac{1}{8}(8x)$
x

105. $-\frac{1}{2}(-2x)$
x

106. $-\frac{1}{4}(-4a)$
a

107. $(3x)\left(\frac{1}{3}\right)$
x

108. $(12x)\left(\frac{1}{12}\right)$
x

109. $(-6y)\left(-\frac{1}{6}\right)$
y

110. $(-10n)\left(-\frac{1}{10}\right)$
n

111. $\frac{1}{3}(9x)$
$3x$

112. $\frac{1}{7}(14x)$
$2x$

113. $-\frac{1}{5}(10x)$
$-2x$

114. $-\frac{1}{8}(16x)$
$-2x$

115. $-\frac{2}{3}(12a^2)$
$-8a^2$

116. $-\frac{5}{8}(24a^2)$
$-15a^2$

117. $(-6x)\left(\frac{1}{3}\right)$
$-2x$

118. $(-10x)\left(\frac{1}{5}\right)$
$-2x$

3.2D Exercises

Simplify.

119. $-(x+2)$
$-x-2$

120. $-(x+7)$
$-x-7$

121. $2(4x-3)$
$8x-6$

122. $5(2x-7)$
$10x-35$

123. $-2(a+7)$
$-2a-14$

124. $-5(a+16)$
$-5a-80$

125. $-3(2y-8)$
$-6y+24$

126. $-5(3y-7)$
$-15y+35$

127. $(5-3b)7$
$35-21b$

128. $(10-7b)2$
$20-14b$

129. $-3(3-5x)$
$-9+15x$

130. $-5(7-10x)$
$-35+50x$

131. $3(5x^2+2x)$
$15x^2+6x$

132. $6(3x^2+2x)$
$18x^2+12x$

133. $-2(-y+9)$
$2y-18$

134. $-5(-2x+7)$
$10x-35$

Simplify.

135. $(-3x - 6)5$
$-15x - 30$

136. $(-2x + 7)7$
$-14x + 49$

137. $2(-3x^2 - 14)$
$-6x^2 - 28$

138. $5(-6x^2 - 3)$
$-30x^2 - 15$

139. $-3(2y^2 - 7)$
$-6y^2 + 21$

140. $-8(3y^2 - 12)$
$-24y^2 + 96$

141. $3(x^2 - y^2)$
$3x^2 - 3y^2$

142. $5(x^2 + y^2)$
$5x^2 + 5y^2$

143. $-2(x^2 - 3y^2)$
$-2x^2 + 6y^2$

144. $-4(x^2 - 5y^2)$
$-4x^2 + 20y^2$

145. $-(6a^2 - 7b^2)$
$-6a^2 + 7b^2$

146. $3(x^2 + 2x - 6)$
$3x^2 + 6x - 18$

147. $4(x^2 - 3x + 5)$
$4x^2 - 12x + 20$

148. $-2(y^2 - 2y + 4)$
$-2y^2 + 4y - 8$

149. $-3(y^2 - 3y - 7)$
$-3y^2 + 9y + 21$

150. $2(-a^2 - 2a + 3)$
$-2a^2 - 4a + 6$

151. $-(3a^2 + 5a - 4)$
$-3a^2 - 5a + 4$

152. $-(8b^2 - 6b + 9)$
$-8b^2 + 6b - 9$

153. $4x - 2(3x + 8)$
$-2x - 16$

154. $6a - (5a + 7)$
$a - 7$

155. $9 - 3(4y + 6)$
$-9 - 12y$

156. $10 - (11x - 3)$
$13 - 11x$

157. $5n - (7 - 2n)$
$7n - 7$

158. $8 - (12 + 4y)$
$-4 - 4y$

159. $-3(-4x^2 + 3x - 4)$
$12x^2 - 9x + 12$

160. $3(2x^2 + xy - 3y^2)$
$6x^2 + 3xy - 9y^2$

161. $5(2x^2 - 4xy - y^2)$
$10x^2 - 20xy - 5y^2$

162. $3(x + 2) - 5(x - 7)$
$-2x + 41$

163. $2(x - 4) - 4(x + 2)$
$-2x - 16$

164. $12(y - 2) + 3(7 - 3y)$
$3y - 3$

165. $6(2y - 7) - 3(3 - 2y)$
$18y - 51$

166. $4[x - 2(x - 3)]$
$-4x + 24$

167. $2[x + 2(x + 7)]$
$6x + 28$

168. $-2[3x + 2(4 - x)]$
$-2x - 16$

169. $-5[2x + 3(5 - x)]$
$5x - 75$

170. $-3[2x - (x + 7)]$
$-3x + 21$

171. $-2[3x - (5x - 2)]$
$4x - 4$

172. $2x - 3[x - 2(4 - x)]$
$-7x + 24$

173. $-7x + 3[x - 7(3 - 2x)]$
$38x - 63$

174. $-5x - 2[2x - 4(x + 7)] - 6$
$-x + 50$

175. $4a - 2[2b - (b - 2a)] + 3b$
b

176. $2x + 3(x - 2y) + 5(3x - 7y)$
$20x - 41y$

177. $5y - 2(y - 3x) + 2(7x - y)$
$y + 20x$

Section 3 Translating Verbal Expressions into Variable Expressions

Objective A   To translate a verbal expression into a variable expression

Reference for Computer Tutor™

One of the major skills required in applied mathematics is to translate a verbal expression into a variable expression. This requires recognizing the verbal phrases that translate into mathematical operations. A partial list of the verbal phrases used to indicate the different mathematical operations is given below.

Addition	added to	6 added to y	$y + 6$
	more than	8 more than x	$x + 8$
	the sum of	the sum of x and z	$x + z$
	increased by	t increased by 9	$t + 9$
	the total of	the total of 5 and y	$5 + y$
Subtraction	minus	x minus 2	$x - 2$
	less than	7 less than t	$t - 7$
	decreased by	m decreased by 3	$m - 3$
	the difference between	the difference between y and 4	$y - 4$
Multiplication	times	10 times t	$10t$
	of	one half of x	$\frac{1}{2}x$
	the product of	the product of y and z	yz
	multiplied by	y multiplied by 11	$11y$
	twice	twice n	$2n$
Division	divided by	x divided by 12	$\frac{x}{12}$
	the quotient of	the quotient of y and z	$\frac{y}{z}$
	the ratio of	the ratio of t to 9	$\frac{t}{9}$
Power	the square of	the square of x	x^2
	the cube of	the cube of a	a^3

In most applications that involve translating phrases into variable expressions, the variable to be used is not given. To translate these phrases, a variable must be assigned to an unknown quantity before the variable expression can be written.

After translating the verbal expression into a variable expression, simplify the variable expression by using the Addition, Multiplication, and Distributive Properties.

Translate and simplify "a number minus the difference between twice the number and eleven."

Step 1   Assign a variable to one of the unknown quantities.   the unknown number: n

Step 2   Use the assigned variable to write an expression for any other unknown quantity.   the difference between twice the number and eleven: $2n - 11$

Step 3   Use the assigned variable to write the variable expression. $n - (2n - 11)$

Step 4   Simplify the variable expression.

$$n - 2n + 11$$
$$-n + 11$$

Example 1   Translate and simplify "the sum of one-fourth of a number and one-eighth of the same number."

Solution   the unknown number: n

one-fourth of the number: $\frac{1}{4}n$

one-eighth of the number: $\frac{1}{8}n$

$$\frac{1}{4}n + \frac{1}{8}n$$
$$\frac{2}{8}n + \frac{1}{8}n$$
$$\frac{3}{8}n$$

Example 2   Translate and simplify "the difference between three-eighths of a number and five-sixths of the same number."

Your solution

$$-\frac{11}{24}n$$

Example 3   Translate and simplify "the total of five times an unknown number and twice the difference between the number and nine."

Solution   the unknown number: n
five times the unknown number: $5n$
twice the difference between the number and nine: $2(n - 9)$

$$5n + 2(n - 9)$$
$$5n + 2n - 18$$
$$7n - 18$$

Example 4   Translate and simplify "four times the sum of six and twice a number."

Your solution

$$24 + 8n$$

Solutions on p. A21

3.3A Exercises

Translate into a variable expression. Then simplify.

1. a number added to the product of three and the number

   $n + 3n$

   $4n$

2. a number decreased by the total of the number and nine

   $n - (n + 9)$

   -9

3. five more than the sum of a number and six

   $(n + 6) + 5$

   $n + 11$

4. a number decreased by the difference between eight and the number

   $n - (8 - n)$

   $2n - 8$

5. a number minus the sum of the number and ten

   $n - (n + 10)$

   -10

6. the difference between one-third of a number and five-eighths of the number

   $\frac{1}{3}n - \frac{5}{8}n$; $-\frac{7}{24}n$

7. the sum of one-sixth of a number and four-ninths of the number

   $\frac{1}{6}n + \frac{4}{9}n$; $\frac{11}{18}n$

8. two more than the total of a number and five

   $(n + 5) + 2$

   $n + 7$

9. the sum of a number divided by three and the number

   $\frac{n}{3} + n$; $\frac{4}{3}n$

10. twice the sum of six times a number and seven

    $2(6n + 7)$

    $12n + 14$

11. fourteen multiplied by one-seventh of a number

    $14\left(\frac{1}{7}n\right)$; $2n$

12. four times the product of six and a number

    $4(6n)$

    $24n$

13. the difference between ten times a number and twice the number

    $10n - 2n$

    $8n$

14. the total of twelve times a number and twice the number

    $12n + 2n$

    $14n$

15. sixteen more than the difference between a number and six

    $(n - 6) + 16$

    $n + 10$

16. a number plus the product of the number and nineteen

    $n + 19n$

    $20n$

17. a number subtracted from the product of the number and four

    $4n - n$

    $3n$

18. eight times the sum of the square of a number and three

    $8(n^2 + 3)$

    $8n^2 + 24$

19. the difference between fifteen times a number and the product of the number and five

    $15n - 5n$

    $10n$

20. two-thirds of the sum of nine times a number and three

    $\frac{2}{3}(9n + 3)$; $6n + 2$

21. fifteen multiplied by the total of ten and the cube of a number

    $15(10 + n^3)$

    $150 + 15n^3$

22. five times the difference between a number and sixty

    $5(n - 60)$

    $5n - 300$

23. six times the difference between a number and seven

    $6(n - 7)$

    $6n - 42$

24. the product of three and the total of a number and twelve

    $3(n + 12)$

    $3n + 36$

Translate into a variable expression. Then simplify.

25. the product of eight and the sum of a number and eleven

$8(n+11)$

$8n + 88$

26. the difference between the square of a number and the total of seventeen and the square of the number

$n^2 - (17 + n^2)$

-17

27. the product of nine and the total of a number and one hundred

$9(n + 100)$

$9n + 900$

28. a number increased by the difference between ten times the number and nine

$n + (10n - 9)$

$11n - 9$

29. ten times the difference between a number and fifty

$10(n - 50)$

$10n - 500$

30. nine less than the total of a number and two

$(n + 2) - 9$

$n - 7$

31. four times the sum of a number and nineteen

$4(n + 19)$

$4n + 76$

32. five increased by one-half of the sum of a number and sixteen

$5 + \frac{1}{2}(n + 16)$

$13 + \frac{1}{2}n$

33. the product of two-thirds and the sum of a number and twelve

$\frac{2}{3}(n + 12)$

$\frac{2}{3}n + 8$

34. a number decreased by the difference between three times the number and eight

$n - (3m - 8)$

$-2n + 8$

35. twelve less than the difference between nine and a number

$(9 - n) - 12$

$-3 - n$

36. thirteen decreased by the sum of a number and fifteen

$13 - (n + 15)$

$-2 - n$

37. ten minus the sum of two-thirds of a number and four

$10 - (\frac{2}{3}n + 4)$

$6 - \frac{2}{3}n$

38. nine more than the quotient of eight times a number and four

$\frac{8n}{4} + 9$

$2n + 9$

39. the sum of three more than the square of a number and twice the square of the number

$(n^2 + 3) + 2n^2$

$3n^2 + 3$

40. the total of five increased by the cube of a number and twice the cube of the number

$(5 + n^3) + 2n^3$

$5 + 3n^3$

41. a number plus seven added to the difference between two and twice the number

$(n + 7) + (2 - 2n)$

$-n + 5$

42. ten more than a number added to the difference between the number and eleven

$(n + 10) + (n - 11)$

$2n - 1$

43. six increased by a number added to twice the difference between the number and three

$(6 + n) + 2(n - 3)$

$3n$

44. the sum of a number and ten added to the difference between the number and twelve

$(n + 10) + (n - 12)$

$2n - 2$

45. a number plus the product of the number minus nine and four

$n + 4(n - 9)$

$5n - 36$

46. eighteen minus the product of two less than a number and eight

$18 - 8(n - 2)$

$34 - 8n$

Calculators and Computers

The $\boxed{+/-}$ key on a calculator changes the sign of the number currently in the display. The $\boxed{+/-}$ key is used to calculate with signed numbers.

Simplify: $-34.982 - (-64.72)$

Enter	Display	Comments
34.982	34.982	
$\boxed{+/-}$	-34.982	The number 34.982 is changed to -34.982.
$\boxed{-}$	-34.982	
64.72	64.72	
$\boxed{+/-}$	-64.72	The number 64.72 is changed to -64.72.
$\boxed{=}$	29.738	$-34.982 - (-64.72) = 29.738$

Simplify: $48.93 \div (-21.3)$

Press the keys shown in the box.

$$48.93 \; \boxed{\div} \; 21.3 \; \boxed{+/-} \; \boxed{=}$$

The answer in the display should be -2.297183.

Evaluating variable expressions with your calculator will at times require the use of the $\boxed{+/-}$ key, the $\boxed{x^2}$ key, and the parentheses keys. The $\boxed{x^2}$ key is used to square the number in the display. Parentheses are used around terms with more than one factor.

Evaluate $c^2 - ab$ when $a = 2$, $b = -3$, and $c = 4$.

Replace a, b, and c by their values. $(4)^2 - (2)(-3)$

Press the keys shown in the box.

$$4 \; \boxed{x^2} \; \boxed{-} \; \boxed{(} \; 2 \; \boxed{\times} \; 3 \; \boxed{+/-} \; \boxed{)} \; \boxed{=}$$

The answer in the display should be 22.

Simplify.

1. $-3.0251 - (-6.297)$ 2. $-3.2(-6.9)$ 3. $0.06768 \div (-0.0235)$

Evaluate the variable expression when $a = 2.7$, $b = -1.6$, and $c = -0.8$.

4. $ac^2 - b$ 5. $b^2 - ac$ 6. $(a + b)^2 - c$

ANSWERS: **1.** 3.2719   **2.** 22.08   **3.** -2.88 **4.** 3.328   **5.** 4.72   **6.** 2.01

Chapter Summary

KEY WORDS

Positive numbers are numbers greater than zero. **Negative numbers** are numbers less than zero. The positive and negative numbers together are called **signed numbers.**

Two numbers that are the same distance from zero on the number line but on opposite sides of zero are called **opposites.** The **additive inverse** of a number is the opposite of the number.

The **absolute value** of a number is its distance from zero on the number line.

A **variable** is a letter that is used to stand for a quantity that is unknown. A **variable expression** is an expression that contains one or more variables. The **terms** of a variable expression are the addends of the expression. A **variable term** is composed of a numerical coefficient and a variable part. **Like terms** of a variable expression are the terms with the same variable part.

The **multiplicative inverse** of a number is the reciprocal of the number.

ESSENTIAL RULES

To **add signed numbers with like signs,** add the absolute value of the numbers. Then attach the sign of the addends. To **add signed numbers with unlike signs,** find the difference between the absolute values of the addends. Then attach the sign of the addend with the larger absolute value.

To **subtract signed numbers,** rewrite the subtraction as the addition of the opposite. Then add.

The **product of two numbers with like signs** is positive. The **product of two numbers with unlike signs** is negative.

The **quotient of two numbers with like signs** is positive. The **quotient of two numbers with unlike signs** is negative.

The Associative Property of Addition	$(a + b) + c = a + (b + c)$
The Commutative Property of Addition	$a + b = b + a$
The Addition Property of Zero	$a + 0 = 0 + a = a$
The Inverse Property of Addition	$a + (-a) = (-a) + a = 0$
The Associative Property of Multiplication	$(ab)c = a(bc)$
The Commutative Property of Multiplication	$ab = ba$
The Multiplication Property of One	$1 \cdot a = a \cdot 1 = a$
The Inverse Property of Multiplication	$a\left(\dfrac{1}{a}\right) = \left(\dfrac{1}{a}\right)a = 1$, where a is not zero
The Distributive Property	$a(b + c) = ab + ac$

Review/Test

1. Place the correct symbol, $<$ or $>$, between the two numbers.
$-4 \; > \; -6.5$

2. Evaluate $-\left|-3\frac{1}{2}\right|$.
$-3\frac{1}{2}$

3. Add: $-6.85 + 2.39$
-4.46

4. Add: $-2\frac{1}{2} + \left(-3\frac{2}{7}\right)$
$-5\frac{11}{14}$

5. Subtract: $20 - (-12)$
32

6. Subtract: $-5\frac{1}{8} - \left(-3\frac{3}{4}\right)$
$-1\frac{3}{8}$

7. Subtract: $-8 - (-2) - (-10) - 3$
1

8. Multiply: $-4.7 \times (-5.6)$
26.32

9. Multiply: $-3\frac{1}{5} \times 1\frac{7}{16}$
$-4\frac{3}{5}$

10. Divide: $-52.38 \div (-1.94)$
27

11. Divide: $-\frac{5}{8} \div 1\frac{1}{2}$
$-\frac{5}{12}$

12. Simplify $4 \times (4 - 7) \div (-2) - 4 \times 8$.
-26

13. Simplify $(-2)^2 - (-3)^2 \div (1 - 4)^2 \times 2 - 6$.
-4

14. Evaluate $b^2 - 3ab$ when $a = 3$ and $b = -2$.
22

15. Simplify $3x - 7y - 12x$.
$-9x - 7y$

16. Simplify $3x + (-12y) - 5x - (-7y)$.
$-2x - 5y$

17. Simplify $\frac{1}{5}(10x)$.
$2x$

18. Simplify $(-3)(12y)$.
$-36y$

19. Simplify $-2(2x - 4)$.
$-4x + 8$

20. Simplify $-5(2x^2 - 3x + 6)$.
$-10x^2 + 15x - 30$

21. Simplify $5(2x + 4) - 3(x - 6)$.
$7x + 38$

22. Simplify $-2[x - 2(x - y)] + 5y$.
$2x + y$

23. Translate and simplify "ten times the difference between a number and three."
$10(n-3)$
$10n - 30$

24. Translate and simplify "eleven added to twice the sum of a number and four."
$11 + 2(n+4)$
$19 + 2n$

Cumulative Review/Test

1. Simplify $\frac{1}{2}(12a)$.
   6a

2. Subtract: $-12 - (-7) - 3 - (-8)$
   0

3. Multiply: $-3.2(-1.09)$
   3.488

4. Simplify $3(8 - 2x)$.
   24 - 6x

5. Simplify $16 - 4(3 - 2)^2 \cdot 4$.
   0

6. Add: $3\frac{1}{4} + \left(-6\frac{5}{8}\right)$
   $-3\frac{3}{8}$

7. Simplify $3[2x - 3(x - 2y)] + 3y$.
   -3x + 21y

8. Simplify $4 - (-2)^2 \div (1 - 2)^2 \cdot 3 + 4$.
   -4

9. Subtract: $8\frac{1}{2} - 3\frac{4}{7}$
   $4\frac{13}{14}$

10. Add: $-8 + 5$
    -3

11. Divide: $-2\frac{1}{7} \div \left(-3\frac{3}{5}\right)$
    $\frac{25}{42}$

12. Evaluate $a^2 - 3b$ when $a = 2$ and $b = -4$.
    16

13. Simplify $\left(-\frac{5}{6}\right)(-36b)$.
    30b

14. Divide: $3\frac{7}{8} \div 1\frac{1}{2}$
    $2\frac{7}{12}$

15. Subtract: $-6\frac{1}{8} - 4\frac{5}{12}$
    $-10\frac{13}{24}$

16. Simplify $4(3x - 2) - 7(x + 5)$.
    5x - 43

17. Simplify $5a - 10b - 12a$.
    -7a - 10b

18. Subtract: $2.907 - 1.09761$
    1.80939

19. Simplify $3^3 \cdot 4^2$.
    432

20. Multiply: $-6(7)\left(-\frac{3}{4}\right)$
    $31\frac{1}{2}$

21. Write $1\frac{1}{4}$ as a decimal.
    1.25

22. Simplify $-2x^2 - (-3x^2) + 4x^2$.
    $5x^2$

23. Simplify $-3(3y^2 - 3y - 7)$.
    $-9y^2 + 9y + 21$

24. Translate and simplify "twelve more than the product of three plus a number and five."
    (3 + n)5 + 12
    27 + 5n

chapter 4

Solving Equations and Inequalities

Objectives

Section 1 Introduction to Equations

Objective A To determine if a given number is a solution of an equation

Reference for Computer Tutor™

An **equation** expresses the equality of two mathematical expressions. The expressions can be either numerical or variable expressions.

$$\left. \begin{array}{l} 9 + 3 = 12 \\ 3x - 2 = 10 \\ y^2 + 4 = 2y - 1 \\ z = 2 \end{array} \right\} \text{Equations}$$

The equation at the right is true if the variable is replaced by 5.

$$x + 8 = 13$$
$$5 + 8 = 13 \quad \text{A true equation}$$

The equation is false if the variable is replaced by 7.

$$7 + 8 = 13 \quad \text{A false equation}$$

A **solution** of an equation is a number that, when substituted for the variable, results in a true equation: 5 is a solution of the equation $x + 8 = 13$; 7 is not a solution of the equation $x + 8 = 13$.

Is -3 a solution of the equation $4x + 18 = x^2 - 3$?

Step 1 Replace the variable by the given number, -3.

Step 2 Evaluate the numerical expressions using the Order of Operations Agreement.

$$\begin{array}{c|c} \multicolumn{2}{c}{4x + 18 = x^2 - 3} \\ \hline 4(-3) + 18 & (-3)^2 - 3 \\ -12 + 18 & 9 - 3 \\ \multicolumn{2}{c}{6 = 6} \end{array}$$

Step 3 Compare the results. If the results are equal, the given number is a solution. If the results are not equal, the given number is not a solution.

Yes, -3 is a solution of the equation $4x + 18 = x^2 - 3$.

Example 1 Is $\frac{2}{3}$ a solution of $12x - 2 = 6x + 2$?

Solution

$$\begin{array}{c|c} \multicolumn{2}{c}{12x - 2 = 6x + 2} \\ \hline 12\left(\frac{2}{3}\right) - 2 & 6\left(\frac{2}{3}\right) + 2 \\ 8 - 2 & 4 + 2 \\ \multicolumn{2}{c}{6 = 6} \end{array}$$

Yes, $\frac{2}{3}$ is a solution.

Example 2 Is $\frac{1}{4}$ a solution of $5 - 4x = 8x + 2$?

Your solution

yes

Solution on p. A23

Example 3 Is -4 a solution of
$4 + 5x = x^2 - 2x$?

Solution

$$4 + 5x = x^2 - 2x$$

$4 + 5(-4)$	$(-4)^2 - 2(-4)$
$4 + (-20)$	$16 - (-8)$
	$-16 \neq 24$ ($\neq$ means is not equal to)

No, -4 is not a solution.

Example 4 Is 5 a solution of
$10x - x^2 = 3x - 10$?

Your solution

no

Reference for Computer Tutor™

Objective B To solve an equation of the form $x + a = b$

To **solve** an equation means to find a solution of the equation. The simplest equation to solve is an equation of the form **variable = constant,** since the constant is the solution.

If $x = 5$, then 5 is the solution of the equation, since $5 = 5$ is a true equation.

The solution of the equation shown at the right is 7.

$x + 2 = 9$ $7 + 2 = 9$

Note that if 4 is added to each side of the equation, the solution is still 7.

$x + 2 + 4 = 9 + 4$
$x + 6 = 13$ $7 + 6 = 13$

If -5 is added to each side of the equation, the solution is still 7.

$x + 2 + (-5) = 9 + (-5)$
$x - 3 = 4$ $7 - 3 = 4$

This illustrates the Addition Property of Equations.

> **Addition Property of Equations**
> The same number can be added to each side of an equation without changing the solution of the equation.
>
> If $a = b$, then $a + c = b + c$.

This property is used in solving equations. Note the effect of adding, to each side of the equation shown above, the opposite of the constant term 2. After simplifying each side of the equation, the equation is in the form *variable = constant*. The solution is the constant.

$x + 2 = 9$
$x + 2 + (-2) = 9 + (-2)$
$x + 0 = 7$
$x = 7$

variable	=	constant

The solution is 7.

In solving an equation, the goal is to rewrite the given equation in the form *variable = constant*. The Addition Property of Equations can be used to rewrite an equation in this form. The Addition Property of Equations is used to **remove a term** from one side of an equation **by adding the opposite of that term** to each side of the equation.

Solve: $y - 6 = 9$

The goal is to rewrite the equation in the form *variable = constant*.

Step 1 Add the opposite of the constant term -6 to each side of the equation. (Addition Property of Equations)

$$y - 6 = 9$$
$$y - 6 + 6 = 9 + 6$$

Step 2 Simplify using the Addition Property of Inverses and the Addition Property of Zero. Now the equation is in the form *variable = constant*.

$$\boxed{y + 0 = 15}$$ Do this step mentally.

$$y = 15$$

Step 3 Write the solution.

The solution is 15.

Check: $y - 6 = 9$
$15 - 6 = 9$
$9 = 9$ A true equation

Example 5

Solve: $x + \frac{1}{3} = -\frac{3}{4}$

Solution

$$x + \frac{1}{3} = -\frac{3}{4}$$

$$x + \frac{1}{3} + \left(-\frac{1}{3}\right) = -\frac{3}{4} + \left(-\frac{1}{3}\right)$$

$$x = -\frac{13}{12}$$

The solution is $-\frac{13}{12}$.

Example 6

Solve: $\frac{1}{2} = x - \frac{2}{3}$

Your solution

$$\frac{7}{6}$$

Solution on p. A23

Objective C   # To solve an equation of the form $ax = b$

Reference for Computer Tutor™

The solution of the equation shown at the right is 3. Note that if each side of the equation is multiplied by 5 the solution is still 3.

$$2x = 6 \qquad\qquad 2 \cdot 3 = 6$$
$$5 \cdot 2x = 5 \cdot 6$$
$$10x = 30 \qquad\qquad 10 \cdot 3 = 30$$

If each side of the equation is multiplied by -4, the solution is still 3.

$$(-4) \cdot 2x = (-4) \cdot 6$$
$$-8x = -24 \qquad -8 \cdot 3 = -24$$

This illustrates the Multiplication Property of Equations.

> ***Multiplication Property of Equations***
> Each side of an equation can be multiplied by the same nonzero number without changing the solution of the equation.
>
> If $a = b$ and $c \neq 0$, then $ac = bc$.

This property is used in solving equations. Note the effect of multiplying each side of the equation shown above by the reciprocal of the coefficient 2. After simplifying each side of the equation, the equation is in the form *variable = constant*. The solution is the constant.

$$2x = 6$$
$$\frac{1}{2} \cdot 2x = \frac{1}{2} \cdot 6$$
$$1x = 3$$
$$x = 3$$

| variable | = | constant. |

The solution is 3

In solving an equation, the goal is to rewrite the given equation in the form *variable = constant*. The Multiplication Property of Equations can be used to rewrite an equation in this form. The Multiplication Property of Equations is used to **remove a coefficient** from one side of an equation **by multiplying each side of the equation by the reciprocal of the coefficient.**

Solve: $4x = 6$

The goal is to rewrite the equation in the form *variable = constant*.

Step 1 Multiply each side of the equation by the reciprocal of the coefficient 4. (Multiplication Property of Equations)

$$4x = 6$$
$$\frac{1}{4} \cdot 4x = \frac{1}{4} \cdot 6$$

Step 2 Simplify using the Multiplication Property of Reciprocals and the Multiplication Property of One. Now the equation is in the form *variable = constant*.

$$1x = \frac{6}{4}$$ Do this step mentally.

$$x = \frac{6}{4} = \frac{3}{2}$$

Step 3 Write the solution.

The solution is $\frac{3}{2}$.

Check:
$$4x = 6$$
$$4\left(\frac{3}{2}\right) = 6$$
$$6 = 6 \quad \text{A true equation}$$

Example 7 Solve: $\frac{3x}{4} = -9$

Solution
$$\frac{3x}{4} = -9$$
$$\frac{4}{3} \cdot \frac{3}{4}x = \frac{4}{3}(-9) \qquad \left[\frac{3x}{4} = \frac{3}{4}x\right]$$
$$x = -12$$
The solution is -12.

Example 8 Solve: $-\frac{2x}{5} = 6$

Your solution
$$-15$$

Example 9 Solve: $5x - 9x = 12$

Solution
$$5x - 9x = 12 \quad \text{Combine like}$$
$$-4x = 12 \quad \text{terms.}$$
$$\left(-\frac{1}{4}\right)(-4x) = \left(-\frac{1}{4}\right)(12)$$
$$x = -3$$
The solution is -3.

Example 10 Solve: $4x - 8x = 16$

Your solution
$$-4$$

Solutions on p. A23

Reference for
Computer
Tutor™

Objective D   To solve an equation of the form $ax + b = c$

In solving an equation of the form $ax + b = c$, the goal is to rewrite the equation in the form *variable = constant*. This requires the application of both the Addition and Multiplication Properties of Equations.

Solve: $\frac{2}{5}x - 3 = -7$

The goal is to rewrite the equation in the form *variable = constant*.

Step 1   Add the opposite of the constant term -3 to each side of the equation. Then simplify.

$$\frac{2}{5}x - 3 = -7$$
$$\frac{2}{5}x - 3 + 3 = -7 + 3$$
$$\frac{2}{5}x = -4$$

Step 2   Multiply each side of the equation by the reciprocal of the coefficient $\frac{2}{5}$. Simplify. Now the equation is in the form *variable = constant*.

$$\frac{5}{2} \cdot \frac{2}{5}x = \frac{5}{2}(-4)$$
$$x = -10$$

Step 3   Write the solution.

The solution is -10.
-10 checks as the solution.

Example 11   Solve: $5 = 9 - 2x$

Solution
$$5 = 9 - 2x$$
$$5 + (-9) = 9 + (-9) - 2x$$
$$-4 = -2x$$
$$\left(-\frac{1}{2}\right)(-4) = \left(-\frac{1}{2}\right)(-2x)$$
$$2 = x$$

The solution is 2.

Example 12   Solve: $2 = 11 + 3x$

Your solution

-3

Example 13   Solve: $2x + 4 - 5x = 10$

Solution
$$2x + 4 - 5x = 10 \quad \text{Combine}$$
$$-3x + 4 = 10 \quad \text{like terms.}$$
$$-3x + 4 + (-4) = 10 + (-4)$$
$$-3x = 6$$
$$-\frac{1}{3}(-3x) = -\frac{1}{3}(6)$$
$$x = -2$$

The solution is -2.

Example 14   Solve: $x - 5 + 4x = 25$

Your solution

6

Solutions on p. A23

4.1A Exercises

1. Is 4 a solution of $2x = 8$?
yes

2. Is 3 a solution of $y + 4 = 7$?
yes

3. Is -1 a solution of $2b - 1 = 3$?
no

4. Is -2 a solution of $3a - 4 = 10$?
no

5. Is 5 a solution of $2x + 5 = 3x$?
yes

6. Is 4 a solution of $3y - 4 = 2y$?
yes

7. Is 0 a solution of $4a + 5 = 3a + 5$?
yes

8. Is 0 a solution of $4 - 3b = 4 - 5b$?
yes

9. Is -2 a solution of $4 - 2n = n + 10$?
yes

10. Is -3 a solution of $5 - m = 2 - 2m$?
yes

11. Is -1 a solution of $y^2 - 1 = 4y + 3$?
no

12. Is -2 a solution of $m^2 - 4 = m + 3$?
no

13. Is 5 a solution of $x^2 + 2x + 1 = (x + 1)^2$?
yes

14. Is -6 a solution of $(n - 2)^2 = n^2 - 4n + 4$?
yes

15. Is 4 a solution of $x(x + 1) = x^2 + 5$?
no

16. Is 3 a solution of $2a(a - 1) = 3a + 3$?
yes

17. Is $-\frac{1}{4}$ a solution of $8t + 1 = -1$?
yes

18. Is $\frac{1}{2}$ a solution of $4y + 1 = 3$?
yes

19. Is $\frac{2}{5}$ a solution of $5m + 1 = 10m - 3$?
no

20. Is $\frac{3}{4}$ a solution of $8x - 1 = 12x + 3$?
no

4.1B Exercises

Solve and check.

21. $x + 5 = 7$
2

22. $y + 3 = 9$
6

23. $b - 4 = 11$
15

24. $z - 6 = 10$
16

25. $2 + a = 8$
6

26. $5 + x = 12$
7

27. $b + 7 = 7$
0

28. $y - 5 = -5$
0

Solve and check.

29. $a - 3 = -5$
-2

30. $x - 6 = -3$
3

31. $z + 9 = 2$
-7

32. $n + 11 = 1$
-10

33. $10 + m = 3$
-7

34. $8 + x = 5$
-3

35. $9 + x = -3$
-12

36. $10 + y = -4$
-14

37. $b - 5 = -3$
2

38. $t - 6 = -4$
2

39. $2 = x + 7$
-5

40. $-8 = n + 1$
-9

41. $4 = m - 11$
15

42. $-6 = y - 5$
-1

43. $4 = -10 + b$
14

44. $m + \frac{2}{3} = -\frac{1}{3}$
-1

45. $c + \frac{3}{4} = -\frac{1}{4}$
-1

46. $x - \frac{1}{2} = \frac{1}{2}$
1

47. $x - \frac{2}{5} = \frac{3}{5}$
1

48. $\frac{5}{8} + y = \frac{1}{8}$
$-\frac{1}{2}$

49. $\frac{4}{9} + a = -\frac{2}{9}$
$-\frac{2}{3}$

50. $m + \frac{1}{2} = -\frac{1}{4}$
$-\frac{3}{4}$

51. $b + \frac{1}{6} = -\frac{1}{3}$
$-\frac{1}{2}$

52. $x + \frac{2}{3} = \frac{3}{4}$
$\frac{1}{12}$

53. $d + 1.3619 = 2.0148$
0.6529

54. $w + 2.932 = 4.801$
1.869

55. $-0.813 + x = -1.096$
-0.283

56. $-1.926 + t = -1.042$
0.884

57. $6.149 = -3.108 + z$
9.257

58. $5.237 = -2.014 + x$
7.251

4.1C Exercises

Solve and check.

59. $5x = 15$
3

60. $4y = 28$
7

61. $3b = -12$
-4

62. $2a = -14$
-7

63. $-3x = 6$
-2

64. $-5m = 20$
-4

65. $-3x = -27$
9

66. $-6n = -30$
5

67. $20 = 4c$
5

68. $18 = 2t$
9

69. $-32 = 8w$
-4

70. $-56 = 7x$
-8

71. $8d = 0$
0

72. $-5x = 0$
0

73. $\frac{x}{3} = 2$
6

74. $\frac{x}{4} = 3$
12

Solve and check.

75. $-\frac{y}{2} = 5$
-10

76. $-\frac{b}{3} = 6$
-18

77. $\frac{3}{4}y = 9$
12

78. $\frac{2}{5}x = 6$
15

79. $-\frac{2}{3}d = 8$
-12

80. $-\frac{3}{5}m = 12$
-20

81. $\frac{2n}{3} = 2$
3

82. $\frac{5x}{6} = -10$
-12

83. $\frac{-3z}{8} = 9$
-24

84. $\frac{-4x}{5} = -12$
15

85. $-6 = -\frac{2}{3}y$
9

86. $-15 = -\frac{3}{5}x$
25

87. $\frac{3}{4}c = \frac{3}{5}$
$\frac{4}{5}$

88. $\frac{2}{9} = \frac{2}{3}y$
$\frac{1}{3}$

89. $-\frac{6}{7} = -\frac{3}{4}b$
$\frac{8}{7}$

90. $5x + 2x = 14$
2

91. $3n + 2n = 20$
4

92. $7d - 4d = 9$
3

93. $10y - 3y = 21$
3

94. $2x - 5x = 9$
-3

4.1D Exercises

Solve and check.

95. $3x + 1 = 10$
3

96. $4y + 3 = 11$
2

97. $2a - 5 = 7$
6

98. $5m - 6 = 9$
3

99. $5 = 4x + 9$
-1

100. $2 = 5b + 12$
-2

101. $2x - 5 = -11$
-3

102. $3n - 7 = -19$
-4

103. $10 = 4 + 3d$
2

104. $13 = 9 + 4z$
1

105. $7 - c = 9$
-2

106. $2 - x = 11$
-9

107. $4 - 3w = -2$
2

108. $5 - 6x = -13$
3

109. $4a - 20 = 0$
5

110. $3y - 9 = 0$
3

111. $6 + 2b = 0$
-3

112. $10 + 5m = 0$
-2

113. $-2x + 5 = 7$
-1

114. $-5d + 3 = -12$
3

115. $-8x - 3 = -19$
2

116. $-7n - 4 = -25$
3

117. $-13 = -11y + 9$
2

118. $2 = 7 - 5a$
1

119. $-3m - 21 = 0$
-7

120. $-5x - 30 = 0$
-6

121. $-4y + 15 = 15$
0

122. $-3x + 19 = 19$
0

Solve and check.

123. $7x - 3 = 3$
$$\frac{6}{7}$$

124. $8y + 3 = 7$
$$\frac{1}{2}$$

125. $14 = 9x + 1$
$$\frac{13}{9}$$

126. $4 = 5b + 6$
$$-\frac{2}{5}$$

127. $11 = 15 + 4n$
$$-1$$

128. $4 = 2 - 3c$
$$-\frac{2}{3}$$

129. $9 - 4x = 6$
$$\frac{3}{4}$$

130. $3t - 2 = 0$
$$\frac{2}{3}$$

131. $9x - 4 = 0$
$$\frac{4}{9}$$

132. $7 - 8z = 0$
$$\frac{7}{8}$$

133. $1 - 3x = 0$
$$\frac{1}{3}$$

134. $12w + 11 = 5$
$$-\frac{1}{2}$$

135. $6y - 5 = -7$
$$-\frac{1}{3}$$

136. $7 + 12x = 3$
$$-\frac{1}{3}$$

137. $9 + 14x = 7$
$$-\frac{1}{7}$$

138. $5 - 6m = 2$
$$\frac{1}{2}$$

139. $7 - 9a = 4$
$$\frac{1}{3}$$

140. $9 = -12c + 5$
$$-\frac{1}{3}$$

141. $10 = -18x + 7$
$$-\frac{1}{6}$$

142. $2y + \frac{1}{3} = \frac{7}{3}$
$$1$$

143. $4a + \frac{3}{4} = \frac{19}{4}$
$$1$$

144. $2n - \frac{3}{4} = \frac{13}{4}$
$$2$$

145. $3x - \frac{5}{6} = \frac{13}{6}$
$$1$$

146. $8t + 13 = 3$
$$-\frac{5}{4}$$

147. $12x + 19 = 3$
$$-\frac{4}{3}$$

148. $-6y + 5 = 13$
$$-\frac{4}{3}$$

149. $-4x + 3 = 9$
$$-\frac{3}{2}$$

150. $\frac{1}{2}a - 3 = 1$
$$8$$

151. $\frac{1}{3}m - 1 = 5$
$$18$$

152. $\frac{2}{5}y + 4 = 6$
$$5$$

153. $\frac{3}{4}n + 7 = 13$
$$8$$

154. $-\frac{2}{3}x + 1 = 7$
$$-9$$

155. $-\frac{3}{8}b + 4 = 10$
$$-16$$

156. $\frac{x}{4} - 6 = 1$
$$28$$

157. $\frac{y}{5} - 2 = 3$
$$25$$

158. $\frac{2x}{3} - 1 = 5$
$$9$$

159. $\frac{3c}{7} - 1 = 8$
$$21$$

160. $9 = 3 - \frac{2x}{7}$
$$-21$$

161. $3 = \frac{3a}{4} + 1$
$$\frac{8}{3}$$

162. $6a + 3 + 2a = 11$
$$1$$

163. $5y + 9 + 2y = 23$
$$2$$

164. $7x - 4 - 2x = 6$
$$2$$

165. $11z - 3 - 7z = 9$
$$3$$

166. $2x - 6x + 1 = 9$
$$-2$$

167. $b - 8b + 1 = -6$
$$1$$

168. $3 = 7x + 9 - 4x$
$$-2$$

169. $-1 = 5m + 7 - m$
$$-2$$

170. $8 = 4n - 6 + 3n$
$$2$$

Section 2   General Equations

To solve an equation of the form $ax + b = cx + d$

Reference for
Computer
Tutor™

In solving an equation of the form $ax + b = cx + d$, the goal is to rewrite the equation in the form *variable = constant*. Begin by rewriting the equation so that there is only one variable term in the equation. Then rewrite the equation so that there is only one constant term.

Solve: $4x - 5 = 6x + 11$

The goal is to rewrite the equation in the form *variable = constant*.

Step 1 Add the opposite of the variable term $6x$ to each side of the equation. Simplify. Now there is only one variable term in the equation.

$$4x - 5 = 6x + 11$$
$$4x + (-6x) - 5 = 6x + (-6x) + 11$$
$$-2x - 5 = 11$$

Step 2 Add the opposite of the constant term -5 to each side of the equation. Simplify. Now there is only one constant term in the equation.

$$-2x - 5 + 5 = 11 + 5$$
$$-2x = 16$$

Step 3 Multiply each side of the equation by the reciprocal of the coefficient -2. Simplify. Now the equation is in the form *variable = constant*.

$$\left(-\frac{1}{2}\right)(-2x) = \left(-\frac{1}{2}\right)(16)$$
$$x = -8$$

Step 4 Write the solution.

The solution is -8.

-8 checks as the solution.

Example 1   Solve: $4x - 5 = 8x - 7$

Solution

$$4x - 5 = 8x - 7$$
$$4x + (-8x) - 5 = 8x + (-8x) - 7$$
$$-4x - 5 = -7$$
$$-4x - 5 + 5 = -7 + 5$$
$$-4x = -2$$
$$\left(-\frac{1}{4}\right)(-4x) = \left(-\frac{1}{4}\right)(-2)$$
$$x = \frac{1}{2}$$

The solution is $\frac{1}{2}$

Example 2   Solve: $5x + 4 = 6 + 10x$

Your solution

$$-\frac{2}{5}$$

Solution on p. A24

Example 3   Solve: $3x + 4 - 5x = 2 - 4x$

Solution
$$3x + 4 - 5x = 2 - 4x$$
$$-2x + 4 = 2 - 4x$$
$$-2x + 4x + 4 = 2 - 4x + 4x$$
$$2x + 4 = 2$$
$$2x + 4 + (-4) = 2 + (-4)$$
$$2x = -2$$
$$\frac{1}{2} \cdot 2x = \frac{1}{2}(-2)$$
$$x = -1$$

The solution is -1.

Example 4   Solve: $5x - 10 - 3x = 6 - 4x$

Solution
$$\frac{8}{3}$$

Solution on p. A24

Objective B   # To solve an equation containing parentheses

4
DISK
FOUR

Reference for
Computer
Tutor™

When an equation contains parentheses, one of the steps in solving the equation requires the use of the Distributive Property.

The Distributive Property is used to remove parentheses from a variable expression. $a(b + c) = ab + ac$

Solve: $4 + 5(2x - 3) = 3(4x - 1)$

The goal is to rewrite the equation in the form *variable = constant*.

Step 1 Use the Distributive Property to remove parentheses. Simplify.

$$4 + 5(2x - 3) = 3(4x - 1)$$
$$4 + 10x - 15 = 12x - 3$$
$$10x - 11 = 12x - 3$$

Step 2 Add the opposite of the variable term $12x$ to each side of the equation. Simplify. Now there is only one variable term in the equation.

$$10x + (-12x) - 11 = 12x + (-12x) - 3$$
$$-2x - 11 = -3$$

Step 3 Add the opposite of the constant term -11 to each side of the equation. Simplify. Now there is only one constant term in the equation.

$$-2x - 11 + 11 = -3 + 11$$
$$-2x = 8$$

Step 4 Multiply each side of the equation by the reciprocal of the coefficient -2. Simplify. Now the equation is in the form *variable = constant*.

$$\left(-\frac{1}{2}\right)(-2x) = \left(-\frac{1}{2}\right)(8)$$
$$x = -4$$

Step 5 Write the solution.

The solution is -4.

-4 checks as the solution.

Example 5   Solve:
$$3x - 4(2 - x) = 3(x - 2) - 4$$

Solution
$$3x - 4(2 - x) = 3(x - 2) - 4$$
$$3x - 8 + 4x = 3x - 6 - 4$$
$$7x - 8 = 3x - 10$$
$$7x + (-3x) - 8 = 3x + (-3x) - 10$$
$$4x - 8 = -10$$
$$4x - 8 + 8 = -10 + 8$$
$$4x = -2$$
$$\frac{1}{4} \cdot 4x = \frac{1}{4} \cdot (-2)$$
$$x = -\frac{1}{2}$$

The solution is $-\frac{1}{2}$.

Example 6   Solve:
$$5x - 4(3 - 2x) = 2(3x - 2) + 6$$

Your solution

2

Example 7   Solve:
$$3[2 - 4(2x - 1)] = 4x - 10$$

Solution
$$3[2 - 4(2x - 1)] = 4x - 10$$
$$3[2 - 8x + 4] = 4x - 10$$
$$3[6 - 8x] = 4x - 10$$
$$18 - 24x = 4x - 10$$
$$18 - 24x + (-4x) = 4x + (-4x) - 10$$
$$18 - 28x = -10$$
$$18 + (-18) - 28x = -10 + (-18)$$
$$-28x = -28$$
$$-\frac{1}{28} \cdot (-28x) = -\frac{1}{28} \cdot (-28)$$
$$x = 1$$

The solution is 1.

Example 8   Solve:
$$-2[3x - 5(2x - 3)] = 3x - 8$$

Your solution

2

Objective C   To solve application problems using a formula

A lever system is shown at the right. It consists of a lever, or bar; a fulcrum; and two forces, F_1 and F_2. The distance d represents the length of the lever, x represents the distance from F_1 to the fulcrum, and $d - x$ represents the distance from F_2 to the fulcrum.

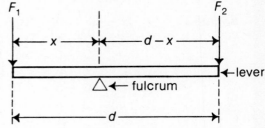

A principle of physics states that when the lever system balances,
$F_1 \cdot x = F_2 \cdot (d - x)$.

Example 9

A lever is 15 ft long. A force of 50 lb is applied to one end of the lever and a force of 100 lb is applied to the other end. Where is the fulcrum located when the system balances?

Strategy

To find the location of the fulcrum when the system balances, replace the variables F_1, F_2, and d in the lever system formula by the given values and solve for x.

Solution

$$F_1 \cdot x = F_2 \cdot (d - x)$$
$$50x = 100(15 - x)$$
$$50x = 1500 - 100x$$
$$50x + 100x = 1500 - 100x + 100x$$
$$150x = 1500$$
$$\frac{1}{150} \cdot 150x = \frac{1}{150} \cdot 1500$$
$$x = 10$$

The fulcrum is 10 ft from the 50-pound force.

Example 10

A lever is 25 ft long. A force of 45 lb is applied to one end of the lever and a force of 80 lb is applied to the other end. What is the location of the fulcrum when the system balances?

Your strategy

Your solution

16 ft from the
45-pound force

Solution on p. A24

4.2A Exercises

Solve and check.

1. $8x + 5 = 4x + 3$
$-\frac{1}{2}$

2. $6y + 2 = y + 17$
3

3. $7m + 4 = 6m + 7$
3

4. $11n + 3 = 10n + 11$
8

5. $5x - 4 = 2x + 5$
3

6. $9a - 10 = 3a + 2$
2

7. $12y - 4 = 9y - 7$
-1

8. $13b - 1 = 4b - 19$
-2

9. $15x - 2 = 4x - 13$
-1

10. $7a - 5 = 2a - 20$
-3

11. $3x + 1 = 11 - 2x$
2

12. $n - 2 = 6 - 3n$
2

13. $2x - 3 = -11 - 2x$
-2

14. $4y - 2 = -16 - 3y$
-2

15. $2b + 3 = 5b + 12$
-3

16. $m + 4 = 3m + 8$
-2

17. $4x - 7 = 5x + 1$
-8

18. $6d - 2 = 7d + 5$
-7

19. $4y - 8 = y - 8$
0

20. $5a + 7 = 2a + 7$
0

21. $6 - 5x = 8 - 3x$
-1

22. $10 - 4n = 16 - n$
-2

23. $5 + 7x = 11 + 9x$
-3

24. $3 - 2y = 15 + 4y$
-2

25. $2x - 4 = 6x$
-1

26. $2b - 10 = 7b$
-2

27. $-3x - 4 = 2x + 6$
-2

28. $8 - 4x = 18 - 5x$
10

29. $6 - 10a = 8 - 9a$
-2

30. $5 - 7m = 2 - 6m$
3

31. $8b + 5 = 5b + 7$
$\frac{2}{3}$

32. $6y - 1 = 2y + 2$
$\frac{3}{4}$

33. $7x - 8 = x - 3$
$\frac{5}{6}$

34. $10x - 3 = 3x - 1$
$\frac{2}{7}$

35. $5n + 3 = 2n + 1$
$-\frac{2}{3}$

36. $8a - 2 = 4a - 5$
$-\frac{3}{4}$

4.2B Exercises

Solve and check.

37. $5x + 2(x + 1) = 23$
3

38. $6y + 2(2y + 3) = 16$
1

39. $9n - 3(2n - 1) = 15$
4

40. $12x - 2(4x - 6) = 28$
4

41. $7a - (3a - 4) = 12$
2

42. $9m - 4(2m - 3) = 11$
-1

43. $2(3x + 1) - 4 = 16$
3

44. $4(2b + 3) - 9 = 11$
1

45. $5(3 - 2y) + 4y = 3$
2

Solve and check.

46. $4(1 - 3x) + 7x = 9$
    -1

47. $10x + 1 = 2(3x + 5) - 1$
    2

48. $5y - 3 = 7 + 4(y - 2)$
    2

49. $4 - 3a = 7 - 2(2a + 5)$
    -7

50. $9 - 5x = 12 - (6x + 7)$
    -4

51. $2x - 5 = 3(4x + 5)$
    -2

52. $3n - 7 = 5(2n + 7)$
    -6

53. $5b + 2(3b + 1) = 3b + 5$
    $\frac{3}{8}$

54. $x + 3(4x - 2) = 7x - 1$
    $\frac{5}{6}$

55. $3y - 7 = 5(2y - 3) + 4$
    $\frac{4}{7}$

56. $2a - 5 = 4(3a + 1) - 2$
    $-\frac{7}{10}$

57. $5 - (9 - 6x) = 2x - 2$
    $\frac{1}{2}$

58. $3[2 - 4(y - 1)] = 3(2y + 8)$
    $-\frac{1}{3}$

59. $5[2 - (2x - 4)] = 2(5 - 3x)$
    5

60. $3a + 2[2 + 3(a - 1)] = 2(3a + 4)$
    $\frac{10}{3}$

61. $5 + 3[1 + 2(2x - 3)] = 6(x + 5)$
    $\frac{20}{3}$

62. $-2[4 - (3b + 2)] = 5 - 2(3b + 6)$
    $-\frac{1}{4}$

63. $-4[x - 2(2x - 3)] + 1 = 2x - 3$
    2

4.2C Exercises

Solve. Use the lever system formula $F_1 \cdot x = F_2 \cdot (d - x)$.

64. A lever is 25 ft long. A force of 26 lb is applied to one end of the lever and a force of 24 lb is applied to the other end. Find the location of the fulcrum when the system balances.

    12 feet from the 26-pound force

65. A lever is 14 ft long. A force of 40 lb is applied to one end of the lever and a force of 30 lb is applied to the other end. Find the location of the fulcrum when the system balances.

    6 ft from the 40-pound force

66. A lever is 10 ft long. At a distance of 8 ft from the fulcrum, a force of 100 lb is applied. How large a force must be applied to the other end of the lever so that the system will balance?

    400 lb

67. A lever is 8 ft long. At a distance of 7 ft from the fulcrum, a force of 80 lb is applied. How large a force must be applied to the other end of the lever so that the system will balance?

    560 lb

Section 3 Application Problems

Objective A   To translate a sentence into an equation and solve

Reference for
Computer
Tutor™

An equation states that two mathematical expressions are equal. Therefore, to translate a sentence into an equation requires recognition of the words or phrases that mean "equals." Some of these phrases are listed below.

equals
is
is equal to   } translate to =
amounts to
represents

Once the sentence is translated into an equation, the equation can be solved by rewriting it in the form *variable = constant*.

Translate "five less than a number is thirteen" into an equation and solve.

Step 1 Assign a variable to the unknown quantity.

The unknown number: n

Step 2 Find two verbal expressions for the same value.

| Five less than a number | is | thirteen |

Step 3 Write a mathematical expression for each verbal expression. Write the equals sign.

$$n - 5 \quad = \quad 13$$

Step 4 Solve the equation.

$$n - 5 + 5 = 13 + 5$$
$$n = 18$$

The number is 18.

Example 1 Translate "three more than twice a number is the number plus six" into an equation and solve.

Solution The unknown number: n

| Three more than twice a number | is | the number plus six |

$$2n + 3 = n + 6$$
$$2n + (-n) + 3 = n + (-n) + 6$$
$$n + 3 = 6$$
$$n + 3 + (-3) = 6 + (-3)$$
$$n = 3$$

The number is 3.

Example 2 Translate "four less than one-third of a number equals five minus two-thirds of the number" into an equation and solve.

Your solution

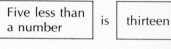

$$\frac{1}{3}n - 4 = 5 - \frac{2}{3}n \ ; $$
$$n = 9$$

Solution on p. A25

Solution on p. A25

Example 3

Translate "four times the sum of a number and three is six less than twice the number" into an equation and solve.

Example 4

Translate "two times the difference between a number and eight is equal to the sum of six times the number and eight" into an equation and solve.

Solution

The unknown number: n

Four times the sum of a number and three	is	six less than twice the number

$$4(n + 3) = 2n - 6$$
$$4n + 12 = 2n - 6$$
$$4n + (-2n) + 12 = 2n + (-2n) - 6$$
$$2n + 12 = -6$$
$$2n + 12 + (-12) = -6 + (-12)$$
$$2n = -18$$
$$\frac{1}{2} \cdot 2n = \frac{1}{2}(-18)$$
$$n = -9$$

The number is -9.

Your solution

$$2(n-8) = 6n + 8;$$
$$n = -6$$

To solve consecutive integer problems

Reference for Computer Tutor™

The integers are the numbers . . . -4, -3, -2, -1, 0, 1, 2, 3, 4, . . . An **even integer** is an integer that is divisible by 2. Examples of even integers are -8, 0, and 22. An **odd integer** is an integer that is not divisible by 2. Examples of odd integers are -17, 1, and 39.

Consecutive integers are integers that follow one another in order. Examples of consecutive integers are shown at the right. (Assume that the variable n represents an integer.)

11, 12, 13
-8, -7, -6
$n, n + 1, n + 2$

Examples of **consecutive even integers** are shown at the right. (Assume that the variable n represents an even integer.)

24, 26, 28
-10, -8, -6
$n, n + 2, n + 4$

Examples of **consecutive odd integers** are shown at the right. (Assume that the variable n represents an odd integer.)

19, 21, 23
-1, 1, 3
$n, n + 2, n + 4$

The sum of three consecutive odd integers is 45. Find the integers.

STRATEGY FOR SOLVING A CONSECUTIVE INTEGER PROBLEM

▷ Let a variable represent one of the integers. Express each of the other integers in terms of that variable. Remember that consecutive integers will differ by 1. Consecutive even or consecutive odd integers differ by 2.

Represent three consecutive odd integers.

First odd integer: n
Second odd integer: $n + 2$
Third odd integer: $n + 4$

▷ Determine the relationship among the integers.

The sum of the three odd integers is 45.

$$n + (n + 2) + (n + 4) = 45$$
$$3n + 6 = 45$$
$$3n = 39$$
$$n = 13$$
$$n + 2 = 13 + 2 = 15$$
$$n + 4 = 13 + 4 = 17$$

The three consecutive odd integers are 13, 15, and 17.

Example 5

Find three consecutive even integers such that three times the second is four more than the sum of the first and third.

Strategy

▷ First even integer: n
Second even integer: $n + 2$
Third even integer: $n + 4$
▷ Three times the second equals four more than the sum of the first and third.

Solution

$$3(n + 2) = n + (n + 4) + 4$$
$$3n + 6 = 2n + 8$$
$$n + 6 = 8$$
$$n = 2$$
$$n + 2 = 2 + 2 = 4$$
$$n + 4 = 2 + 4 = 6$$

The three even integers are 2, 4, and 6.

Example 6

Find three consecutive integers whose sum is -6.

Your strategy

Your solution

$$-3, \ -2, \ -1$$

Solution on p. A25

Reference for
Computer
Tutor™

Objective C   To solve age problems

The goal of an age problem is to determine the age of a person or an object.

A painting is 20 years old and a sculpture is 10 years old. How many years ago was the painting three times as old as the sculpture was then?

STRATEGY FOR SOLVING AN AGE PROBLEM

▷ Represent the ages in terms of numerical or variable expressions. To represent a past age, subtract from the present age. To represent a future age, add to the present age. The results can be recorded in a table.

The number of years ago: x

	Present age	Past age
Painting	20	$20 - x$
Sculpture	10	$10 - x$

▷ Determine the relationship among the ages.

At a past age, the painting was three times as old as the sculpture was then.

$$20 - x = 3(10 - x)$$
$$20 - x = 30 - 3x$$
$$20 + 2x = 30$$
$$2x = 10$$
$$x = 5$$

Five years ago the painting was three times as old as the sculpture.

Example 7

A stamp collector has a 3¢ stamp that is 25 years older than a 5¢ stamp. In 18 years, the 3¢ stamp will be twice as old as the 5¢ stamp will be then. How old are the stamps now?

Strategy

▷ Present age of 5¢ stamp: x

	Present	Future
3¢ stamp	$x + 25$	$x + 43$
5¢ stamp	x	$x + 18$

▷ At a future age, the 3¢ stamp will be twice as old as the 5¢ stamp.

Solution

$$2(x + 18) = x + 43$$
$$2x + 36 = x + 43$$
$$x + 36 = 43$$
$$x = 7$$
$$x + 25 = 7 + 25 = 32$$

The 3¢ stamp is 32 years old and the 5¢ stamp is 7 years old.

Example 8

A half-dollar is now 25 years old. A dime is 15 years old. How many years ago was the half-dollar twice as old as the dime?

Your strategy

Your solution

5 years

Objective D

Reference for
Computer
Tutor™

To solve uniform motion problems

A train that travels constantly in a straight line at 50 mph is in *uniform motion*. **Uniform motion** means that the speed of an object does not change.

The solution of a uniform motion problem is based on the equation $d = rt$, where d is the distance traveled, r is the rate of travel, and t is the time spent traveling.

A train traveled at a speed of 55 mph for 3 hours. The distance traveled by the train can be found by the equation $d = rt$.

The rate is 55 mph. The time is 3 hours.

$$d = rt$$
$$d = 55(3)$$
$$d = 165$$

The train traveled 165 mi.

A car leaves a town traveling at 40 mph. Two hours later, a second car leaves the same town, on the same road, traveling at 60 mph. In how many hours will the second car be passing the first car?

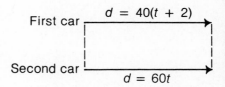

STRATEGY FOR SOLVING A UNIFORM MOTION PROBLEM

▷ For each object, write a numerical or variable expression for the distance, rate, and time. The results can be recorded in a table.

The first car traveled 2 hours longer than the second car.

Unknown time for the second car: t
Time for the first car: $t + 2$

	Rate, r	·	Time, t	=	Distance, d
First car	40	·	$t + 2$	=	$40(t + 2)$
Second car	60	·	t	=	$60t$

▷ Determine how the distances traveled by each object are related. For example, the total distance traveled by both objects may be known or it may be known that the two objects traveled the same distance.

The two cars travel the same distance.

$$40(t + 2) = 60t$$
$$40t + 80 = 60t$$
$$80 = 20t$$
$$4 = t$$

The second car will be passing the first car in 4 hours.

Example 9

Two cars, the second car traveling 10 mph faster than the first car, start at the same time from the same point and travel in opposite directions. In 3 hours they are 300 mi apart. Find the rate of each car.

Strategy

▷ Rate of 1st car: r
Rate of 2nd car: $r + 10$

	Rate	Time	Distance
1st car	r	3	$3r$
2nd car	$r + 10$	3	$3(r + 10)$

▷ The total distance traveled by the two cars is 300 mi.

Solution

$$3r + 3(r + 10) = 300$$
$$3r + 3r + 30 = 300$$
$$6r + 30 = 300$$
$$6r = 270$$
$$r = 45$$
$$r + 10 = 45 + 10 = 55$$

The first car is traveling 45 mph.
The second car is traveling 55 mph.

Example 11

How far can a bicycling club ride out into the country at a speed of 12 mph and return over the same road at 8 mph if they travel a total of 10 hours?

Strategy

▷ Time spent riding out: t
Time spent riding back: $10 - t$

	Rate	Time	Distance
Out	12	t	$12t$
Back	8	$10 - t$	$8(10 - t)$

▷ The distance out equals the distance back.

Solution

$$12t = 8(10 - t)$$
$$12t = 80 - 8t$$
$$20t = 80$$
$$t = 4 \text{ (The time is 4 hours.)}$$

The distance out $= 12t = 12(4) = 48$ mi.
The club can ride 48 mi into the country.

Example 10

Two trains, one traveling at twice the speed of the other, start at the same time from stations 288 mi apart and travel toward each other. In 3 hours, the trains pass each other. Find the rate of each train.

Your strategy

Your solution

32 mph; 64 mph

Example 12

On a survey mission, a pilot flew out to a parcel of land and back in 5 hours. The rate out was 150 mph and the rate returning was 100 mph. How far away was the parcel of land?

Your strategy

Your solution

300 mi

Solutions on p. A26

4.3A Exercises

Translate into an equation and solve.

1. The sum of a number and twelve is ten. Find the number.

$$x + 12 = 10;$$
$$x = -2$$

2. The difference between a number and five is two. Find the number.

$$x - 5 = 2;$$
$$x = 7$$

3. Two-thirds of a number is six. Find the number.

$$\frac{2}{3}x = 6;$$
$$x = 9$$

4. The quotient of a number and seven is the opposite of three. Find the number.

$$\frac{x}{7} = -3;$$
$$x = -21$$

5. The difference between twelve and the product of five and a number equals seven. Find the number.

$$12 - 5x = 7;$$
$$x = 1$$

6. The sum of six times a number and five is the opposite of thirteen. Find the number.

$$6x + 5 = -13;$$
$$x = -3$$

7. The sum of three times a number and the number is twelve. Find the number.

$$3x + x = 12;$$
$$x = 3$$

8. The difference between five times a number and twice the number is nine. Find the number.

$$5x - 2x = 9;$$
$$x = 3$$

9. The total of twice a number and the sum of the number and three equals fifteen. Find the number.

$$2x + (x + 3) = 15;$$
$$x = 4$$

10. The difference between twice a number and three times the sum of the number and three is equal to fourteen. Find the number.

$$2x - 3(x + 3) = 14;$$
$$x = -23$$

11. Three times the sum of a number and two is fifteen. Find the number.

$$3(x + 2) = 15;$$
$$x = 3$$

12. Five times the difference between a number and four equals thirty. Find the number.

$$5(x - 4) = 30;$$
$$x = 10$$

13. Four times a number is equal to ten more than twice the number. Find the number.

$$4x = 2x + 10;$$
$$x = 5$$

14. Twice a number is twenty less than the product of seven and the number. Find the number.

$$2x = 7x - 20;$$
$$x = 4$$

15. The sum of a number and four equals eight less than the product of three and the number. Find the number.

$$x + 4 = 3x - 8;$$
$$x = 6$$

16. A number minus three is equal to the difference between six times the number and eighteen. Find the number.

$$x - 3 = 6x - 18;$$
$$x = 3$$

17. Four times the difference between three times a number and one is equal to six more than twice the number. Find the number.

$$4(3x - 1) = 2x + 6;$$
$$x = 1$$

18. Five times the sum of a number and one equals four less than twice the number. Find the number.

$$5(x + 1) = 2x - 4;$$
$$x = -3$$

4.3B Exercises

Solve.

19. The sum of three consecutive integers is 48. Find the integers.

    15, 16, 17

20. The sum of three consecutive integers is 60. Find the integers.

    19, 20, 21

21. The sum of three consecutive even integers is 66. Find the integers.

    20, 22, 24 .

22. The sum of three consecutive even integers is 42. Find the integers.

    12, 14, 16

23. The sum of three consecutive odd integers is 51. Find the integers.

    15, 17, 19

24. The sum of three consecutive odd integers is 75. Find the integers.

    23, 25, 27

25. Find two consecutive even integers such that three times the first equals twice the second.

    4, 6

26. Find two consecutive even integers such that four times the first is three times the second.

    6, 8

27. Five times the first of two consecutive odd integers equals three times the second. Find the integers.

    3, 5

28. Seven times the first of two consecutive odd integers is five times the second. Find the integers.

    5, 7

29. Find three consecutive integers whose sum is negative twenty-one.

    −8, −7, −6

30. Find three consecutive even integers whose sum is negative eighteen.

    −8, −6, −4

31. Twice the smallest of three consecutive odd integers is seven more than the largest. Find the integers.

    11, 13, 15

32. Three times the smallest of three consecutive even integers is four more than twice the largest. Find the integers.

    12, 14, 16

33. Find three consecutive odd integers such that three times the middle integer is one more than the sum of the first and third.

    −1, 1, 3

34. Find three consecutive even integers such that three times the middle integer is four more than the sum of the first and third.

    2, 4, 6

4.3C Exercises

Solve.

35. A book dealer has an autographed, first-edition book that is 35 years old and a reprint of the book that is 7 years old. In how many years will the autographed first edition be three times as old as the reprint will be then?

7 years

36. A collector of hand woven rugs has an oval rug that is 42 years old and a circular rug that is 14 years old. How many years ago was the oval rug five times as old as the circular rug was then?

7 years

37. A coin collector has a dime that is 24 years older than a nickel. In 8 years the dime will be twice as old as the nickel will be then. Find the present age of the dime and nickel.

nickel: 16 years
dime: 40 years

38. An oil painting is 10 years older than a lithograph. Five yeas ago the painting was twice as old as the lithograph was then. Find the present age of each.

lithograph: 15 years
painting: 25 years

39. An art collector has a porcelain vase that is 15 years old and a crystal vase that is 95 years old. In how many years will the crystal vase be three times as old as the porcelain vase will be then?

25 years

40. A stamp collector has a 2¢ stamp that is 20 years old and a 3¢ stamp that is 16 years old. How many years ago was the 2¢ stamp twice as old as the 3¢ stamp was then?

12 years

41. An antique butterchurn is 85 years old and an antique ice box is 75 years old. How many years ago was the butterchurn twice the age the ice box was then?

65 years

42. A diamond ring is 2 years old and a ruby ring is 22 years old. In how many years will the ruby ring be twice the age the diamond ring will be then?

18 years

43. An antique car is 45 years older than a replica of the car. In 13 years, the antique car will be four times as old as the replica will be then. Find the present ages of the two cars.

antique: 47 years
replica: 2 years

44. A gold coin is 84 years older than a silver coin. Twenty years ago, the gold coin was three times as old as the silver coin was then. Find the present ages of the two coins.

silver coin: 62 years
gold coin: 146 years

45. The sum of the ages of an oil painting and a watercolor is 20 years. The oil painting one year from now will be nine times the age of the watercolor one year ago. Find the present age of each painting.

watercolor: 3 years
oil painting: 17 years

46. The sum of the ages of two cars is 8 years. Two years ago the age of the older car was three times the age the younger car was then. Find the present age of each car.

newer car: 3 years
older car: 5 years

47. The sum of the ages of a 5¢ coin and a 10¢ coin is 12. Two years from now the age of the 5¢ coin will equal the age of the 10¢ coin two years ago. Find the present age of each coin.

5¢ coin: 4 years
10¢ coin: 8 years

48. The sum of the ages of two children is 18. Six years from now the age of the older child will be twice the age of the younger child. Find the present ages of the two children.

younger child: 4 years
older child: 14 years

4.3D Exercises

Solve.

49. Two cyclists start from the same point and ride in opposite directions. One cyclist rides twice as fast as the other. In three hours they are 72 mi apart. Find the rate of each cyclist.

    8 mph and 16 mph

50. Two small planes start from the same point and fly in opposite directions. The first plane is flying 25 mph slower than the second plane. In two hours the planes are 430 mi apart. Find the rate of each plane.

    95 mph and 120 mph

51. A family drove to a resort at an average speed of 30 mph and later returned over the same road at an average speed of 50 mph. Find the distance to the resort if the total driving time was 8 hours.

    150 mi

52. As part of flight training, a student pilot was required to fly to an airport and then return. The average speed to the airport was 90 mph, and the average speed returning was 120 mph. Find the distance between the two airports if the total flying time was 7 hours.

    360 mi

53. Running at an average rate of 8 m/s, a sprinter ran to the end of a track and then jogged back to the starting point at an average rate of 3 m/s. The sprinter took 55 seconds to run to the end of the track and jog back. Find the length of the track.

    120 m

54. Three campers left their campsite by canoe and paddled downstream at an average rate of 8 mph. They then turned around and paddled back upstream at an average rate of 4 mph to return to their campsite. How long did it take the campers to canoe downstream if the total trip took 1 hour?

    20 min

55. A car traveling at 48 mph overtakes a cyclist who, riding at 12 mph, has had a 3-hour head start. How far from the starting point does the car overtake the cyclist?

    48 mi

56. A jet plane traveling at 600 mph overtakes a propeller-driven plane that has had a 2-hour head start. The propeller-driven plane is traveling at 200 mph. How far from the starting point does the jet overtake the propeller-driven plane?

    600 mi

57. On a 195-mile trip, a car traveled at an average speed of 45 mph and then reduced the speed to 30 mph for the remainder of the trip. The trip took a total of 5 hours. For how long did the car travel at each speed?

    3 hours at 45 mph
    2 hours at 30 mph

58. A 555-mile, 5-hour plane trip was flown at two speeds. For the first part of the trip, the average speed was 105 mph. For the remainder of the trip, the average speed was 115 mph. For how long did the plane fly at each speed?

    2 hours at 105 mph
    3 hours at 115 mph

59. A bus traveled on a straight road for 2 hours at an average speed of 20 mph faster than it traveled on a winding road. The time spent on the winding road was 3 hours. Find the average speed on the winding road if the total trip was 200 mi.

    32 mph

60. After a sailboat had been on the water for 3 hours, a change in wind direction reduced the average speed of the boat by 5 mph. The entire distance sailed was 57 mi. The total time spent sailing was 6 hours. How far did the sailboat travel in the first 3 hours?

    36 mi

Section 4 Introduction to Inequalities

Objective A   To graph the solution set of an inequality on the number line

Reference for
Computer
Tutor™

A **set** is a collection of objects. The objects in a set are called the **elements** of the set.

An expression that contains the symbol >, <, ≥ (is greater than or equal to), or ≤ (is less than or equal to) is called an **inequality.** An inequality expresses the relative order of two mathematical expressions. The expressions can be either numerical or variable expressions.

$$4 > 2$$
$$3x \leq 7$$
$$x^2 - 2x > y + 4$$
$\Big\}$ Inequalities

The **solution set of an inequality** is a set of real numbers and can be graphed on the number line.

Graph the solution set of $x > 1$.

The solution set is the real numbers greater than 1. The circle on the graph indicates that 1 is not included in the solution set. Every number greater than 1 is an element of the solution set.

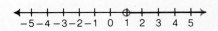

Graph the solution set of $x \geq 1$.

The dot at 1 indicates that 1 is included in the solution set.

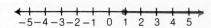

Graph the solution set of $x < -1$.

The numbers less than -1 are to the left of -1 on the number line.

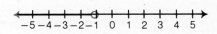

Example 1   Graph the solution set of $x < 5$.

Solution   The solution set is the numbers less than 5.

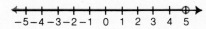

Example 2   Graph the solution set of $x > -2$.

Your solution

Solution on p. A26

| Objective B | To solve an inequality using the Addition Property of Inequalities |

Reference for
Computer
Tutor™

The **solution set of an inequality** is a set of numbers, each element of which, when substituted for the variable, results in a true inequality.

The inequality at the right is true if the variable is replaced by 7, 9.3, or $\frac{15}{2}$.

$$x + 3 > 8$$

$$\left.\begin{array}{l} 7 + 3 > 8 \\ 9.3 + 3 > 8 \\ \frac{15}{2} + 3 > 8 \end{array}\right\} \text{True inequalities}$$

The inequality is false if the variable is replaced by 4, 1.5, or $-\frac{1}{2}$.

$$\left.\begin{array}{l} 4 + 3 > 8 \\ 1.5 + 3 > 8 \\ -\frac{1}{2} + 3 > 8 \end{array}\right\} \text{False inequalities}$$

There are many values of the variable x that will make the inequality $x + 3 > 8$ true. The solution set of $x + 3 > 8$ is any number greater than 5.

The graph of the solution
set of $x + 3 > 8$

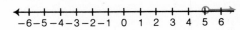

To solve an inequality, rewrite the given inequality in the form *variable > constant* or *variable < constant*. The Addition Property of Inequalities is used to rewrite an inequality in this form.

| **Addition Property of Inequalities** | |
| The same number can be added to each side of an inequality without changing the solution set of the inequality. | If $a > b$, then $a + c > b + c$.
 If $a < b$, then $a + c < b + c$. |

The Addition Property of Inequalities also holds true for an inequality containing the symbol ≥ or ≤.

The Addition Property of Inequalities is used when, in order to rewrite an inequality in the form *variable > constant* or *variable < constant*, a term must be removed from one side of the inequality. Add the opposite of the term to each side of the inequality.

To rewrite the inequality at the right, add the opposite of the constant term 4 to each side of the inequality. Then simplify.

$$x + 4 < 5$$
$$x + 4 + (-4) < 5 + (-4)$$
$$x < 1$$

The graph of the solution
set of $x + 4 < 5$

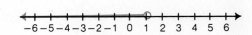

Solve: $x - 3 \geq 7$

Add the opposite of the constant term -3 to each side of the equation.

$$x - 3 \geq 7$$
$$x - 3 + 3 \geq 7 + 3$$

Simplify.

$$x \geq 10$$

Solve: $5x - 6 \leq 4x - 4$

Step 1　Add the opposite of the variable term $4x$ to each side of the inequality. Simplify.

$$5x - 6 \leq 4x - 4$$
$$5x + (-4x) - 6 \leq 4x + (-4x) - 4$$
$$x - 6 \leq -4$$

Step 2　Add the opposite of the constant term -6 to each side of the inequality. Simplify.

$$x - 6 + 6 \leq -4 + 6$$
$$x \leq 2$$

Example 3　Solve and graph the solution set of $x + 5 > 3$.

Solution
$$x + 5 > 3$$
$$x + 5 + (-5) > 3 + (-5)$$
$$x > -2$$

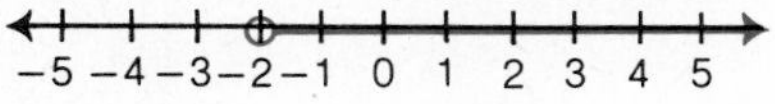

<!-- number line from -5 to 5, open circle at -2, arrow to right -->
$$\xleftarrow{\quad} \; \underset{-5\,-4\,-3\,-2\,-1\;\;0\;\;1\;\;2\;\;3\;\;4\;\;5}{\circ} \; \xrightarrow{\quad}$$

Example 4　Solve and graph the solution set of $x + 2 < -2$.

Your solution

$$x < -4$$

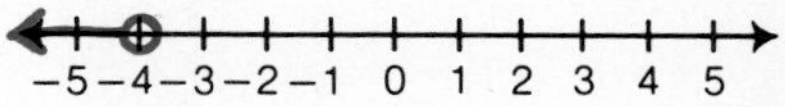

<!-- number line from -5 to 5, open circle at -4, arrow to left -->
$$\xleftarrow{\quad} \; \underset{-5\,-4\,-3\,-2\,-1\;\;0\;\;1\;\;2\;\;3\;\;4\;\;5}{\circ} \; \xrightarrow{\quad}$$

Example 5　Solve: $7x - 14 \leq 6x - 16$

Solution
$$7x - 14 \leq 6x - 16$$
$$7x + (-6x) - 14 \leq 6x + (-6x) - 16$$
$$x - 14 \leq -16$$
$$x - 14 + 14 \leq -16 + 14$$
$$x \leq -2$$

Example 6　Solve: $5x + 3 > 4x + 5$

Your solution

$$x > 2$$

Solutions on p. A26

4
DISK FOUR
Reference for Computer Tutor™

Objective C　## To solve an inequality using the Multiplication Property of Inequalities

In solving an inequality, the goal is to rewrite the given inequality in the form *variable > constant* or *variable < constant*. The Multiplication Property of Inequalities is used when, in order to rewrite an inequality in this form, a coefficient must be removed from one side of the inequality.

Multiplication Property of Inequalities

Rule 1

Each side of an inequality can be multiplied by the same positive number without changing the solution set of the inequality.

If $a > b$ and $c > 0$, then $ac > bc$.

$5 > 4$
$5(2) > 4(2)$
$10 > 8$ A true inequality

If $a < b$ and $c > 0$, then $ac < bc$.

$6 < 9$
$6(3) < 9(3)$
$18 < 27$ A true inequality

Rule 2

If each side of an inequality is multiplied by the same negative number and the inequality symbol is reversed, then the solution set of the inequality is not changed.

If $a > b$ and $c < 0$, then $ac < bc$.

$5 > 4$
$5(-2) < 4(-2)$
$-10 < -8$ A true inequality

If $a < b$ and $c < 0$, then $ac > bc$.

$6 < 9$
$6(-3) > 9(-3)$
$-18 > -27$ A true inequality

Copyright © 1989 HMCo

The Multiplication Property of Inequalities also holds true for an inequality containing the symbol $\geq$ or $\leq$.

To rewrite the inequality at the right, multiply each side of the inequality by the reciprocal of the coefficient -2.

$-2x \leq 8$

Since $-\frac{1}{2}$ is a negative number, the inequality symbol must be reversed.

$-\frac{1}{2}(-2x) \geq -\frac{1}{2}(8)$

Simplify.

$x \geq -4$

The graph of the solution set of $-2x \leq 8$

$-5\ -4\ -3\ -2\ -1\ \ 0\ \ 1\ \ 2\ \ 3\ \ 4\ \ 5$

Solve: $-5x \leq 8$

Multiply each side of the inequality by the reciprocal of the coefficient -5.

$-5x \leq 8$

Since $-\frac{1}{5}$ is a negative number, the inequality symbol must be reversed.

$-\frac{1}{5}(-5x) \geq -\frac{1}{5}(8)$

Simplify.

$x \geq -\frac{8}{5}$

Example 7   Solve: $-\frac{5}{8}x \leq \frac{5}{12}$

Solution
$-\frac{5}{8}x \leq \frac{5}{12}$

$-\frac{8}{5}\left(-\frac{5}{8}x\right) \geq -\frac{8}{5}\left(\frac{5}{12}\right)$

$x \geq -\frac{2}{3}$

Example 8   Solve: $-\frac{3}{4}x \geq 18$

Your solution

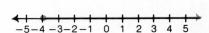
$x \leq -24$

4.4A Exercises

Graph the solution set.

1. $x > 2$

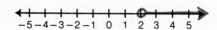

2. $x \geq -1$

3. $x \leq 0$

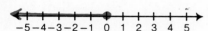

4. $x < 4$

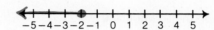

5. $x \geq 3$

6. $x \leq -2$

4.4B Exercises

Solve and graph the solution set.

7. $x - 5 > -2$

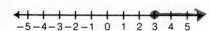 $x > 3$

8. $x - 3 > -2$

$x > 1$

9. $n + 4 \geq 7$

$n \geq 3$

10. $x + 5 \geq 3$

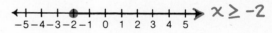 $x \geq -2$

11. $x - 6 \leq -10$

$x \leq -4$

12. $y - 8 \leq -11$

$y \leq -3$

Solve.

13. $y - 3 \geq -12$

$y \geq -9$

14. $x + 8 \geq -14$

$x \geq -22$

15. $3x - 5 < 2x + 7$

$x < 12$

16. $5x + 4 < 4x - 10$

$x < -14$

17. $2x + 4 < x - 7$

$x < -11$

18. $9x + 7 < 8x - 7$

$x < -14$

19. $4x - 8 \leq 2 + 3x$

$x \leq 10$

20. $5b - 9 < 3 + 4b$

$b < 12$

21. $d + \frac{1}{2} < \frac{1}{3}$

$d < -\frac{1}{6}$

22. $x - \frac{3}{8} < \frac{5}{6}$

$x < \frac{29}{24}$

23. $x + \frac{5}{8} \geq -\frac{2}{3}$

$x \geq -\frac{31}{24}$

24. $y + \frac{5}{12} \geq -\frac{3}{4}$

$y \geq -\frac{7}{6}$

Solve.

25. $6x - \frac{1}{3} \leq 5x - \frac{1}{2}$

    $x \leq -\frac{1}{6}$

26. $3x + \frac{5}{8} > 2x + \frac{5}{6}$

    $x > \frac{5}{24}$

27. $3.8x < 2.8x - 3.8$

    $x < -3.8$

28. $1.2x < 0.2x - 7.3$

    $x < -7.3$

29. $x + 5.8 \leq 4.6$

    $x \leq -1.2$

30. $n - 3.82 \leq 3.95$

    $n \leq 7.77$

31. $x - 3.5 < 2.1$

    $x < 5.6$

32. $x - 0.23 \leq 0.47$

    $x \leq 0.70$

4.4C Exercises

Solve and graph the solution set.

33. $8x \leq -24$

    $x \leq -3$

34. $5y \geq 15$

    $y \geq 3$

35. $24x > -48$

    $x > -2$

36. $3x > 0$

    $x > 0$

37. $-8x > 8$

    $x < -1$

38. $-2n \leq -8$

    $n \geq 4$

Solve.

39. $-5y \geq 20$

    $y \leq -4$

40. $3x < 5$

    $x < \frac{5}{3}$

41. $6x \leq -1$

    $x \leq -\frac{1}{6}$

42. $2x \leq -5$

    $x \leq -\frac{5}{2}$

43. $\frac{5}{6}n < 15$

    $n < 18$

44. $\frac{3}{4}x < 12$

    $x < 16$

45. $-\frac{2}{3}x \leq 4$

    $x \geq -6$

46. $-\frac{3}{7}x \leq 6$

    $x \geq -14$

47. $-\frac{2}{11}b \geq -6$

    $b \leq 33$

48. $-\frac{4}{7}x \geq -12$

    $x \leq 21$

49. $\frac{2}{3}n < \frac{1}{2}$

    $n < \frac{3}{4}$

50. $\frac{3}{5}x < \frac{7}{10}$

    $x < \frac{7}{6}$

51. $-\frac{2}{3}x \geq \frac{4}{7}$

    $x \leq -\frac{6}{7}$

52. $-\frac{3}{8}x \geq \frac{9}{14}$

    $x \leq -\frac{12}{7}$

53. $-\frac{3}{5}x < -\frac{6}{7}$

    $x > \frac{10}{7}$

54. $-\frac{4}{5}x < -\frac{8}{15}$

    $x > \frac{2}{3}$

55. $1.5x \leq 6.30$

    $x \leq 4.2$

56. $-3.5d > 7.35$

    $d < -2.1$

57. $4.25m > -34$

    $m > -8$

58. $-3.9x \geq -19.5$

    $x \leq 5$

Section 5   General Inequalities

Objective A   To solve general inequalities

Reference for
Computer
Tutor™

In solving an inequality, frequently the application of both the Addition and Multiplication Properties of Inequalities is required.

Solve: $3x - 2 < 5x + 4$

Step 1	Add the opposite of the variable term $5x$ to each side of the inequality. Simplify.	$3x - 2 < 5x + 4$ $3x + (-5x) - 2 < 5x + (-5x) + 4$ $-2x - 2 < 4$
Step 2	Add the opposite of the constant term -2 to each side of the inequality. Simplify.	$-2x - 2 + 2 < 4 + 2$ $-2x < 6$
Step 3	Multiply each side of the inequality by the reciprocal of the coefficient -2. Since $-\frac{1}{2}$ is a negative number, the inequality symbol must be reversed. Simplify.	$-\frac{1}{2}(-2x) > -\frac{1}{2}(6)$ $x > -3$

When an inequality contains parentheses, one of the steps in solving the inequality requires the use of the Distributive Property.

Solve: $-2(x - 7) > 3 - 4(2x - 3)$

Step 1	Use the Distributive Property to remove parentheses. Simplify.	$-2(x - 7) > 3 - 4(2x - 3)$ $-2x + 14 > 3 - 8x + 12$ $-2x + 14 > 15 - 8x$
Step 2	Add the opposite of the variable term $-8x$ to each side of the inequality. Simplify.	$-2x + 8x + 14 > 15 - 8x + 8x$ $6x + 14 > 15$
Step 3	Add the opposite of the constant term 14 to each side of the inequality. Simplify.	$6x + 14 + (-14) > 15 + (-14)$ $6x > 1$
Step 4	Multiply each side of the inequality by the reciprocal of the coefficient 6. Simplify.	$\frac{1}{6} \cdot 6x > \frac{1}{6} \cdot 1$ $x > \frac{1}{6}$

Example 1 Solve: $7x - 3 \le 3x + 17$

Solution
$$7x - 3 \le 3x + 17$$
$$7x + (-3x) - 3 \le 3x + (-3x) + 17$$
$$4x - 3 \le 17$$
$$4x - 3 + 3 \le 17 + 3$$
$$4x \le 20$$
$$\frac{1}{4} \cdot 4x \le \frac{1}{4} \cdot 20$$
$$x \le 5$$

Example 2 Solve: $5 - 4x > 9 - 8x$

Your solution

$$x > 1$$

Solution on p. A27

Example 3 Solve:
$$3(3 - 2x) \geq -5x - 2(3 - x)$$

Solution
$$3(3 - 2x) \geq -5x - 2(3 - x)$$
$$9 - 6x \geq -5x - 6 + 2x$$
$$9 - 6x \geq -3x - 6$$
$$9 - 6x + 3x \geq -3x + 3x - 6$$
$$9 - 3x \geq -6$$
$$9 + (-9) - 3x \geq -6 + (-9)$$
$$-3x \geq -15$$
$$-\frac{1}{3}(-3x) \leq -\frac{1}{3}(-15)$$
$$x \leq 5$$

Example 4 Solve:
$$8 - 4(3x + 5) \leq 6(x - 8)$$

Your solution

$$x \geq 2$$

Solution on p. A27

Objective B   To solve application problems

Example 5

A student must have at least 450 points out of 500 points on five tests to receive an A in a course. One student's results on the first four tests were 94, 87, 77, and 95. What scores on the last test will enable the student to receive an A in the course?

Strategy

To find the scores, write and solve an inequality using N to represent the score on the last test.

Solution

Total number of points on the 5 tests	is greater than or equal to	450

$$94 + 87 + 77 + 95 + N \geq 450$$
$$353 + N \geq 450$$
$$353 + (-353) + N \geq 450 + (-353)$$
$$N \geq 97$$

The student's score on the last test must be equal to or greater than 97.

Example 6

Company A rents cars for $8 a day and 10¢ for every mile driven. Company B rents cars for $10 a day and 8¢ per mile driven. You want to rent a car for one week. What is the maximum number of miles you can drive a Company A car if it is to cost you less than a Company B car?

Your strategy

Your solution

699 mi

Solution on p. A27

4.5A Exercises

Solve.

1. $4x - 8 < 2x$
$$x < 4$$

2. $7x - 4 < 3x$
$$x < 1$$

3. $2x - 8 > 4x$
$$x < -4$$

4. $3y - 5 \leq -7y$
$$y \leq \frac{1}{2}$$

5. $3y + 2 > 7y$
$$y < \frac{1}{2}$$

6. $8 - 3x \leq 5x$
$$x \geq 1$$

7. $10 - 3x \leq 7x$
$$x \geq 1$$

8. $6 - 4x > -8x$
$$x > -\frac{3}{2}$$

9. $3x + 2 \geq 5x - 8$
$$x \leq 5$$

10. $2n - 9 \geq 5n + 4$
$$n \leq -\frac{13}{3}$$

11. $5x - 2 < 3x - 2$
$$x < 0$$

12. $3x + 5 \geq 6x - 4$
$$x \leq 3$$

13. $4x - 3 < 5 - 8x$
$$x < \frac{2}{3}$$

14. $8x - 9 > 3x - 9$
$$x > 0$$

15. $0.1(180 + x) > x$
$$x < 20$$

16. $x > 0.2(50 + x)$
$$x > 12.5$$

17. $0.15x + 55 > 0.10x + 80$
$$x > 500$$

18. $-3.6b + 16 < 2.8b + 25.6$
$$b > -1.5$$

19. $2(3x - 1) > 3x + 4$
$$x > 2$$

20. $5(2x + 7) > -4x - 7$
$$x > -3$$

21. $3(2x - 5) \geq 8x - 5$
$$x \leq -5$$

22. $5x - 8 \geq 7x - 9$
$$x \leq \frac{1}{2}$$

23. $2(2y - 5) \leq 3(5 - 2y)$
$$y \leq \frac{5}{2}$$

24. $2(5x - 8) \leq 7(x - 3)$
$$x \leq -\frac{5}{3}$$

25. $5(2 - x) > 3(2x - 5)$
$$x < \frac{25}{11}$$

26. $4(3d - 1) > 3(2 - 5d)$
$$d > \frac{10}{27}$$

27. $5(x - 2) > 9x - 3(2x - 4)$
$$x > 11$$

28. $3x - 2(3x - 5) > 4(2x - 1)$
$$x < \frac{14}{11}$$

29. $4 - 3(3 - n) \leq 3(2 - 5n)$
$$n \leq \frac{11}{18}$$

30. $15 - 5(3 - 2x) \leq 4(x - 3)$
$$x \leq -2$$

31. $2x - 3(x - 4) \geq 4 - 2(x - 7)$
$$x \geq 6$$

32. $4 + 2(3 - 2y) \leq 4(3y - 5) - 6y$
$$y \geq 3$$

4.5B Exercises

Solve.

33. Eight less than a number is greater than ten. Find the smallest integer that will satisfy the inequality.

19

34. Four less than the product of six and a number is greater than three plus the product of five and the number. Find the smallest integer that will satisfy the inequality.

8

35. Three-eighths of a number is less than or equal to nine-sixteenths. Find the largest number that will satisfy the inequality.

$\frac{3}{2}$

36. Two-thirds of a number is greater than or equal to seven-twelfths. Find the smallest number that will satisfy the inequality.

$\frac{7}{8}$

37. A student must have at least 320 points out of 400 points on four tests to receive a B in a history course. One student's results on the first three tests were 82, 71, and 94. What scores on the last test will enable the student to receive at least a B in the course?

73 or better

38. A student received a 63, a 73, a 94, and an 80 on four tests in a psychology course. What scores on the last test will enable the student to receive a minimum of 400 points?

90 or better

39. A marketing representative receives payments of $1560, $1980, and $1270 in commissions during a three-month period. What is the minimum commission the marketing representative must earn during the fourth month in order to earn a minimum of $6000 during the four-month period?

$1190

40. A plumber's annual income for the last four years was $37,520, $29,860, $45,832, and $26,440. What is the minimum annual income the plumber must earn this year in order to have earned $150,000 during the five-year period?

$10,348

41. Five times the sum of a number and four is less than three times the number. Find the largest integer that will satisfy the inequality.

−11

42. The quotient of a number and two is less than twice the difference between the number and six. Find the smallest integer that will satisfy the inequality.

9

43. Company A rents cars for $12 a day and 12¢ for every mile driven. Company B rents cars for $30 per day with unlimited mileage. What is the maximum number of miles per day you can drive a Company A car if it is to cost you less than a Company B car?

149 mi

44. Company A rents cars for $15 a day and 10¢ for every mile driven. Company B rents cars for $35 a day with unlimited mileage. You want to rent a car for one week. What is the maximum number of miles you can drive a Company A car if it is to cost you less than a Company B car?

1399 mi

45. Company A rents cars for $12 a day and 12¢ for every mile driven. Company B rents cars for $8 a day and 20¢ per mile driven. You want to rent a car for one week. What is the maximum number of miles you can drive a Company B car if it is to cost you less than a Company A car?

349 mi

46. Company A rents cars for $10 a day and 20¢ for every mile driven. Company B rents cars for $20 a day and 10¢ for every mile driven. You want to rent a car for one week. What is the maximum number of miles you can drive a Company A car if it is to cost you less than a Company B car?

699 mi

Calculators and Computers

Solving equations is a *learned* skill and requires practice. To provide you with additional practice, the program SOLVE A FIRST-DEGREE EQUATION on the Student Disk will allow you to practice solving the following three types of equations:

1. $ax + b = c$

2. $ax + b = cx + d$

3. Equations with parentheses

After you select the type of equation you want to practice, a problem will be displayed on the screen. Using paper and pencil, solve the problem.

When you are ready, press the RETURN key and the complete solution will be displayed. Compare your solution with the displayed solution. Note that all answers are rounded to the nearest hundredth.

After you have completed a problem, you may continue practicing the type of problem you have selected, return to the main menu and select a different type of problem, or quit the program.

As you work the problems, remember the order in which the skills used to solve equations are used:

1. Remove parentheses.

2. Get all variable terms on one side of the equation and simplify.

3. Get all constant terms on the other side of the equation and simplify.

4. Multiply both sides of the equation by the reciprocal of the coefficient of the variable term.

To practice solving inequalities, use the program FIRST-DEGREE INEQUALITIES on the Student Disk. Three levels of difficulty are provided, with the first level being the easiest and the third level being the most difficult.

Once you choose the level of difficulty, the program will display a problem. Using paper and pencil, solve the inequality.

When you are ready, press the RETURN key and compare your solution with the one on the screen. Note that the answers are rounded to the nearest hundredth.

After you complete a problem, you may continue practicing at the same level, return to the main menu and select a different level of difficulty, or quit the program.

Chapter Summary

KEY WORDS

An **equation** expresses the equality of two mathematical expressions. A **solution** of an equation is a number that, when substituted for the variable, results in a true equation. To **solve** an equation means to find a solution of the equation. The goal is to rewrite the equation in the form **variable = constant.**

Consecutive integers are integers that follow one another in order.

Uniform motion means that an object at a constant speed moves in a straight line.

A **set** is a collection of objects. The objects in a set are called the **elements** of the set.

An **inequality** is an expression that contains the symbol $<$, $>$, $\le$, or $\ge$. The **solution set of an inequality** is a set of numbers, each element of which, when substituted for the variable, results in a true inequality.

ESSENTIAL RULES

Addition Property of Equations

The same number can be added to each side of an equation without changing the solution of the equation.
If $a = b$, then $a + c = b + c$.

Multiplication Property of Equations

Each side of an equation can be multiplied by the same nonzero number without changing the solution of the equation.
If $a = b$ and $c \ne 0$, then $ac = bc$.

Uniform Motion Equation

Distance = rate $\times$ time
$D = r \times t$

Addition Property of Inequalities

The same number can be added to each side of an inequality without changing the solution set of the inequality.
If $a > b$, then $a + c > b + c$.
If $a < b$, then $a + c < b + c$.

The Addition Property of Inequalities also holds true for an inequality containing the symbol $\ge$ or $\le$.

Multiplication Property of Inequalities

Rule 1 Each side of an inequality can be multiplied by the same **positive number** without changing the solution set of the inequality.
If $a > b$ and $c > 0$, then $ac > bc$.
If $a < b$ and $c > 0$, then $ac < bc$.

Rule 2 If each side of an inequality is multiplied by the same **negative number** and the inequality symbol is reversed, then the solution set of the inequality is not changed.
If $a > b$ and $c < 0$, then $ac < bc$.
If $a < b$ and $c < 0$, then $ac > bc$.

The Multiplication Property of Inequalities also holds true for an inequality containing the symbol $\ge$ or $\le$.

Review/Test

1. Is -2 a solution of $x^2 - 3x = 2x - 6$?
   no

2. Is $\frac{2}{3}$ a solution of $6x - 7 = 3 - 9x$?
   yes

3. Solve: $x - 3 = -8$
   -5

4. Solve: $\frac{3}{4}x = -9$
   -12

5. Solve: $3x - 5 = -14$
   -3

6. Solve: $7 - 4x = -13$
   5

7. Solve: $3x - 2 = 5x + 8$
   -5

8. Solve: $6 - 5x = 5x + 11$
   $-\frac{1}{2}$

9. Solve: $5x - 2(4x - 3) = 6x + 9$
   $-\frac{1}{3}$

10. Solve: $9 - 3(2x - 5) = 12 + 5x$
    $\frac{12}{11}$

11. Graph the solution set of $x > -2$.

    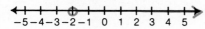

12. Solve and graph the solution set of $4 + x < 1$.

    $x < -3$

13. Solve: $x + \frac{1}{2} > \frac{5}{8}$

    $x > \frac{1}{8}$

14. Solve and graph the solution set of $\frac{2}{3}x \geq 2$.

    $x \geq 3$

15. Solve: $-\frac{3}{8}x \leq 5$

    $x \geq -\frac{40}{3}$

16. Solve: $3(2x - 5) \geq 8x - 9$

    $x \leq -3$

17. Solve: $6x - 3(2 - 3x) < 4(2x - 7)$

    $x < -\frac{22}{7}$

18. A lever is 30 ft long. A force of 20 lb is applied to one end of the lever and a force of 40 lb is applied to the other end. Where is the fulcrum located when the system balances? Use the lever system formula $F_1 \cdot x = F_2 \cdot (d - x)$.

    20 ft from 20-pound force

19. Translate "the difference between three times a number and fifteen is twenty-seven" into an equation and solve.

    $3n - 15 = 27$; $n = 14$

20. Find three consecutive odd integers such that three times the first integer is one less than the sum of the second and third integers.

    5, 7, 9

21. The age of a 20¢ stamp is 5 years, and the age of a 4¢ stamp is 35 years. In how many years will the 4¢ stamp be three times the age the 20¢ stamp will be then?

    10 years

22. Two planes start at the same point and fly in opposite directions. The first plane is flying 100 mph faster than the second plane. In three hours the two planes are 1050 mi apart. Find the rate of each plane.

    225 mph; 125 mph

23. Five more than a number is less than -3. Find the largest integer that will satisfy the inequality.

    -9

24. Four times the sum of a number and five is less than three times the number. Find the largest integer that will satisfy the inequality.

    -21

Cumulative Review/Test

1. Solve: $5x - 8 \le 4x + 1$
   $x \le 9$

2. Solve: $5x - 8 = 12x + 13$
   -3

3. Find the prime factorization of 160.
   $2 \cdot 2 \cdot 2 \cdot 2 \cdot 2 \cdot 5$

4. Graph the solution set of $4x > -8$.
   $x > -2$

5. Is -3 a solution of $x^2 + 6x + 9 = x + 3$?
   yes

6. Find the LCM of 9, 12, and 18.
   36

7. Divide: $8.09\overline{)16.0976}$
   Round to the nearest thousandth.
   1.990

8. Solve: $x - 4 = -9$
   -5

9. Evaluate $3(a - c) - 2ab$ when $a = 2$, $b = 3$, and $c = -4$.
   6

10. Solve: $-\frac{4}{5}x > 12$
    $x < -15$

11. Solve: $6 - 2(5x - 8) = 3x - 4$
    2

12. Find the GCF of 28 and 42.
    14

13. Solve: $7x - 8 = -2x$
    $\frac{8}{9}$

14. Simplify $2[5a - 3(2 - 5a) - 8]$.
    $40a - 28$

15. Subtract: $10\frac{1}{6} - 4\frac{5}{9}$
    $5\frac{11}{18}$

16. Solve: $15 - 3(5x - 7) < 2(7 - 2x)$
    $x > 2$

17. Simplify $2a - (-3b) - 7a - 5b$.
    $-5a - 2b$

18. Solve: $\frac{3}{5}x = -15$
    -25

19. Divide: $3\frac{1}{3} \div \frac{5}{7}$
    $4\frac{2}{3}$

20. Translate "the difference between twelve and the product of five and a number is negative eighteen" into an equation and solve.
    $12 - 5x = -18$; $x = 6$

21. A lever is 40 ft long. A force of 25 lb is applied to one end of the lever and a force of 15 lb is applied to the other end. Find the location of the fulcrum when the system balances. Use the lever system formula $F_1 \cdot x = F_2 \cdot (d - x)$.
    15 ft from the 25-pound force

22. Three times the second of three consecutive even integers is 14 more than the sum of the first and third integers. Find the middle even integer.
    14

23. The age of a gold coin is 17 years, and the age of a silver coin is 42 years. In how many years will the silver coin be twice the age the gold coin will be then?
    8 years

24. Company A rents cars for $6 a day and 25¢ for every mile driven. Company B rents cars for $15 a day and 10¢ per mile. You want to rent a car for 6 days. What is the maximum number of miles you can drive a Company A car if it is to cost you less than a Company B car?
    359 mi

chapter 5 Proportion and Percent

Objectives

5.1A   To write the ratio of two quantities in simplest form

5.1B   To write unit rates

5.1C   To solve a proportion

5.1D   To solve application problems

5.2A   To write a percent as a fraction or a decimal

5.2B   To write a fraction or a decimal as a percent

5.3A   To solve the basic percent equation

5.3B   To solve percent problems using proportions

5.3C   To solve application problems

5.4A   To solve investment problems

5.4B   To solve value mixture problems

5.4C   To solve percent mixture problems

Section 1 — Ratio, Rate, and Proportion

Objective A   ## To write the ratio of two quantities in simplest form

Reference for
Computer
Tutor™

Quantities such as 3 feet, 12 cents, or 9 cars are number quantities written with **units.**

$$
\left.
\begin{array}{l}
3 \text{ feet} \\
12 \text{ cents} \\
9 \text{ cars}
\end{array}
\right\} \text{units}
$$

These are only some examples of units. Shirts, dollars, trees, miles, and gallons are further examples.

A **ratio** is the comparison of two quantities that have the *same* units. This comparison can be written in three different ways:

1. as a fraction,
2. as two numbers separated by a colon (:),
3. as two numbers separated by the word TO.

Therefore, the ratio of the lengths of two boards, one 8 ft long and the other 10 ft long, can be written:

1. $\dfrac{8\,\text{ft}}{10\,\text{ft}} = \dfrac{8}{10} = \dfrac{4}{5}$
2. $8\,\text{ft}{:}10\,\text{ft} = 8{:}10 = 4{:}5$
3. $8\,\text{ft TO } 10\,\text{ft} = 8 \text{ TO } 10 = 4 \text{ TO } 5$

A ratio is in **simplest form** when the two numbers do not have a common factor. Notice that the units are not written.

This ratio means that the smaller board is $\dfrac{4}{5}$ the length of the longer board.

Example 1	Write the comparison $6 to $8 as a ratio in simplest form using a fraction.	**Example 2**	Write the comparison 20 lb to 24 lb as a ratio in simplest form using a fraction.
Solution	$\dfrac{\$6}{\$8} = \dfrac{6}{8} = \dfrac{3}{4}$	**Your solution**	$\dfrac{5}{6}$

Solution on p. A29

Objective B   ## To write unit rates

Reference for
Computer
Tutor™

A **rate** is a comparison of two quantities that have different units. A rate is written as a fraction.

A distance runner ran 26 mi in 4 hours. The distance-to-time rate is written:

$$\frac{26\,\text{mi}}{4\,\text{hours}} = \frac{13\,\text{mi}}{2\,\text{hours}}$$

A rate is in **simplest form** when the numbers that form the rate have no common factors. Notice that the units are written as part of the rate.

A **unit rate** is a rate in which the number in the denominator is 1.

$\frac{\$3.25}{1\,lb}$ or \$3.25/lb is read "\$3.25 per pound."

To find a unit rate, divide the number in the numerator of the rate by the number in the denominator of the rate.

A car traveled 344 mi on 16 gal of gasoline. To find the miles per gallon (the unit rate), divide the numerator of the rate by the denominator of the rate.

$\frac{344\,mi}{16\,gal}$ is the rate.

$$16\overline{)344.0}^{21.5}$$

21.5 mi/gal is the unit rate.

Example 3	Write "300 ft in 8 seconds" as a unit rate.	**Example 4**	Write "260 mi in 8 hours" as a unit rate.
Solution	$\frac{300\,ft}{8\,seconds}$	**Your solution**	32.5 mi/hour
	$8\overline{)300.0}^{37.5}$		
	37.5 ft/second		

Solution on p. A29

Objective C   To solve a proportion

Reference for
Computer
Tutor™

A **proportion** is an equation that states the equality of two ratios or rates.

$\frac{30\,mi}{4\,hours} = \frac{15\,mi}{2\,hours}$

Note that the units of the numerators are the same and the units of the denominators are the same.

$\frac{3}{5} = \frac{9}{15}$

In a proportion, the "cross products" are equal. For the proportion $\frac{2}{3} = \frac{8}{12}$,

$$\frac{2}{3} \times \frac{8}{12} \Rightarrow \begin{array}{l} 3 \times 8 = 24 \\ 2 \times 12 = 24 \end{array}$$

Sometimes one of the numbers in a proportion is unknown. In this case, it is necessary to *solve* the proportion.

Solve the proportion $\frac{4}{x} = \frac{2}{3}$.

$$\frac{4}{x} = \frac{2}{3}$$

Find the cross products.

$$4 \cdot 3 = x \cdot 2$$

Solve for x.

$$12 = 2x$$
$$6 = x$$

The solution is 6.

Example 5 Solve $\frac{x}{12} = \frac{25}{60}$ and check.

Solution
$$x \cdot 60 = 12 \cdot 25$$
$$60x = 300$$
$$x = 5$$

Check:

$$\frac{5}{12} \diagdown \frac{25}{60} \Rightarrow 12 \times 25 = 300$$
$$5 \times 60 = 300$$

The solution is 5.

Example 6 Solve $\frac{x}{14} = \frac{3}{7}$ and check.

Your solution

6

Example 7 Solve $\frac{4}{9} = \frac{x}{16}$.
Round to the nearest tenth.

Solution
$$4 \cdot 16 = 9 \cdot x$$
$$64 = 9x$$
$$7.1 \approx x$$

Note: A rounded answer is an approximation. Therefore, the answer to a check will not be exact.

The solution is 7.1.

Example 8 Solve $\frac{5}{8} = \frac{x}{20}$.
Round to the nearest tenth.

Your solution

12.5

Solutions on p. A29

Example 9   Solve $\dfrac{8}{x+3} = \dfrac{4}{x}$.

Solution
$$8 \cdot x = 4(x+3)$$
$$8x = 4x + 12$$
$$4x = 12$$
$$x = 3$$

The solution is 3.

Example 10   Solve $\dfrac{2}{x+3} = \dfrac{6}{5x+5}$.

Your solution

2

Solution on p. A29

Objective D   To solve application problems

Example 11   The cost of building a patio cover was $450 for labor and $800 for materials. What is the ratio, as a fraction in simplest form, of the cost of materials to the total cost for labor and materials?

Strategy   To find the ratio, write the ratio of the cost of materials ($450) to the total cost ($450 + $800) in simplest form.

Solution
$$\frac{\$450}{\$450 + \$800} = \frac{450}{1250} = \frac{9}{25}$$

The ratio is $\dfrac{9}{25}$.

Example 12   A company spends $20,000 a month for television advertising and $15,000 a month for radio advertising. What is the ratio, as a fraction in simplest form, of the cost of radio advertising to the total cost of radio and television advertising?

Your strategy

Your solution

$\dfrac{3}{7}$

Example 13   A grocery store sells 3 tomatoes for 98 cents. What is the cost per tomato to the nearest tenth of a cent?

Strategy   To find the cost per tomato, divide the cost for 3 tomatoes (98¢) by the number of tomatoes (3).

Solution
$$\begin{array}{r} 32.66 \approx 32.7 \\ 3)\overline{98.00} \end{array}$$

The cost is 32.7¢ per tomato.

Example 14   A cyclist rode 47 mi in 3 hours. What is the miles-per-hour rate to the nearest tenth?

Your strategy

Your solution

15.7 mi/hour

Solutions on p. A29

Example 15   The dosage of a certain medication is 2 oz for every 50 lb of body weight. How many ounces of this medication are required for a person who weighs 175 lb?

Strategy   To find the number of ounces required, write and solve a proportion using n to represent the number of ounces of medication for a 175-pound person.

Solution
$$\frac{2 \text{ oz}}{50 \text{ lb}} = \frac{n \text{ oz}}{175 \text{ lb}}$$
$$2 \cdot 175 = 50 \cdot n$$
$$350 = 50n$$
$$7 = n$$

For a 175-pound person, 7 oz of medication are required.

Example 16   Three tablespoons of a liquid plant fertilizer are to be added to every 4 gal of water. How many tablespoons of fertilizer are required for 10 gal of water?

Your strategy

Your solution

7.5 tablespoons

Example 17   An investment of $500 earns $60 each year. At the same rate, how much additional money must be invested to earn $90 each year?

Strategy   To find the additional amount of money that must be invested, write and solve a proportion using x to represent the additional money. Then $500 + x$ is the total amount invested.

Solution
$$\frac{\$60}{\$500} = \frac{\$90}{\$500 + x}$$
$$60(500 + x) = 500(90)$$
$$30{,}000 + 60x = 45{,}000$$
$$60x = 15{,}000$$
$$x = 250$$

An additional $250 must be invested.

Example 18   Three ounces of medication are required for a 150-pound adult. At the same rate, how many additional ounces of medication are required for a 200-pound adult?

Your strategy

Your solution

1 additional ounce

Solutions on p. A30

5.1A Exercises

Write the comparison as a ratio in simplest form using a fraction, a colon (:), and the word TO.

1. 3 qt to 15 qt
$\frac{1}{5}$; 1:5; 1 to 5

2. 6 lb to 8 lb
$\frac{3}{4}$; 3:4; 3 to 4

3. $40 to $20
$\frac{2}{1}$; 2:1; 2 to 1

4. 10 ft to 2 ft
$\frac{5}{1}$; 5:1; 5 to 1

5. 6 mi to 6 mi
$\frac{1}{1}$; 1:1; 1 to 1

6. 8 days to 12 days
$\frac{2}{3}$; 2:3; 2 to 3

7. 35 cents to 50 cents
$\frac{7}{10}$; 7:10; 7 to 10

8. 28 in. to 36 in.
$\frac{7}{9}$; 7:9; 7 to 9

9. 30 m to 60 m
$\frac{1}{2}$; 1:2; 1 to 2

10. 25 gal to 100 gal
$\frac{1}{4}$; 1:4; 1 to 4

11. 32 oz to 16 oz
$\frac{2}{1}$; 2:1; 2 to 1

12. 12 L to 4 L
$\frac{3}{1}$; 3:1; 3 to 1

Write the comparison as a ratio in simplest form using a fraction.

13. 12 m to 18 m
$\frac{2}{3}$

14. $20 to $28
$\frac{5}{7}$

15. 8 tons to 16 tons
$\frac{1}{2}$

16. 8 mi to 40 mi
$\frac{1}{5}$

17. 27 yd to 18 yd
$\frac{3}{2}$

18. 28 km to 20 km
$\frac{7}{5}$

5.1B Exercises

Write as a unit rate.

19. 10 ft in 4 seconds
2.5 ft/second

20. 816 mi in 6 days
136 mi/day

21. $1300 earned in 4 weeks
$325/week

22. 1100 trees on 10 acres
110 trees/acre

23. 3750 words on 15 pages
250 words/page

24. $32.97 earned in 7 hours
$4.71/hour

25. 628.8 mi in 12 hours
52.4 mi/hour

26. 388.8 mi in 8 hours
48.6 mi/hour

27. 344.4 mi on 12.3 gal
28 mi/gal

28. 409.40 mi on 11.5 gal
35.6 mi/gal

29. $349.80 for 212 lb
$1.65/lb

30. $11.05 for 3.4 lb
$3.25/lb

5.1C Exercises

Solve. Round to the nearest tenth.

31. $\dfrac{x}{12} = \dfrac{3}{4}$

9

32. $\dfrac{6}{x} = \dfrac{2}{3}$

9

33. $\dfrac{4}{9} = \dfrac{x}{27}$

12

34. $\dfrac{16}{9} = \dfrac{64}{x}$

36

35. $\dfrac{n}{45} = \dfrac{17}{135}$

5.7

36. $\dfrac{n}{5} = \dfrac{7}{8}$

4.4

37. $\dfrac{4}{n} = \dfrac{9}{5}$

2.2

38. $\dfrac{8}{5} = \dfrac{n}{6}$

9.6

39. $\dfrac{n}{11} = \dfrac{32}{4}$

88

40. $\dfrac{3}{4} = \dfrac{8}{n}$

10.7

41. $\dfrac{5}{12} = \dfrac{n}{8}$

3.3

42. $\dfrac{36}{20} = \dfrac{12}{n}$

6.7

43. $\dfrac{15}{n} = \dfrac{65}{100}$

23.1

44. $\dfrac{n}{15} = \dfrac{21}{12}$

26.3

45. $\dfrac{40}{n} = \dfrac{15}{8}$

21.3

46. $\dfrac{32}{n} = \dfrac{1}{3}$

96

47. $\dfrac{x+3}{12} = \dfrac{5}{6}$

7

48. $\dfrac{3}{5} = \dfrac{x-4}{10}$

10

49. $\dfrac{18}{x+4} = \dfrac{9}{5}$

6

50. $\dfrac{2}{11} = \dfrac{20}{x-3}$

113

51. $\dfrac{2}{x} = \dfrac{4}{x+1}$

1

52. $\dfrac{16}{x-2} = \dfrac{8}{x}$

−2

53. $\dfrac{x+3}{4} = \dfrac{x}{8}$

−6

54. $\dfrac{x-6}{3} = \dfrac{x}{5}$

15

55. $\dfrac{2}{x-1} = \dfrac{6}{2x+1}$

4

56. $\dfrac{9}{x+2} = \dfrac{3}{x-2}$

4

57. $\dfrac{x+3}{5} = \dfrac{3}{4}$

0.8

58. $\dfrac{2x}{7} = \dfrac{x-2}{14}$

−0.7

59. $\dfrac{4}{x} = \dfrac{7}{x+2}$

2.7

60. $\dfrac{5}{x+3} = \dfrac{2}{x-1}$

3.7

5.1D Exercises

Solve.

61. One computer prints 80 letters on one line while a second computer prints 96 letters on one line. Write the ratio of the number of letters per line of the first computer to the number of letters per line of the second computer as a fraction in simplest form.

$\dfrac{5}{6}$

62. The average annual rainfall in one Washington city is 75 in. A second city in Washington has an average annual rainfall of 25 in. Write the ratio of the average rainfall of the second city to the average rainfall of the first city as a fraction in simplest form.

$\dfrac{1}{3}$

Solve.

63. A house had an original value of $90,000 but increased in value to $126,000 in two years.
    a. What is the amount of increase?
    b. What is the ratio of the increase to the original value?

    a. $36,000

    b. $\frac{2}{5}$

64. The original value of a compact car was $9600. Two years later the car had a value of $4200.
    a. What is the amount of decrease?
    b. What is the ratio of the decrease in value to the original value?

    a. $5400

    b. $\frac{9}{16}$

65. A chef earns $100 in 8 hours. What is the chef's wage per hour?

    $12.50

66. A mechanic earns $18,000 in 12 months. What is the mechanic's wage per month?

    $1500

67. Five quarts of oil cost $4.80. What is the cost per quart?

    $.96

68. Twenty feet of lumber cost $138.40. What is the cost per foot?

    $6.92

69. An investor purchased 350 shares of stock for $12,600. Find the cost per share.

    $36

70. You own 300 shares of Lumex stock and receive a dividend of $729.00. Find the dividend per share.

    $2.43

71. A company's cost to produce 1000 ballpoint pens was $250. The company sold the pens to a retail store for $450. What was the company's profit per pen?

    $.20

72. A florist purchased 150 roses for $405. During one week, the florist sold all the roses and received $825. What was the florist's profit per rose?

    $2.80

73. A salt water solution is made by dissolving 2 lb of salt in 5 gal of water. At this rate, how many pounds of salt are required for 25 gal of water?

    10 lb

74. A building contractor estimates that three overhead lights are needed for every 250 ft² of floor space. Using this estimate, how many light fixtures are necessary for a 10,000-square-foot office building?

    120

75. A pre-election survey showed that 2 out of every 5 voters would vote in an election. At this rate, how many people would be expected to vote in a city of 25,000?

    10,000 people

76. A quality control inspector found 2 defective electric blenders in a shipment of 100 blenders. At this rate, how many blenders would be defective in a shipment of 5000?

    100

Solve.

77. A landscape designer estimates that 6 pieces of lumber are necessary for each 25 ft² of patio wood decking. Using this estimate, how many square feet of decking can be made from 36 pieces of lumber?

150 ft²

78. A carpet manufacturer uses 2 lb of wool for every 3 lb of nylon in a certain grade of carpet. At this rate, how many pounds of nylon are required for 250 lb of wool?

375 lb

79. The license fee for a car that cost $5500 was $66. At the same rate, what is the license fee for a car that costs $7500?

$90

80. The real estate tax for a home that costs $75,000 is $750. At this rate, what is the cost of a home for which the real estate tax is $562.50?

$56,250

81. In a wildlife preserve, 16 deer are captured, tagged, and then released. Later, 30 deer are captured. Two of the 30 are found to have tags. Estimate the number of deer in the preserve.

240 deer

82. In a lake, 50 fish are caught, tagged, and then released. Later 70 fish are caught. Five of the 70 are found to have tags. Estimate the number of fish in the lake.

700

83. A liquid plant food is prepared by using 1 gal of water for each 2 oz of plant food. At this rate, how many ounces of plant food are required for 4 gal of water?

8 oz

84. The directions on a bag of lawn fertilizer recommend 2 lb of fertilizer for every 100 ft² of lawn. At this rate, how many pounds of fertilizer are used on a lawn that measures 2500 ft²?

50 lb

85. The scale on a map is 1 in. equals 6 mi. What is the distance between two points that measure 7 in. on the map?

42 mi

86. The scale on the plans for a new house is 1 in. equals 2 ft. How long is a room that measures $5\frac{1}{2}$ in. on the drawing?

11 ft

87. A stock investment of 100 shares paid a dividend of $124. At this rate, how many additional shares are required to earn a dividend of $186?

50 shares

88. A chef estimates that 50 lb of vegetables will serve 130 people. Using this estimate, how many additional pounds will be necessary to serve 156 people?

10 lb

89. A caterer estimates that 3 gal of fruit punch will serve 40 people. How much additional punch is necessary to serve 60 people?

$1\frac{1}{2}$ gal

90. A farmer estimates that 5600 bushels of wheat can be harvested from 160 acres of land. Using this estimate, how many additional acres are needed to harvest 8120 bushels of wheat?

72 acres

Section **2**   # Introduction to Percent

Objective A   ## To write a percent as a fraction or a decimal

Reference for
Computer
Tutor™

"A population growth rate of 3%," "a manufacturer's discount of 25%," and "an 8% increase in pay" are typical examples of the many ways in which percent is used in applied problems. **Percent** means "parts of 100." Thus, 27% means 27 parts of 100.

In applied problems involving a percent, it is usually necessary either to rewrite the percent as a fraction or a decimal, or to rewrite a fraction or a decimal as a percent.

To write a percent as a fraction, drop the percent sign and multiply by $\frac{1}{100}$.

Write 27% as a fraction.

Drop the percent sign and multiply by $\frac{1}{100}$. $27\% = 27\left(\frac{1}{100}\right) = \frac{27}{100}$

To write a percent as a decimal, drop the percent sign and multiply by 0.01.

Write 33% as a decimal.

Drop the percent sign. $33\% \quad = \quad 33(0.01) \quad = \quad 0.33$
Then multiply by 0.01.

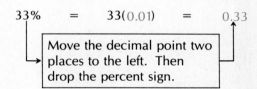
Move the decimal point two places to the left. Then drop the percent sign.

Example 1   Write 130% as a fraction and as a decimal.

Solution $130\% = 130\left(\frac{1}{100}\right) = \frac{130}{100} = 1\frac{3}{10}$
$130\% = 130(0.01) = 1.30$

Example 2   Write 125% as a fraction and as a decimal.

Your solution $1\frac{1}{4} \; ; \; 1.25$

Example 3   Write $33\frac{1}{3}\%$ as a fraction.

Solution $33\frac{1}{3}\% = 33\frac{1}{3}\left(\frac{1}{100}\right) = \frac{100}{3}\left(\frac{1}{100}\right) = \frac{1}{3}$

Example 4   Write $16\frac{2}{3}\%$ as a fraction.

Your solution $\frac{1}{6}$

Example 5   Write 0.25% as a decimal.

Solution $0.25\% = 0.25(0.01) = 0.0025$

Example 6   Write 0.5% as a decimal.

Your solution 0.005

Solutions on p. A30

Reference for
Computer
Tutor™

Objective B   To write a fraction or a decimal as a percent

A fraction or decimal can be written as a percent by multiplying by 100%.

Write $\frac{5}{8}$ as a percent.

Multiply by 100%.

$$\frac{5}{8} = \frac{5}{8}(100\%) = \frac{500}{8}\% = 62.5\% \text{ or } 62\frac{1}{2}\%$$

Write 0.82 as a percent.

Multiply by 100%.

$$0.82 = 0.82(100\%) = 82\%$$

Move the decimal point two places to the right. Then write the percent sign.

Example 7   Write 0.027 as a percent.

Solution $0.027 = 0.027(100\%) = 2.7\%$

Example 8   Write 0.043 as a percent.

Your solution
                  4.3 %

Example 9   Write 1.34 as a percent.

Solution $1.34 = 1.34(100\%) = 134\%$

Example 10   Write 2.57 as a percent.

Your solution
                  257 %

Example 11   Write $\frac{5}{6}$ as a percent. Round to the nearest tenth of a percent.

Solution $\frac{5}{6} = \frac{5}{6}(100\%) = \frac{500}{6}\% \approx 83.3\%$

Example 12   Write $\frac{5}{9}$ as a percent. Round to the nearest tenth of a percent.

Your solution
                  55.6 %

Example 13   Write $\frac{7}{16}$ as a percent. Write the remainder in fractional form.

Solution $\frac{7}{16} = \frac{7}{16}(100\%) = \frac{700}{16}\% = 43\frac{3}{4}\%$

Example 14   Write $\frac{9}{16}$ as a percent. Write the remainder in fractional form.

Your solution
                  56$\frac{1}{4}$ %

Solutions on p. A30

5.2A Exercises

Write as a fraction and as a decimal.

1. 75%
$\frac{3}{4}$; 0.75

2. 40%
$\frac{2}{5}$; 0.40

3. 50%
$\frac{1}{2}$; 0.50

4. 10%
$\frac{1}{10}$; 0.10

5. 120%
$1\frac{1}{5}$; 1.20

6. 25%
$\frac{1}{4}$; 0.25

7. 150%
$1\frac{1}{2}$; 1.50

8. 100%
1 ; 1.00

9. 64%
$\frac{16}{25}$; 0.64

10. 88%
$\frac{22}{25}$; 0.88

11. 160%
$1\frac{3}{5}$; 1.60

12. 45%
$\frac{9}{20}$; 0.45

13. 70%
$\frac{7}{10}$; 0.70

14. 55%
$\frac{11}{20}$; 0.55

15. 32%
$\frac{8}{25}$; 0.32

16. 19%
$\frac{19}{100}$; 0.19

17. 87%
$\frac{87}{100}$; 0.87

18. 5%
$\frac{1}{20}$; 0.05

19. 2%
$\frac{1}{50}$; 0.02

20. 450%
$4\frac{1}{2}$; 4.50

21. 380%
$3\frac{4}{5}$; 3.80

22. 8%
$\frac{2}{25}$; 0.08

23. 4%
$\frac{1}{25}$; 0.04

24. 18%
$\frac{9}{50}$; 0.18

Write as a fraction.

25. $11\frac{1}{9}$%
$\frac{1}{9}$

26. $4\frac{2}{7}$%
$\frac{3}{70}$

27. $12\frac{1}{2}$%
$\frac{1}{8}$

28. $37\frac{1}{2}$%
$\frac{3}{8}$

29. $31\frac{1}{4}$%
$\frac{5}{16}$

30. $3\frac{1}{8}$%
$\frac{1}{32}$

31. $66\frac{2}{3}$%
$\frac{2}{3}$

32. $45\frac{5}{11}$%
$\frac{5}{11}$

33. $15\frac{3}{8}$%
$\frac{123}{800}$

34. $\frac{3}{8}$%
$\frac{3}{800}$

35. $6\frac{2}{3}$%
$\frac{1}{15}$

36. $\frac{1}{4}$%
$\frac{1}{400}$

37. $\frac{1}{2}$%
$\frac{1}{200}$

38. $5\frac{3}{4}$%
$\frac{23}{400}$

39. $68\frac{3}{4}$%
$\frac{11}{16}$

40. $6\frac{1}{4}$%
$\frac{1}{16}$

41. $83\frac{1}{3}$%
$\frac{5}{6}$

42. $8\frac{2}{3}$%
$\frac{13}{150}$

Write as a decimal.

43. 7.3%
0.073

44. 9.1%
0.091

45. 15.8%
0.158

46. 16.7%
0.167

47. 0.3%
0.003

48. 0.9%
0.009

49. 9.15%
0.0915

50. 121.2%
1.212

51. 18.23%
0.1823

52. 62.14%
0.6214

53. 0.15%
0.0015

54. 0.27%
0.0027

55. 6.5%
0.065

56. 12.3%
0.123

57. 2%
0.02

58. 8.25%
0.0825

59. 5.05%
0.0505

60. 80.4%
0.804

5.2B Exercises

Write as a percent.

61. 0.15
15%

62. 0.37
37%

63. 0.05
5%

64. 0.02
2%

65. 0.175
17.5%

66. 0.125
12.5%

67. 1.15
115%

68. 1.36
136%

69. 0.62
62%

70. 0.96
96%

71. 3.165
316.5%

72. 2.142
214.2%

73. 0.008
0.8%

74. 0.004
0.4%

75. 0.065
6.5%

76. 0.083
8.3%

77. 0.73
73%

78. 0.13
13%

79. 0.7
70%

80. 0.2
20%

81. 1.03
103%

82. 2.09
209%

83. 1.012
101.2%

84. 3.106
310.6%

Write as a percent. Round to the nearest tenth.

85. $\frac{27}{50}$
54%

86. $\frac{83}{100}$
83%

87. $\frac{1}{3}$
33.3%

88. $\frac{3}{8}$
37.5%

89. $\frac{5}{11}$
45.5%

90. $\frac{4}{9}$
44.4%

91. $\frac{7}{8}$
87.5%

92. $\frac{9}{20}$
45%

93. $1\frac{2}{3}$
166.7%

94. $2\frac{1}{2}$
250%

95. $1\frac{2}{7}$
128.6%

96. $1\frac{11}{12}$
191.7%

97. $\frac{37}{100}$
37%

98. $\frac{2}{5}$
40%

99. $\frac{1}{8}$
12.5%

100. $\frac{1}{6}$
16.7%

101. $\frac{7}{40}$
17.5%

102. $1\frac{7}{9}$
177.8%

Write as a percent. Write the remainder in fractional form.

103. $\frac{17}{50}$
34%

104. $\frac{17}{25}$
68%

105. $\frac{3}{8}$
$37\frac{1}{2}$%

106. $\frac{9}{16}$
$56\frac{1}{4}$%

107. $\frac{5}{14}$
$35\frac{5}{7}$%

108. $\frac{3}{19}$
$15\frac{15}{19}$%

109. $\frac{3}{16}$
$18\frac{3}{4}$%

110. $\frac{4}{7}$
$57\frac{1}{7}$%

111. $1\frac{1}{4}$
125%

112. $2\frac{5}{8}$
$262\frac{1}{2}$%

113. $1\frac{5}{9}$
$155\frac{5}{9}$%

114. $1\frac{13}{16}$
$181\frac{1}{4}$%

115. $\frac{15}{50}$
30%

116. $\frac{12}{25}$
48%

117. $\frac{7}{30}$
$23\frac{1}{3}$%

118. $\frac{1}{3}$
$33\frac{1}{3}$%

119. $\frac{3}{11}$
$27\frac{3}{11}$%

120. $\frac{2}{9}$
$22\frac{2}{9}$%

Section **3**   The Percent Equation

Objective A   To solve the basic percent equation

Reference for
Computer
Tutor™

The solution of a problem that involves a percent requires solving the basic percent equation shown at the right.	**BASIC PERCENT EQUATION**
	Percent × Base = Amount
	$P \quad \times \quad B \quad = \quad A$

In any percent problem, two parts of the equation are given, and one is unknown.

To translate a problem involving a percent into an equation, remember that the word "of" translates to "multiply" and the word "is" translates to "=." The base usually follows the word "of."

20% of what number is 30?

Given: $P = 20\% = 0.20$
$\quad\quad\quad A = 30$
Unknown: Base

$$P \times B = A$$
$$(0.20)B = 30$$
$$\frac{1}{0.20}(0.20)B = \frac{1}{0.20}(30)$$
$$B = 150$$

The number is 150.

Find 25% of 200.

Given: $P = 25\% = 0.25$
$\quad\quad\quad B = 200$
Unknown: Amount

$$P \times B = A$$
$$0.25(200) = A$$
$$50 = A$$

25% of 200 is 50.

In most cases, the percent is written as a decimal before solving the basic percent equation. However, some percents are more easily written as a fraction. For example,

$$33\frac{1}{3}\% = \frac{1}{3} \qquad 66\frac{2}{3}\% = \frac{2}{3} \qquad 16\frac{2}{3}\% = \frac{1}{6} \qquad 83\frac{1}{3}\% = \frac{5}{6}$$

Example 1   12 is $33\frac{1}{3}\%$ of what number?

Solution

$$12 = \frac{1}{3}B \quad \left(33\frac{1}{3}\% = \frac{1}{3}\right)$$
$$3 \cdot 12 = 3 \cdot \frac{1}{3}B$$
$$36 = B$$

The number is 36.

Example 2   27 is what percent of 60?

Your solution

45%

Solution on p. A31

Reference for
Computer
Tutor™

Objective B — To solve percent problems using proportions

The percent problems in the last objective were solved using the basic percent equation. Those problems can also be solved using proportions.

The proportion method is based on writing two ratios. One ratio is the percent ratio, written as $\frac{percent}{100}$. The second ratio is the amount-to-base ratio, written as $\frac{amount}{base}$. These two ratios form the proportion

$$\frac{percent}{100} = \frac{amount}{base}$$

To use the proportion method, first identify the percent, the amount, and the base (the base usually follows the phrase "percent of").

What is 23% of 45?	What percent of 25 is 4?	12 is 60% of what number?
$\frac{23}{100} = \frac{n}{45}$	$\frac{n}{100} = \frac{4}{25}$	$\frac{60}{100} = \frac{12}{n}$
$23 \cdot 45 = 100 \cdot n$	$n \cdot 25 = 100 \cdot 4$	$60 \cdot n = 100 \cdot 12$
$1035 = 100n$	$25n = 400$	$60n = 1200$
$10.35 = n$	$n = 16$	$n = 20$

Example 3 15% of what is 7? Round to the nearest hundredth.

Solution
$$\frac{15}{100} = \frac{7}{n}$$
$$15 \cdot n = 100 \cdot 7$$
$$15n = 700$$
$$n \approx 46.67$$

The number is 46.67

Example 4 26% of what is 22? Round to the nearest hundredth.

Your solution

84.62

Example 5 30% of 63 is what?

Solution
$$\frac{30}{100} = \frac{n}{63}$$
$$30 \cdot 63 = 100 \cdot n$$
$$1890 = 100n$$
$$18.90 = n$$

The number is 18.90

Example 6 16% of 132 is what?

Your solution

21.12

Solutions on p. A31

Reference for
Computer
Tutor™

Objective C   To solve application problems

The key to solving a percent problem is identifying the percent, the base, and the amount. The base usually follows the word "of."

Examples 7, 8, 9, and 10 below are solved using the basic percent equation. Examples 11, 12, 13, and 14 on the next page are solved using proportions.

Example 7   A student answered 76 of the 80 questions on a test correctly. What percent of the questions were answered correctly?

Strategy   To find the percent of the questions answered correctly, solve the basic percent equation using $B = 80$ and $A = 76$. The percent is unknown.

Solution

$$P \times B = A$$
$$P(80) = 76$$
$$P(80)\left(\frac{1}{80}\right) = 76\left(\frac{1}{80}\right)$$
$$P = 0.95$$

95% of the questions were answered correctly.

Example 8   A quality control inspector found that 6 out of 200 wheel bearings inspected were defective. What percent of the wheel bearings were defective?

Your strategy

Your solution

3%

Example 9   A new labor contract increased an employee's hourly wage by 5%. What is the amount of increase for an employee who was making $9.60 an hour?

Strategy   To find the amount of increase, solve the basic percent equation using $B = 9.60$ and $P = 5\% = 0.05$. The amount is unknown.

Solution

$$P \times B = A$$
$$(0.05)(9.60) = A$$
$$0.48 = A$$

The amount of increase is $.48.

Example 10   A company was producing 2500 gal of paint each week. Due to a decrease in demand for the paint, the company reduced its weekly production by 500 gal. What percent decrease does this represent?

Your strategy

Your solution

20%

Copyright © 1989 HMCo

Solutions on pp. A31–32

Example 11   An antique dealer found that 86% of the 250 items that were sold during one month sold for under $1000. How many items sold for under $1000?

Strategy   To find the number of items that sold for under $1000, write and solve a proportion using n to represent the number of items sold for under $1000 (amount). The percent is 86% and the base is 250.

Solution
$$\frac{86}{100} = \frac{n}{250}$$
$$86 \cdot 250 = 100 \cdot n$$
$$21{,}500 = 100n$$
$$215 = n$$

215 items sold for under $1000.

Example 12   Last year it snowed 64% of the 150 days of the ski season at a resort. How many days did it snow?

Your strategy

Your solution
96 days

Example 13   In a test of the strength of nylon rope, 5 pieces of the 25 pieces tested did not meet the test standards. What percent of the nylon ropes tested did meet the standards?

Strategy   To find the percent of ropes tested that met the standards:
▷ Find the number of ropes that met the test standards (25 − 5).
▷ Write and solve a proportion using n to represent the percent of ropes that met the test standards. The base is 25. The amount is the number of ropes that met the standards.

Solution   25 − 5 = 20 ropes met test standards
$$\frac{n}{100} = \frac{20}{25}$$
$$n \cdot 25 = 100 \cdot 20$$
$$25n = 2000$$
$$n = 80$$

80% of the ropes tested did meet the test standards.

Example 14   Five ballpoint pens in a box of 200 were found to be defective. What percent of the pens were not defective?

Your strategy

Your solution
$97\frac{1}{2}$

Solutions on p. A32

5.3A Exercises

Solve using the basic percent equation.

1. 26% of 250 is what?

   65

2. What is 18% of 150?

   27

3. 37 is what percent of 148?

   25%

4. What percent of 150 is 33?

   22%

5. 68% of what is 51?

   75

6. 126 is 84% of what?

   150

7. What percent of 344 is 43?

   12.5%

8. 750 is what percent of 50?

   1500%

9. 82 is 20.5% of what?

   400

10. 2.4% of what is 21?

    875

11. What is 6.5% of 300?

    19.5

12. 96% of 75 is what?

    72

13. What is $33\frac{1}{3}$% of 27?

    9

14. Find $16\frac{2}{3}$% of 30.

    5

15. What percent of 12 is 3?

    25%

16. 120% of what is 6?

    5

17. Find 125% of 16.

    20

18. What is 250% of 12?

    30

5.3B Exercises

Solve using proportions.

19. 12 is what percent of 50?

    24%

20. What percent of 125 is 50?

    40%

21. Find 18% of 40.

    7.2

22. What is 25% of 60?

    15

23. 12% of what is 48?

    400

24. 45% of what is 9?

    20

25. 7.4 is what percent of 50?

    14.8%

26. 50.5% of 124 is what?

    62.62

27. What is 87.4% of 255?

    222.87

28. 10 is what percent of 15?

    $66\frac{2}{3}$%

29. 12 is what percent of 6?

    200%

30. Find 15.4% of 50.

    7.7

31. What is 18.5% of 46?

    8.51

32. 1 is 0.5% of what?

    200

33. 3 is 1.5% of what?

    200

34. Find 125% of 32.

    40

35. 14 is 175% of what?

    8

36. What is 250% of 18?

    45

5.3C Exercises

Solve.

37. A prescribed medication will cure an illness in 37 out of 50 patients who have the disease. What percent of the patients who have the disease will be cured by the medication?

    74%

38. A charity organization spent 12% of the $24,500 it collected for administrative expenses. How much of the amount collected was paid for administrative expenses?

    $2940

39. A meat market reduced the price of pork to $2.07 per pound, which is 90% of the original price. What was the original price?

    $2.30

40. A medium-size computer can be purchased for $44,000, which is 55% of the cost five years ago. What was the cost of the computer five years ago?

    $80,000

41. An engineer estimates that 32% of the gasoline used by a car is used efficiently. Using this estimate, how many gallons out of 20 gal of gasoline are used efficiently?

    6.4 gal

42. Approximately 80% of the air in the atmosphere is nitrogen. Using this estimate, how many liters of nitrogen are in a box that contains 500 L of air?

    400 L

43. The value of a car today is $66\frac{2}{3}$% of its value two years ago. The value of the car two years ago was $6000. What is the value of the car today?

    $4000

44. An appliance store estimates that 15% of the washing machines it sells will require service within one year. Using this estimate, how many washing machines were sold in a year in which 27 new machines were serviced?

    180

45. The normal underwater visibility off the coast of an island is 30 ft. Unusual turbulence reduced the visibility by 12 ft. What percent decrease does this represent?

    40%

46. The seating capacity of a baseball stadium, which had seated 50,000, was expanded by 6250 seats. What percent increase does this represent?

    12.5%

47. The number of take-offs and landings at a municipal airport this year was 303,750. This represents 112.5% of last year's take-offs and landings. How many take-offs and landings were there last year?

    270,000

48. A company's budget for the development of a new product is $250,000. Of this amount, $50,000 is for materials. What percent of the total budget is for materials?

    20%

49. A monthly state income tax is 11% of that amount earned over $1700. What state income tax does a person pay on a salary of $2600?

    $99

50. In a test of 20 antifreeze solutions, 3 solutions froze above an acceptable temperature. What percent of the solutions did not freeze above the acceptable temperature?

    85%

Section 4 Application Problems

Objective A   To solve investment problems

Reference for
Computer
Tutor™

The annual simple interest that an investment earns is given by the equation $I = Pr$, where I is the simple interest, P is the principal, or the amount invested, and r is the simple interest rate.

The annual interest rate on a $2500 investment is 11%. Find the annual simple interest earned on the investment.

Given: $P = \$2500$ $I = Pr$
         $r = 11\% = 0.11$ $I = 2500(0.11)$
Unknown: I $I = 275$

The annual simple interest is $275.

An investor has a total of $10,000 to deposit into two simple interest accounts. On one account, the annual simple interest rate is 7%. On the second account, the annual simple interest rate is 11%. How much should be invested in each account so that the total annual interest earned is $1000?

STRATEGY FOR SOLVING A PROBLEM INVOLVING MONEY DEPOSITED IN TWO SIMPLE INTEREST ACCOUNTS

▷ For each amount invested, write a numerical or variable expression for the principal, the interest rate, and the interest earned. The results can be recorded in a table.

The sum of the amounts at each   Amount invested at 7%: x
interest rate is $10,000.   Amount invested at 11%: $\$10,000 - x$

	Principal, P	·	Interest rate, r	=	Interest earned, I
Amount at 7%	x	·	0.07	=	$0.07x$
Amount at 11%	$10,000 - x$	·	0.11	=	$0.11(10,000 - x)$

▷ Determine how the amounts of interest earned on each amount are related. For example, the total interest earned by both accounts may be known or it may be known that the interest earned on one account is equal to the interest earned by the other account.

The total annual interest $0.07x + 0.11(10,000 - x) = 1000$
earned is $1000. $0.07x + 1100 - 0.11x = 1000$
                                        $-0.04x + 1100 = 1000$
                                            $-0.04x = -100$
                                                $x = 2500$
                      $10,000 - x = 10,000 - 2500 = 7500$

The amount invested at 7% is $2500.
The amount invested at 11% is $7500.

Example 1

An investment counselor invested 75% of a client's money in a 9% annual simple interest money market fund. The remainder was invested in 7% annual simple interest government securities. Find the amount invested in each if the total annual interest earned is $3825.

Example 2

An investment of $5000 is made at an annual simple interest rate of 8%. How much additional money must be invested at 11% so that the total interest earned will be 9% of the total investment?

Strategy

▷ Amount invested: x
Amount invested at 7%: $0.25x$
Amount invested at 9%: $0.75x$

	Principal	Rate	Interest
Amount at 7%	$0.25x$	0.07	$0.0175x$
Amount at 9%	$0.75x$	0.09	$0.0675x$

▷ The sum of the interest earned by the two investments equals the total annual interest earned ($3825).

Your strategy

Solution

$0.0175x + 0.0675x = 3825$
$\qquad\qquad 0.085x = 3825$
$\qquad\qquad\qquad x = 45{,}000$

$0.25x = 0.25(45{,}000) = 11{,}250$

$0.75x = 0.75(45{,}000) = 33{,}750$

The amount invested at 7% is $11,250.
The amount invested at 9% is $33,750.

Your solution

$ 2500

Solution on p. A33

| Objective B | To solve value mixture problems |

A value mixture problem involves combining two ingredients that have different prices into a single blend. For example, a coffee merchant may blend two types of coffee into a single blend, or a candy manufacturer may combine two types of candy to sell as a "variety pack."

The solution of a value mixture problem is based on the equation $V = AC$, where V is the value of an ingredient, A is the amount of the ingredient, and C is the cost per unit of the ingredient.

The value of 12 lb of walnuts costing $1.60 per pound can be found by the equation $V = AC$.

The amount is 12 lb. The cost per pound is $1.60.

$$V = AC$$
$$V = 12(1.60)$$
$$V = 19.20$$

The value of the 12 lb of walnuts is $19.20.

A coffee merchant wants to make 6 lb of a blend of coffee costing $5 per pound. The blend is made using a $6 grade and a $3 grade of coffee. How many pounds of each of these grades should be used?

STRATEGY FOR SOLVING A VALUE MIXTURE PROBLEM

▷ For each ingredient in the mixture, write a numerical or variable expression for the amount of the ingredient used, the unit cost of the ingredient, and the value of the amount used. For the blend, write a numerical or variable expression for the amount, the unit cost of the blend, and the value of the amount. The results can be recorded in a table.

The sum of the amounts is 6 lb.

Amount of $6 coffee: x
Amount of $3 coffee: $6 - x$

	Amount, A	·	Unit cost, C	=	Value, V
$6 grade	x	·	$6	=	6x
$3 grade	6 − x	·	$3	=	3(6 − x)
$5 blend	6	·	$5	=	5(6)

▷ Determine how the values of each ingredient are related. Use the fact that the sum of the values of each ingredient is equal to the value of the blend.

The sum of the values of the $6 grade and the $3 grade is equal to the value of the $5 blend.

$$6x + 3(6 - x) = 5(6)$$
$$6x + 18 - 3x = 30$$
$$3x + 18 = 30$$
$$3x = 12$$
$$x = 4$$

$$6 - x = 6 - 4 = 2$$

The merchant must use 4 lb of the $6 coffee and 2 lb of the $3 coffee.

Example 3

How many ounces of a silver alloy that costs $4 an ounce must be mixed with 10 oz of an alloy that costs $6 an ounce to make a mixture that costs $4.32 an ounce?

Example 4

A gardener has 20 lb of a lawn fertilizer that costs $.80 per pound. How many pounds of a fertilizer that costs $.55 per pound should be mixed with the 20 lb of lawn fertilizer to produce a mixture that costs $.75 per pound?

Strategy

▷ Ounces of $4 alloy: x

	Amount	Cost	Value
$4 alloy	x	$4	$4x$
$6 alloy	10	$6	6(10)
$4.32 mixture	$10 + x$	$4.32	$4.32(10 + x)$

▷ The sum of the values before mixing equals the value after mixing.

Your strategy

Solution

$$4x + 6(10) = 4.32(10 + x)$$
$$4x + 60 = 43.2 + 4.32x$$
$$-0.32x + 60 = 43.2$$
$$-0.32x = -16.8$$
$$x = 52.5$$

52.5 oz of the $4 silver alloy must be used.

Your solution

5 lb

Solution on p. A33

Objective C   To solve percent mixture problems

The amount of a substance in a solution can be given as a percent of the total solution. For example, a 5% salt water solution means that 5% of the total solution is salt. The remaining 95% is water.

The solution of a percent mixture problem is based on the equation $Q = Ar$, where Q is the quantity of a substance in the solution, r is the percent of concentration, and A is the amount of solution.

A 500-milliliter bottle contains a 4% solution of hydrogen peroxide. Find the amount of hydrogen peroxide in the solution.

Given: $A = 500$ $Q = Ar$
       $r = 4\% = 0.04$ $Q = 500(0.04)$
Unknown: Q $Q = 20$

The bottle contains 20 ml of hydrogen peroxide.

How many gallons of a 20% salt solution must be mixed with 6 gal of a 30% salt solution to make a 22% salt solution?

STRATEGY FOR SOLVING A PERCENT MIXTURE PROBLEM

▷ For each solution, write a numerical or variable expression for the amount of solution, percent of concentration, and the quantity of the substance in the solution. The results can be recorded in a table.

The unknown quantity of 20% solution: x

	Amount of solution, A	·	Percent of concentration, r	=	Quantity of substance, Q
20% solution	x	·	0.20	=	$0.20x$
30% solution	6	·	0.30	=	$0.30(6)$
22% solution	$x + 6$	·	0.22	=	$0.22(x + 6)$

▷ Determine how the quantities of the substance in each solution are related. Use the fact that the sum of the quantities of the substances being mixed is equal to the quantity of the substance after mixing.

The sum of the quantities of the substances in the 20% solution and the 30% solution is equal to the quantity of the substance in the 22% solution.

$$0.20x + 0.30(6) = 0.22(x + 6)$$
$$0.20x + 1.80 = 0.22x + 1.32$$
$$-0.02x + 1.80 = 1.32$$
$$-0.02x = -0.48$$
$$x = 24$$

24 gal of the 20% solution are required.

Example 5

A chemist wishes to make 2 L of an 8% acid solution by mixing a 10% acid solution and a 5% acid solution. How many liters of each solution should the chemist use?

Strategy

▷ Liters of 10% solution: x
Liters of 5% solution: $2 - x$

	Amount	Percent	Quantity
10%	x	0.10	$0.10x$
5%	$2 - x$	0.05	$0.05(2 - x)$
8%	2	0.08	$0.08(2)$

▷ The sum of the quantities before mixing is equal to the quantity after mixing.

Solution

$$0.10x + 0.05(2 - x) = 0.08(2)$$
$$0.10x + 0.10 - 0.05x = 0.16$$
$$0.05x + 0.10 = 0.16$$
$$0.05x = 0.06$$
$$x = 1.2$$
$$2 - x = 2 - 1.2 = 0.8$$

The chemist needs 1.2 L of the 10% solution and 0.8 L of the 5% solution.

Example 6

A pharmacist dilutes 5 L of a 12% solution by adding water. How many liters of water are added to make an 8% solution?

Your strategy

Your solution

2.5 L

Solution on p. A33

5.4A Exercises

Solve.

1. A total of $5000 is deposited into two simple interest accounts. On one account the annual simple interest rate is 6%, while on the second account the annual simple interest rate is 9%. How much should be invested in each account so that the total annual interest earned is $390?

$2000 at 6%
$3000 at 9%

2. An investment club invested a part of $10,000 in a 7.5% annual simple interest account and the remainder in a 9% annual simple interest account. The amount of interest earned for one year was $795. How much was invested in each account?

$7000 at 7.5%
$3000 at 9%

3. An investment of $4000 is made at an annual simple interest rate of 9%. How much additional money must be invested at an annual simple interest rate of 6% so that the total interest earned is 8% of the total investment?

$2000

4. An investment of $3500 is made at an annual simple interest rate of 7%. How much additional money must be invested at an annual simple interest rate of 10% so that the total interest earned is 9% of the total investment?

$7000

5. A total of $4000 is invested into two simple interest accounts. On one account the annual simple interest rate is 9%, while on the second account the annual simple interest rate is 6%. How much should be invested in each account so that the interest earned by each account is the same?

$1600 at 9%
$2400 at 6%

6. An investment advisor deposited a total of $6000 into two money market funds. One fund earns 7% annual simple interest, while a second tax-free fund earns 5% annual simple interest. How much must be invested in each fund so that the interest earned by each is the same?

$3500 at 5%
$2500 at 7%

7. An accountant deposited an amount of money into a 6% annual simple interest account. Another deposit, $2000 more than the first, was placed in an 8.8% annual simple interest account. The total interest earned on both investments for one year was $546. How much money was deposited in the 6% account?

$2500

8. A deposit was made into a 6% annual simple interest savings account. Another deposit, $3500 less than the first, was placed in a 10% annual simple interest bond market account. The total interest earned on both accounts for one year was $450. How much money was deposited in the 6% account?

$5000

9. An investment of $12,000 is made in a 10.5% simple interest account. How much additional money must be deposited into an 8% simple interest account so that the total interest earned on both accounts is 9.5% of the total investment?

$8000

10. To provide for retirement income, an engineer purchases a $10,000 bond. The simple interest rate on the bond is 8.5%. How much money must be invested in additional bonds that have an interest rate of 9.25% so that the total interest earned each year is $2700?

$20,000

Solve.

11. A stock broker's client has $25,000 to invest. The broker recommends that part of the $25,000 be placed in 7.5% tax-free municipal bonds and the remainder in 9.25% commercial bonds. How much should be invested in each type of bond so that the total interest earned is $2050?

    $15,000 at 7.5%
    $10,000 at 9.25%

12. A corporation gave a university $250,000 to support research assistants in science. The university deposited some of the money in an 8% simple interest account and the remainder in a 6.5% simple interest account. How much should be deposited in each so that the total interest earned is $18,875?

    $175,000 at 8%
    $75,000 at 6.5%

5.4B Exercises

Solve.

13. A butcher combined hamburger that cost $2.50 per pound with hamburger that cost $3.10 per pound. How many pounds of each were used to make an 80-pound mixture costing $2.65 per pound?

    60 lb of $2.50
    20 lb of $3.10

14. A butcher combined hamburger that cost $4.40 per kilogram with hamburger that cost $8.40 per kilogram. How many kilograms of each were used to make a mixture of 50 kg costing $6.00 per kilogram?

    30 kg at $4.40
    20 kg at $8.40

15. How many ounces of pure gold that cost $400 an ounce must be mixed with 20 oz of an alloy that cost $220 an ounce to make an alloy costing $300 an ounce?

    16 oz

16. A goldsmith combined pure gold that cost $675 per ounce with an alloy costing $325 per ounce. How many ounces of each should be used to make 5 oz of a gold alloy costing $465 per ounce?

    2 oz of pure gold
    3 oz of the alloy

17. Find the cost per pound of a mixture made from 12 lb of chocolate that cost $4.00 per pound and 30 lb of chocolate that cost $2.25 per pound.

    $2.75 per pound

18. How many kilograms of chocolates that cost $7.00 per kilogram must be mixed with 20 kg of chocolates that cost $3.50 per kilogram to make a box of mixed chocolates costing $4.50 per kilogram?

    8 kg

19. A grocer combined cranberry juice that cost $3.25 per gallon with apple juice that cost $2.25 per gallon. How many gallons of each should be used to make 100 gal of cranapple juice costing $2.50 per gallon?

    25 gal of cranberry
    75 gal of apple

20. Find the cost per liter of a mixture made from 40 L of cranberry juice that cost $1.00 per liter and 120 L of apple juice that cost $.60 per liter.

    $.70

21. How many pounds of walnuts that cost $1.60 per pound must be mixed with 18 lb of cashews that cost $2.50 per pound to make a mixture that costs $1.90 per pound?

    36 lb

22. A grocer combined peanuts that cost $2.50 per kilogram with walnuts that cost $4.50 per kilogram. How many kilograms of each were used to make a 100-kilogram mixture costing $3.24 per kilogram?

    63 kg of peanuts
    37 kg of walnuts

Solve.

23. Find the cost per pound of a mixture of coffee made from 25 lb of coffee that cost $4.82 per pound and 40 lb of coffee that cost $3.00 per pound.
    $3.70/pound

24. How many kilograms of coffee that cost $9 per kilogram must be mixed with 16 kg of coffee that cost $5 per kilogram to make a mixture that costs $6.50 per kilogram?
    9.6 kg

25. How many pounds of cheese that cost $4.20 per pound must be mixed with 12 lb of cheese that cost $2.25 per pound to make a grated cheese topping that costs $3.40 per pound?
    17.25 lb

26. Find the cost per kilogram of a grated cheese mixture made from 8 kg of cheese that cost $9.20 per kilogram and 12 kg of cheese that cost $5.50 per kilogram.
    $6.98

27. To make a feed for cattle, a feed store operator combined soybeans that cost $8 per bushel with corn that cost $3 per bushel. How many bushels of each were used to make a mixture of 5000 bushels costing $4.50 per bushel?
    1500 bushels of soybeans
    3500 bushels of corn

28. How many bushels of soybeans that cost $7.50 per bushel must be mixed with 2400 bushels of corn that cost $3.25 per bushel to make a mixture that costs $4.50 per bushel?
    1000 bushels

29. Find the cost per ounce of a mixture of 200 oz of silver that cost $5.50 per ounce and 500 oz of an alloy that cost $2.00 per ounce.
    $3/oz

30. A silversmith combined a silver alloy that cost $4.30 per ounce with an alloy that cost $1.80 per ounce. How many ounces of each were used to make a mixture of 100 oz costing $2.50 per ounce?
    28 oz of the $4.30 silver alloy
    72 oz of the $1.80 alloy

31. How many liters of face cream that cost $80 per liter must be mixed with 6 L of face cream that cost $25 per liter to make a face cream that costs $36 per liter?
    1.5 L

32. Find the cost per ounce of a face cream mixture made from 40 oz of face cream that cost $4.40 per ounce and 100 oz of face cream that cost $2.30 per ounce.
    $2.90

5.4C Exercises

Solve.

33. A farmer has some cream that is 21% butterfat and some that is 15% butterfat. How many gallons of each must be mixed to produce 60 gal of cream that is 19% butterfat?
    40 gal of the 21% butterfat
    20 gal of the 15% butterfat

34. A chemist has some 8% hydrogen peroxide and some 5% hydrogen peroxide solution. How many milliliters of each should be mixed to make a 300-milliliter solution that is 6% hydrogen peroxide?
    100 mL of the 8% solution
    200 mL of the 5% solution

35. How many grams of pure acid must be added to 40 g of a 20% acid solution to make a solution that is 36% acid?
    10 g

36. How many ounces of pure water must be added to 60 oz of a 15% salt solution to make a salt solution that is 10% salt?
    30 oz

Solve.

37. A hygenist mixed 50 L of a 36% disinfectant solution with 40 L of water. What is the percent concentration of the resulting solution?

    20%

38. A researcher mixed 80 lb of a 30% aluminum alloy with 120 lb of a 25% aluminum alloy. What is the percent concentration of the resulting alloy?

    27%

39. A syrup manufacturer has some pure maple syrup and some that is 85% maple syrup. How many liters of each should be mixed to make 150 L that is 96% maple syrup?

    40 L of 85% maple syrup
    110 L of pure syrup

40. A butcher has some hamburger that is 20% fat and some that is 15% fat. How many pounds of each should be mixed to make 50 lb of hamburger that is 18% fat?

    30 lb of 20% fat
    20 lb of 15% fat

41. A 100-pound bag of animal feed is 40% oats. How many pounds of oats must be added to this feed to produce a mixture that is 50% oats?

    20 lb

42. A goldsmith has 10 g of a 50% gold alloy. How many grams of pure gold should be added to the alloy to make an alloy that is 75% gold?

    10 g

43. Ten grams of sugar are added to a 40-gram serving of a breakfast cereal that is 30% sugar. What is the percent concentration of sugar in the resulting mixture?

    44%

44. Thirty ounces of pure grapefruit juice are added to 50 oz of a fruit punch that is 20% grapefruit juice. What is the percent concentration of grapefruit juice in the resulting mixture?

    50%

45. A clothing manufacturer has some fiber that is 20% polyester and some that is 50% polyester. How many pounds of each fiber should be woven together to produce 600 lb of a fabric that is 35% polyester?

    300 lb of 20% polyester
    300 lb of 50% polyester

46. A nurse wants to make 50 ml of a 16% salt solution. How many milliliters each of a 13% salt solution and an 18% salt solution should be mixed to produce the desired solution?

    20 mL of 13% solution
    30 mL of 18% solution

47. A baker mixed some flour that was 40% wheat with 80 lb of flour that was 30% wheat to make a mixture that is 32% wheat. How many pounds of the 40% wheat flour were used?

    20 lb

48. A manufacturer mixed a chemical that was 60% fire retardant with 70 lb of a chemical that was 80% fire retardant to make a mixture that is 74% fire retardant. How much of the 60% mixture was used?

    30 lb

49. A 200-pound alloy of tin that is 35% tin is mixed with 300 lb of another tin alloy. The resulting alloy is 20% tin. Find the percent of tin in the 300-pound alloy.

    10%

50. A silversmith mixes 50 g of one alloy that is 50% silver with 150 g of another silver alloy. The resulting alloy is 68% silver. Find the percent of silver in the 150-gram alloy.

    74%

Calculators and Computers

A percent can be entered on a calculator in one of two ways:

1. Enter the percent as a decimal. Remember that to write a percent as a decimal, drop the percent sign and multiply by 0.01. For example, 12% would be entered as the decimal 0.12.

2. Enter the percent using the ⬚%⬚ key.

The following examples illustrate the use of the ⬚%⬚ key.

25% of 87 is what?

Press the keys shown in the box.　　　 25 ⬚%⬚ ⬚×⬚ 87 ⬚=⬚

The answer 21.75 should be displayed; 25% of 87 is 21.75.

45 is what percent of 75?

Press the keys shown in the box.　　　 45 ⬚÷⬚ 75 ⬚%⬚ ⬚=⬚

The answer 60 should be displayed; 45 is 60% of 75.

53 is 25% of what?

Press the keys shown in the box.　　　 53 ⬚÷⬚ 25 ⬚%⬚ ⬚=⬚

The answer 212 should be displayed; 53 is 25% of 212.

Solve.

1. 16% of 50 is what?

2. 24 is what percent of 60?

3. 171 is 38% of what?

4. Find 0.06% of 250.

5. What percent of 6 is 1.2?

6. 180% of what is 21.6?

7. 80% of 16.25 is what?

8. 4.2 is what percent of 175?

9. 0.56 is 0.7% of what?

10. What is 6.5% of 300?

11. What percent of 99.5 is 41.79?

12. 30% of what is 2.7?

13. 50.5% of 124 is what?

14. 7.4 is what percent of 50?

15. 82 is 20.5% of what?

ANSWERS:　**1.** 8　　**2.** 40%　　**3.** 450　　**4.** 0.15　　**5.** 20%　　**6.** 12　　**7.** 13　　**8.** 2.4%　　**9.** 80　　**10.** 19.5
　　　11. 42%　　**12.** 9　　**13.** 62.62　　**14.** 14.8%　　**15.** 400

Chapter Summary

KEY WORDS

A **ratio** is the quotient of two quantities that have the same unit.

A **rate** is the quotient of two quantities that have different units.

A **proportion** is an equation that states the equality of two ratios or rates.

Percent means "parts of 100."

ESSENTIAL RULES

In a proportion, the "cross products" are equal. For the proportion $\frac{a}{b} = \frac{c}{d}$, $a \cdot d = b \cdot c$.

To **write a percent as a fraction,** drop the percent sign and multiply by $\frac{1}{100}$.

To **write a percent as a decimal,** drop the percent sign and multiply by 0.01.

To **write a decimal or a fraction as a percent,** multiply by 100%.

The proportion used for solving percent problems is $\frac{\text{percent}}{100} = \frac{\text{amount}}{\text{base}}$.

The Basic Percent Equation	Percent $\times$ Base = Amount $P \quad \times \quad B \ = \quad A$
The Annual Simple Interest Equation	Simple interest = Principal $\times$ Simple interest rate $I \qquad = \qquad P \quad \times \qquad\qquad r$
The Value Mixture Equation	Value = Amount $\times$ Unit cost $V \ = \quad A \quad \times \quad C$
The Percent Mixture Equation	Quantity = Amount $\times$ Percent concentration $Q \quad = \quad A \quad \times \qquad\qquad r$

Review/Test

1. Write the comparison 6 qt to 18 qt as a ratio in simplest form using a fraction.
$\frac{1}{3}$

2. Write "$27,000 earned in 12 months" as a unit rate.
$2250/month

3. Solve the proportion $\frac{3}{x+4} = \frac{5}{x+6}$.
−1

4. Write 60% as a fraction and as a decimal.
$\frac{3}{5}$; 0.60

5. Write $62\frac{1}{2}$% as a fraction.
$\frac{5}{8}$

6. Write 18.2% as a decimal.
0.182

7. Write 0.375 as a percent.
37.5%

8. Write $\frac{4}{5}$ as a percent.
80%

9. Write $\frac{7}{8}$ as a percent. Write the remainder in fractional form.
$87\frac{1}{2}$%

10. 20 is what percent of 16?
125%

11. 15% of what number is 12?
80

12. 42.5 is 150% of what number? Round to the nearest tenth.
28.3

13. A small plane used 2 qt of oil on a 1200-mile trip. At this rate, how many quarts of oil would be used on a trip of 2000 mi?
$3\frac{1}{3}$ qt

14. A salt water solution is formed by mixing 4 lb of salt with 10 gal of water. At this rate, how many additional pounds of salt are required for 15 gal of water?
2 additional pounds

15. The value of a personal computer today is $24,000. This is 80% of the computer's value last year. Find the value of the computer last year.
$30,000

16. A student missed 7 out of 80 questions on a math exam. What percent of the questions did the student answer correctly? Round to the nearest tenth of a percent.
91.3%

17. A manufacturer of transistors expects 1.1% of its transistors to be defective. In a batch of 350,000 transistors, how many does the manufacturer expect to be defective?
3850 transistors

18. In the last 200 hours of a computer operation, the computer malfunctioned 8% of the time. For how many hours did the computer operate properly?
184 hours

19. A total of $7000 is deposited into two simple interest accounts. On one account, the annual simple interest rate is 7%, while on the second account the annual simple interest rate is 9%. How much is invested in each account if the total annual interest earned is $600?
$1500 at 7%; $5500 at 9%

20. A deposit of $4000 is made into an account that earns 6% simple interest. How much additional money must be deposited into an account that pays 8.8% simple interest if the total interest earned is to be 8% of the total investment?
$10,000

21. A coffee merchant wants to make 12 lb of a blend of coffee costing $6 per pound. The blend is made using a $7 grade and a $4 grade of coffee. How many pounds of each of these grades should be used?
8 lb at $7/lb; 4 lb at $4/lb

22. How many grams of a gold alloy that costs $5 a gram must be mixed with 40 g of a gold alloy that costs $8 a gram to make an alloy that costs $6 a gram?
80 g

23. How many gallons of a 15% acid solution must be mixed with 5 gal of a 20% acid solution to make a 16% acid solution?
20 gal

24. How many ounces of pure water must be added to 20 oz of a 15% salt solution to make a 6% salt solution?
30 oz

Cumulative Review/Test

1. Write $2 \cdot 2 \cdot 2 \cdot 2 \cdot 3 \cdot 3 \cdot 3$ in exponential notation.

   $2^4 \cdot 3^3$

2. Write $\frac{2}{25}$ as a percent.

   8%

3. Add: $2\frac{1}{3} + 3\frac{1}{2} + 4\frac{5}{8}$

   $10\frac{11}{24}$

4. Simplify $-2 + (-8) - (-16)$.

   6

5. Find $83\frac{1}{3}\%$ of 24.

   20

6. 24 is what percent of 18?

   $133\frac{1}{3}\%$

7. Solve the proportion $\frac{2}{x-2} = \frac{12}{x-3}$.

   $\frac{9}{5}$

8. Write 0.075 as a percent.

   7.5%

9. Evaluate $b^2 - (a - b)^2$ when $a = 3$ and $b = -2$.

   -21

10. Reduce $\frac{10}{24}$ to simplest form.

    $\frac{5}{12}$

11. Simplify $18 \div (7 - 4)^2 + 2$.

    4

12. Write $16\frac{2}{3}\%$ as a fraction.

    $\frac{1}{6}$

13. 30% of what is 12?

    40

14. Simplify $2x - 3y - (-4x) + 7y$.

    $6x + 4y$

15. Subtract: $3.0902 - 1.9706$

    1.1196

16. Solve the proportion $\frac{7}{8} = \frac{20}{n}$. Round to the nearest tenth.

    22.9

17. Write 80% as a fraction.

    $\frac{4}{5}$

18. Simplify $-3[x - 2(x - 3) - 4]$.

    $3x - 6$

19. Solve: $-2x - 3(4 - 2x) = 5x + 4$

    -16

20. A life insurance policy costs $16 for every $1000 of coverage. At this rate, how much additional money would a policy of $5000 cost?

    $\$64$

21. A survey of 250 librarians showed that 50 of the libraries had a particular reference book. What percent of the libraries had the reference book?

    20%

22. A deposit of $12,000 is made into an account that earns 9% simple interest. How much additional money must be deposited in an account that pays 6% simple interest so that the total interest earned is 8% of the total investment?

    $\$6000$

23. How many grams of gold alloy that costs $4 a gram must be mixed with 30 g of a gold alloy that costs $7 a gram to make an alloy that costs $5 a gram?

    60 g

24. How many ounces of pure water must be added to 70 oz of a 10% salt solution to make a 7% salt solution?

    30 oz

chapter **6** Polynomials

Objectives

6.1A   To add polynomials

6.1B   To subtract polynomials

6.2A   To multiply monomials

6.2B   To simplify powers of monomials

6.2C   To multiply polynomials

6.2D   To multiply two binomials

6.2E   To multiply binomials that have special products

6.3A   To divide monomials

6.3B   To divide a polynomial by a monomial

6.3C   To divide polynomials

6.4A   To simplify expressions containing negative and zero exponents

6.4B   To convert from decimal notation to scientific notation and from scientific notation to decimal notation

6.4C   To solve application problems

Section **1**

Addition and Subtraction of Polynomials

Objective A

To add polynomials

Reference for
Computer
Tutor™

A **monomial** is a number, a variable, or a product of numbers and variables.

$3x^2$ and $4x^3y^5$ are monomials.

$\frac{1}{x}$ is not a monomial because a variable appears in the denominator.

A **polynomial** is a variable expression in which the terms are monomials.

A **monomial** is a polynomial of *one* term. $5x^3$ is a monomial.

A **binomial** is a polynomial of *two* terms. $5y^2 - 3x$ is a binomial.

A **trinomial** is a polynomial of *three* terms. $6xy - 2r^2s + 4r$ is a trinomial.

Polynomials with more than three terms do not have special names.

The terms of a polynomial in one variable are usually arranged so that the exponents of the variable decrease from left to right. This is called **descending order.**

$$4x^3 - 3x^2 + 6x - 1$$

$$5y^4 - 2y^3 + y^2 - 7y + 8$$

The **degree of a polynomial** in one variable is its largest exponent.

The degree of $4x^3 - 3x^2 + 6x - 1$ is 3.

The degree of $5y^4 - 2y^3 + y^2 - 7y + 8$ is 4.

Polynomials can be added, using either a vertical or a horizontal format, by combining like terms.

Simplify $(2x^2 + x - 1) + (3x^3 + 4x^2 - 5)$. Use a vertical format.

Arrange the terms of each polynomial in descending order with like terms in the same column.
Combine the terms in each column.

$$\begin{array}{r} 2x^2 + x - 1 \\ + \underline{3x^3 + 4x^2 \quad\ - 5} \\ 3x^3 + 6x^2 + x - 6 \end{array}$$

Simplify $(3x^3 - 7x + 2) + (7x^2 + 2x - 7)$. Use a horizontal format.

Use the Commutative and Associative Properties of Addition to rearrange and group like terms.

$(3x^3 - 7x + 2) + (7x^2 + 2x - 7)$

$\boxed{3x^3 + 7x^2 + (-7x + 2x) + (2 - 7)}$ Do this step mentally.

Combine like terms.

$3x^3 + 7x^2 - 5x - 5$

Write the polynomial in descending order.

Example 1

Write the polynomial in descending order.
$3x^2 - 5 + 4x^3 - 2x$

Solution

$4x^3 + 3x^2 - 2x - 5$

Example 2

Write the polynomial in descending order.
$x + 6x^2 - 1 + 5x^3$

Your solution

$5x^3 + 6x^2 + x - 1$

Example 3

Identify the degree of the polynomial.
$8x^3 - 2x^2 - 7$

Solution

The largest exponent on the variable x is 3.

The degree of $8x^3 - 2x^2 - 7$ is 3.

Example 4

Identify the degree of the polynomial.
$9x^4 - 3x^2 + 11$

Your solution

4

Example 5

Simplify $(7y^2 - 6y + 9) + (-8y^2 - 2)$.
Use a vertical format.

Solution

$$\begin{array}{r} 7y^2 - 6y + 9 \\ + \;-8y^2 \qquad\; - 2 \\ \hline -y^2 - 6y + 7 \end{array}$$

Example 6

Simplify $(2x^2 + 4x - 3) + (5x^2 - 6x)$.
Use a vertical format.

Your solution

$7x^2 - 2x - 3$

Example 7

Simplify $(-4x^2 - 3xy + 2y^2) + (3x^2 - 4y^2)$.
Use a horizontal format.

Solution

$(-4x^2 - 3xy + 2y^2) + (3x^2 - 4y^2) =$
$-x^2 - 3xy - 2y^2$

Example 8

Simplify $(-3x^2 + 2y^2) + (-8x^2 + 9xy)$.
Use a horizontal format.

Your solution

$-11x^2 + 9xy + 2y^2$

Solutions on p. A35

Reference for Computer Tutor™

Objective B   To subtract polynomials

The **opposite** of the polynomial $x^2 - 2x + 3$ is $-(x^2 - 2x + 3)$.

To simplify the opposite of a polynomial, change the sign of every term inside the parentheses.

$$-(x^2 - 2x + 3) = -x^2 + 2x - 3$$

Polynomials can be subtracted using either a vertical or horizontal format. To subtract, add the opposite of the second polynomial to the first.

Simplify $(-3x^2 - 7) - (-8x^2 + 3x - 4)$. Use a vertical format.

Arrange the terms of each polynomial in descending order with like terms in the same column.
Rewrite subtraction as addition of the opposite.
Combine the terms in each column.

$$\begin{array}{r} -3x^2 \qquad - 7 \\ -\ -8x^2 + 3x - 4 \\ \hline \end{array} = \begin{array}{r} -3x^2 \qquad - 7 \\ +\ \ 8x^2 - 3x + 4 \\ \hline 5x^2 - 3x - 3 \end{array}$$

Simplify $(5x^2 - 3x + 4) - (-3x^3 - 2x + 8)$. Use a horizontal format.

Rewrite subtraction as addition of the opposite.
Combine like terms.
Write the polynomial in descending order.

$$(5x^2 - 3x + 4) - (-3x^3 - 2x + 8)$$
$$(5x^2 - 3x + 4) + (3x^3 + 2x - 8)$$
$$3x^3 + 5x^2 - x - 4$$

Example 9

Simplify $(6y^2 - 3y - 1) - (7y^2 - y)$.
Use a vertical format.

Solution

$$\begin{array}{r} 6y^2 - 3y - 1 \\ -\ 7y^2 - \ \ y \\ \hline \end{array} = \begin{array}{r} 6y^2 - 3y - 1 \\ +\ -7y^2 + \ \ y \\ \hline -y^2 - 2y - 1 \end{array}$$

Example 10

Simplify $(8y^2 - 4xy + x^2) - (2y^2 - xy + 5x^2)$.
Use a vertical format.

Your solution

$$6y^2 - 3xy - 4x^2$$

Example 11

Simplify $(4x^3 - 3x - 7) - (7x^2 - 4x - 2)$.
Use a horizontal format.

Solution

$$(4x^3 - 3x - 7) - (7x^2 - 4x - 2)$$
$$(4x^3 - 3x - 7) + (-7x^2 + 4x + 2)$$
$$4x^3 - 7x^2 + x - 5$$

Example 12

Simplify $(-3a^2 - 4a + 2) - (5a^3 + 2a - 6)$.
Use a horizontal format.

Your solution

$$-5a^3 - 3a^2 - 6a + 8$$

Solutions on p. A35

6.1A Exercises

Write the polynomial in descending order.

1. $8x^2 - 2x + 3x^3 - 6$
$$3x^3 + 8x^2 - 2x - 6$$

2. $7y - 8 + 2y^2 + 4y^3$
$$4y^3 + 2y^2 + 7y - 8$$

3. $2a - 3a^2 + 5a^3 + 1$
$$5a^3 - 3a^2 + 2a + 1$$

4. $b - 3b^2 + b^4 - 2b^3$
$$b^4 - 2b^3 - 3b^2 + b$$

5. $5 + r^5 - 6r^2 + r^3$
$$r^5 + r^3 - 6r^2 + 5$$

6. $8x^2 - 2x^6 + x^4 + 7$
$$-2x^6 + x^4 + 8x^2 + 7$$

7. $1 - y^4$
$$-y^4 + 1$$

8. $4 - b^2$
$$-b^2 + 4$$

9. $3 - 9a^2 + a$
$$-9a^2 + a + 3$$

Identify the degree of the polynomial.

10. $9x^5 + 3x^3 - 4x$
$$5$$

11. $3y^4 - 2y^2 + 10$
$$4$$

12. $6b^8 - 5b^6 + 7b^4$
$$8$$

13. $a^6 - 2a^4 + a^2 - 8$
$$6$$

14. $5r + 1$
$$1$$

15. $9x - 2$
$$1$$

Simplify. Use a vertical format.

16. $(x^2 + 7x) + (-3x^2 - 4x)$
$$-2x^2 + 3x$$

17. $(3y^2 - 2y) + (5y^2 + 6y)$
$$8y^2 + 4y$$

18. $(y^2 + 4y) + (-4y - 8)$
$$y^2 - 8$$

19. $(3x^2 + 9x) + (6x - 24)$
$$3x^2 + 15x - 24$$

20. $(2x^2 + 6x + 12) + (3x^2 + x + 8)$
$$5x^2 + 7x + 20$$

21. $(x^2 + x + 5) + (3x^2 - 10x + 4)$
$$4x^2 - 9x + 9$$

22. $(x^3 - 7x + 4) + (2x^2 + x - 10)$
$$x^3 + 2x^2 - 6x - 6$$

23. $(3y^3 + y^2 + 1) + (-4y^3 - 6y - 3)$
$$-y^3 + y^2 - 6y - 2$$

24. $(2a^3 - 7a + 1) + (-3a^2 - 4a + 1)$
$$2a^3 - 3a^2 - 11a + 2$$

25. $(5r^3 - 6r^2 + 3r) + (r^2 - 2r - 3)$
$$5r^3 - 5r^2 + r - 3$$

Simplify. Use a horizontal format.

26. $(4x^2 + 2x) + (x^2 + 6x)$
$$5x^2 + 8x$$

27. $(-3y^2 + y) + (4y^2 + 6y)$
$$y^2 + 7y$$

28. $(4x^2 - 5xy) + (3x^2 + 6xy - 4y^2)$
$$7x^2 + xy - 4y^2$$

29. $(2x^2 - 4y^2) + (6x^2 - 2xy + 4y^2)$
$$8x^2 - 2xy$$

30. $(2a^2 - 7a + 10) + (a^2 + 4a + 7)$
$$3a^2 - 3a + 17$$

31. $(-6x^2 + 7x + 3) + (3x^2 + x + 3)$
$$-3x^2 + 8x + 6$$

Simplify. Use a horizontal format.

32. $(5x^3 + 7x - 7) + (10x^2 - 8x + 3)$

$5x^3 + 10x^2 - x - 4$

33. $(3y^3 + 4y + 9) + (2y^2 + 4y - 21)$

$3y^3 + 2y^2 + 8y - 12$

34. $(2r^2 - 5r + 7) + (3r^3 - 6r)$

$3r^3 + 2r^2 - 11r + 7$

35. $(3y^3 + 4y + 14) + (-4y^2 + 21)$

$3y^3 - 4y^2 + 4y + 35$

36. $(3x^2 + 7x + 10) + (-2x^3 + 3x + 1)$

$-2x^3 + 3x^2 + 10x + 11$

37. $(7x^3 + 4x - 1) + (2x^2 - 6x + 2)$

$7x^3 + 2x^2 - 2x + 1$

6.1B Exercises

Simplify. Use a vertical format.

38. $(x^2 - 6x) - (x^2 - 10x)$

$4x$

39. $(y^2 + 4y) - (y^2 + 10y)$

$-6y$

40. $(2y^2 - 4y) - (-y^2 + 2)$

$3y^2 - 4y - 2$

41. $(-3a^2 - 2a) - (4a^2 - 4)$

$-7a^2 - 2a + 4$

42. $(x^2 - 2x + 1) - (x^2 + 5x + 8)$

$-7x - 7$

43. $(3x^2 + 2x - 2) - (5x^2 - 5x + 6)$

$-2x^2 + 7x - 8$

44. $(4x^3 + 5x + 2) - (-3x^2 + 2x + 1)$

$4x^3 + 3x^2 + 3x + 1$

45. $(5y^2 - y + 2) - (-2y^3 + 3y - 3)$

$2y^3 + 5y^2 - 4y + 5$

46. $(2y^3 + 6y - 2) - (y^3 + y^2 + 4)$

$y^3 - y^2 + 6y - 6$

47. $(-2x^2 - x + 4) - (-x^3 + 3x - 2)$

$x^3 - 2x^2 - 4x + 6$

Simplify. Use a horizontal format.

48. $(y^2 - 10xy) - (2y^2 + 3xy)$

$-y^2 - 13xy$

49. $(x^2 - 3xy) - (-2x^2 + xy)$

$3x^2 - 4xy$

50. $(3x^2 + x - 3) - (x^2 + 4x - 2)$

$2x^2 - 3x - 1$

51. $(5y^2 - 2y + 1) - (-3y^2 - y - 2)$

$8y^2 - y + 3$

52. $(-2x^3 + x - 1) - (-x^2 + x - 3)$

$-2x^3 + x^2 + 2$

53. $(2x^2 + 5x - 3) - (3x^3 + 2x - 5)$

$-3x^3 + 2x^2 + 3x + 2$

54. $(4a^3 - 2a + 1) - (a^3 - 2a + 3)$

$3a^3 - 2$

55. $(b^2 - 8b + 7) - (4b^3 - 7b - 8)$

$-4b^3 + b^2 - b + 15$

56. $(4y^3 - y - 1) - (2y^2 - 3y + 3)$

$4y^3 - 2y^2 + 2y - 4$

57. $(3x^2 - 2x - 3) - (2x^3 - 2x^2 + 4)$

$-2x^3 + 5x^2 - 2x - 7$

Section **2** Multiplication of Polynomials

Objective A To multiply monomials

Reference for
Computer
Tutor™

Recall that in the exponential expression x^5, x is the base and 5 is the exponent. The exponent indicates the number of times the base occurs as a factor.

The product of exponential expressions with the *same* base can be simplified by writing each expression in factored form and writing the result with an exponent.

$$x^3 \cdot x^2 = \overbrace{(x \cdot x \cdot x)}^{3 \text{ factors}} \cdot \overbrace{(x \cdot x)}^{2 \text{ factors}}$$
$$\underbrace{\qquad\qquad\qquad}_{5 \text{ factors}}$$
$$= x \cdot x \cdot x \cdot x \cdot x$$
$$= x^5$$

Note that adding the exponents results in the same product.

$$x^3 \cdot x^2 = x^{3+2} = x^5$$

> **Rule for Multiplying Exponential Expressions**
> If m and n are integers, then $x^m \cdot x^n = x^{m+n}$.

Simplify $a^2 \cdot a^6 \cdot a$.

The bases are the same.
Add the exponents.

$$a^2 \cdot a^6 \cdot a \;\boxed{= a^{2+6+1}} \quad \text{Do this step mentally.}$$
$$= a^9$$

Simplify $(2xy)(3x^2y)$.

Use the Commutative and Associative Properties of Multiplication to rearrange and group factors.
Multiply variables with like bases by adding the exponents.

$$(2xy)(3x^2y) = (2 \cdot 3)(x \cdot x^2)(y \cdot y)$$
$$\boxed{= 6x^{1+2}y^{1+1}} \quad \text{Do this step mentally.}$$
$$= 6x^3y^2$$

Example 1

Simplify $(-4y)(5y^3)$.

Solution

$(-4y)(5y^3) = (-4 \cdot 5)(y \cdot y^3) = -20y^4$

Example 2

Simplify $(3x^2)(6x^3)$.

Your solution

$18x^5$

Example 3

Simplify $(2x^2y)(-5xy^4)$.

Solution

$(2x^2y)(-5xy^4) = [2(-5)](x^2 \cdot x)(y \cdot y^4) = -10x^3y^5$

Example 4

Simplify $(-3xy^2)(-4x^2y^3)$.

Your solution

$12x^3y^5$

| Objective B | To simplify powers of monomials |

Reference for
Computer
Tutor™

A power of a monomial can be simplified by rewriting the expression in factored form and then using the Rule for Multiplying Exponential Expressions.

$$(x^2)^3 = x^2 \cdot x^2 \cdot x^2$$
$$= x^{2+2+2}$$
$$= x^6$$

$$(x^4y^3)^2 = (x^4y^3)(x^4y^3)$$
$$= x^4 \cdot y^3 \cdot x^4 \cdot y^3$$
$$= (x^4 \cdot x^4)(y^3 \cdot y^3)$$
$$= x^{4+4}y^{3+3}$$
$$= x^8y^6$$

Note that multiplying each exponent inside the parentheses by the exponent outside the parentheses gives the same result.

$$(x^2)^3 = x^{2\cdot3} = x^6$$

$$(x^4y^3)^2 = x^{4\cdot2}y^{3\cdot2} = x^8y^6$$

Rule for Simplifying Powers of Exponential Expressions
If m and n are integers, then $(x^m)^n = x^{m \cdot n}$.

Rule for Simplifying Powers of Products
If m, n, and p are integers, then $(x^m \cdot y^n)^p = x^{m \cdot p}y^{n \cdot p}$.

Simplify $(x^5)^2$.

Multiply the exponents.

$$(x^5)^2 \;\boxed{= x^{5\cdot2}}$$
$$= x^{10}$$

Do this step mentally.

Simplify $(3a^2b)^3$.

Multiply each exponent inside the parentheses by the exponent outside the parentheses.

$$(3a^2b)^3 \;\boxed{= 3^{1\cdot3}a^{2\cdot3}b^{1\cdot3}}$$
$$= 3^3a^6b^3$$
$$= 27a^6b^3$$

Do this step mentally.

Example 5

Simplify $(2xy^3)^4$.

Solution

$$(2xy^3)^4 = 2^4x^4y^{12} = 16x^4y^{12}$$

Example 6

Simplify $(3x)(2x^2y)^3$.

Your solution

$$24x^7y^3$$

Example 7

Simplify $(-2x)(-3xy^2)^3$.

Solution

$$(-2x)(-3xy^2)^3 = (-2x)(-3)^3x^3y^6 =$$
$$(-2x)(-27)x^3y^6 = [-2(-27)](x \cdot x^3)y^6 = 54x^4y^6$$

Example 8

Simplify $(3x^2)^2(-2xy^2)^3$.

Your solution

$$-72x^7y^6$$

| Objective C | To multiply polynomials |

Reference for Computer Tutor™

To multiply a polynomial by a monomial, use the Distributive Property and the Rule for Multiplying Exponential Expressions.

Simplify $-2x(x^2 - 4x - 3)$.

Use the Distributive Property.

$$-2x(x^2 - 4x - 3)$$

Use the Rule for Multiplying Exponential Expressions.

$$-2x(x^2) - (-2x)(4x) - (-2x)(3)$$

Do this step mentally.

$$-2x^3 + 8x^2 + 6x$$

Multiplication of two polynomials requires the repeated application of the Distributive Property.

$$(y - 2)(y^2 + 3y + 1) =$$
$$(y - 2)(y^2) + (y - 2)(3y) + (y - 2)(1) =$$
$$y^3 - 2y^2 + 3y^2 - 6y + y - 2 =$$
$$y^3 + y^2 - 5y - 2$$

A more convenient method of multiplying two polynomials is to use a vertical format, similar to that used for multiplication of whole numbers.

Multiply each term in the trinomial by -2.
Multiply each term in the trinomial by y.
Write like terms in the same column.
Add the terms in each column.

$$
\begin{array}{r}
y^2 + 3y + 1 \\
\times \quad\quad y - 2 \\
\hline
-2y^2 - 6y - 2 \\
y^3 + \;\; 3y^2 + \;\; y \\
\hline
y^3 + \quad y^2 - 5y - 2
\end{array}
$$

Simplify $(a^2 - 3)(a + 5)$.

Multiply each term of $a^2 - 3$ by 5.
Multiply each term of $a^2 - 3$ by a.
Arrange the terms in descending order.
Add the terms in each column.

$$
\begin{array}{r}
a^2 - \;\; 3 \\
\times \quad a + \;\; 5 \\
\hline
5a^2 \quad\quad - 15 \\
a^3 \quad\quad - 3a \\
\hline
a^3 + 5a^2 - 3a - 15
\end{array}
$$

Example 9

Simplify $(5x + 4)(-2x)$.

Solution

$(5x + 4)(-2x) = -10x^2 - 8x$

Example 10

Simplify $(-2y + 3)(-4y)$.

Your solution

$$8y^2 - 12y$$

Example 11

Simplify $x^3(2x^2 - 3x + 2)$.

Solution

$x^3(2x^2 - 3x + 2) = 2x^5 - 3x^4 + 2x^3$

Example 12

Simplify $-a^2(3a^2 + 2a - 7)$.

Your solution

$$-3a^4 - 2a^3 + 7a^2$$

Solutions on p. A35

Solutions on p. A35

Example 13

Simplify $(2b^3 - b + 1)(2b + 3)$.

Solution

$$
\begin{array}{r}
2b^3 - b + 1 \\
\times 2b + 3 \\
\hline
6b^3 - 3b + 3 \\
4b^4 + - 2b^2 + 2b \\
\hline
4b^4 + 6b^3 - 2b^2 - b + 3
\end{array}
$$

Example 14

Simplify $(2y^3 + 2y^2 - 3)(3y - 1)$.

Your solution

$6y^4 + 4y^3 - 2y^2 - 9y + 3$

Example 15

Simplify $(x^2 - 1)(x + 3)$.

Solution

$$
\begin{array}{r}
x^2 - 1 \\
\times x + 3 \\
\hline
3x^2 - 3 \\
x^3 - x \\
\hline
x^3 + 3x^2 - x - 3
\end{array}
$$

Example 16

Simplify $(a^3 - 2)(a + 7)$.

Your solution

$a^4 + 7a^3 - 2a - 14$

Copyright © 1989 HMCo

Objective D   To multiply two binomials

Reference for
Computer
Tutor™

It is frequently necessary to find the product of two binomials. The product can be found using a method called **FOIL,** which is based on the Distributive Property. The letters of FOIL stand for **F**irst, **O**uter, **I**nner, and **L**ast.

Simplify $(2x + 3)(x + 5)$.

Multiply the **F**irst terms. $(2x + 3)(x + 5)$ $2x \cdot x = 2x^2$

Multiply the **O**uter terms. $(2x + 3)(x + 5)$ $2x \cdot 5 = 10x$

Multiply the **I**nner terms. $(2x + 3)(x + 5)$ $3 \cdot x = 3x$

Multiply the **L**ast terms. $(2x + 3)(x + 5)$ $3 \cdot 5 = 15$

Add the products. $(2x + 3)(x + 5)$
Combine like terms.

$$
\begin{array}{cccc}
\text{F} & \text{O} & \text{I} & \text{L} \\
= 2x^2 & + 10x & + 3x & + 15 \\
= 2x^2 & + 13x & & + 15
\end{array}
$$

Simplify $(4x - 3)(3x - 2)$.

$(4x - 3)(3x - 2)$ $\boxed{= 4x(3x) + 4x(-2) + (-3)(3x) + (-3)(-2)}$ Do this step mentally.

$$= 12x^2 - 8x - 9x + 6$$
$$= 12x^2 - 17x + 6$$

Simplify $(3x - 2y)(x + 4y)$.

$(3x - 2y)(x + 4y)$ $\boxed{= 3x(x) + 3x(4y) + (-2y)(x) + (-2y)(4y)}$ Do this step mentally.

$$= 3x^2 + 12xy - 2xy - 8y^2$$
$$3x^2 + 10xy - 8y^2$$

Example 17

Simplify $(y + 4)(y - 7)$.

Solution

$$(y + 4)(y - 7) = y^2 - 7y + 4y - 28$$
$$= y^2 - 3y - 28$$

Example 18

Simplify $(b - 5)(b + 8)$.

Your solution

$$b^2 + 3b - 40$$

Example 19

Simplify $(2a - 1)(3a - 2)$.

Solution

$$(2a - 1)(3a - 2) = 6a^2 - 4a - 3a + 2$$
$$= 6a^2 - 7a + 2$$

Example 20

Simplify $(4y - 5)(2y - 3)$.

Your solution

$$8y^2 - 22y + 15$$

Example 21

Simplify $(3x - 2)(4x + 3)$.

Solution

$$(3x - 2)(4x + 3) = 12x^2 + 9x - 8x - 6$$
$$= 12x^2 + x - 6$$

Example 22

Simplify $(3b + 2)(3b - 5)$.

Your solution

$$9b^2 - 9b - 10$$

Example 23

Simplify $(2x - 3y)(3x + 4y)$.

Solution

$$(2x - 3y)(3x + 4y) =$$
$$6x^2 + 8xy - 9xy - 12y^2 =$$
$$6x^2 - xy - 12y^2$$

Example 24

Simplify $(4x - y)(2x + 3y)$.

Your solution

$$8x^2 + 10xy - 3y^2$$

Solutions on p. A36

Objective E	To multiply binomials that have special products

6
DISK SIX

Reference for
Computer
Tutor™

Using FOIL, a pattern for the product of the sum and difference of two terms and for the square of a binomial can be found.

The Sum and Difference of Two Terms $(a + b)(a - b) = a^2 - ab + ab - b^2$
$$= a^2 - b^2$$

Square of first term —
Square of second term —

The Square of a Binomial $(a + b)^2 = (a + b)(a + b) = a^2 + ab + ab + b^2$
$$= a^2 + 2ab + b^2$$

Square of first term —
Twice the product of the two terms —
Square of last term —

Simplify $(2x + 3)(2x - 3)$.

$(2x + 3)(2x - 3)$ is the sum and difference of two terms.

$(2x + 3)(2x - 3)$ $= (2x)^2 - 3^2$ Do this step mentally.

$= 4x^2 - 9$

Simplify $(3x - 2)^2$.

$(3x - 2)^2$ is the square of a binomial.

$(3x - 2)^2$ $= (3x)^2 + 2(3x)(-2) + (-2)^2$ Do this step mentally.

$= 9x^2 - 12x + 4$

Example 25

Simplify $(4z - 2w)(4z + 2w)$.

Solution

$(4z - 2w)(4z + 2w) = 16z^2 - 4w^2$

Example 26

Simplify $(2a + 5c)(2a - 5c)$.

Your solution

$4a^2 - 25c^2$

Example 27

Simplify $(2r - 3s)^2$.

Solution

$(2r - 3s)^2 = 4r^2 - 12rs + 9s^2$

Example 28

Simplify $(3x + 2y)^2$.

Your solution

$9x^2 + 12xy + 4y^2$

Solutions on p. A36

6.2A Exercises

Simplify.

1. $x(2x)$
$2x^2$

2. $(-3y)(y)$
$-3y^2$

3. $(3x)(4x)$
$12x^2$

4. $(7y^3)(7y^2)$
$49y^5$

5. $(-2a^3)(-3a^4)$
$6a^7$

6. $(5a^6)(-2a^5)$
$-10a^{11}$

7. $(x^2y)(xy^4)$
x^3y^5

8. $(x^2y^4)(xy^7)$
x^3y^{11}

9. $(-2x^4)(5x^5y)$
$-10x^9y$

10. $(-3a^3)(2a^2b^4)$
$-6a^5b^4$

11. $(x^2y^4)(x^5y^4)$
x^7y^8

12. $(a^2b^4)(ab^3)$
a^3b^7

13. $(2xy)(-3x^2y^4)$
$-6x^3y^5$

14. $(-3a^2b)(-2ab^3)$
$6a^3b^4$

15. $(x^2yz)(x^2y^4)$
x^4y^5z

16. $(-ab^2c)(a^2b^5)$
$-a^3b^7c$

17. $(a^2b^3)(ab^2c^4)$
$a^3b^5c^4$

18. $(x^2y^3z)(x^3y^4)$
x^5y^7z

19. $(-a^2b^2)(a^3b^6)$
$-a^5b^8$

20. $(xy^4)(-xy^3)$
$-x^2y^7$

21. $(-6a^3)(a^2b)$
$-6a^5b$

22. $(2a^2b^3)(-4ab^2)$
$-8a^3b^5$

23. $(-5y^4z)(-8y^6z^5)$
$40y^{10}z^6$

24. $(3x^2y)(-4xy^2)$
$-12x^3y^3$

25. $(x^2y)(yz)(xyz)$
$x^3y^3z^2$

26. $(xy^2z)(x^2y)(z^2y^2)$
$x^3y^5z^3$

27. $(-2x^2y^3)(3xy)(-5x^3y^4)$
$30x^6y^8$

28. $(4a^2b)(-3a^3b^4)(a^5b^2)$
$-12a^{10}b^7$

29. $(3ab^2)(-2abc)(4ac^2)$
$-24a^3b^3c^3$

30. $(3a^2b)(-6bc)(2ac^2)$
$-36a^3b^2c^3$

6.2B Exercises

Simplify.

31. $(2^2)^3$
64

32. $(3^2)^2$
81

33. $(-2)^2$
4

34. $(-3)^3$
-27

35. $(-2^2)^3$
-64

36. $(-2^3)^3$
-512

37. $(x^3)^3$
x^9

38. $(y^4)^2$
y^8

39. $(x^7)^2$
x^{14}

40. $(y^5)^3$
y^{15}

41. $(-x^2)^2$
x^4

42. $(-x^2)^3$
$-x^6$

43. $(2x)^2$
$4x^2$

44. $(3y)^3$
$27y^3$

45. $(-2x^2)^3$
$-8x^6$

46. $(-3y^3)^2$
$9y^6$

47. $(x^2y^3)^2$
x^4y^6

48. $(x^3y^4)^5$
$x^{15}y^{20}$

49. $(3x^2y)^2$
$9x^4y^2$

50. $(-2ab^3)^4$
$16a^4b^{12}$

Simplify.

51. $(a^2)(3a^2)^3$
$$27a^8$$

52. $(b^2)(2a^3)^4$
$$16a^{12}b^2$$

53. $(-2x)(2x^3)^2$
$$-8x^7$$

54. $(2y)(-3y^4)^3$
$$-54y^{13}$$

55. $(x^2y)(x^2y)^3$
$$x^8y^4$$

56. $(a^3b)(ab)^3$
$$a^6b^4$$

57. $(ab^2)^2(ab)^2$
$$a^4b^6$$

58. $(x^2y)^2(x^3y)^3$
$$x^{13}y^5$$

59. $(-2x)(-2x^3y)^3$
$$16x^{10}y^3$$

60. $(-3y)(-4x^2y^3)^3$
$$192x^6y^{10}$$

61. $(ab^2)(-2a^2b)^3$
$$-8a^7b^5$$

62. $(a^2b^2)(-3ab^4)^2$
$$9a^4b^{10}$$

63. $(-2a^3)(3a^2b)^3$
$$-54a^9b^3$$

64. $(-3b^2)(2ab^2)^3$
$$-24a^3b^8$$

65. $(-3ab)^2(-2ab)^3$
$$-72a^5b^5$$

66. $(-3ab^2)^3(-3ab)^3$
$$729a^6b^9$$

6.2C Exercises

Simplify.

67. $x(x-2)$
$$x^2-2x$$

68. $y(3-y)$
$$-y^2+3y$$

69. $-x(x+7)$
$$-x^2-7x$$

70. $-y(7-y)$
$$y^2-7y$$

71. $3a^2(a-2)$
$$3a^3-6a^2$$

72. $4b^2(b+8)$
$$4b^3+32b^2$$

73. $-5x^2(x^2-x)$
$$-5x^4+5x^3$$

74. $-6y^2(y+2y^2)$
$$-12y^4-6y^3$$

75. $2x(6x^2-3x)$
$$12x^3-6x^2$$

76. $3y(4y-y^2)$
$$-3y^3+12y^2$$

77. $(2x-4)3x$
$$6x^2-12x$$

78. $(3y-2)y$
$$3y^2-2y$$

79. $(3x+4)x$
$$3x^2+4x$$

80. $(2x+1)2x$
$$4x^2+2x$$

81. $-xy(x^2-y^2)$
$$-x^3y+xy^3$$

82. $-x^2y(2xy-y^2)$
$$-2x^3y^2+x^2y^3$$

83. $x(2x^3-3x+2)$
$$2x^4-3x^2+2x$$

84. $y(-3y^2-2y+6)$
$$-3y^3-2y^2+6y$$

85. $-a(-2a^2-3a-2)$
$$2a^3+3a^2+2a$$

86. $-b(5b^2+7b-35)$
$$-5b^3-7b^2+35b$$

87. $x^2(3x^4-3x^2-2)$
$$3x^6-3x^4-2x^2$$

88. $y^3(-4y^3-6y+7)$
$$-4y^6-6y^4+7y^3$$

89. $2y^2(-3y^2-6y+7)$
$$-6y^4-12y^3+14y^2$$

90. $4x^2(3x^2-2x+6)$
$$12x^4-8x^3+24x^2$$

91. $(a^2+3a-4)(-2a)$
$$-2a^3-6a^2+8a$$

92. $(b^3-2b+2)(-5b)$
$$-5b^4+10b^2-10b$$

93. $-3y^2(-2y^2+y-2)$
$$6y^4-3y^3+6y^2$$

94. $-5x^2(3x^2-3x-7)$
$$-15x^4+15x^3+35x^2$$

Simplify.

95. $xy(x^2 - 3xy + y^2)$

$x^3y - 3x^2y^2 + xy^3$

96. $ab(2a^2 - 4ab - 6b^2)$

$2a^3b - 4a^2b^2 - 6ab^3$

97. $(x^2 + 3x + 2)(x + 1)$

$x^3 + 4x^2 + 5x + 2$

98. $(x^2 - 2x + 7)(x - 2)$

$x^3 - 4x^2 + 11x - 14$

99. $(a^2 - 3a + 4)(a - 3)$

$a^3 - 6a^2 + 13a - 12$

100. $(x^2 - 3x + 5)(2x - 3)$

$2x^3 - 9x^2 + 19x - 15$

101. $(-2b^2 - 3b + 4)(b - 5)$

$-2b^3 + 7b^2 + 19b - 20$

102. $(-a^2 + 3a - 2)(2a - 1)$

$-2a^3 + 7a^2 - 7a + 2$

103. $(-2x^2 + 7x - 2)(3x - 5)$

$-6x^3 + 31x^2 - 41x + 10$

104. $(-a^2 - 2a + 3)(2a - 1)$

$-2a^3 - 3a^2 + 8a - 3$

105. $(x^2 + 5)(x - 3)$

$x^3 - 3x^2 + 5x - 15$

106. $(y^2 - 2y)(2y + 5)$

$2y^3 + y^2 - 10y$

107. $(x^3 - 3x + 2)(x - 4)$

$x^4 - 4x^3 - 3x^2 + 14x - 8$

108. $(y^3 + 4y^2 - 8)(2y - 1)$

$2y^4 + 7y^3 - 4y^2 - 16y + 8$

109. $(5y^2 + 8y - 2)(3y - 8)$

$15y^3 - 16y^2 - 70y + 16$

110. $(3y^2 + 3y - 5)(4y - 3)$

$12y^3 + 3y^2 - 29y + 15$

111. $(5a^3 - 5a + 2)(a - 4)$

$5a^4 - 20a^3 - 5a^2 + 22a - 8$

112. $(3b^3 - 5b^2 + 7)(6b - 1)$

$18b^4 - 33b^3 + 5b^2 + 42b - 7$

113. $(y^3 + 2y^2 - 3y + 1)(y + 2)$

$y^4 + 4y^3 + y^2 - 5y + 2$

114. $(2a^3 - 3a^2 + 2a - 1)(2a - 3)$

$4a^4 - 12a^3 + 13a^2 - 8a + 3$

6.2D Exercises

Simplify.

115. $(x + 1)(x + 3)$

$x^2 + 4x + 3$

116. $(y + 2)(y + 5)$

$y^2 + 7y + 10$

117. $(a - 3)(a + 4)$

$a^2 + a - 12$

118. $(b - 6)(b + 3)$

$b^2 - 3b - 18$

119. $(y + 3)(y - 8)$

$y^2 - 5y - 24$

120. $(x + 10)(x - 5)$

$x^2 + 5x - 50$

121. $(y - 7)(y - 3)$

$y^2 - 10y + 21$

122. $(a - 8)(a - 9)$

$a^2 - 17a + 72$

123. $(2x + 1)(x + 7)$

$2x^2 + 15x + 7$

124. $(y + 2)(5y + 1)$

$5y^2 + 11y + 2$

125. $(3x - 1)(x + 4)$

$3x^2 + 11x - 4$

126. $(7x - 2)(x + 4)$

$7x^2 + 26x - 8$

127. $(4x - 3)(x - 7)$

$4x^2 - 31x + 21$

128. $(2x - 3)(4x - 7)$

$8x^2 - 26x + 21$

129. $(3y - 8)(y + 2)$

$3y^2 - 2y - 16$

130. $(5y - 9)(y + 5)$

$5y^2 + 16y - 45$

131. $(3x + 7)(3x + 11)$

$9x^2 + 54x + 77$

132. $(5a + 6)(6a + 5)$

$30a^2 + 61a + 30$

133. $(7a - 16)(3a - 5)$

$21a^2 - 83a + 80$

134. $(5a - 12)(3a - 7)$

$15a^2 - 71a + 84$

Simplify.

135. $(x + y)(2x + y)$

$2x^2 + 3xy + y^2$

136. $(2a + b)(a + 3b)$

$2a^2 + 7ab + 3b^2$

137. $(3x - 4y)(x - 2y)$

$3x^2 - 10xy + 8y^2$

138. $(2a - b)(3a + 2b)$

$6a^2 + ab - 2b^2$

139. $(5a - 3b)(2a + 4b)$

$10a^2 + 14ab - 12b^2$

140. $(2x + y)(x - 2y)$

$2x^2 - 3xy - 2y^2$

141. $(3x - 7y)(3x + 5y)$

$9x^2 - 6xy - 35y^2$

142. $(2x + 3y)(5x + 7y)$

$10x^2 + 29xy + 21y^2$

143. $(5x + 3y)(7x + 2y)$

$35x^2 + 31xy + 6y^2$

144. $(3a - 2b)(2a - 7b)$

$6a^2 - 25ab + 14b^2$

145. $(5a - b)(7a - b)$

$35a^2 - 12ab + b^2$

146. $(a - 9b)(2a + 7b)$

$2a^2 - 11ab - 63b^2$

147. $(2a + 5b)(7a - 2b)$

$14a^2 + 31ab - 10b^2$

148. $(10a - 3b)(10a - 7b)$

$100a^2 - 100ab + 21b^2$

149. $(12a - 5b)(3a - 4b)$

$36a^2 - 63ab + 20b^2$

150. $(5x + 12y)(3x + 4y)$

$15x^2 + 56xy + 48y^2$

151. $(11x + 2y)(3x + 7y)$

$33x^2 + 83xy + 14y^2$

152. $(2x - 15y)(7x + 4y)$

$14x^2 - 97xy - 60y^2$

153. $(5x + 2y)(2x - 5y)$

$10x^2 - 21xy - 10y^2$

154. $(8x - 3y)(7x - 5y)$

$56x^2 - 61xy + 15y^2$

155. $(2x - 9y)(8x - 3y)$

$16x^2 - 78xy + 27y^2$

6.2E Exercises

Simplify.

156. $(y - 5)(y + 5)$

$y^2 - 25$

157. $(y + 6)(y - 6)$

$y^2 - 36$

158. $(2x + 3)(2x - 3)$

$4x^2 - 9$

159. $(4x - 7)(4x + 7)$

$16x^2 - 49$

160. $(x + 1)^2$

$x^2 + 2x + 1$

161. $(y - 3)^2$

$y^2 - 6y + 9$

162. $(3a - 5)^2$

$9a^2 - 30a + 25$

163. $(6x - 5)^2$

$36x^2 - 60x + 25$

164. $(3x - 7)(3x + 7)$

$9x^2 - 49$

165. $(9x - 2)(9x + 2)$

$81x^2 - 4$

166. $(2a + b)^2$

$4a^2 + 4ab + b^2$

167. $(x + 3y)^2$

$x^2 + 6xy + 9y^2$

168. $(x - 2y)^2$

$x^2 - 4xy + 4y^2$

169. $(2x - 3y)^2$

$4x^2 - 12xy + 9y^2$

170. $(4 - 3y)(4 + 3y)$

$16 - 9y^2$

171. $(2 + 5x)(2 - 5x)$

$4 - 25x^2$

172. $(5x + 2y)^2$

$25x^2 + 20xy + 4y^2$

173. $(2a - 9b)^2$

$4a^2 - 36ab + 81b^2$

174. $(3 - 5y)^2$

$9 - 30y + 25y^2$

175. $(2 + 7x)^2$

$4 + 28x + 49x^2$

Section 3 | Division of Polynomials

Objective A | ## To divide monomials

Reference for
Computer
Tutor™

The quotient of two exponential expressions with the *same* base can be simplified by writing each expression in factored form, canceling the common factors, and then writing the result with an exponent.

$$\frac{x^5}{x^2} = \frac{\overset{1}{\cancel{x}} \cdot \overset{1}{\cancel{x}} \cdot x \cdot x \cdot x}{\underset{1}{\cancel{x}} \cdot \underset{1}{\cancel{x}}} = x^3$$

$$\frac{x^4}{x^6} = \frac{\overset{1}{\cancel{x}} \cdot \overset{1}{\cancel{x}} \cdot \overset{1}{\cancel{x}} \cdot \overset{1}{\cancel{x}}}{\underset{1}{\cancel{x}} \cdot \underset{1}{\cancel{x}} \cdot \underset{1}{\cancel{x}} \cdot \underset{1}{\cancel{x}} \cdot x \cdot x} = \frac{1}{x^2}$$

Note that subtracting the smaller exponent from the larger exponent results in the same quotient.

$$\frac{x^5}{x^2} = \frac{x^{5-2}}{1} = x^3$$

$$\frac{x^4}{x^6} = \frac{1}{x^{6-4}} = \frac{1}{x^2}$$

Rule for Dividing Exponential Expressions

If m and n are integers and $x \neq 0$, then $\dfrac{x^m}{x^n} = x^{m-n}$ if $m > n$

and $\dfrac{x^m}{x^n} = \dfrac{1}{x^{n-m}}$ if $m < n$.

Simplify $\dfrac{x^7}{x^2}$.

$7 > 2$
The bases are the same.
Subtract the exponent in the denominator from the exponent in the numerator.

$$\frac{x^7}{x^2} \boxed{= x^{7-2}} \quad \begin{array}{l}\text{Do this step}\\\text{mentally.}\end{array}$$
$$= x^5$$

Simplify $\dfrac{a^3}{a^9}$.

$3 < 9$
The bases are the same.
Subtract the exponent in the numerator from the exponent in the denominator.

$$\frac{a^3}{a^9} \boxed{= \frac{1}{a^{9-3}}} \quad \begin{array}{l}\text{Do this step}\\\text{mentally.}\end{array}$$
$$= \frac{1}{a^6}$$

Simplify $\dfrac{x^4 y^2}{-xy^3}$.

Negative signs are placed in front of a fraction.

$$\frac{x^4 y^2}{-xy^3} = -\frac{x^4 y^2}{xy^3}$$

Divide variables with like bases by subtracting the exponents.

$$\boxed{= -\frac{x^{4-1}}{y^{3-2}}} \quad \begin{array}{l}\text{Do this step}\\\text{mentally.}\end{array}$$
$$= -\frac{x^3}{y}$$

Simplify $\dfrac{10x^3y^5}{4x^6y^2}$.

Factor the coefficients.
Cancel the common factors.

$$\dfrac{10x^3y^5}{4x^6y^2} = \dfrac{\overset{1}{\cancel{2}} \cdot 5x^3y^5}{\underset{1}{\cancel{2}} \cdot 2x^6y^2}$$

Divide variables with like bases by subtracting the exponents.

$$= \boxed{\dfrac{5y^{5-2}}{2x^{6-3}}}$$ Do this step mentally.

$$= \dfrac{5y^3}{2x^3}$$

Example 1

Simplify $\dfrac{-16x^4}{4x^9}$.

Solution

$$\dfrac{-16x^4}{4x^9} = -\dfrac{\overset{1}{\cancel{2}} \cdot \overset{1}{\cancel{2}} \cdot 2 \cdot 2x^4}{\underset{1}{\cancel{2}} \cdot \underset{1}{\cancel{2}}x^9} = -\dfrac{4}{x^5}$$

Example 2

Simplify $\dfrac{42y^{12}}{-14y^{17}}$.

Your solution

$$-\dfrac{3}{y^5}$$

Example 3

Simplify $\dfrac{-28x^4y^3}{6xy}$.

Solution

$$\dfrac{-28x^4y^3}{6xy} = -\dfrac{\overset{1}{\cancel{2}} \cdot 2 \cdot 7x^4y^3}{\underset{1}{\cancel{2}} \cdot 3xy} = -\dfrac{14x^3y^2}{3}$$

Example 4

Simplify $\dfrac{12r^4s^2}{-8r^3s}$.

Your solution

$$-\dfrac{3rs}{2}$$

Example 5

Simplify $\dfrac{(-3ab)^2}{9a^3b}$.

Solution

$$(-3)^2 = 9$$

$$\dfrac{(-3ab)^2}{9a^3b} = \dfrac{(-3)^2a^2b^2}{9a^3b} = \dfrac{\overset{1}{\cancel{3}} \cdot \overset{1}{\cancel{3}}a^2b^2}{\underset{1}{\cancel{3}} \cdot \underset{1}{\cancel{3}}a^3b} = \dfrac{b}{a}$$

Example 6

Simplify $\dfrac{(2x^2y)^3}{-4xy^5}$.

Your solution

$$-\dfrac{2x^5}{y^2}$$

Solutions on p. A36

| Objective B | To divide a polynomial by a monomial |

Reference for
Computer
Tutor™

Note that $\frac{8 + 4}{2}$ can be simplified by first adding the terms in the numerator and then dividing the result. It can also be simplified by first dividing each term in the numerator by the denominator and then adding the result.

$$\frac{8 + 4}{2} = \frac{12}{2} = 6$$

$$\frac{8 + 4}{2} = \frac{8}{2} + \frac{4}{2} = 4 + 2 = 6$$

To divide a polynomial by a monomial, divide each term in the numerator by the denominator, and write the sum of the quotients.

$$\frac{a + b}{c} = \frac{a}{c} + \frac{b}{c}$$

Simplify $\frac{6x^2 + 4x}{2x}$.

Divide each term of the polynomial by the monomial.
Simplify each expression.

$$\frac{6x^2 + 4x}{2x} = \frac{6x^2}{2x} + \frac{4x}{2x}$$
$$= 3x + 2$$

Check: $2x(3x + 2) = 6x^2 + 4x$

Example 7

Simplify $\frac{6x^3 - 3x^2 + 9x}{3x}$.

Solution

$$\frac{6x^3 - 3x^2 + 9x}{3x} = \frac{6x^3}{3x} - \frac{3x^2}{3x} + \frac{9x}{3x}$$
$$= 2x^2 - x + 3$$

Example 8

Simplify $\frac{4x^3y + 8x^2y^2 - 4xy^3}{2xy}$.

Your solution

$$2x^2 + 4xy - 2y^2$$

Example 9

Simplify $\frac{12x^2y - 6xy + 4x^2}{2xy}$.

Solution

$$\frac{12x^2y - 6xy + 4x^2}{2xy} = \frac{12x^2y}{2xy} - \frac{6xy}{2xy} + \frac{4x^2}{2xy}$$
$$= 6x - 3 + \frac{2x}{y}$$

Example 10

Simplify $\frac{24x^2y^2 - 18xy + 6y}{6xy}$.

Your solution

$$4xy - 3 + \frac{1}{x}$$

Solutions on pp. A36–37

| Objective C | To divide polynomials |

Reference for
Computer
Tutor™

To divide polynomials, use a method similar to that used for division of whole numbers. The same equation used to check division of whole numbers is used to check polynomial division.

Dividend = (quotient × divisor) + remainder

Simplify $(x^2 - 5x + 8) \div (x - 3)$.

Step 1

$$\begin{array}{r} x \phantom{{}-5x+8} \\ x-3\overline{)x^2 - 5x + 8} \\ \underline{x^2 - 3x} \downarrow \\ -2x + 8 \end{array}$$

Think: $x\overline{)x^2} = \dfrac{x^2}{x} = x$

Multiply: $x(x - 3) = x^2 - 3x$

Subtract: $(x^2 - 5x) - (x^2 - 3x) = -2x$

Step 2

$$\begin{array}{r} x - 2 \\ x-3\overline{)x^2 - 5x + 8} \\ \underline{x^2 - 3x} \\ -2x + 8 \\ \underline{-2x + 6} \\ 2 \end{array}$$

Think: $x\overline{)-2x} = \dfrac{-2x}{x} = -2$

Multiply: $-2(x - 3) = -2x + 6$

Subtract: $(-2x + 8) - (-2x + 6) = 2$

The remainder is 2.

Check: $(x - 2)(x - 3) + 2 = x^2 - 3x - 2x + 6 + 2 = x^2 - 5x + 8$

$(x^2 - 5x + 8) \div (x - 3) = x - 2 + \dfrac{2}{x-3}$

Simplify $(6x + 2x^3 + 26) \div (x + 2)$.

Arrange the terms in descending order.
There is no term of x^2 in $2x^3 + 6x + 26$.
Insert a zero for the missing term
so that like terms will be in columns.

$$\begin{array}{r} 2x^2 - 4x + 14 \\ x+2\overline{)2x^3 + 0 + 6x + 26} \\ \underline{2x^3 + 4x^2} \\ -4x^2 + 6x \\ \underline{-4x^2 - 8x} \\ 14x + 26 \\ \underline{14x + 28} \\ -2 \end{array}$$

$(2x^3 + 6x + 26) \div (x + 2) = 2x^2 - 4x + 14 - \dfrac{2}{x+2}$

Example 11

Simplify $(x^2 - 1) \div (x + 1)$.

Solution

Insert a zero for
the missing term.

$$\begin{array}{r} x - 1 \\ x+1\overline{)x^2 + 0 - 1} \\ \underline{x^2 + x} \\ -x - 1 \\ \underline{-x - 1} \\ 0 \end{array}$$

$(x^2 - 1) \div (x + 1) = x - 1$

Example 12

Simplify $(2x^3 + x^2 - 8x - 3) \div (2x - 3)$.

Your solution

$x^2 + 2x - 1 - \dfrac{6}{2x-3}$

6.3A Exercises

Simplify.

1. $\dfrac{3x^2}{x}$

$3x$

2. $\dfrac{4y^2}{2y}$

$2y$

3. $\dfrac{2x^2}{-2x}$

$-x$

4. $\dfrac{-8y^2}{4y}$

$-2y$

5. $\dfrac{12x^4}{3x}$

$4x^3$

6. $\dfrac{5x^2}{15x}$

$\dfrac{x}{3}$

7. $\dfrac{-16x}{4x^3}$

$-\dfrac{4}{x^2}$

8. $\dfrac{27y}{-12y^3}$

$-\dfrac{9}{4y^2}$

9. $\dfrac{a^4b^5}{a^3b^9}$

$\dfrac{a}{b^4}$

10. $\dfrac{a^5b^7}{a^8b^2}$

$\dfrac{b^5}{a^3}$

11. $\dfrac{x^3y^4}{x^3y}$

y^3

12. $\dfrac{x^4y^5}{x^2y^5}$

x^2

13. $\dfrac{(3x)^2}{15x^2}$

$\dfrac{3}{5}$

14. $\dfrac{(4y)^2}{2y}$

$8y$

15. $\dfrac{(6b)^3}{(-3b^2)^2}$

$\dfrac{24}{b}$

16. $\dfrac{(-3a^2)^3}{(9a)^2}$

$-\dfrac{a^4}{3}$

17. $\dfrac{-36a^4b^7}{60a^5b^9}$

$-\dfrac{3}{5ab^2}$

18. $\dfrac{-50a^2b^7}{45ab^2}$

$-\dfrac{10ab^5}{9}$

19. $\dfrac{12a^2b^3}{-27a^2b^2}$

$-\dfrac{4b}{9}$

20. $\dfrac{-16xy^4}{96x^4y^4}$

$-\dfrac{1}{6x^3}$

21. $\dfrac{-8x^2y^4}{44y^2z^5}$

$-\dfrac{2x^2y^2}{11z^5}$

22. $\dfrac{22a^2b^4}{-132b^3c^2}$

$-\dfrac{a^2b}{6c^2}$

23. $\dfrac{-(8a^2b^4)^3}{64a^3b^8}$

$-8a^3b^4$

24. $\dfrac{-(14ab^4)^2}{28a^4b^2}$

$-\dfrac{7b^6}{a^2}$

25. $\dfrac{-20a^3b^4}{-45ab^7}$

$\dfrac{4a^2}{9b^3}$

26. $\dfrac{-14x^6y^4}{-70x^3y}$

$\dfrac{x^3y^3}{5}$

27. $\dfrac{x^4y^7z}{x^2y^5z^4}$

$\dfrac{x^2y^2}{z^3}$

28. $\dfrac{x^2y^4z^2}{x^3yz^5}$

$\dfrac{y^3}{xz^3}$

29. $\dfrac{(-2ab^2)^3}{-8ab^7}$

$\dfrac{a^2}{b}$

30. $\dfrac{(-3x^3y)^2}{-12xy^5}$

$-\dfrac{3x^5}{4y^3}$

6.3B Exercises

Simplify.

31. $\dfrac{2x+2}{2}$

$x+1$

32. $\dfrac{5y+5}{5}$

$y+1$

33. $\dfrac{10a-25}{5}$

$2a-5$

34. $\dfrac{16b-40}{8}$

$2b-5$

35. $\dfrac{3a^2+2a}{a}$

$3a+2$

36. $\dfrac{6y^2+4y}{y}$

$6y+4$

37. $\dfrac{4b^3-3b}{b}$

$4b^2-3$

38. $\dfrac{12x^2-7x}{x}$

$12x-7$

39. $\dfrac{3x^2-6x}{3x}$

$x-2$

40. $\dfrac{10y^2-6y}{2y}$

$5y-3$

41. $\dfrac{5x^2-10x}{-5x}$

$-x+2$

42. $\dfrac{3y^2-27y}{-3y}$

$-y+9$

43. $\dfrac{x^3+3x^2-5x}{x}$

x^2+3x-5

44. $\dfrac{a^3-5a^2+7a}{a}$

a^2-5a+7

45. $\dfrac{x^6-3x^4-x^2}{x^2}$

x^4-3x^2-1

46. $\dfrac{a^8-5a^5-3a^3}{a^2}$

a^6-5a^3-3a

47. $\dfrac{5x^2y^2+10xy}{5xy}$

$xy+2$

48. $\dfrac{8x^2y^2-24xy}{8xy}$

$xy-3$

49. $\dfrac{9y^6-15y^3}{-3y^3}$

$-3y^3+5$

50. $\dfrac{4x^4-6x^2}{-2x^2}$

$-2x^2+3$

51. $\dfrac{3x^2-2x+1}{x}$

$3x-2+\dfrac{1}{x}$

52. $\dfrac{8y^2+2y-3}{y}$

$8y+2-\dfrac{3}{y}$

53. $\dfrac{-3x^2+7x-6}{x}$

$-3x+7-\dfrac{6}{x}$

54. $\dfrac{2y^2-6y+9}{y}$

$2y-6+\dfrac{9}{y}$

Simplify.

55. $\dfrac{16a^2b - 20ab + 24ab^2}{4ab}$

$$4a - 5 + 6b$$

56. $\dfrac{22a^2b + 11ab - 33ab^2}{11ab}$

$$2a + 1 - 3b$$

57. $\dfrac{9x^2y + 6xy - 3xy^2}{xy}$

$$9x + 6 - 3y$$

6.3C Exercises

Simplify.

58. $(x^2 + 2x + 1) \div (x + 1)$

$$x + 1$$

59. $(x^2 + 10x + 25) \div (x + 5)$

$$x + 5$$

60. $(a^2 - 6a + 9) \div (a - 3)$

$$a - 3$$

61. $(b^2 - 14b + 49) \div (b - 7)$

$$b - 7$$

62. $(x^2 - x - 6) \div (x - 3)$

$$x + 2$$

63. $(y^2 + 2y - 35) \div (y + 7)$

$$y - 5$$

64. $(2x^2 + 5x + 2) \div (x + 2)$

$$2x + 1$$

65. $(2y^2 - 13y + 21) \div (y - 3)$

$$2y - 7$$

66. $(4x^2 - 16) \div (2x + 4)$

$$2x - 4$$

67. $(2y^2 + 7) \div (y - 3)$

$$2y + 6 + \dfrac{25}{y-3}$$

68. $(x^2 + 1) \div (x - 1)$

$$x + 1 + \dfrac{2}{x-1}$$

69. $(x^2 + 4) \div (x + 2)$

$$x - 2 + \dfrac{8}{x+2}$$

70. $(6x^2 - 7x) \div (3x - 2)$

$$2x - 1 - \dfrac{2}{3x-2}$$

71. $(6y^2 + 2y) \div (2y + 4)$

$$3y - 5 + \dfrac{10}{y+2}$$

72. $(5x^2 + 7x) \div (x - 1)$

$$5x + 12 + \dfrac{12}{x-1}$$

73. $(6x^2 - 5) \div (x + 2)$

$$6x - 12 + \dfrac{19}{x+2}$$

74. $(a^2 + 5a + 10) \div (a + 2)$

$$a + 3 + \dfrac{4}{a+2}$$

75. $(b^2 - 8b - 9) \div (b - 3)$

$$b - 5 - \dfrac{24}{b-3}$$

76. $(2y^2 - 9y + 8) \div (2y + 3)$

$$y - 6 + \dfrac{26}{2y+3}$$

77. $(x^4 - x^2 - 6) \div (x^2 + 2)$

$$x^2 - 3$$

78. $(x^4 + 3x^2 - 10) \div (x^2 - 2)$

$$x^2 + 5$$

79. $(12a^2 - 25a - 7) \div (3a - 7)$

$$4a + 1$$

80. $(12x^2 - 23x + 5) \div (4x - 1)$

$$3x - 5$$

81. $(x^3 + 3x^2 + 5x + 3) \div (x + 1)$

$$x^2 + 2x + 3$$

82. $(x^3 - 6x^2 + 7x - 2) \div (x - 1)$

$$x^2 - 5x + 2$$

Section 4 Negative and Zero Exponents

Objective A

To simplify expressions containing negative and zero exponents

Reference for
Computer
Tutor™

Note that when an exponential expression is divided by itself, the result contains a zero exponent.

$$\frac{x^3}{x^3} = x^{3-3} = x^0$$

When the same expression is simplified by factoring and canceling, the result is 1.

$$\frac{x^3}{x^3} = \frac{\overset{1}{\cancel{x}} \cdot \overset{1}{\cancel{x}} \cdot \overset{1}{\cancel{x}}}{\underset{1}{\cancel{x}} \cdot \underset{1}{\cancel{x}} \cdot \underset{1}{\cancel{x}}} = 1$$

To insure that the two answers are equal, a number or variable to the zero power must be equal to 1.

$$x^0 = 1, x \neq 0$$

Negative integers, as well as positive, can be used as exponents. The rules that have been developed for exponential expressions can be extended to include negative integers.

$$x^m \cdot x^n = x^{m+n}$$
$$a^{-2} \cdot a^3 = a^{-2+3} = a$$

$$(x^m)^n = x^{m \cdot n}$$
$$(a^{-2})^3 = a^{-2 \cdot 3} = a^{-6}$$

$$(x^m \cdot y^n)^p = x^{m \cdot p} y^{n \cdot p}$$
$$(a^{-2}b^4)^{-3} = a^{-2(-3)}b^{4(-3)} = a^6 b^{-12}$$

The Rule for Dividing Exponential Expressions can be stated as a single rule.

$$\frac{x^m}{x^n} = x^{m-n}$$
$$\frac{a^2}{a^5} = a^{2-5} = a^{-3}$$

The meaning of a negative exponent can be developed using the rules presented in this chapter.

The exponential expressions at the right are multiplied by adding the exponents. The product is a^0, or 1.

$$a^4 \cdot a^{-4} = a^{4+(-4)} = a^0 = 1$$

Recall that a number times its reciprocal is equal to 1.

$$a^4 \cdot \frac{1}{a^4} = 1$$

Since $a^4 \cdot a^{-4} = 1$, and $a^4 \cdot \frac{1}{a^4} = 1$, then a^{-4} must equal $\frac{1}{a^4}$.

Rule of Negative Exponents

If n is a positive integer and $x \neq 0$, then $x^{-n} = \frac{1}{x^n}$ and $\frac{1}{x^{-n}} = x^n$.

An exponential expression is considered in simplest form when written with a positive exponent.

A number with a negative exponent can be written with a positive exponent and then evaluated.

Write 2^{-3} with a positive exponent. Then evaluate.

Write the expression with a positive exponent.

$$2^{-3} = \frac{1}{2^3}$$

Evaluate.

$$= \frac{1}{8}$$

Simplify $\frac{x^{-4}y^6}{xy^{-2}}$.

Divide variables with like bases by subtracting the exponents.

$$\frac{x^{-4}y^6}{xy^{-2}} \quad \boxed{= x^{-4-1}y^{6-(-2)}} \qquad \text{Do this step}$$
$$\text{mentally.}$$

Write the expression with positive exponents.

$$= x^{-5}y^8$$

$$= \frac{y^8}{x^5}$$

Example 1

Write $\frac{3^{-3}}{3^2}$ with a positive exponent.

Then evaluate.

Solution

$$\frac{3^{-3}}{3^2} = 3^{-5} = \frac{1}{3^5} = \frac{1}{243}$$

Example 2

Write $\frac{2^{-2}}{2^3}$ with a positive exponent.

Then evaluate.

Your solution

$$\frac{1}{32}$$

Example 3

Simplify $(-2x)(3x^{-2})^{-3}$.

Solution

$$(-2x)(3x^{-2})^{-3} = (-2x)(3^{-3}x^6) =$$
$$\frac{-2x \cdot x^6}{3^3} = -\frac{2x^7}{27}$$

Example 4

Simplify $(-2x^2)(x^{-3}y^{-4})^{-2}$.

Your solution

$$-2x^8y^8$$

Example 5

Simplify $\frac{(2ab^{-2})^{-2}}{ab^2}$.

Solution

$$\frac{(2ab^{-2})^{-2}}{ab^2} = \frac{2^{-2}a^{-2}b^4}{ab^2} = 2^{-2}a^{-3}b^2 = \frac{b^2}{2^2a^3} = \frac{b^2}{4a^3}$$

Example 6

Simplify $\frac{(3x^{-2}y)^3}{9xy^0}$.

Your solution

$$\frac{3y^3}{x^7}$$

Reference for Computer Tutor™

| Objective B | To convert from decimal notation to scientific notation and from scientific notation to decimal notation |

Very large and very small numbers are encountered in the fields of science and engineering. For example, the mass of the electron is 0.00000000000000000000000000009 g. Numbers such as this one are difficult to read and write, so a more convenient system for writing such numbers has been developed. It is called **scientific notation.**

To express a number in scientific notation, write the number as the product of a number between 1 and 10 and a power of 10. The form for scientific notation is $a \times 10^n$, where a is a number between 1 and 10.

For numbers greater than 10, move the decimal point to the right of the first digit. The exponent n is positive and equal to the number of places the decimal point has been moved.

$$965{,}000 = 9.65 \times 10^5$$
$$3{,}600{,}000 = 3.6 \times 10^6$$
$$92{,}000{,}000{,}000 = 9.2 \times 10^{10}$$

For numbers less than 1, move the decimal point to the right of the first nonzero digit. The exponent n is negative. The absolute value of the exponent is equal to the number of places the decimal point has been moved.

$$0.0002 = 2 \times 10^{-4}$$
$$0.0000000974 = 9.74 \times 10^{-8}$$
$$0.000000000086 = 8.6 \times 10^{-11}$$

Converting a number written in scientific notation to decimal notation requires moving the decimal point.

When the exponent is positive, move the decimal point to the right the same number of places as the exponent.

$$1.32 \times 10^4 = 13{,}200$$
$$1.4 \times 10^8 = 140{,}000{,}000$$

When the exponent is negative, move the decimal point to the left the same number of places as the absolute value of the exponent.

$$1.32 \times 10^{-2} = 0.0132$$
$$1.4 \times 10^{-4} = 0.00014$$

Numerical calculations involving numbers that have more digits than the hand-held calculator is able to handle can be performed using scientific notation.

Simplify: $\dfrac{220{,}000 \times 0.000000092}{0.0000011}$

Write the numbers in scientific notation.

Simplify.

$$\frac{220{,}000 \times 0.000000092}{0.0000011} = \frac{2.2 \times 10^5 \times 9.2 \times 10^{-8}}{1.1 \times 10^{-6}}$$

$$= \frac{(2.2)(9.2) \times 10^{5 + (-8) - (-6)}}{1.1}$$

$$= 18.4 \times 10^3 = 18{,}400$$

Example 7   Write 0.000041 in scientific notation.

Solution $0.000041 = 4.1 \times 10^{-5}$

Example 8   Write 942,000,000 in scientific notation.

Your solution

$$9.42 \times 10^8$$

Solution on p. A37

Example 9   Write 3.3×10^7 in decimal notation.

Solution $3.3 \times 10^7 = 33,000,000$

Example 11   Simplify:
$$\frac{2,400,000,000 \times 0.0000063}{0.00009 \times 480}$$

Solution

$$\frac{2,400,000,000 \times 0.0000063}{0.00009 \times 480} =$$

$$\frac{2.4 \times 10^9 \times 6.3 \times 10^{-6}}{9 \times 10^{-5} \times 4.8 \times 10^2} =$$

$$\frac{(2.4)(6.3) \times 10^{9 + (-6) - (-5) - 2}}{(9)(4.8)} =$$

$$0.35 \times 10^6 = 350,000$$

Example 10   Write 2.7×10^{-5} in decimal notation.

Your solution   0.000027

Example 12   Simplify:
$$\frac{5,600,000 \times 0.000000081}{900 \times 0.000000028}$$

Your solution

18,000

Solutions on p. A37

| Objective C | To solve application problems |

Example 13   How many miles does light travel in one day? The speed of light is 186,000 mi/s. Write the answer in scientific notation.

Strategy   To find the distance traveled:
▷ Write the speed of light in scientific notation.
▷ Write the number of seconds in one day in scientific notation.
▷ Use the equation $d = rt$, where r is the speed of light and t is the number of seconds in one day.

Solution

$186,000 = 1.86 \times 10^5$
$24 \cdot 60 \cdot 60 = 86,400 = 8.64 \times 10^4$
$d = rt$
$d = (1.86 \times 10^5)(8.64 \times 10^4)$
$d = 1.86 \times 8.64 \times 10^9$
$d = 16.0704 \times 10^9$
$d = 1.60704 \times 10^{10}$

Light travels 1.60704×10^{10} mi in one day.

Example 14   How long does it take light to travel to the earth from the sun? The sun is 9.3×10^7 mi from the earth and light travels 1.86×10^5 mi/s. Write the answer in scientific notation.

Your strategy

Your solution

5×10^2 seconds

Solution on p. A38

6.4A Exercises

Write with a positive exponent, then evaluate.

1. 5^{-2}
$\dfrac{1}{5^2} = \dfrac{1}{25}$

2. 3^{-3}
$\dfrac{1}{3^3} = \dfrac{1}{27}$

3. $\dfrac{3^{-2}}{3}$
$\dfrac{1}{3^3} = \dfrac{1}{27}$

4. $\dfrac{5^{-3}}{5}$
$\dfrac{1}{5^4} = \dfrac{1}{625}$

5. $\dfrac{2^{-3}}{2^3}$
$\dfrac{1}{2^6} = \dfrac{1}{64}$

6. $\dfrac{3^{-2}}{3^2}$
$\dfrac{1}{3^4} = \dfrac{1}{81}$

Simplify.

7. x^{-2}
$\dfrac{1}{x^2}$

8. y^{-10}
$\dfrac{1}{y^{10}}$

9. a^{-6}
$\dfrac{1}{a^6}$

10. b^{-4}
$\dfrac{1}{b^4}$

11. $x^2 y^{-3}$
$\dfrac{x^2}{y^3}$

12. $a^{-2} b$
$\dfrac{b}{a^2}$

13. $x^{-1} y^{-2}$
$\dfrac{1}{xy^2}$

14. $x^{-3} y^{-4}$
$\dfrac{1}{x^3 y^4}$

15. $x^{-3} x^4$
x

16. $x \cdot x^{-2}$
$\dfrac{1}{x}$

17. $a^{-3} a^{-4}$
$\dfrac{1}{a^7}$

18. $a^{-2} a^{-5}$
$\dfrac{1}{a^7}$

19. $\dfrac{x^{-2}}{x^2}$
$\dfrac{1}{x^4}$

20. $\dfrac{x^{-1}}{x}$
$\dfrac{1}{x^2}$

21. $\dfrac{a^{-3}}{a^5}$
$\dfrac{1}{a^8}$

22. $\dfrac{a^{-10}}{a^{10}}$
$\dfrac{1}{a^{20}}$

23. $\dfrac{x^{-2} y}{x}$
$\dfrac{y}{x^3}$

24. $\dfrac{x^4 y^{-3}}{x^2}$
$\dfrac{x^2}{y^3}$

25. $\dfrac{a^{-2} b}{b^0}$
$\dfrac{b}{a^2}$

26. $\dfrac{a^2 b^{-4}}{b^0}$
$\dfrac{a^2}{b^4}$

27. $(a^2)^{-2}$
$\dfrac{1}{a^4}$

28. $(b^3)^{-3}$
$\dfrac{1}{b^9}$

29. $(a^{-3})^2$
$\dfrac{1}{a^6}$

30. $(y^{-4})^3$
$\dfrac{1}{y^{12}}$

31. $(x^{-2})^{-3}$
x^6

32. $(y^{-3})^{-4}$
y^{12}

33. $(a^{-6})^{-3}$
a^{18}

34. $(a^{-1})^{-3}$
a^3

35. $(ab^{-1})^0$
1

36. $(a^2 b)^0$
1

37. $(x^{-2} y^2)^2$
$\dfrac{y^4}{x^4}$

38. $(x^{-3} y^{-1})^2$
$\dfrac{1}{x^6 y^2}$

39. $\dfrac{x^2 y^{-4}}{xy}$
$\dfrac{x}{y^5}$

40. $\dfrac{ab^{-5}}{a^7 b}$
$\dfrac{1}{a^6 b^6}$

41. $\dfrac{x^{-2} y}{x^2 y^{-3}}$
$\dfrac{y^4}{x^4}$

42. $\dfrac{a^{-3} b}{a^{-1} b^2}$
$\dfrac{1}{a^2 b}$

43. $(x^2 y^{-1})^{-2}$
$\dfrac{y^2}{x^4}$

44. $(a^{-1} b^{-1})^{-4}$
$a^4 b^4$

45. $(-2xy^{-2})^3$
$-\dfrac{8x^3}{y^6}$

46. $(-3x^{-1} y^2)^2$
$\dfrac{9y^4}{x^2}$

47. $(4x^2 y^{-3})^2$
$\dfrac{16x^4}{y^6}$

48. $(2a^{-3} b^2)^3$
$\dfrac{8b^6}{a^9}$

49. $(2x^{-1})(x^{-3})$
$\dfrac{2}{x^4}$

50. $(-2x^{-5})x^7$
$-2x^2$

51. $(-5a^2)(a^{-5})^2$
$-\dfrac{5}{a^8}$

52. $(2a^{-3})(a^7 b^{-1})^3$
$\dfrac{2a^{18}}{b^3}$

53. $(3ab^{-2})(2a^{-1} b)^{-3}$
$\dfrac{3a^4}{8b^5}$

54. $\dfrac{a^{-1} b^{-1}}{ab}$
$\dfrac{1}{a^2 b^2}$

55. $\dfrac{a^{-3} b^{-4}}{a^2 b^2}$
$\dfrac{1}{a^5 b^6}$

56. $\dfrac{3x^{-2} y^2}{6xy^2}$
$\dfrac{1}{2x^3}$

57. $\dfrac{2x^{-2} y}{8xy^{-3}}$
$\dfrac{y^4}{4x^3}$

58. $\dfrac{2x^{-1} y^{-4}}{4xy^{-2}}$
$\dfrac{1}{2x^2 y^2}$

59. $\dfrac{(x^{-1} y)^2}{xy^2}$
$\dfrac{1}{x^3}$

60. $\dfrac{(x^{-2} y)^2}{x^{-3} y^3}$
$\dfrac{1}{xy}$

61. $\dfrac{(x^{-3} y^{-2})^2}{x^6 y^8}$
$\dfrac{1}{x^{12} y^{12}}$

62. $\dfrac{(a^{-2} y^3)^{-3}}{a^{-2} y}$
$\dfrac{a^8}{y^{10}}$

6.4B Exercises

Write in scientific notation.

63. 0.00000467
4.67×10^{-6}

64. 0.0000000017
1.7×10^{-10}

65. 4,300,000
4.3×10^{6}

66. 9,800,000,000
9.8×10^{9}

Write in decimal notation.

67. 1.23×10^{-7}
0.000000123

68. 6.2×10^{-12}
0.0000000000062

69. 6.34×10^{5}
$634,000$

70. 4.35×10^{9}
$4,350,000,000$

Simplify.

71. (0.0000065)(3,200,000,000,000)
$20,800,000$

72. (480,000)(0.0000000096)
0.004608

73. $(3 \times 10^{-12})(5 \times 10^{16})$
$150,000$

74. $(8.9 \times 10^{-5})(3.2 \times 10^{-6})$
0.0000000002848

75. $\frac{9 \times 10^{-3}}{6 \times 10^{5}}$
0.000000015

76. $\frac{2.7 \times 10^{4}}{3 \times 10^{-6}}$
$9,000,000,000$

77. $\frac{4800}{0.00000024}$
$20,000,000,000$

78. $\frac{0.00056}{0.000000000004}$
$140,000,000$

6.4C Exercises

Solve. Write the answer in scientific notation.

79. How many kilometers does light travel in one day? The speed of light is 300,000 km/s.
2.592×10^{10} km

80. How many meters does light travel in 8 hours? The speed of light is 300,000,000 m/s.
8.64×10^{12} m

81. The mass of the earth is 5.9×10^{27} g. The mass of the sun is 2×10^{33} g. How many times heavier is the sun than the earth?
3.38983×10^{5} times heavier

82. The distance to the sun is 9.3×10^{7} mi. A satellite leaves the earth traveling at a constant speed of 1×10^{5} mph. How long would it take for the satellite to reach the sun if such a trip were possible?
9.3×10^{2} hours

83. One light year, an astronomical unit of distance, is the distance that light will travel in one year. Light travels 1.86×10^{5} mi/s. Find the measure of one light year in miles. Use a 360-day year.
5.785344×10^{12} mi

84. The light from the star Alpha Centauri takes 4.3 years to reach the earth. Light travels at 1.86×10^{5} mi/s. How far is Alpha Centauri from the earth? Use a 360-day year.
2.4876979×10^{13} mi

Calculators and Computers

One way to evaluate a polynomial using a calculator is to first express the polynomial in a form that suggests a sequence of steps on the calculator. To illustrate this method, consider the polynomial $4x^2 - 5x + 2$. First the polynomial is rewritten as:

$$4x^2 - 5x + 2 = (4x - 5)x + 2$$

To evaluate the polynomial, substitute the given value of x and then work through the rewritten expression from left to right. Three examples of this method are shown below.

Evaluate $5x^2 - 2x + 4$ when $x = 3$.

Rewrite the polynomial.

$$5x^2 - 2x + 4 = (5x - 2)x + 4$$

Replace x in the rewritten expression by the given value.

$$(5 \cdot 3 - 2) \cdot 3 + 4$$

Work through the expression from left to right.

$$\boxed{(} \ 5 \ \boxed{\times} \ 3 \ \boxed{-} \ 2 \ \boxed{)} \ \boxed{\times} \ 3 \ \boxed{+} \ 4 \ \boxed{=}$$

The result in the display should be 43.

Evaluate $2x^3 - 4x^2 + 7x - 12$ when $x = 4$.

Rewrite the polynomial.

$$2x^3 - 4x^2 + 7x - 12 = [(2x - 4)x + 7]x - 12$$

Replace x in the rewritten expression by the given value.

$$[(2 \cdot 4 - 4) \cdot 4 + 7] \cdot 4 - 12$$

Work through the expression from left to right.

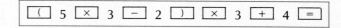

The result in the display should be 80.

Evaluate $4x^2 - 3x + 5$ when $x = -2$.

Rewrite the polynomial.

$$4x^2 - 3x + 5 = (4x - 3)x + 5$$

Replace x in the rewritten expression by the given value.

$$[4 \cdot (-2) - 3] \cdot (-2) + 5$$

Work through the expression from left to right.

$$\boxed{(} \ 4 \ \boxed{\times} \ 2 \ \boxed{+/-} \ \boxed{-} \ 3 \ \boxed{)} \ \boxed{\times} \ 2 \ \boxed{+/-} \ \boxed{+} \ 5 \ \boxed{=}$$

The result in the display should be 27.

Evaluate for the given value of x.

1. $2x^2 - 3x + 7; x = 4$ 2. $3x^2 + 7x - 12; x = -3$ 3. $3x^3 - 2x^2 + 6x - 8; x = 3$

ANSWERS: **1.** 27   **2.** -6 **3.** 73

Chapter Summary

KEY WORDS

A **monomial** is a number, a variable, or a product of numbers and variables.

A **polynomial** is a variable expression in which the terms are monomials.

A **monomial** is a polynomial of one term.
A **binomial** is a polynomial of two terms.
A **trinomial** is a polynomial of three terms.

When the terms of a polynomial in one variable are arranged so that the exponents of the variable decrease from left to right, the polynomial is written in **descending order.**

The **degree of a polynomial** in one variable is the largest exponent on a variable.

The product of two binomials can be found using the **FOIL** method. The letters of FOIL stand for **F**irst, **O**uter, **I**nner, and **L**ast.

A number written in **scientific notation** is a number written in the form $a \times 10^n$, where a is a number between 1 and 10.

ESSENTIAL RULES

Rule for Multiplying Exponential Expressions

If m and n are integers, then $x^m \cdot x^n = x^{m+n}$.

Rule for Simplifying Powers of Exponential Expressions

If m and n are integers, then $(x^m)^n = x^{m \cdot n}$.

Rule for Simplifying Powers of Products

If m, n, and p are integers, then $(x^m \cdot y^n)^p = x^{m \cdot p} y^{n \cdot p}$.

The Sum and Difference of Two Terms

$(a + b)(a - b) = a^2 - b^2$

The Square of a Binomial

$(a + b)^2 = a^2 + 2ab + b^2$
$(a - b)^2 = a^2 - 2ab + b^2$

Rule for Dividing Exponential Expressions

If m and n are integers and $x \neq 0$, then

$\dfrac{x^m}{x^n} = x^{m-n}$ if $m > n$ and

$\dfrac{x^m}{x^n} = \dfrac{1}{x^{n-m}}$ if $m < n$.

Rule of Negative Exponents

If n is a positive integer and $x \neq 0$, then $x^{-n} = \dfrac{1}{x^n}$ and $\dfrac{1}{x^{-n}} = x^n$.

	Review/Test

1. Write the polynomial in descending order.
$5x - 2x^2 + 3 - 8x^3$

$-8x^3 - 2x^2 + 5x + 3$

2. Identify the degree of the polynomial.
$6x^4 - x^2 + 7$

4

3. Simplify
$(3x^3 - 2x^2 - 4) + (8x^2 - 8x + 7)$.

$3x^3 + 6x^2 - 8x + 3$

4. Simplify
$(3a^2 - 2a - 7) - (5a^3 + 2a - 10)$.

$-5a^3 + 3a^2 - 4a + 3$

5. Simplify $(-2xy^2)(3x^2y^4)$.

$-6x^3y^6$

6. Simplify $(x^2y^3)^4$.

x^8y^{12}

7. Simplify $2x(2x^2 - 3x)$.

$4x^3 - 6x^2$

8. Simplify $-3y^2(-2y^2 + 3y - 6)$.

$6y^4 - 9y^3 + 18y^2$

9. Simplify $(x - 3)(x^2 - 4x + 5)$.

$x^3 - 7x^2 + 17x - 15$

10. Simplify $(-2x^3 + x^2 - 7)(2x - 3)$.

$-4x^4 + 8x^3 - 3x^2 - 14x + 21$

11. Simplify $(a - 2b)(a + 5b)$.

$a^2 + 3ab - 10b^2$

12. Simplify $(2x - 7y)(5x - 4y)$.

$10x^2 - 43xy + 28y^2$

13. Simplify $(4y - 3)(4y + 3)$.

$16y^2 - 9$

14. Simplify $(2x - 5)^2$.

$4x^2 - 20x + 25$

15. Simplify $\frac{12x^2}{-3x^8}$.

$-\frac{4}{x^6}$

16. Simplify $\frac{(3xy^3)^3}{3x^4y^3}$.

$\frac{9y^6}{x}$

17. Simplify $\frac{16x^5 - 8x^3 + 20x}{4x}$.

$4x^4 - 2x^2 + 5$

18. Simplify $(x^2 + 6x - 7) \div (x - 1)$.

$x + 7$

19. Simplify $(4x^2 - 7) \div (2x - 3)$.

$2x + 3 + \frac{2}{2x-3}$

20. Simplify $(a^2b^{-3})^2$.

$\frac{a^4}{b^6}$

21. Simplify $(-2ab^{-3})(3a^{-2}b^4)$.

$-\frac{6b}{a}$

22. Write 0.00000005 in scientific notation.

5×10^{-8}

23. Write 3.9×10^{-2} in decimal notation.

0.039

24. A space vehicle travels 2.4×10^5 mi from the earth to the moon at an average velocity of 2×10^4 mph. How long does it take the space vehicle to reach the moon? Write the answer in scientific notation.

1.2×10 hours

Cumulative Review/Test

1. Simplify $(3b - 2)(5b - 7)$.

    $15b^2 - 31b + 14$

2. Simplify
    $(3y^3 - 5y + 8) - (-2y^2 + 5y + 8)$.

    $3y^3 + 2y^2 - 10y$

3. Solve: $12 = -\frac{3}{4}x$

    -16

4. Simplify $\frac{-18a^3 + 12a^2 - 6}{-3a^2}$.

    $6a - 4 + \frac{2}{a^2}$

5. Multiply: $1\frac{3}{4} \times 2\frac{2}{5}$

    $4\frac{1}{5}$

6. 35.2 is what percent of 160?

    22%

7. Simplify $(-2x^{-2}y)(-3x^{-4}y)$.

    $\frac{6y^2}{x^6}$

8. Simplify $-2y^2(-3y^2 - 4y + 8)$.

    $6y^4 + 8y^3 - 16y^2$

9. Place the correct symbol, $<$ or $>$, between the two numbers.

    $\frac{5}{9} > 0.5$

10. Simplify $\left(-\frac{1}{2}\right)^3 \div \left(\frac{3}{8} - \frac{5}{6}\right) + 2$.

    $2\frac{3}{11}$

11. Simplify $(3b + 2)^2$.

    $9b^2 + 12b + 4$

12. Write 8.1×10^{-4} in decimal notation.

    0.00081

13. Simplify $(12x)\left(-\frac{3}{4}\right)$.

    $-9x$

14. Simplify $(a^2 - 4a - 21) \div (a + 3)$.

    $a - 7$

15. Simplify $(2a - 7)(5a^2 - 2a + 3)$.

    $10a^3 - 39a^2 + 20a - 21$

16. Evaluate $-|-6.8|$.

    -6.8

17. Simplify $(4 \times 10^{-8})(6 \times 10^4)$.

    0.0024

18. Solve: $2x - 9 = 3x + 7$

    -16

19. Simplify $\frac{(-2a^2b^3)^2}{8a^4b^8}$.

    $\frac{1}{2b^2}$

20. Simplify $(a^3b^5)^3$.

    a^9b^{15}

21. Simplify
    $(4b^3 - 7b^2 - 7) + (3b^2 - 8b + 3)$.

    $4b^3 - 4b^2 - 8b - 4$

22. Simplify $(4xy^3)(-2x^2y^3)$.

    $-8x^3y^6$

23. Translate and simplify "the product of four and the sum of two consecutive integers."

    $4[n + (n+1)]$;

    $8n + 4$

24. How long does it take light to travel to the earth from the moon when the moon is 232,500 mi from the earth? Light travels 1.86×10^5 mi/s.

    1.25 seconds

chapter 7 Factoring

Objectives

7.1A To find the greatest common factor (GCF) of two or more monomials

7.1B To factor a monomial from a polynomial

7.2A To factor a trinomial of the form $x^2 + bx + c$

7.2B To factor completely

7.3A To factor a trinomial of the form $ax^2 + bx + c$

7.3B To factor completely

7.4A To factor the difference of two perfect squares

7.4B To factor a perfect square trinomial

7.4C To factor a common binomial factor

7.4D To factor completely

Section 1 Monomial Factors

Objective A

To find the greatest common factor (GCF) of two or more monomials

Reference for
Computer
Tutor™

The **greatest common factor (GCF)** of two or more integers is the greatest integer that is a factor of all of the integers.

$$24 = 2 \cdot 2 \cdot 2 \cdot 3$$
$$60 = 2 \cdot 2 \cdot 3 \cdot 5$$
$$GCF = 2 \cdot 2 \cdot 3 = 12$$

The GCF of two or more monomials is the product of the GCF of the coefficients and the common variable factors.

$$6x^3y = 2 \cdot 3 \cdot x \cdot x \cdot x \cdot y$$
$$8x^2y^2 = 2 \cdot 2 \cdot 2 \cdot x \cdot x \cdot y \cdot y$$
$$GCF = 2 \cdot x \cdot x \cdot y = 2x^2y$$

Note that the exponent of each variable in the GCF is the same as the *smallest* exponent of that variable in either of the monomials.

The GCF of $6x^3y$ and $8x^2y^2$ is $2x^2y$

Find the GCF of $12a^4b$ and $18a^2b^2c$.

$$12a^4b = 2 \cdot 2 \cdot 3 \cdot a^4 \cdot b$$
$$18a^2b^2c = 2 \cdot 3 \cdot 3 \cdot a^2 \cdot b^2 \cdot c$$
$$GCF = 2 \cdot 3 \cdot a^2 \cdot b = 6a^2b$$

The common variable factors are a^2 and b. c is not a common variable factor.

Example 1

Find the GCF of $4x^4y$ and $18x^2y^6$.

Solution

$$4x^4y = 2 \cdot 2 \cdot x^4 \cdot y$$
$$18x^2y^6 = 2 \cdot 3 \cdot 3 \cdot x^2 \cdot y^6$$

The GCF is $2x^2y$.

Example 2

Find the GCF of $12x^3y^6$ and $15x^2y^3$.

Your solution

$3x^2y^3$

Example 3

Find the GCF of $4a^3b$, $12ab^2$, and $6a^2b^2$.

Solution

$$4a^3b = 2 \cdot 2 \cdot a^3 \cdot b$$
$$12ab^2 = 2 \cdot 2 \cdot 3 \cdot a \cdot b^2$$
$$6a^2b^2 = 2 \cdot 3 \cdot a^2 \cdot b^2$$

The GCF is $2ab$.

Example 4

Find the GCF of $8a^4bc$, $12ab^3$, and $20abc^2$.

Your solution

$4ab$

Solutions on p. A39

**Reference for
Computer
Tutor™**

Objective B   To factor a monomial from a polynomial

The Distributive Property is used to multiply factors of a polynomial. To **factor** a polynomial means to write the polynomial as a product of other polynomials.

```
           ┌──── Multiply ────┐
                               ↓
  Factors              Polynomial

 2x(x + 5)     =       2x² + 10x
     ↑                     │
     └──────── Factor ──────┘
```

In the example above, $2x$ is the GCF of the terms $2x^2$ and $10x$. It is a **common monomial factor** of the terms. $x + 5$ is a **binomial factor** of $2x^2 + 10x$.

Factor $8a^2b^2 - 6ab$.

Find the GCF of the terms of the polynomial.

$$8a^2b^2 = 2 \cdot 2 \cdot 2 \cdot a^2 \cdot b^2$$
$$6ab = 2 \cdot 3 \cdot a \cdot b$$
The GCF is $2ab$.

Divide each term of the polynomial by the GCF.

$$\frac{8a^2b^2}{2ab} = 4ab \qquad \frac{-6ab}{2ab} = -3$$

Do this step mentally.

Use the quotients to rewrite the polynomial, expressing each term as a product with the GCF as one of the factors.

$$8a^2b^2 - 6ab = 2ab(4ab) + 2ab(-3)$$

Use the Distributive Property to write the polynomial as a product of factors.

$$= 2ab(4ab - 3)$$

Check: $2ab(4ab - 3) = 8a^2b^2 - 6ab$

Factor $5x^3 - 35x^2 + 10x$.

Find the GCF of the terms of the polynomial.

$$5x^3 = 5 \cdot x^3$$
$$35x^2 = 5 \cdot 7 \cdot x^2$$
$$10x = 2 \cdot 5 \cdot x$$
The GCF is $5x$.

Divide each term of the polynomial by the GCF.

$$\frac{5x^3}{5x} = x^2 \qquad \frac{-35x^2}{5x} = -7x \qquad \frac{10x}{5x} = 2$$

Do this step mentally.

Use the quotients to rewrite the polynomial, expressing each term as a product with the GCF as one of the factors.

$$5x^3 - 35x^2 + 10x = 5x(x^2) + 5x(-7x) + 5x(2)$$

Use the Distributive Property to write the polynomial as a product of factors.

$$= 5x(x^2 - 7x + 2)$$

Example 5

Factor $8x^2 + 2xy$.

Solution

$8x^2 = 2 \cdot 2 \cdot 2 \cdot x^2$
$2xy = 2 \cdot x \cdot y$
The GCF is $2x$.

$8x^2 + 2xy = 2x(4x) + 2x(y) = 2x(4x + y)$

Example 6

Factor $14a^2 - 21a^4b$.

Your solution

$7a^2(2 - 3a^2b)$

Example 7

Factor $6x^3 - 12x^2 + 30x$.

Solution

$6x^3 = 2 \cdot 3 \cdot x^3$
$12x^2 = 2 \cdot 2 \cdot 3 \cdot x^2$
$30x = 2 \cdot 3 \cdot 5 \cdot x$
The GCF is $6x$.

$6x^3 - 12x^2 + 30x =$
$6x(x^2) + 6x(-2x) + 6x(5) =$
$6x(x^2 - 2x + 5)$

Example 8

Factor $18a^4 + 27a^3 - 9a^2$.

Your solution

$9a^2(2a^2 + 3a - 1)$

Example 9

Factor $16x^2y + 8x^4y^2 - 12x^4y^5$.

Solution

$16x^2y = 2 \cdot 2 \cdot 2 \cdot 2 \cdot x^2 \cdot y$
$8x^4y^2 = 2 \cdot 2 \cdot 2 \cdot x^4 \cdot y^2$
$12x^4y^5 = 2 \cdot 2 \cdot 3 \cdot x^4 \cdot y^5$
The GCF is $4x^2y$.

$16x^2y + 8x^4y^2 - 12x^4y^5 =$
$4x^2y(4) + 4x^2y(2x^2y) + 4x^2y(-3x^2y^4) =$
$4x^2y(4 + 2x^2y - 3x^2y^4)$

Example 10

Factor $6x^4y^2 - 9x^3y^2 + 12x^2y^4$.

Your solution

$3x^2y^2(2x^2 - 3x + 4y^2)$

Solutions on p. A39

7.1A Exercises

Find the greatest common factor.

1. x^7, x^3
x^3

2. y^6, y^{12}
y^6

3. x^2y^4, xy^6
xy^4

4. a^5b^3, a^3b^8
a^3b^3

5. $x^2y^4z^6, xy^8z^2$
xy^4z^2

6. ab^2c^3, a^3b^2c
ab^2c

7. $a^3b^2c^3, ab^4c^3$
ab^2c^3

8. x^3y^2z, x^4yz^5
x^3yz

9. $3x^4, 12x^2$
$3x^2$

10. $12x, 30x^2$
$6x$

11. $16a^3, 18a$
$2a$

12. $8y^3, 12y^6$
$4y^3$

13. $14a^3, 49a^7$
$7a^3$

14. $12y^2, 27y^4$
$3y^2$

15. $3x^2y^2, 5ab^2$
1

16. $8x^2y^3, 7ab^4$
1

17. $9a^2b^4, 24a^4b^2$
$3a^2b^2$

18. $15a^4b^2, 9ab^5$
$3ab^2$

19. $ab^3, 4a^2b, 12a^2b^3$
ab

20. $12x^2y, x^4y, 16x$
x

21. $18ab^2, a^3b^3, 27a^2b$
ab

22. $2x^2y, 4xy, 8x$
$2x$

23. $16x^2, 8x^4y^2, 12xy$
$4x$

24. $3x^2y^2, 6x, 9x^3y^3$
$3x$

25. $4a^2b^3, 8a^3, 12ab^4$
$4a$

26. $8a^3bc, 2ab^3c, 6a^2b^2$
$2ab$

27. $6m^2n^2, 9m^3n^3, 18m^4n^4$
$3m^2n^2$

28. $21x^2y, 14y^2z, 35xz^2$
7

7.1B Exercises

Factor.

29. $5a + 5$
$5(a + 1)$

30. $7b - 7$
$7(b - 1)$

31. $6 - 18x$
$6(1 - 3x)$

32. $8 - 4y$
$4(2 - y)$

33. $2x^2 - 20$
$2(x^2 - 10)$

34. $3y^2 - 24$
$3(y^2 - 8)$

35. $16 - 8a^2$
$8(2 - a^2)$

36. $12 + 12y^2$
$12(1 + y^2)$

37. $8x + 12$
$4(2x + 3)$

38. $16a - 24$
$8(2a - 3)$

39. $30a - 6$
$6(5a - 1)$

40. $20b + 5$
$5(4b + 1)$

Factor.

41. $7x^2 - 3x$
$$x(7x - 3)$$

42. $12y^2 - 5y$
$$y(12y - 5)$$

43. $3a^2 + 5a^5$
$$a^2(3 + 5a^3)$$

44. $12b^3 + 4b^4$
$$4b^3(3 + b)$$

45. $9x - 5x^2$
$$x(9 - 5x)$$

46. $14y^2 + 11y$
$$y(14y + 11)$$

47. $6b^3 - 5b^2$
$$b^2(6b - 5)$$

48. $2x^4 - 4x$
$$2x(x^3 - 2)$$

49. $3y^4 - 9y$
$$3y(y^3 - 3)$$

50. $10x^4 - 12x^2$
$$2x^2(5x^2 - 6)$$

51. $12a^5 - 32a^2$
$$4a^2(3a^3 - 8)$$

52. $8a^8 - 4a^5$
$$4a^5(2a^3 - 1)$$

53. $16y^4 - 8y^7$
$$8y^4(2 - y^3)$$

54. $x^2y^2 - xy$
$$xy(xy - 1)$$

55. $a^2b^2 + ab$
$$ab(ab + 1)$$

56. $m^3n^2 + mn$
$$mn(m^2n + 1)$$

57. $m^4n^2 - m^2n^4$
$$m^2n^2(m^2 - n^2)$$

58. $3x^2y^4 - 6xy$
$$3xy(xy^3 - 2)$$

59. $12a^2b^5 - 9ab$
$$3ab(4ab^4 - 3)$$

60. $x^2y - xy^3$
$$xy(x - y^2)$$

61. $a^2b + a^4b^2$
$$a^2b(1 + a^2b)$$

62. $2a^5b + 3xy^3$
$$2a^5b + 3xy^3$$

63. $5x^2y - 7ab^3$
$$5x^2y - 7ab^3$$

64. $6a^2b^3 - 12b^2$
$$6b^2(a^2b - 2)$$

65. $8x^2y^3 - 4x^2$
$$4x^2(2y^3 - 1)$$

66. $a^3 - 3a^2 + 5a$
$$a(a^2 - 3a + 5)$$

67. $b^3 - 5b^2 - 7b$
$$b(b^2 - 5b - 7)$$

68. $5x^2 - 15x + 35$
$$5(x^2 - 3x + 7)$$

69. $8y^2 - 12y + 32$
$$4(2y^2 - 3y + 8)$$

70. $3x^3 + 6x^2 + 9x$
$$3x(x^2 + 2x + 3)$$

71. $5y^3 - 20y^2 + 10y$
$$5y(y^2 - 4y + 2)$$

72. $2x^4 - 4x^3 + 6x^2$
$$2x^2(x^2 - 2x + 3)$$

73. $3y^4 - 9y^3 - 6y^2$
$$3y^2(y^2 - 3y - 2)$$

74. $2x^3 + 6x^2 - 14x$
$$2x(x^2 + 3x - 7)$$

75. $3y^3 - 9y^2 + 24y$
$$3y(y^2 - 3y + 8)$$

76. $2y^5 - 3y^4 + 7y^3$
$$y^3(2y^2 - 3y + 7)$$

77. $6a^5 - 3a^3 - 2a^2$
$$a^2(6a^3 - 3a - 2)$$

78. $x^3y - 3x^2y^2 + 7xy^3$
$$xy(x^2 - 3xy + 7y^2)$$

79. $2a^2b - 5a^2b^2 + 7ab^2$
$$ab(2a - 5ab + 7b)$$

80. $5y^3 + 10y^2 - 25y$
$$5y(y^2 + 2y - 5)$$

81. $4b^5 + 6b^3 - 12b$
$$2b(2b^4 + 3b^2 - 6)$$

82. $3a^2b^2 - 9ab^2 + 15b^2$
$$3b^2(a^2 - 3a + 5)$$

83. $8x^2y^2 - 4x^2y + x^2$
$$x^2(8y^2 - 4y + 1)$$

Section 2 Factoring Polynomials of the Form $x^2 + bx + c$

Objective A To factor a trinomial of the form $x^2 + bx + c$

Reference for Computer Tutor™

Trinomials of the form $x^2 + bx + c$, where b and c are integers, are shown at the right.

$x^2 + 8x + 12, b = 8, \quad c = 12$
$x^2 - 7x + 12, b = -7, c = 12$
$x^2 - 2x - 15, b = -2, c = -15$

To **factor** a trinomial of this form means to express the trinomial as the product of two binomials.

Trinomials expressed as the product of binomials are shown at the right.

$x^2 + 8x + 12 = (x + 6)(x + 2)$
$x^2 - 7x + 12 = (x - 3)(x - 4)$
$x^2 - 2x - 15 = (x + 3)(x - 5)$

The method by which factors of a trinomial are found is based upon FOIL. Consider the following binomial products, noting the relationship between the constant terms of the binomials and the terms of the trinomials.

Signs in the binomials are the same

$(x + 6)(x + 2) = x^2 + 2x + 6x + (6)(2) \quad = x^2 + 8x + 12$
sum of 6 and 2 —————
product of 6 and 2 —————

$(x - 3)(x - 4) = x^2 - 4x - 3x + (-3)(-4) = x^2 - 7x + 12$
sum of -3 and -4 —————
product of -3 and -4 —————

Signs in the binomials are opposite

$(x + 3)(x - 5) = x^2 - 5x + 3x + (3)(-5) \quad = x^2 - 2x - 15$
sum of 3 and -5 —————
product of 3 and -5 —————

$(x - 4)(x + 6) = x^2 + 6x - 4x + (-4)(6) \quad = x^2 + 2x - 24$
sum of -4 and 6 —————
product of -4 and 6 —————

Important Relationships

1. When the constant term of the trinomial is positive, the constant terms of the binomials have the same sign. They are both positive when the coefficient of the x term in the trinomial is positive. They are both negative when the coefficient of the x term in the trinomial is negative.

2. When the constant term of the trinomial is negative, the constant terms of the binomials have opposite signs.

3. In the trinomial, the coefficient of x is the sum of the constant terms of the binomials.

4. In the trinomial, the constant term is the product of the constant terms of the binomials.

The following trinomial factoring patterns help to summarize the relationships stated on the previous page.

Trinomial	Factoring Pattern
$x^2 + bx + c$	$(x + \blacksquare)(x + \blacksquare)$
$x^2 - bx + c$	$(x - \blacksquare)(x - \blacksquare)$
$x^2 + bx - c$	$(x + \blacksquare)(x - \blacksquare)$
$x^2 - bx - c$	$(x + \blacksquare)(x - \blacksquare)$

Factor $x^2 + 7x + 10$.

The constant term is positive.
The coefficient of x is positive.
The binomial constants will be positive.

$(x + \blacksquare)(x + \blacksquare)$

Find two positive factors of 10 whose sum is 7.

Factors	Sum
+1, +10	11
+2 +5	7

Write the factors of the trinomial.

$(x + 2)(x + 5)$

Check:
$(x + 2)(x + 5) = x^2 + 5x + 2x + 10$
$= x^2 + 7x + 10$

Factor $x^2 - 8x - 9$.

The constant term is negative.
The signs of the binomial constants will be opposites.

$(x + \blacksquare)(x - \blacksquare)$

Find two factors of 9, one of which is positive and one of which is negative, whose sum is -8.

Factors	Sum
−1, +9	8
+1, −9	−8
+3, −3	0

Once the sum of -8 is found, other factors need not be tried.

Write the factors of the trinomial.

$(x + 1)(x - 9)$

Check:
$(x + 1)(x - 9) = x^2 - 9x + x - 9$
$= x^2 - 8x - 9$

When only integers are used, some trinomials do not factor. For example, to factor $x^2 + 5x + 3$, it would be necessary to find two positive integers whose product is 3 and whose sum is 5. This is not possible, since the only positive factors of 3 are 1 and 3, and the sum of 1 and 3 is 4. This trinomial is **nonfactorable over the integers.** Binomials of the form $x + a$ or $x - a$ are also nonfactorable over the integers.

Example 1

Factor $x^2 - 8x + 15$.

Solution

$(x - \blacksquare)(x - \blacksquare)$

Factors	Sum
$-1, -15$	-16
$-3, -5$	-8

$(x - 3)(x - 5)$

$x^2 - 8x + 15 = (x - 3)(x - 5)$

Example 2

Factor $x^2 - 9x + 20$.

Your solution

$(x - 4)(x - 5)$

Example 3

Factor $x^2 + 6x - 27$.

Solution

$(x + \blacksquare)(x - \blacksquare)$

Factors	Sum
$+1, -27$	-26
$-1, +27$	26
$+3, -9$	-6
$-3, +9$	6

$(x + 9)(x - 3)$

$x^2 + 6x - 27 = (x + 9)(x - 3)$

Example 4

Factor $x^2 + 3x - 18$.

Your solution

$(x + 6)(x - 3)$

Solutions on p. A39

Solutions on p. A39

Objective B   ## To factor completely

Reference for
Computer
Tutor™

A polynomial is factored completely when it is written as a product of factors that are nonfactorable over the integers.

Factor $3x^3 + 15x^2 + 18x$.

Find the GCF of the terms of the polynomial.

The GCF is $3x$.

Factor out the GCF.

$3x^3 + 15x^2 + 18x =$

$3x(x^2) + 3x(5x) + 3x(6) =$ Do this step mentally.

$3x(x^2 + 5x + 6)$

Factor the trinomial.
Find two positive factors of 6 whose sum is 5.

$3x(x + \blacksquare)(x + \blacksquare)$

Factors	Sum
$+1, +6$	7
$+2, +3$	5

Write the product of the GCF and the factors of the trinomial.

$3x(x + 2)(x + 3)$

Check: $3x(x + 2)(x + 3) =$
$3x(x^2 + 3x + 2x + 6) =$
$3x(x^2 + 5x + 6) =$
$3x^3 + 15x^2 + 18x$

Factor $x^2 + 9xy + 20y^2$.

The terms have no common factor.
There are two variables.
Find two positive factors of 20 whose
sum is 9.

$(x + \blacksquare y)(x + \blacksquare y)$

Factors	Sum
+1, +20	21
+2, +10	12
+4 +5	9

Write the factors of the trinomial.

$(x + 4y)(x + 5y)$

Check: $(x + 4y)(x + 5y) =$
$x^2 + 5xy + 4xy + 20y^2 =$
$x^2 + 9xy + 20y^2$

Example 5

Factor $2x^2y + 12xy - 14y$.

Solution

The GCF is $2y$.
$2x^2y + 12xy - 14y = 2y(x^2 + 6x - 7)$
Factor the trinomial.
$2y(x + \blacksquare)(x - \blacksquare)$

Factors	Sum
+1, −7	−6
−1, +7	6

$2y(x + 7)(x - 1)$
$2x^2y + 12xy - 14y = 2y(x + 7)(x - 1)$

Example 6

Factor $3a^2b - 18ab - 81b$.

Your solution

$3b(a + 3)(a - 9)$

Example 7

Factor $4x^2 - 40xy + 84y^2$.

Solution

The GCF is 4.
$4x^2 - 40xy + 84y^2 = 4(x^2 - 10xy + 21y^2)$
Factor the trinomial.
$4(x - \blacksquare y)(x - \blacksquare y)$

Factors	Sum
−1, −21	−22
−3, −7	−10

$4(x - 3y)(x - 7y)$
$4x^2 - 40xy + 84y^2 = 4(x - 3y)(x - 7y)$

Example 8

Factor $3x^2 - 9xy - 12y^2$.

Your solution

$3(x + y)(x - 4y)$

Solutions on p. A40

7.2A Exercises

Factor.

1. $x^2 + 3x + 2$
$(x + 1)(x + 2)$

2. $x^2 + 5x + 6$
$(x + 2)(x + 3)$

3. $x^2 - x - 2$
$(x + 1)(x - 2)$

4. $x^2 + x - 6$
$(x + 3)(x - 2)$

5. $a^2 + a - 12$
$(a + 4)(a - 3)$

6. $a^2 - 2a - 35$
$(a + 5)(a - 7)$

7. $a^2 - 3a + 2$
$(a - 1)(a - 2)$

8. $a^2 - 5a + 4$
$(a - 1)(a - 4)$

9. $a^2 + a - 2$
$(a + 2)(a - 1)$

10. $a^2 - 2a - 3$
$(a + 1)(a - 3)$

11. $b^2 - 6b + 9$
$(b - 3)(b - 3)$

12. $b^2 + 8b + 16$
$(b + 4)(b + 4)$

13. $b^2 + 7b - 8$
$(b + 8)(b - 1)$

14. $y^2 - y - 6$
$(y + 2)(y - 3)$

15. $y^2 + 6y - 55$
$(y + 11)(y - 5)$

16. $z^2 - 4z - 45$
$(z + 5)(z - 9)$

17. $y^2 - 5y + 6$
$(y - 2)(y - 3)$

18. $y^2 - 8y + 15$
$(y - 3)(y - 5)$

19. $z^2 - 14z + 45$
$(z - 5)(z - 9)$

20. $z^2 - 14z + 49$
$(z - 7)(z - 7)$

21. $z^2 - 12z - 160$
$(z + 8)(z - 20)$

22. $p^2 + 2p - 35$
$(p + 7)(p - 5)$

23. $p^2 + 12p + 27$
$(p + 3)(p + 9)$

24. $p^2 - 6p + 8$
$(p - 2)(p - 4)$

25. $x^2 + 20x + 100$
$(x + 10)(x + 10)$

26. $x^2 + 18x + 81$
$(x + 9)(x + 9)$

27. $b^2 + 9b + 20$
$(b + 4)(b + 5)$

28. $b^2 + 13b + 40$
$(b + 5)(b + 8)$

29. $x^2 - 11x - 42$
$(x + 3)(x - 14)$

30. $x^2 + 9x - 70$
$(x + 14)(x - 5)$

31. $b^2 - b - 20$
$(b + 4)(b - 5)$

32. $b^2 + 3b - 40$
$(b + 8)(b - 5)$

33. $y^2 - 14y - 51$
$(y + 3)(y - 17)$

34. $y^2 - y - 72$
$(y + 8)(y - 9)$

35. $p^2 - 4p - 21$
$(p + 3)(p - 7)$

36. $p^2 + 16p + 39$
$(p + 3)(p + 13)$

37. $y^2 - 8y + 32$
nonfactorable

38. $y^2 - 9y + 81$
nonfactorable

39. $x^2 - 20x + 75$
$(x - 5)(x - 15)$

40. $p^2 + 24p + 63$
$(p + 3)(p + 21)$

41. $x^2 - 15x + 56$
$(x - 7)(x - 8)$

42. $x^2 + 21x + 38$
$(x + 2)(x + 19)$

43. $x^2 + x - 56$
$(x + 8)(x - 7)$

44. $x^2 + 5x - 36$
$(x + 9)(x - 4)$

45. $a^2 - 21a - 72$
$(a + 3)(a - 24)$

46. $a^2 - 7a - 44$
$(a + 4)(a - 11)$

47. $a^2 - 15a + 36$
$(a - 3)(a - 12)$

48. $a^2 - 21a + 54$
$(a - 3)(a - 18)$

49. $z^2 - 9z - 136$
$(z + 8)(z - 17)$

50. $z^2 + 14z - 147$
$(z + 21)(z - 7)$

51. $c^2 - c - 90$
$(c + 9)(c - 10)$

52. $c^2 - 3c - 180$
$(c + 12)(c - 15)$

7.2B Exercises

Factor.

53. $2x^2 + 6x + 4$

$2(x+1)(x+2)$

54. $3x^2 + 15x + 18$

$3(x+2)(x+3)$

55. $3a^2 + 3a - 18$

$3(a+3)(a-2)$

56. $4x^2 - 4x - 8$

$4(x+1)(x-2)$

57. $ab^2 + 2ab - 15a$

$a(b+5)(b-3)$

58. $ab^2 + 7ab - 8a$

$a(b+8)(b-1)$

59. $xy^2 - 5xy + 6x$

$x(y-2)(y-3)$

60. $xy^2 + 8xy + 15x$

$x(y+3)(y+5)$

61. $z^3 - 7z^2 + 12z$

$z(z-3)(z-4)$

62. $2a^3 + 6a^2 + 4a$

$2a(a+1)(a+2)$

63. $3y^3 - 15y^2 + 18y$

$3y(y-2)(y-3)$

64. $4y^3 + 12y^2 - 72y$

$4y(y+6)(y-3)$

65. $3x^2 + 3x - 36$

$3(x+4)(x-3)$

66. $2x^3 - 2x^2 - 4x$

$2x(x+1)(x-2)$

67. $5z^2 - 15z - 140$

$5(z+4)(z-7)$

68. $6z^2 + 12z - 90$

$6(z+5)(z-3)$

69. $2a^3 + 8a^2 - 64a$

$2a(a+8)(a-4)$

70. $3a^3 - 9a^2 - 54a$

$3a(a+3)(a-6)$

71. $x^2 - 5xy + 6y^2$

$(x-2y)(x-3y)$

72. $x^2 + 4xy - 21y^2$

$(x+7y)(x-3y)$

73. $a^2 - 9ab + 20b^2$

$(a-4b)(a-5b)$

74. $a^2 - 15ab + 50b^2$

$(a-5b)(a-10b)$

75. $x^2 - 3xy - 28y^2$

$(x+4y)(x-7y)$

76. $s^2 + 2st - 48t^2$

$(s+8t)(s-6t)$

77. $y^2 - 15yz - 41z^2$

nonfactorable

78. $y^2 + 85yz + 36z^2$

nonfactorable

79. $z^4 - 12z^3 + 35z^2$

$z^2(z-5)(z-7)$

80. $z^4 + 2z^3 - 80z^2$

$z^2(z+10)(z-8)$

81. $b^4 - 22b^3 + 120b^2$

$b^2(b-10)(b-12)$

82. $b^4 - 3b^3 - 10b^2$

$b^2(b+2)(b-5)$

83. $2y^4 - 26y^3 - 96y^2$

$2y^2(y+3)(y-16)$

84. $x^4 + 7x^3 - 8x^2$

$x^2(x+8)(x-1)$

85. $3y^4 + 54y^3 + 135y^2$

$3y^2(y+3)(y+15)$

86. $4x^2y + 20xy - 56y$

$4y(x+7)(x-2)$

87. $3x^2y - 6xy - 45y$

$3y(x+3)(x-5)$

88. $3x^3 - 36x^2 + 81x$

$3x(x-3)(x-9)$

89. $4x^3 + 4x^2 - 24x$

$4x(x+3)(x-2)$

90. $5x^3 + 30x^2 + 40x$

$5x(x+2)(x+4)$

91. $5p^2 + 25p - 420$

$5(p+12)(p-7)$

92. $5x^4 - 30x^3 + 40x^2$

$5x^2(x-2)(x-4)$

93. $15ab^2 + 45ab - 60a$

$15a(b+4)(b-1)$

94. $20a^2b - 100ab + 120b$

$20b(a-2)(a-3)$

95. $3yx^2 + 36yx - 135y$

$3y(x+15)(x-3)$

96. $4yz^2 - 52yz + 88y$

$4y(z-2)(z-11)$

Section 3 Factoring Polynomials of the Form $ax^2 + bx + c$

Objective A   To factor a trinomial of the form $ax^2 + bx + c$

**Reference for
Computer
Tutor™**

Trinomials of the form $ax^2 + bx + c$, where a, b, and c are integers and $a \neq 0$, are shown at the right.

$3x^2 - x + 4$, $a = 3$, $b = -1$, $c = 4$

$6x^2 + 8x - 6$, $a = 6$, $b = 8$, $c = -6$

To factor a trinomial of this form, a trial-and-error method is used. Trial factors are written, using the factors of a and c to write the binomials. Then FOIL is used to check for b, the coefficient of the middle term.

To reduce the number of trial factors that must be considered, remember the following.

1. Use the signs of the constant and the coefficient of x in the trinomial to determine the signs of the terms in the binomial factors.

Trinomial	Factoring Pattern
$ax^2 + bx + c$	$(\ x + \ )(\ x + \ )$
$ax^2 - bx + c$	$(\ x - \ )(\ x - \ )$
$ax^2 - bx - c$	$(\ x + \ )(\ x - \ )$ or $(\ x - \ )(\ x + \ )$
$ax^2 + bx - c$	$(\ x + \ )(\ x - \ )$ or $(\ x - \ )(\ x + \ )$

2. If the terms of the trinomial do not have a common factor, then the two terms in either one of the binomial factors will not have a common factor.

Factor $2x^2 - 7x + 3$.

The terms have no common factor.
The constant term is positive.
The coefficient of x is negative.
The binomial constants will be negative.

$(\ x - \ )(\ x - \ )$

Write the factors of 2 (the coefficient of x^2). These factors will be the coefficients of the x terms in the binomial factors.

Factors of 2: 1, 2

Write the negative factors of 3 (the constant term). These factors will be the constants in the binomial factors.

Factors of 3: -1, -3

Write trial factors. Writing the 1 when it is the coefficient of x may be helpful. Use the Outer and Inner products of FOIL to determine the middle term of the trinomial.
Write the factors of the trinomial.

Trial Factors	Middle Term
$(1x - 1)(2x - 3)$	$-3x - 2x = -5x$
$(1x - 3)(2x - 1)$	$-x - 6x = -7x$

$(x - 3)(2x - 1)$

Check: $(x - 3)(2x - 1) =$
$\qquad 2x^2 - x - 6x + 3 =$
$\qquad 2x^2 - 7x + 3$

Factor $6x^2 - x - 2$.

The terms have no common factor.	(▢ x + ▢)(▢ x − ▢)
The constant term is negative.	or
The signs of the binomial constants will be opposites.	(▢ x − ▢)(▢ x + ▢)

Write the factors of 6. These factors will be the coefficients of the x terms in the binomial factors.

Factors of 6: 1, 6
          2, 3

Write the factors of -2. These factors will be the constants in the binomial factors.

Factors of -2: $-1, +2$
              $+1, -2$

Write the trial factors.
Use the <u>O</u>uter and <u>I</u>nner terms of FOIL to determine the middle term of the trinomial.
It is not necessary to test trial factors that have a common factor. For example, $6x + 2$ need not be tested because it has a common factor of 2. Once a trial solution has the correct middle term, other trial factors need not be tried.

Trial Factors	Middle Term
$(1x - 1)(6x + 2)$	Common factor
$(1x + 2)(6x - 1)$	$-x + 12x = 11x$
$(1x + 1)(6x - 2)$	Common factor
$(1x - 2)(6x + 1)$	$x - 12x = -11x$
$(2x - 1)(3x + 2)$	$4x - 3x = x$
$(2x + 2)(3x - 1)$	Common factor
$(2x + 1)(3x - 2)$	$-4x + 3x = -x$
$(2x - 2)(3x + 1)$	Common factor

Write the factors of the trinomial.

$(2x + 1)(3x - 2)$

Check: $(2x + 1)(3x - 2) =$
        $6x^2 - 4x + 3x - 2 =$
        $6x^2 - x - 2$

Example 1

Factor $3x^2 + x - 2$.

Solution

(▢ x + ▢)(▢ x − ▢) or (▢ x − ▢)(▢ x + ▢)
Factors of 3: 1, 3   Factors of -2: $+1, -2$
                                    $-1, +2$

Trial Factors	Middle Term
$(1x + 1)(3x - 2)$	$-2x + 3x = x$
$(1x - 2)(3x + 1)$	$x - 6x \quad = -5x$
$(1x - 1)(3x + 2)$	$2x - 3x \quad = -x$
$(1x + 2)(3x - 1)$	$-x + 6x \quad = 5x$

$(x + 1)(3x - 2)$
$3x^2 + x - 2 = (x + 1)(3x - 2)$

Example 2

Factor $2x^2 - x - 3$.

Your solution

$(x + 1)(2x - 3)$

Solution on p. A40

Reference for
Computer
Tutor™

Objective B	

To factor completely

Factor $3x^3 - 23x^2 + 14x$.

Find the GCF of the terms of the polynomial.

The GCF is x.

Factor out the GCF.

$3x^3 - 23x^2 + 14x = x(3x^2 - 23x + 14)$

Factor the trinomial.

$x(\blacksquare x - \blacksquare)(\blacksquare x - \blacksquare)$

Write the factors of 3.

Factors of 3: 1, 3

Write the negative factors of 14.

Factors of 14: $-1, -14$
$\qquad\qquad -2, -7$

Write trial factors. Writing the 1 when it is the coefficient of x may be helpful.
Determine the middle term of the trinomial.

Trial Factors	Middle Term
$(1x - 1)(3x - 14)$	$-14x - 3x = -17x$
$(1x - 14)(3x - 1)$	$-x - 42x = -43x$
$(1x - 2)(3x - 7)$	$-7x - 6x = -13x$
$(1x - 7)(3x - 2)$	$-2x - 21x = -23x$

Write the product of the GCF and the factors of the trinomial.

$x(x - 7)(3x - 2)$

Check: $x(x - 7)(3x - 2) =$
$\qquad x(3x^2 - 2x - 21x + 14) =$
$\qquad x(3x^2 - 23x + 14) =$
$\qquad 3x^3 - 23x^2 + 14x$

Factor $15 - 2x - x^2$.

The terms have no common factor.
The coefficient of x^2 is -1.
The signs of the binomials will be opposites.

$(\blacksquare + \blacksquare x)(\blacksquare - \blacksquare x)$

or

$(\blacksquare - \blacksquare x)(\blacksquare + \blacksquare x)$

Write the factors of 15.

Factors of 15: 1, 15
$\qquad\qquad\quad 3, 5$

Write the factors of -1.

Factors of -1: 1, -1

Write trial factors.
Determine the middle term of the trinomial.

Trial Factors	Middle Term
$(1 + 1x)(15 - 1x)$	$-x + 15x = 14x$
$(1 - 1x)(15 + 1x)$	$x - 15x = -14x$
$(3 + 1x)(5 - 1x)$	$-3x + 5x = 2x$
$(3 - 1x)(5 + 1x)$	$3x - 5x = -2x$

Write the factors of the trinomial.

$(3 - x)(5 + x)$

Check: $(3 - x)(5 + x) = 15 + 3x - 5x - x^2$
$\qquad\qquad\qquad\qquad = 15 - 2x - x^2$

Example 3

Factor $2x^2y + 19xy - 10y$.

Solution

The GCF is y.
$2x^2y + 19xy - 10y = y(2x^2 + 19x - 10)$
Factor the trinomial
$y(\ \square\ x + \ \square\ )(\ \square\ x - \ \square\ )$ or $y(\ \square\ x - \ \square\ )(\ \square\ x + \ \square\ )$
Factors of 2: 1, 2   Factors of -10: $+1, -10$
                                   $-1, +10$
                                   $+2, -5$
                                   $-2, +5$

Trial Factors	Middle Term
$(1x + 1)(2x - 10)$	Common factor
$(1x - 10)(2x + 1)$	$x - 20x = -19x$
$(1x - 1)(2x + 10)$	Common factor
$(1x + 10)(2x - 1)$	$-x + 20x = 19x$
$(1x + 2)(2x - 5)$	$-5x + 4x = -x$
$(1x - 5)(2x + 2)$	Common factor
$(1x - 2)(2x + 5)$	$5x - 4x = x$
$(1x + 5)(2x - 2)$	Common factor

$y(x + 10)(2x - 1)$
$2x^2y + 19xy - 10y = y(x + 10)(2x - 1)$

Example 4

Factor $4a^2b^2 + 26a^2b - 14a^2$.

Your solution

$2a^2(b + 7)(2b - 1)$

Example 5

Factor $12x - 32x^2 - 12x^3$.

Solution

The GCF is $4x$.
$12x - 32x^2 - 12x^3 = 4x(3 - 8x - 3x^2)$
Factor the trinomial.
$4x(\ \square\ + \ \square\ x)(\ \square\ - \ \square\ x)$ or $4x(\ \square\ - \ \square\ x)(\ \square\ + \ \square\ x)$
Factors of 3: 1, 3   Factors of -3: $+1, -3$
                                   $-1, +3$

Trial Factors	Middle Term
$(1 + 1x)(3 - 3x)$	Common factor
$(1 - 3x)(3 + 1x)$	$x - 9x = -8x$
$(1 - 1x)(3 + 3x)$	Common factor
$(1 + 3x)(3 - 1x)$	$-x + 9x = 8x$

$4x(1 - 3x)(3 + x)$
$12x - 32x^2 - 12x^3 = 4x(1 - 3x)(3 + x)$

Example 6

Factor $12y + 12y^2 - 45y^3$.

Your solution

$3y(2 - 3y)(2 + 5y)$

Copyright © 1989 HMCo

Solutions on pp. A40–41

7.3A Exercises

Factor.

1. $2x^2 + 3x + 1$
$(x+1)(2x+1)$

2. $5x^2 + 6x + 1$
$(x+1)(5x+1)$

3. $2y^2 + 7y + 3$
$(y+3)(2y+1)$

4. $3y^2 + 7y + 2$
$(y+2)(3y+1)$

5. $2a^2 - 3a + 1$
$(a-1)(2a-1)$

6. $3a^2 - 4a + 1$
$(a-1)(3a-1)$

7. $2b^2 - 11b + 5$
$(b-5)(2b-1)$

8. $3b^2 - 13b + 4$
$(b-4)(3b-1)$

9. $2x^2 + x - 1$
$(x+1)(2x-1)$

10. $4x^2 - 3x - 1$
$(x-1)(4x+1)$

11. $2x^2 - 5x - 3$
$(x-3)(2x+1)$

12. $3x^2 + 5x - 2$
$(x+2)(3x-1)$

13. $2t^2 - t - 10$
$(t+2)(2t-5)$

14. $2t^2 + 5t - 12$
$(t+4)(2t-3)$

15. $3p^2 - 16p + 5$
$(p-5)(3p-1)$

16. $6p^2 + 5p + 1$
$(2p+1)(3p+1)$

17. $12y^2 - 7y + 1$
$(3y-1)(4y-1)$

18. $6y^2 - 5y + 1$
$(2y-1)(3y-1)$

19. $6z^2 - 7z + 3$
nonfactorable

20. $9z^2 + 3z + 2$
nonfactorable

21. $6t^2 - 11t + 4$
$(2t-1)(3t-4)$

22. $10t^2 + 11t + 3$
$(2t+1)(5t+3)$

23. $8x^2 + 33x + 4$
$(x+4)(8x+1)$

24. $7x^2 + 50x + 7$
$(x+7)(7x+1)$

25. $5x^2 - 62x - 7$
nonfactorable

26. $9x^2 - 13x - 4$
nonfactorable

27. $12y^2 + 19y + 5$
$(3y+1)(4y+5)$

28. $5y^2 - 22y + 8$
$(y-4)(5y-2)$

29. $7a^2 + 47a - 14$
$(a+7)(7a-2)$

30. $11a^2 - 54a - 5$
$(a-5)(11a+1)$

31. $3b^2 - 16b + 16$
$(b-4)(3b-4)$

32. $6b^2 - 19b + 15$
$(2b-3)(3b-5)$

33. $2z^2 - 27z - 14$
$(z-14)(2z+1)$

34. $4z^2 + 5z - 6$
$(z+2)(4z-3)$

35. $3p^2 + 22p - 16$
$(p+8)(3p-2)$

36. $7p^2 + 19p + 10$
$(p+2)(7p+5)$

Factor.

37. $6x^2 - 17x + 12$
$(2x - 3)(3x - 4)$

38. $15x^2 - 19x + 6$
$(3x - 2)(5x - 3)$

39. $5b^2 + 33b - 14$
$(b + 7)(5b - 2)$

40. $8x^2 - 30x + 25$
$(2x - 5)(4x - 5)$

41. $6a^2 + 7a - 24$
$(2a - 3)(3a + 8)$

42. $14a^2 + 15a - 9$
$(2a + 3)(7a - 3)$

43. $4z^2 + 11z + 6$
$(z + 2)(4z + 3)$

44. $6z^2 - 25z + 14$
$(2z - 7)(3z - 2)$

45. $22p^2 + 51p - 10$
$(2p + 5)(11p - 2)$

46. $14p^2 - 41p + 15$
$(2p - 5)(7p - 3)$

47. $8y^2 + 17y + 9$
$(y + 1)(8y + 9)$

48. $12y^2 - 145y + 12$
$(y - 12)(12y - 1)$

49. $18t^2 - 9t - 5$
$(3t + 1)(6t - 5)$

50. $12t^2 + 28t - 5$
$(2t + 5)(6t - 1)$

51. $6b^2 + 71b - 12$
$(b + 12)(6b - 1)$

52. $8b^2 + 65b + 8$
$(b + 8)(8b + 1)$

53. $9x^2 + 12x + 4$
$(3x + 2)(3x + 2)$

54. $25x^2 - 30x + 9$
$(5x - 3)(5x - 3)$

55. $6b^2 - 13b + 6$
$(2b - 3)(3b - 2)$

56. $20b^2 + 37b + 15$
$(4b + 5)(5b + 3)$

57. $33b^2 + 34b - 35$
$(3b + 5)(11b - 7)$

58. $15b^2 - 43b + 22$
$(3b - 2)(5b - 11)$

59. $18y^2 - 39y + 20$
$(3y - 4)(6y - 5)$

60. $24y^2 + 41y + 12$
$(3y + 4)(8y + 3)$

61. $15a^2 + 26a - 21$
$(3a + 7)(5a - 3)$

62. $6a^2 + 23a + 21$
$(2a + 3)(3a + 7)$

63. $8y^2 - 26y + 15$
$(2y - 5)(4y - 3)$

64. $18y^2 - 27y + 4$
$(3y - 4)(6y - 1)$

65. $8z^2 + 2z - 15$
$(2z + 3)(4z - 5)$

66. $10z^2 + 3z - 4$
$(2z - 1)(5z + 4)$

67. $15x^2 - 82x + 24$
nonfactorable

68. $13z^2 + 49z - 8$
nonfactorable

69. $10z^2 - 29z + 10$
$(2z - 5)(5z - 2)$

70. $15z^2 - 44z + 32$
$(3z - 4)(5z - 8)$

71. $36z^2 + 72z + 35$
$(6z + 5)(6z + 7)$

72. $16z^2 + 8z - 35$
$(4z - 5)(4z + 7)$

7.3B Exercises

Factor.

73. $4x^2 + 6x + 2$
$2(x+1)(2x+1)$

74. $12x^2 + 33x - 9$
$3(x+3)(4x-1)$

75. $15y^2 - 50y + 35$
$5(y-1)(3y-7)$

76. $30y^2 + 10y - 20$
$10(y+1)(3y-2)$

77. $2x^3 - 11x^2 + 5x$
$x(x-5)(2x-1)$

78. $2x^3 - 3x^2 - 5x$
$x(x+1)(2x-5)$

79. $3a^2b - 16ab + 16b$
$b(a-4)(3a-4)$

80. $2a^2b - ab - 21b$
$b(a+3)(2a-7)$

81. $3z^2 + 95z + 10$
nonfactorable

82. $8z^2 - 36z + 1$
nonfactorable

83. $3x^2 + xy - 2y^2$
$(x+y)(3x-2y)$

84. $6x^2 + 10xy + 4y^2$
$2(x+y)(3x+2y)$

85. $3a^2 + 5ab - 2b^2$
$(a+2b)(3a-b)$

86. $2a^2 - 9ab + 9b^2$
$(a-3b)(2a-3b)$

87. $4y^2 - 11yz + 6z^2$
$(y-2z)(4y-3z)$

88. $2y^2 + 7yz + 5z^2$
$(2y+5z)(y+z)$

89. $12 - x - x^2$
$(3-x)(4+x)$

90. $2 + x - x^2$
$(1+x)(2-x)$

91. $28 + 3z - z^2$
$(4+z)(7-z)$

92. $15 - 2z - z^2$
$(3-z)(5+z)$

93. $8 - 7x - x^2$
$(1-x)(8+x)$

94. $12 + 11x - x^2$
$(1+x)(12-x)$

95. $9x^2 + 33x - 60$
$3(x+5)(3x-4)$

96. $16x^2 - 16x - 12$
$4(2x+1)(2x-3)$

97. $80y^2 - 36y + 4$
$4(4y-1)(5y-1)$

98. $24y^2 - 24y - 18$
$6(2y+1)(2y-3)$

99. $8z^3 + 14z^2 + 3z$
$z(2z+3)(4z+1)$

100. $6z^3 - 23z^2 + 20z$
$z(2z-5)(3z-4)$

101. $6x^2y - 11xy - 10y$
$y(2x-5)(3x+2)$

102. $8x^2y - 27xy + 9y$
$y(x-3)(8x-3)$

103. $24x^2 - 52x + 24$
$4(2x-3)(3x-2)$

104. $60x^2 + 95x + 20$
$5(3x+4)(4x+1)$

105. $35a^4 + 9a^3 - 2a^2$
$a^2(5a+2)(7a-1)$

106. $15a^4 + 26a^3 + 7a^2$
$a^2(3a+1)(5a+7)$

107. $15b^2 - 115b + 70$
$5(b-7)(3b-2)$

108. $25b^2 + 35b - 30$
$5(b+2)(5b-3)$

Factor.

109. $3x^2 - 26xy + 35y^2$

$$(x - 7y)(3x - 5y)$$

110. $4x^2 + 16xy + 15y^2$

$$(2x + 3y)(2x + 5y)$$

111. $216y^2 - 3y - 3$

$$3(8y - 1)(9y + 1)$$

112. $360y^2 + 4y - 4$

$$4(9y + 1)(10y - 1)$$

113. $21 - 20x - x^2$

$$(1 - x)(21 + x)$$

114. $18 + 17x - x^2$

$$(1 + x)(18 - x)$$

115. $15a^2 + 11ab - 14b^2$

$$(3a - 2b)(5a + 7b)$$

116. $15a^2 - 31ab + 10b^2$

$$(3a - 5b)(5a - 2b)$$

117. $33z - 8z^2 - z^3$

$$z(3 - z)(11 + z)$$

118. $24z + 10z^2 - z^3$

$$z(2 + z)(12 - z)$$

119. $10x^3 + 12x^2 + 2x$

$$2x(x + 1)(5x + 1)$$

120. $9x^3 - 39x^2 + 12x$

$$3x(x - 4)(3x - 1)$$

121. $10t^2 - 5t - 50$

$$5(t + 2)(2t - 5)$$

122. $16t^2 + 40t - 96$

$$8(t + 4)(2t - 3)$$

123. $3p^3 - 16p^2 + 5p$

$$p(p - 5)(3p - 1)$$

124. $6p^3 + 5p^2 + p$

$$p(2p + 1)(3p + 1)$$

125. $26z^2 + 98z - 24$

$$2(z + 4)(13z - 3)$$

126. $30z^2 - 87z + 30$

$$3(2z - 5)(5z - 2)$$

127. $10y^3 - 44y^2 + 16y$

$$2y(y - 4)(5y - 2)$$

128. $14y^3 + 94y^2 - 28y$

$$2y(y + 7)(7y - 2)$$

129. $4yz^3 + 5yz^2 - 6yz$

$$yz(z + 2)(4z - 3)$$

130. $2yz^3 - 17yz^2 + 8yz$

$$yz(z - 8)(2z - 1)$$

131. $20b^4 + 41b^3 + 20b^2$

$$b^2(4b + 5)(5b + 4)$$

132. $6b^4 - 13b^3 + 6b^2$

$$b^2(2b - 3)(3b - 2)$$

133. $12a^3 + 14a^2 - 48a$

$$2a(2a - 3)(3a + 8)$$

134. $42a^3 + 45a^2 - 27a$

$$3a(2a + 3)(7a - 3)$$

135. $36p^2 - 9p^3 - p^4$

$$p^2(3 - p)(12 + p)$$

136. $9x^2y - 30xy^2 + 25y^3$

$$y(3x - 5y)(3x - 5y)$$

137. $8x^2y - 38xy^2 + 35y^3$

$$y(2x - 7y)(4x - 5y)$$

138. $9x^3y - 24x^2y^2 + 16xy^3$

$$xy(3x - 4y)(3x - 4y)$$

139. $9x^3y + 12x^2y + 4xy$

$$xy(3x + 2)(3x + 2)$$

140. $9a^3b - 9a^2b^2 - 10ab^3$

$$ab(3a + 2b)(3a - 5b)$$

141. $2a^3b - 11a^2b^2 + 5ab^3$

$$ab(a - 5b)(2a - b)$$

Section 4 Special Factoring

Objective A To factor the difference of two perfect squares

Reference for Computer Tutor™

The product of a term and itself is called a **perfect square.** The exponents of variables of perfect squares are always even numbers.

Term		Perfect Square
2	$2 \cdot 2 =$	4
x	$x \cdot x =$	x^2
$3y^3$	$3y^3 \cdot 3y^3 =$	$9y^6$

The **square root** of a perfect square is one of the two equal factors of the perfect square. "$\sqrt{}$," called a radical, is the symbol for square root. To find the exponent of the square root of a variable term, multiply the exponent by $\frac{1}{2}$.

$$\sqrt{4} = 2$$
$$\sqrt{x^2} = x$$
$$\sqrt{9y^6} = 3y^3$$

The difference of two perfect squares is the product of the sum and difference of two terms.

Sum and Difference of Two Terms		Difference of Two Perfect Squares
$(a + b)(a - b)$	$=$	$a^2 - b^2$

The factors of the difference of two perfect squares are the sum and difference of the square roots of the perfect squares.

$a^2 + b^2$ is the *sum* of two perfect squares. It is nonfactorable over the integers.

Factor $x^2 - 16$.

Write $x^2 - 16$ as the difference of two perfect squares.
The factors are the sum and difference of the square roots of the perfect squares.

$$x^2 - 16 = x^2 - 4^2$$
$$= (x + 4)(x - 4)$$

Check: $(x + 4)(x - 4) = x^2 - 4x + 4x - 16$
$$= x^2 - 16$$

Factor $x^2 - 10$.

Since 10 is not a perfect square, $x^2 - 10$ cannot be written as the difference of two perfect squares. $x^2 - 10$ is nonfactorable over the integers.

Example 1

Factor $16x^2 - y^2$.

Solution

$16x^2 - y^2 = (4x)^2 - y^2 = (4x + y)(4x - y)$

Example 3

Factor $z^6 - 25$.

Solution

$z^6 - 25 = (z^3)^2 - 5^2 = (z^3 + 5)(z^3 - 5)$

Example 2

Factor $25a^2 - b^2$.

Your solution

$(5a + b)(5a - b)$

Example 4

Factor $n^8 - 36$.

Your solution

$(n^4 + 6)(n^4 - 6)$

Solutions on p. A42

Objective B   ## To factor a perfect square trinomial

Reference for
Computer
Tutor™

A perfect square trinomial is the square of a binomial.

Square of a Binomial		Perfect Square Trinomial
$(a + b)^2$	$= (a + b)(a + b) =$	$a^2 + 2ab + b^2$
$(a - b)^2$	$= (a - b)(a - b) =$	$a^2 - 2ab + b^2$

In factoring a perfect square trinomial, remember that the terms of the binomial are the square roots of the perfect squares of the trinomial. The sign in the binomial is the sign of the middle term of the trinomial.

Factor $x^2 + 10x + 25$.

Check that the trinomial is a perfect square.

$\sqrt{x^2} = x$
$\sqrt{25} = 5$ $2(5x) = 10x$
The trinomial is a perfect square.

Write the factors as the square of a binomial.

$(x + 5)^2$

Check: $(x + 5)^2 = (x + 5)(x + 5)$
$= x^2 + 5x + 5x + 25$
$= x^2 + 10x + 25$

Factor $x^2 + 10x - 25$.

Since the constant term is negative, $x^2 + 10x - 25$ is not a perfect square trinomial. $x^2 + 10x - 25$ is nonfactorable over the integers.

Example 5

Factor $y^2 - 14y + 49$.

Solution

$\sqrt{y^2} = y$
$\sqrt{49} = 7$ $2(7y) = 14y$
The trinomial is a perfect square.
$y^2 - 14y + 49 = (y - 7)^2$

Example 6

Factor $a^2 + 20a + 100$.

Your solution

$(a + 10)^2$

Example 7

Factor $9x^2 - 24xy + 16y^2$.

Solution

$\sqrt{9x^2} = 3x$
$\sqrt{16y^2} = 4y$ $2(3x \cdot 4y) = 24xy$
The trinomial is a perfect square.
$9x^2 - 24xy + 16y^2 = (3x - 4y)^2$

Example 8

Factor $25a^2 - 30ab + 9b^2$.

Your solution

$(5a - 3b)^2$

Solutions on p. A42

Objective C   To factor a common binomial factor

Reference for
Computer
Tutor™

In the examples at the right, the binomials in parentheses are called binomial factors.

$2a(a + b)^2$
$3xy(x - y)$

The Distributive Property is used to factor a common binomial factor from an expression.

Factor $6(x - 3) + y^2(x - 3)$.

The common binomial factor is $x - 3$. Use the Distributive Property to write the expression as a product of factors.

$6(x - 3) + y^2(x - 3) =$
$(x - 3)(6 + y^2)$

Factor $2x(a - b) + 5(b - a)$.

Rewrite the expression as a difference of terms that have a common factor. Note that
$(b - a) = (-a + b) = -(a - b)$

$2x(a - b) + 5(b - a)$
$2x(a - b) + 5[-(a - b)]$ Do this step mentally.
$2x(a - b) - 5(a - b)$
$(a - b)(2x - 5)$

Write the expression as a product of factors.

Copyright © 1989 HMCo

Example 9

Factor $4x(3x - 2) - 7(3x - 2)$.

Solution

$4x(3x - 2) - 7(3x - 2) = (3x - 2)(4x - 7)$

Example 10

Factor $5x(2x + 3) - 4(2x + 3)$.

Your solution

$(2x + 3)(5x - 4)$

Example 11

Factor $5a(2x - 7) + 2(7 - 2x)$.

Solution

$5a(2x - 7) + 2(7 - 2x) =$
$5a(2x - 7) - 2(2x - 7) = (2x - 7)(5a - 2)$

Example 12

Factor $2y(5x - 2) - 3(2 - 5x)$.

Your solution

$(5x - 2)(2y + 3)$

Solutions on p. A42

Objective D   ## To factor completely

Reference for Computer Tutor™

When factoring a polynomial completely, ask the following questions about the polynomial.

1. Is there a common factor? If so, factor out the common factor.

2. Is the polynomial the difference of two perfect squares? If so, factor.

3. Is the polynomial a perfect square trinomial? If so, factor.

4. Is the polynomial a trinomial that is the product of two binomials? If so, factor.

5. Is each factor nonfactorable over the integers? If not, factor.

Example 13

Factor $3x^2 - 48$.

Solution

The GCF is 3.
$3x^2 - 48 = 3(x^2 - 16)$
Factor the difference of two perfect squares.
$3(x + 4)(x - 4)$

$3x^2 - 48 = 3(x + 4)(x - 4)$

Example 14

Factor $12x^3 - 75x$.

Your solution

$3x(2x + 5)(2x - 5)$

Example 15

Factor $x^2(x - 3) + 4(3 - x)$.

Solution

The common binomial factor is $x - 3$.
$x^2(x - 3) + 4(3 - x) =$
$x^2(x - 3) - 4(x - 3) = (x - 3)(x^2 - 4)$
Factor the difference of two perfect squares.
$(x - 3)(x + 2)(x - 2)$

$x^2(x - 3) + 4(3 - x) = (x - 3)(x + 2)(x - 2)$

Example 16

Factor $a^2(b - 7) + (7 - b)$.

Your solution

$(b - 7)(a + 1)(a - 1)$

Example 17

Factor $4x^2y^2 + 12xy^2 + 9y^2$.

Solution

The GCF is y^2.
$4x^2y^2 + 12xy^2 + 9y^2 = y^2(4x^2 + 12x + 9)$
Factor the perfect square trinomial.
$y^2(2x + 3)^2$

$4x^2y^2 + 12xy^2 + 9y^2 = y^2(2x + 3)^2$

Example 18

Factor $4x^3 + 28x^2 - 120x$.

Your solution

$4x(x + 10)(x - 3)$

Solutions on p. A42

7.4A Exercises

Factor.

1. $x^2 - 4$
$(x+2)(x-2)$

2. $x^2 - 9$
$(x+3)(x-3)$

3. $a^2 - 81$
$(a+9)(a-9)$

4. $a^2 - 49$
$(a+7)(a-7)$

5. $4x^2 - 1$
$(2x+1)(2x-1)$

6. $9x^2 - 16$
$(3x+4)(3x-4)$

7. $x^6 - 9$
$(x^3+3)(x^3-3)$

8. $y^{12} - 64$
$(y^6+8)(y^6-8)$

9. $25x^2 - 1$
$(5x+1)(5x-1)$

10. $4x^2 - 1$
$(2x+1)(2x-1)$

11. $1 - 49x^2$
$(1+7x)(1-7x)$

12. $1 - 64x^2$
$(1+8x)(1-8x)$

13. $t^2 + 36$
nonfactorable

14. $x^2 + 64$
nonfactorable

15. $x^4 - y^2$
$(x^2+y)(x^2-y)$

16. $b^4 - 16a^2$
$(b^2+4a)(b^2-4a)$

17. $9x^2 - 16y^2$
$(3x+4y)(3x-4y)$

18. $25z^2 - y^2$
$(5z+y)(5z-y)$

19. $x^2y^2 - 4$
$(xy+2)(xy-2)$

20. $a^2b^2 - 25$
$(ab+5)(ab-5)$

7.4B Exercises

Factor.

21. $y^2 + 2y + 1$
$(y+1)^2$

22. $y^2 + 14y + 49$
$(y+7)^2$

23. $a^2 - 2a + 1$
$(a-1)^2$

24. $x^2 + 8x - 16$
nonfactorable

25. $z^2 - 18z - 81$
nonfactorable

26. $x^2 - 12x + 36$
$(x-6)^2$

27. $x^2 + 2xy + y^2$
$(x+y)^2$

28. $x^2 + 6xy + 9y^2$
$(x+3y)^2$

29. $4a^2 + 4a + 1$
$(2a+1)^2$

30. $25x^2 + 10x + 1$
$(5x+1)^2$

31. $64a^2 - 16a + 1$
$(8a-1)^2$

32. $9a^2 + 6a + 1$
$(3a+1)^2$

33. $16b^2 + 8b + 1$
$(4b+1)^2$

34. $4a^2 - 20a + 25$
$(2a-5)^2$

35. $4b^2 + 28b + 49$
$(2b+7)^2$

36. $9a^2 - 42a + 49$
$(3a-7)^2$

37. $25a^2 + 30ab + 9b^2$
$(5a+3b)^2$

38. $4a^2 - 12ab + 9b^2$
$(2a-3b)^2$

39. $49x^2 + 28xy + 4y^2$
$(7x+2y)^2$

40. $4y^2 - 36yz + 81z^2$
$(2y-9z)^2$

7.4C Exercises

Factor.

41. $x(a+b) + 2(a+b)$
$(a+b)(x+2)$

42. $a(x+y) + 4(x+y)$
$(x+y)(a+4)$

43. $x(b+2) - y(b+2)$
$(b+2)(x-y)$

44. $a(y-4) - b(y-4)$
$(y-4)(a-b)$

45. $z(x-3) - (x-3)$
$(x-3)(z-1)$

46. $a(y+7) - (y+7)$
$(y+7)(a-1)$

Factor.

47. $x(b - 2c) + y(b - 2c)$
$(b - 2c)(x + y)$

48. $2x(x - 3) - (x - 3)$
$(x - 3)(2x - 1)$

49. $a(x - 2) + 5(2 - x)$
$(x - 2)(a - 5)$

50. $a(x - 7) + b(7 - x)$
$(x - 7)(a - b)$

51. $b(y - 2) - 2a(y - 2)$
$(y - 2)(b - 2a)$

52. $x(a - 3) - 2y(a - 3)$
$(a - 3)(x - 2y)$

53. $b(y - 3) + 3(3 - y)$
$(y - 3)(b - 3)$

54. $c(a - 2) - b(2 - a)$
$(a - 2)(c + b)$

55. $a(x - y) - 2(y - x)$
$(x - y)(a + 2)$

7.4D Exercises

Factor.

56. $5x^2 - 5$
$5(x + 1)(x - 1)$

57. $2x^2 - 18$
$2(x + 3)(x - 3)$

58. $x^3 + 4x^2 + 4x$
$x(x + 2)^2$

59. $y^3 - 10y^2 + 25y$
$y(y - 5)^2$

60. $x^4 + 2x^3 - 35x^2$
$x^2(x + 7)(x - 5)$

61. $a^4 - 11a^3 + 24a^2$
$a^2(a - 3)(a - 8)$

62. $5b^2 + 75b + 180$
$5(b + 3)(b + 12)$

63. $6y^2 - 48y + 72$
$6(y - 2)(y - 6)$

64. $3a^2 + 36a + 10$
nonfactorable

65. $5a^2 - 30a + 4$
nonfactorable

66. $2x^2y + 16xy - 66y$
$2y(x + 11)(x - 3)$

67. $3a^2b + 21ab - 54b$
$3b(a + 9)(a - 2)$

68. $x^2y^2 - 7xy^2 - 8y^2$
$y^2(x + 1)(x - 8)$

69. $a^2b^2 + 3a^2b - 88a^2$
$a^2(b + 11)(b - 8)$

70. $a^2b^2 - 10ab^2 + 25b^2$
$b^2(a - 5)^2$

71. $a^2b^2 + 6ab^2 + 9b^2$
$b^2(a + 3)^2$

72. $12a^3b - a^2b^2 - ab^3$
$ab(3a - b)(4a + b)$

73. $2x^3y - 7x^2y^2 + 6xy^3$
$xy(x - 2y)(2x - 3y)$

74. $12a^3 - 12a^2 + 3a$
$3a(2a - 1)^2$

75. $18a^3 + 24a^2 + 8a$
$2a(3a + 2)^2$

76. $x^4 - 25x^2$
$x^2(x + 5)(x - 5)$

77. $a^4 - 16$
$(a + 2)(a - 2)(a^2 + 4)$

78. $a(2x - 2) + b(2x - 2)$
$2(x - 1)(a + b)$

79. $4a(x - 3) - 2b(x - 3)$
$2(x - 3)(2a - b)$

80. $x^2(x - 2) - (x - 2)$
$(x - 2)(x + 1)(x - 1)$

81. $y^2(a - b) - (a - b)$
$(a - b)(y + 1)(y - 1)$

82. $a(x^2 - 4) + b(x^2 - 4)$
$(x + 2)(x - 2)(a + b)$

Calculators and Computers

Remember, when factoring a polynomial, to ask the following questions about the polynomial.

1. Is there a common factor? If so, factor out the common factor.

2. Is the polynomial the difference of two perfect squares? If so, factor.

3. Is the polynomial a perfect square trinomial? If so, factor.

4. Is the polynomial a trinomial that is the product of two binomials? If so, factor.

5. Is each factor nonfactorable over the integers? If not, factor.

Factoring polynomials is an important part of the study of algebra and is a *learned* skill requiring practice. The program FACTORING on the Student Disk will provide you with additional practice in factoring.

Once the program FACTORING is loaded, a menu will appear on the screen. You may select to practice polynomials of the form

(1) $x^2 + bx + c$ or

(2) $ax^2 + bx + c$.

The option of quitting the program is also given on the menu screen.

After you have selected the type of polynomial you wish to factor, the program will present you with a polynomial to factor. When you have tried to factor the polynomial using paper and pencil, press the RETURN key on the keyboard. The correct factorization will be displayed.

Note that the difference of two squares is a polynomial of the form $ax^2 + bx + c$ in which $b = 0$. Therefore, you will be provided with practice on factoring the difference of two squares if you select to factor polynomials of the form $x^2 + bx + c$ or polynomials of the form $ax^2 + bx + c$.

You may practice factoring polynomials of either form for as long as you like. At the end of each problem, you may select to continue practicing or to return to the menu screen.

Chapter Summary

KEY WORDS

The **greatest common factor (GCF)** of two or more integers is the greatest integer that is a factor of all the integers.

To **factor** a polynomial means to write the polynomial as a product of other polynomials.

To **factor** a trinomial of the form $ax^2 + bx + c$ means to express the trinomial as the product of two binomials.

A polynomial that does not factor using only integers is **nonfactorable over the integers.**

The product of a term and itself is a **perfect square.**

The **square root** of a perfect square is one of the two equal factors of the perfect square.

ESSENTIAL RULES

The Basic Factoring Patterns for a Trinomial

$$x^2 + bx + c = (x + \;\;)(x + \;\;)$$

$$x^2 - bx + c = (x - \;\;)(x - \;\;)$$

$$x^2 + bx - c = (x + \;\;)(x - \;\;)$$

$$x^2 - bx - c = (x + \;\;)(x - \;\;)$$

$$ax^2 + bx + c = (\;\;x + \;\;)(\;\;x + \;\;)$$

$$ax^2 - bx + c = (\;\;x - \;\;)(\;\;x - \;\;)$$

$$ax^2 + bx - c = (\;\;x + \;\;)(\;\;x - \;\;)$$

$$ax^2 - bx - c = (\;\;x + \;\;)(\;\;x - \;\;)$$

The factors of the difference of two perfect squares are the sum and difference of two terms.

$$a^2 - b^2 = (a + b)(a - b)$$

A perfect square trinomial is the square of a binomial.

$$a^2 + 2ab + b^2 = (a + b)^2$$

$$a^2 - 2ab + b^2 = (a - b)^2$$

Review/Test

1. Find the GCF of $12a^2b^3$ and $16ab^6$.

$4ab^3$

2. Factor $6x^3 - 8x^2 + 10x$.

$2x(3x^2 - 4x + 5)$

3. Factor $p^2 + 5p + 6$.

$(p + 2)(p + 3)$

4. Factor $a^2 - 19a + 48$.

$(a - 3)(a - 16)$

5. Factor $x^2 + 2x - 15$.

$(x + 5)(x - 3)$

6. Factor $x^2 - 9x - 36$.

$(x + 3)(x - 12)$

7. Factor $5x^2 - 45x - 15$.

$5(x^2 - 9x - 3)$

8. Factor $2y^4 - 14y^3 - 16y^2$.

$2y^2(y + 1)(y - 8)$

9. Factor $2x^2 + 4x - 5$.

nonfactorable

10. Factor $6x^2 + 19x + 8$.

$(2x + 1)(3x + 8)$

11. Factor $12x^2 - x - 1$.

$(3x - 1)(4x + 1)$

12. Factor $8x^2 + 20x - 48$.

$4(x + 4)(2x - 3)$

13. Factor $6x^2y^2 + 9xy^2 + 12y^2$.

$3y^2(2x^2 + 3x + 4)$

14. Factor $b^2 - 16$.

$(b + 4)(b - 4)$

15. Factor $4x^2 - 49y^2$.

$(2x + 7y)(2x - 7y)$

16. Factor $p^2 + 12p + 36$.

$(p + 6)^2$

17. Factor $4a^2 - 12ab + 9b^2$.

$(2a - 3b)^2$

18. Factor $a(x - 2) + b(x - 2)$.

$(x - 2)(a + b)$

19. Factor $x(p + 1) - (p + 1)$.

$(p + 1)(x - 1)$

20. Factor $3a^2 - 75$.

$3(a + 5)(a - 5)$

21. Factor $3x^2 + 12xy + 12y^2$.

$3(x + 2y)^2$

22. Factor $y^3 - 9y$.

$y(y + 3)(y - 3)$

23. Factor $12a^2 - 36a + 27$.

$3(2a - 3)^2$

24. Factor $x(a^2 - b^2) - y(a^2 - b^2)$.

$(a + b)(a - b)(x - y)$

Cumulative Review/Test

1. Simplify $-2[4x - 2(3 - 2x) - 8x]$.

   12

2. Factor $3y(x - 3) - 2(x - 3)$.

   $(x - 3)(3y - 2)$

3. Factor $p^2 - 9p - 10$.

   $(p + 1)(p - 10)$

4. Subtract: $-2 - (-3) - 5 - (-11)$

   7

5. Simplify $(3 - 7)^2 \div (-2) - 3 \cdot (-4)$.

   4

6. Factor $x^2 - 5xy - 14y^2$.

   $(x - 7y)(x + 2y)$

7. Evaluate $-2a^2 \div 2b - c$ when $a = -4$, $b = 2$, and $c = -1$.

   -31

8. Simplify $-\frac{3}{4}(-20x^2)$.

   $15x^2$

9. Factor $9x^2 + 15x - 14$.

   $(3x - 2)(3x + 7)$

10. Solve: $-\frac{5}{7}x = -\frac{10}{21}$

    $\frac{2}{3}$

11. Find the GCF of $12x^3y^2$ and $42xy^6$.

    $6xy^2$

12. Factor $18a^3 + 57a^2 + 30a$.

    $3a(2a + 5)(3a + 2)$

13. Factor $18x^2 - 48xy + 32y^2$.

    $2(3x - 4y)^2$

14. Solve: $3x - 2 = 12 - 5x$

    $\frac{7}{4}$

15. Factor $4x^2 + 28xy + 49y^2$.

    $(2x + 7y)^2$

16. 120% of what number is 54?

    45

17. Simplify $(x^{-4}y^3)^2$.

    $\frac{y^6}{x^8}$

18. Factor $15xy^2 - 20xy^4$.

    $5xy^2(3 - 4y^2)$

19. Solve:
    $-2 + 4[3x - 2(4 - x) - 3] = 4x + 2$

    3

20. Simplify $(-3a^3b^2)^2$.

    $9a^6b^4$

21. Factor $36a^2 - 49b^2$.

    $(6a + 7b)(6a - 7b)$

22. Simplify $(x + 2)(x^2 - 5x + 4)$.

    $x^3 - 3x^2 - 6x + 8$

23. Find three consecutive even integers such that five times the middle integer is twelve more than twice the sum of the first and third.

    10, 12, and 14

24. A family drove to a resort at an average speed of 42 mph and later returned over the same road at an average speed of 56 mph. Find the distance to the resort if the total driving time was 7 hours.

    168 mi

chapter 8

Algebraic Fractions

Objectives

Section 1 Multiplication and Division of Algebraic Fractions

Objective A   To simplify an algebraic fraction

Reference for
Computer
Tutor™

A fraction in which the numerator or denominator is a variable expression is called an **algebraic fraction.** Examples of algebraic fractions are shown at the right.

$$\frac{5}{z}, \quad \frac{x^2 + 1}{2x - 1}, \quad \frac{y^2 - 3}{3xy + 1}$$

Care must be exercised with algebraic fractions to assure that when the variables are replaced with numbers, the resulting denominator is not zero.

Consider the algebraic fraction at the right. The value of x cannot be 2, since the denominator would then be zero and division by zero is not defined.

$$\frac{3x^2 + 1}{x^2 - 4}$$

$$\frac{3 \cdot 2^2 + 1}{2^2 - 4} = \frac{13}{0}$$

An algebraic fraction is in **simplest form** when the numerator and denominator have no common factors.

Simplify: $\dfrac{x^2 - 4}{x^2 - 2x - 8}$

Factor the numerator and denominator.

$$\frac{x^2 - 4}{x^2 - 2x - 8} = \frac{(x - 2)(x + 2)}{(x - 4)(x + 2)}$$

Cancel the common factors.

$$= \frac{(x - 2)\overset{1}{\cancel{(x + 2)}}}{(x - 4)\underset{1}{\cancel{(x + 2)}}}$$

Write the answer in simplest form.

$$= \frac{x - 2}{x - 4}$$

Recall from Chapter 7 that $(b - a) = (-a + b) = -(a - b)$.

Therefore, $\dfrac{b - a}{a - b} = \dfrac{-(a - b)}{a - b} = \dfrac{-1}{1} = -1$.

Simplify: $\dfrac{6 - 2x}{x - 3}$

Factor the numerator.

$$\frac{6 - 2x}{x - 3} = \frac{2(3 - x)}{x - 3}$$

Cancel the common factors.

$$= \frac{2\overset{-1}{\cancel{(3 - x)}}}{\underset{1}{\cancel{x - 3}}}$$

$$\frac{3 - x}{x - 3} = \frac{-(x - 3)}{x - 3} = \frac{-1}{1}$$

Write the answer in simplest form.

$$= -2$$

Simplify: $\dfrac{10 + 3x - x^2}{x^2 - 4x - 5}$

Factor the numerator and the denominator.

$$\dfrac{10 + 3x - x^2}{x^2 - 4x - 5} = \dfrac{(5 - x)(2 + x)}{(x - 5)(x + 1)}$$

Cancel the common factors.

$$\dfrac{5 - x}{x - 5} = \dfrac{-(x - 5)}{x - 5} = \dfrac{-1}{1}$$

$$= \dfrac{\overset{-1}{\cancel{(5 - x)}}(2 + x)}{\underset{1}{\cancel{(x - 5)}}(x + 1)}$$

Write the answer in simplest form.

$$= -\dfrac{x + 2}{x + 1}$$

Example 1

Simplify: $\dfrac{4x^3y^4}{6x^4y}$

Solution

$\dfrac{4x^3y^4}{6x^4y} = \dfrac{\overset{1}{\cancel{2}} \cdot 2x^3y^4}{\underset{1}{\cancel{2}} \cdot 3x^4y} = \dfrac{2y^3}{3x}$ Use rules of exponents.

Example 2

Simplify: $\dfrac{6x^5y}{12x^2y^3}$

Your solution

$$\dfrac{x^3}{2y^2}$$

Example 3

Simplify: $\dfrac{9 - x^2}{x^2 + x - 12}$

Solution

$\dfrac{9 - x^2}{x^2 + x - 12} = \dfrac{\overset{-1}{\cancel{(3 - x)}}(3 + x)}{\underset{1}{\cancel{(x - 3)}}(x + 4)} = -\dfrac{x + 3}{x + 4}$

Example 4

Simplify: $\dfrac{x^2 + 2x - 24}{16 - x^2}$

Your solution

$$-\dfrac{x + 6}{x + 4}$$

Example 5

Simplify: $\dfrac{x^2 + 2x - 15}{x^2 - 7x + 12}$

Solution

$\dfrac{x^2 + 2x - 15}{x^2 - 7x + 12} = \dfrac{(x + 5)\overset{1}{\cancel{(x - 3)}}}{\underset{1}{\cancel{(x - 3)}}(x - 4)} = \dfrac{x + 5}{x - 4}$

Example 6

Simplify: $\dfrac{x^2 + 4x - 12}{x^2 - 3x + 2}$

Your solution

$$\dfrac{x + 6}{x - 1}$$

Solutions on p. A44

Objective B   To multiply algebraic fractions

The product of two fractions is a fraction whose numerator is the product of the numerators of the two fractions and whose denominator is the product of the denominators of the two fractions.

$$\frac{a}{b} \cdot \frac{c}{d} = \frac{ac}{bd}$$

$$\frac{2}{3} \cdot \frac{4}{5} = \frac{8}{15}$$

$$\frac{3x}{y} \cdot \frac{2}{z} = \frac{6x}{yz}$$

$$\frac{x+2}{x} \cdot \frac{3}{x-2} = \frac{3x+6}{x^2-2x}$$

Simplify: $\dfrac{x^2 + 3x}{x^2 - 3x - 4} \cdot \dfrac{x^2 - 5x + 4}{x^2 + 2x - 3}$

$$\frac{x^2 + 3x}{x^2 - 3x - 4} \cdot \frac{x^2 - 5x + 4}{x^2 + 2x - 3} =$$

Factor the numerator and denominator of each fraction.

$$\frac{x(x+3)}{(x-4)(x+1)} \cdot \frac{(x-4)(x-1)}{(x+3)(x-1)} =$$

Multiply.
Cancel the common factors.

$$\frac{\overset{1}{x(x+3)}\overset{1}{(x-4)}\overset{1}{(x-1)}}{(x-4)(x+1)(x+3)(x-1)} =$$

Write the answer in simplest form.

$$\frac{x}{x+1}$$

Example 7

Simplify: $\dfrac{10x^2 - 15x}{12x - 8} \cdot \dfrac{3x - 2}{20x - 25}$

Solution

$$\frac{10x^2 - 15x}{12x - 8} \cdot \frac{3x - 2}{20x - 25} =$$

$$\frac{5x(2x - 3)}{4(3x - 2)} \cdot \frac{(3x - 2)}{5(4x - 5)} =$$

$$\frac{\overset{1}{5}x(2x - 3)\overset{1}{(3x - 2)}}{2 \cdot 2(3x - 2)5(4x - 5)} =$$

$$\frac{x(2x - 3)}{4(4x - 5)}$$

Example 8

Simplify: $\dfrac{12x^2 + 3x}{10x - 15} \cdot \dfrac{8x - 12}{9x + 18}$

Your solution

$$\frac{4x(4x + 1)}{15(x + 2)}$$

Example 9

Simplify: $\dfrac{x^2 + x - 6}{x^2 + 7x + 12} \cdot \dfrac{x^2 + 3x - 4}{4 - x^2}$

Solution

$$\dfrac{x^2 + x - 6}{x^2 + 7x + 12} \cdot \dfrac{x^2 + 3x - 4}{4 - x^2} =$$

$$\dfrac{(x + 3)(x - 2)}{(x + 3)(x + 4)} \cdot \dfrac{(x + 4)(x - 1)}{(2 - x)(2 + x)} =$$

$$\dfrac{\overset{1}{\cancel{(x + 3)}}\overset{-1}{\cancel{(x - 2)}}\overset{1}{\cancel{(x + 4)}}(x - 1)}{\underset{1}{\cancel{(x + 3)}}\underset{1}{\cancel{(x + 4)}}\underset{1}{\cancel{(2 - x)}}(2 + x)} = -\dfrac{x - 1}{x + 2}$$

Example 10

Simplify: $\dfrac{x^2 + 2x - 15}{9 - x^2} \cdot \dfrac{x^2 - 3x - 18}{x^2 - 7x + 6}$

Your solution

$$-\dfrac{x + 5}{x - 1}$$

Solution on p. A44

Objective C   ## To divide algebraic fractions

8
DISK
EIGHT

Reference for
Computer
Tutor™

The **reciprocal** of a fraction is a fraction with the numerator and denominator interchanged.

$$\text{Fraction} \left\{ \begin{array}{ll} \dfrac{a}{b} & \dfrac{b}{a} \\[2mm] x^2 = \dfrac{x^2}{1} & \dfrac{1}{x^2} \\[2mm] \dfrac{x + 2}{x} & \dfrac{x}{x + 2} \end{array} \right\} \text{Reciprocal}$$

To divide two fractions, multiply by the reciprocal of the divisor.

$$\dfrac{a}{b} \div \dfrac{c}{d} = \dfrac{a}{b} \cdot \dfrac{d}{c} = \dfrac{ad}{bc}$$

$$\dfrac{4}{x} \div \dfrac{y}{5} = \dfrac{4}{x} \cdot \dfrac{5}{y} = \dfrac{20}{xy}$$

$$\dfrac{x + 4}{x} \div \dfrac{x - 2}{4} = \dfrac{x + 4}{x} \cdot \dfrac{4}{x - 2} = \dfrac{4(x + 4)}{x(x - 2)}$$

The basis for the division rule is shown at the right.

$$\dfrac{a}{b} \div \dfrac{c}{d} = \dfrac{\dfrac{a}{b} \cdot \dfrac{d}{c}}{\dfrac{c}{d} \cdot \dfrac{d}{c}} = \dfrac{\dfrac{a}{b} \cdot \dfrac{d}{c}}{\dfrac{c}{d} \cdot \dfrac{d}{c}} = \dfrac{\dfrac{a}{b} \cdot \dfrac{d}{c}}{1} = \dfrac{a}{b} \cdot \dfrac{d}{c}$$

Simplify: $\dfrac{3x^4 y^2}{8a^3 b} \div \dfrac{9xy}{4ab}$

Rewrite division as multiplication by the reciprocal of the divisor.

Multiply.

Write the answer in simplest form.

$$\dfrac{3x^4 y^2}{8a^3 b} \div \dfrac{9xy}{4ab} = \dfrac{3x^4 y^2}{8a^3 b} \cdot \dfrac{4ab}{9xy}$$

$$= \dfrac{3x^4 y^2 \cdot 4ab}{8a^3 b \cdot 9xy}$$

$$= \dfrac{x^3 y}{6a^2}$$

Example 11

Simplify: $\dfrac{5ab}{12x^3y} \div \dfrac{15a^3b^2}{4x^5y^6}$

Solution

$\dfrac{5ab}{12x^3y} \div \dfrac{15a^3b^2}{4x^5y^6} =$

$\dfrac{5ab}{12x^3y} \cdot \dfrac{4x^5y^6}{15a^3b^2} =$

$\dfrac{5ab \cdot 4x^5y^6}{12x^3y \cdot 15a^3b^2} =$

$\dfrac{x^2y^5}{9a^2b}$

Example 12

Simplify: $\dfrac{16x^4y^3}{3a^5b^2} \div \dfrac{2xy^3}{9a^6b^5}$

Your solution

$24ab^3x^3$

Example 13

Simplify: $\dfrac{xy^2 - 3x^2y}{z^2} \div \dfrac{6x^2 - 2xy}{z^3}$

Solution

$\dfrac{xy^2 - 3x^2y}{z^2} \div \dfrac{6x^2 - 2xy}{z^3} =$

$\dfrac{xy^2 - 3x^2y}{z^2} \cdot \dfrac{z^3}{6x^2 - 2xy} =$

$\dfrac{xy(\overset{-1}{\cancel{y - 3x}}) \cdot z^3}{z^2 \cdot 2x(\underset{1}{\cancel{3x - y}})} = -\dfrac{yz}{2}$

Example 14

Simplify: $\dfrac{a^2}{4bc^2 - 2b^2c} \div \dfrac{a}{6bc - 3b^2}$

Your solution

$\dfrac{3a}{2c}$

Example 15

Simplify: $\dfrac{2x^2 + 5x + 2}{2x^2 + 3x - 2} \div \dfrac{3x^2 + 13x + 4}{2x^2 + 7x - 4}$

Solution

$\dfrac{2x^2 + 5x + 2}{2x^2 + 3x - 2} \div \dfrac{3x^2 + 13x + 4}{2x^2 + 7x - 4} =$

$\dfrac{2x^2 + 5x + 2}{2x^2 + 3x - 2} \cdot \dfrac{2x^2 + 7x - 4}{3x^2 + 13x + 4} =$

$\dfrac{(2x + 1)(\overset{1}{\cancel{x + 2}})}{(\underset{1}{\cancel{2x - 1}})(\underset{1}{\cancel{x + 2}})} \cdot \dfrac{(\overset{1}{\cancel{2x - 1}})(\overset{1}{\cancel{x + 4}})}{(3x + 1)(\underset{1}{\cancel{x + 4}})} = \dfrac{2x + 1}{3x + 1}$

Example 16

Simplify: $\dfrac{3x^2 + 26x + 16}{3x^2 - 7x - 6} \div \dfrac{2x^2 + 9x - 5}{x^2 + 2x - 15}$

Your solution

$\dfrac{x + 8}{2x - 1}$

Solutions on p. A44

8.1A Exercises

Simplify.

1. $\dfrac{9x^3}{12x^4}$

   $\dfrac{3}{4x}$

2. $\dfrac{16x^2y}{24xy^3}$

   $\dfrac{2x}{3y^2}$

3. $\dfrac{(x+3)^2}{(x+3)^3}$

   $\dfrac{1}{x+3}$

4. $\dfrac{(2x-1)^5}{(2x-1)^4}$

   $2x-1$

5. $\dfrac{3n-4}{4-3n}$

   -1

6. $\dfrac{5-2x}{2x-5}$

   -1

7. $\dfrac{6y(y+2)}{9y^2(y+2)}$

   $\dfrac{2}{3y}$

8. $\dfrac{12x^2(3-x)}{18x(3-x)}$

   $\dfrac{2x}{3}$

9. $\dfrac{6x(x-5)}{8x^2(5-x)}$

   $-\dfrac{3}{4x}$

10. $\dfrac{14x^3(7-3x)}{21x(3x-7)}$

    $-\dfrac{2x^2}{3}$

11. $\dfrac{10-5y}{y-2}$

    -5

12. $\dfrac{18-6a}{a-3}$

    -6

13. $\dfrac{a^2+4a}{ab+4b}$

    $\dfrac{a}{b}$

14. $\dfrac{x^2-3x}{2x-6}$

    $\dfrac{x}{2}$

15. $\dfrac{4-6x}{3x^2-2x}$

    $-\dfrac{2}{x}$

16. $\dfrac{5xy-3y}{9-15x}$

    $-\dfrac{y}{3}$

17. $\dfrac{y^2-3y+2}{y^2-4y+3}$

    $\dfrac{y-2}{y-3}$

18. $\dfrac{x^2+5x+6}{x^2+8x+15}$

    $\dfrac{x+2}{x+5}$

19. $\dfrac{x^2+3x-10}{x^2+2x-8}$

    $\dfrac{x+5}{x+4}$

20. $\dfrac{a^2+7a-8}{a^2+6a-7}$

    $\dfrac{a+8}{a+7}$

21. $\dfrac{x^2+x-12}{x^2-6x+9}$

    $\dfrac{x+4}{x-3}$

22. $\dfrac{x^2+8x+16}{x^2-2x-24}$

    $\dfrac{x+4}{x-6}$

23. $\dfrac{x^2-3x-10}{25-x^2}$

    $-\dfrac{x+2}{x+5}$

24. $\dfrac{4-y^2}{y^2-3y-10}$

    $\dfrac{2-y}{y-5}$

25. $\dfrac{2x^3+2x^2-4x}{x^3+2x^2-3x}$

    $\dfrac{2(x+2)}{x+3}$

26. $\dfrac{3x^3-12x}{6x^3-24x^2+24x}$

    $\dfrac{x+2}{2(x-2)}$

27. $\dfrac{6x^2-7x+2}{6x^2+5x-6}$

    $\dfrac{2x-1}{2x+3}$

28. $\dfrac{2n^2-9n+4}{2n^2-5n-12}$

    $\dfrac{2n-1}{2n+3}$

29. $\dfrac{x^2+3x-28}{24-2x-x^2}$

    $-\dfrac{x+7}{x+6}$

30. $\dfrac{x^2+2x-3}{5-4x-x^2}$

    $-\dfrac{x+3}{x+5}$

31. $\dfrac{8+2y-y^2}{y^2+y-20}$

    $-\dfrac{y+2}{y+5}$

32. $\dfrac{1-x^2}{x^2+8x-9}$

    $-\dfrac{x+1}{x+9}$

8.1B Exercises

Simplify.

33. $\dfrac{8x^2}{9y^3} \cdot \dfrac{3y^2}{4x^3}$

$$\dfrac{2}{3xy}$$

34. $\dfrac{4a^2b^3}{15x^5y^2} \cdot \dfrac{25x^3y}{16ab}$

$$\dfrac{5ab^2}{12x^2y}$$

35. $\dfrac{12x^3y^4}{7a^2b^3} \cdot \dfrac{14a^3b^4}{9x^2y^2}$

$$\dfrac{8abxy^2}{3}$$

36. $\dfrac{18a^4b^2}{25x^2y^3} \cdot \dfrac{50x^5y^6}{27a^6b^2}$

$$\dfrac{4x^3y^3}{3a^2}$$

37. $\dfrac{3x - 6}{5x - 20} \cdot \dfrac{10x - 40}{27x - 54}$

$$\dfrac{2}{9}$$

38. $\dfrac{8x - 12}{14x + 7} \cdot \dfrac{42x + 21}{32x - 48}$

$$\dfrac{3}{4}$$

39. $\dfrac{3x^2 + 2x}{2xy - 3y} \cdot \dfrac{2xy^3 - 3y^3}{3x^3 + 2x^2}$

$$\dfrac{y^2}{x}$$

40. $\dfrac{4a^2x - 3a^2}{2by + 5b} \cdot \dfrac{2b^3y + 5b^3}{4ax - 3a}$

$$ab^2$$

41. $\dfrac{x^2 + 5x + 4}{x^3y^2} \cdot \dfrac{x^2y^3}{x^2 + 2x + 1}$

$$\dfrac{y(x + 4)}{x(x + 1)}$$

42. $\dfrac{x^2 + x - 2}{xy^2} \cdot \dfrac{x^3y}{x^2 + 5x + 6}$

$$\dfrac{x^2(x - 1)}{y(x + 3)}$$

43. $\dfrac{x^4y^2}{x^2 + 3x - 28} \cdot \dfrac{x^2 - 49}{xy^4}$

$$\dfrac{x^3(x - 7)}{y^2(x - 4)}$$

44. $\dfrac{x^5y^3}{x^2 + 13x + 30} \cdot \dfrac{x^2 + 2x - 3}{x^7y^2}$

$$\dfrac{y(x - 1)}{x^2(x + 10)}$$

45. $\dfrac{2x^2 - 5x}{2xy + y} \cdot \dfrac{2xy^2 + y^2}{5x^2 - 2x^3}$

$$-\dfrac{y}{x}$$

46. $\dfrac{3a^3 + 4a^2}{5ab - 3b} \cdot \dfrac{3b^3 - 5ab^3}{3a^2 + 4a}$

$$-ab^2$$

47. $\dfrac{x^2 - 2x - 24}{x^2 - 5x - 6} \cdot \dfrac{x^2 + 5x + 6}{x^2 + 6x + 8}$

$$\dfrac{x + 3}{x + 1}$$

48. $\dfrac{x^2 - 8x + 7}{x^2 + 3x - 4} \cdot \dfrac{x^2 + 3x - 10}{x^2 - 9x + 14}$

$$\dfrac{x + 5}{x + 4}$$

49. $\dfrac{x^2 + 2x - 35}{x^2 + 4x - 21} \cdot \dfrac{x^2 + 3x - 18}{x^2 + 9x + 18}$

$$\dfrac{x - 5}{x + 3}$$

50. $\dfrac{y^2 + y - 20}{y^2 + 2y - 15} \cdot \dfrac{y^2 + 4y - 21}{y^2 + 3y - 28}$

$$1$$

Simplify.

51. $\dfrac{x^2 - 3x - 4}{x^2 + 6x + 5} \cdot \dfrac{x^2 + 5x + 6}{8 + 2x - x^2}$

$-\dfrac{x+3}{x+5}$

52. $\dfrac{25 - n^2}{n^2 - 2n - 35} \cdot \dfrac{n^2 - 8n - 20}{n^2 - 3n - 10}$

$-\dfrac{n-10}{n-7}$

53. $\dfrac{12x^2 - 6x}{x^2 + 6x + 5} \cdot \dfrac{2x^4 + 10x^3}{4x^2 - 1}$

$\dfrac{12x^4}{(x+1)(2x+1)}$

54. $\dfrac{8x^3 + 4x^2}{x^2 - 3x + 2} \cdot \dfrac{x^2 - 4}{16x^2 + 8x}$

$\dfrac{x(x+2)}{2(x-1)}$

55. $\dfrac{16 + 6x - x^2}{x^2 - 10x - 24} \cdot \dfrac{x^2 - 6x - 27}{x^2 - 17x + 72}$

$-\dfrac{x+3}{x-12}$

56. $\dfrac{x^2 - 11x + 28}{x^2 - 13x + 42} \cdot \dfrac{x^2 + 7x + 10}{20 - x - x^2}$

$-\dfrac{x+2}{x-6}$

57. $\dfrac{2x^2 + 5x + 2}{2x^2 + 7x + 3} \cdot \dfrac{x^2 - 7x - 30}{x^2 - 6x - 40}$

$\dfrac{x+2}{x+4}$

58. $\dfrac{x^2 - 4x - 32}{x^2 - 8x - 48} \cdot \dfrac{3x^2 + 17x + 10}{3x^2 - 22x - 16}$

$\dfrac{x+5}{x-12}$

59. $\dfrac{2x^2 + x - 3}{2x^2 - x - 6} \cdot \dfrac{2x^2 - 9x + 10}{2x^2 - 3x + 1}$

$\dfrac{2x-5}{2x-1}$

60. $\dfrac{3y^2 + 14y + 8}{2y^2 + 7y - 4} \cdot \dfrac{2y^2 + 9y - 5}{3y^2 + 16y + 5}$

$\dfrac{3y+2}{3y+1}$

61. $\dfrac{6x^2 - 11x + 4}{6x^2 + x - 2} \cdot \dfrac{12x^2 + 11x + 2}{8x^2 + 14x + 3}$

$\dfrac{3x-4}{2x+3}$

62. $\dfrac{6 - x - 2x^2}{4x^2 + 3x - 10} \cdot \dfrac{3x^2 + 7x - 20}{2x^2 + 5x - 12}$

$-\dfrac{3x-5}{4x-5}$

Copyright © 1989 HMCo

8.1C Exercises

Simplify.

63. $\dfrac{4x^2y^3}{15a^2b^3} \div \dfrac{6xy}{5a^3b^5}$

$\dfrac{2ab^2xy^2}{9}$

64. $\dfrac{9x^3y^4}{16a^4b^2} \div \dfrac{45x^4y^2}{14a^7b}$

$\dfrac{7a^3y^2}{40bx}$

65. $\dfrac{6x - 12}{8x + 32} \div \dfrac{18x - 36}{10x + 40}$

$\dfrac{5}{12}$

66. $\dfrac{28x + 14}{45x - 30} \div \dfrac{14x + 7}{30x - 20}$

$\dfrac{4}{3}$

67. $\dfrac{6x^3 + 7x^2}{12x - 3} \div \dfrac{6x^2 + 7x}{36x - 9}$

$3x$

68. $\dfrac{5a^2y + 3a^2}{2x^3 + 5x^2} \div \dfrac{10ay + 6a}{6x^3 + 15x^2}$

$\dfrac{3a}{2}$

Simplify.

69. $\dfrac{x^2 + 4x + 3}{x^2y} \div \dfrac{x^2 + 2x + 1}{xy^2}$

$$\dfrac{y(x+3)}{x(x+1)}$$

70. $\dfrac{x^3y^2}{x^2 - 3x - 10} \div \dfrac{xy^4}{x^2 - x - 20}$

$$\dfrac{x^2(x+4)}{y^2(x+2)}$$

71. $\dfrac{x^2 - 49}{x^4y^3} \div \dfrac{x^2 - 14x + 49}{x^4y^3}$

$$\dfrac{x+7}{x-7}$$

72. $\dfrac{x^2y^5}{x^2 - 11x + 30} \div \dfrac{xy^6}{x^2 - 7x + 10}$

$$\dfrac{x(x-2)}{y(x-6)}$$

73. $\dfrac{4ax - 8a}{c^2} \div \dfrac{2y - xy}{c^3}$

$$-\dfrac{4ac}{y}$$

74. $\dfrac{3x^2y - 9xy}{a^2b} \div \dfrac{3x^2 - x^3}{ab^2}$

$$-\dfrac{3by}{ax}$$

75. $\dfrac{x^2 - 5x + 6}{x^2 - 9x + 18} \div \dfrac{x^2 - 6x + 8}{x^2 - 9x + 20}$

$$\dfrac{x-5}{x-6}$$

76. $\dfrac{x^2 + 3x - 40}{x^2 + 2x - 35} \div \dfrac{x^2 + 2x - 48}{x^2 + 3x - 18}$

$$\dfrac{(x+6)(x-3)}{(x+7)(x-6)}$$

77. $\dfrac{x^2 + 2x - 15}{x^2 - 4x - 45} \div \dfrac{x^2 + x - 12}{x^2 - 5x - 36}$

$$1$$

78. $\dfrac{y^2 - y - 56}{y^2 + 8y + 7} \div \dfrac{y^2 - 13y + 40}{y^2 - 4y - 5}$

$$1$$

79. $\dfrac{8 + 2x - x^2}{x^2 + 7x + 10} \div \dfrac{x^2 - 11x + 28}{x^2 - x - 42}$

$$-\dfrac{x+6}{x+5}$$

80. $\dfrac{x^2 - x - 2}{x^2 - 7x + 10} \div \dfrac{x^2 - 3x - 4}{40 - 3x - x^2}$

$$-\dfrac{x+8}{x-4}$$

81. $\dfrac{2x^2 - 3x - 20}{2x^2 - 7x - 30} \div \dfrac{2x^2 - 5x - 12}{4x^2 + 12x + 9}$

$$\dfrac{2x+3}{x-6}$$

82. $\dfrac{6n^2 + 13n + 6}{4n^2 - 9} \div \dfrac{6n^2 + n - 2}{4n^2 - 1}$

$$\dfrac{2n+1}{2n-3}$$

83. $\dfrac{9x^2 - 16}{6x^2 - 11x + 4} \div \dfrac{6x^2 + 11x + 4}{8x^2 + 10x + 3}$

$$\dfrac{4x+3}{2x-1}$$

84. $\dfrac{15 - 14x - 8x^2}{4x^2 + 4x - 15} \div \dfrac{4x^2 + 13x - 12}{3x^2 + 13x + 4}$

$$-\dfrac{3x+1}{2x-3}$$

85. $\dfrac{8x^2 + 18x - 5}{10x^2 - 9x + 2} \div \dfrac{8x^2 + 22x + 15}{10x^2 + 11x - 6}$

$$\dfrac{(2x+5)(4x-1)}{(2x-1)(4x+5)}$$

86. $\dfrac{10 + 7x - 12x^2}{8x^2 - 2x - 15} \div \dfrac{6x^2 - 13x + 5}{10x^2 - 13x + 4}$

$$\dfrac{(3x+2)(5-4x)(5x-4)}{(2x-3)(4x+5)(3x-5)}$$

Section 2 | Addition and Subtraction of Algebraic Fractions

Objective A | To find the least common multiple (LCM) of two or more polynomials

Reference for Computer Tutor™

The **least common multiple (LCM)** of two or more numbers is the smallest number that contains the prime factorization of each number.

The LCM of 12 and 18 is 36. 36 contains the prime factors of 12 and the prime factors of 18.

$$12 = 2 \cdot 2 \cdot 3$$
$$18 = 2 \cdot 3 \cdot 3$$

$$\text{LCM} = 36 = \overbrace{2 \cdot \underbrace{2 \cdot 3 \cdot 3}}$$
Factors of 12
Factors of 18

The least common multiple of two or more polynomials is the simplest polynomial that contains the factors of each polynomial.

To find the LCM of two or more polynomials, first factor each polynomial completely. The LCM is the product of each factor the greatest number of times it occurs in any one factorization.

Find the LCM of $4x^2 + 4x$ and $x^2 + 2x + 1$.

The LCM of the polynomials is the product of the LCM of the numerical coefficients and each variable factor the greatest number of times it occurs in any one factorization.

$$4x^2 + 4x = 4x(x + 1) = 2 \cdot 2 \cdot x(x + 1)$$
$$x^2 + 2x + 1 = (x + 1)(x + 1)$$

Factors of $4x^2 + 4x$

$$\text{LCM} = \overbrace{2 \cdot 2 \cdot x\underbrace{(x + 1)(x + 1)}} = 4x(x + 1)(x + 1)$$
Factors of $x^2 + 2x + 1$

Example 1

Find the LCM of $4x^2y$ and $6xy^2$.

Solution

$4x^2y = 2 \cdot 2 \cdot x \cdot x \cdot y \qquad 6xy^2 = 2 \cdot 3 \cdot x \cdot y \cdot y$
$\text{LCM} = 2 \cdot 2 \cdot 3 \cdot x \cdot x \cdot y \cdot y = 12x^2y^2$

Example 3

Find the LCM of $x^2 - x - 6$ and $9 - x^2$.

Solution

$x^2 - x - 6 = (x - 3)(x + 2)$
$9 - x^2 = -(x^2 - 9) = -(x + 3)(x - 3)$
$\text{LCM} = (x - 3)(x + 2)(x + 3)$

Example 2

Find the LCM of $8uv^2$ and $12uw$.

Your solution

$24uv^2w$

Example 4

Find the LCM of $m^2 - 6m + 9$ and $m^2 - 2m - 3$.

Your solution

$(m - 3)(m - 3)(m + 1)$

Solutions on p. A45

Reference for
Computer
Tutor™

Objective B	## To express two fractions in terms of the LCM of their denominators

When adding and subtracting fractions, it is frequently necessary to express two or more fractions in terms of a common denominator. This common denominator is the LCM of the denominators of the fractions.

Write the fractions $\frac{x + 1}{4x^2}$ and $\frac{x - 3}{6x^2 - 12x}$ in terms of the LCM of the denominators.

Find the LCM of the denominators.

The LCM is $12x^2(x - 2)$.

$$\frac{x + 1}{4x^2} = \frac{x + 1}{4x^2} \cdot \frac{3(x - 2)}{3(x - 2)} = \frac{3x^2 - 3x - 6}{12x^2(x - 2)} \longleftarrow$$

For each fraction, multiply the numerator and denominator by the factors whose product with the denominator is the LCM.

$$\frac{x - 3}{6x^2 - 12x} = \frac{x - 3}{6x(x - 2)} \cdot \frac{2x}{2x} = \frac{2x^2 - 6x}{12x^2(x - 2)} \longleftarrow$$

LCM

Example 5

Write the fractions $\frac{x + 2}{3x^2}$ and $\frac{x - 1}{8xy}$ in terms of the LCM of the denominators.

Solution

The LCM is $24x^2y$.

$$\frac{x + 2}{3x^2} = \frac{x + 2}{3x^2} \cdot \frac{8y}{8y} = \frac{8xy + 16y}{24x^2y}$$

$$\frac{x - 1}{8xy} = \frac{x - 1}{8xy} \cdot \frac{3x}{3x} = \frac{3x^2 - 3x}{24x^2y}$$

Example 6

Write the fractions $\frac{x - 3}{4xy^2}$ and $\frac{2x + 1}{9y^2z}$ in terms of the LCM of the denominators.

Your solution

$$\frac{8x^2 + 4x}{36xy^2z}$$

Example 7

Write the fractions $\frac{2x - 1}{2x - x^2}$ and $\frac{x}{x^2 + x - 6}$ in terms of the LCM of the denominators.

Solution

$$\frac{2x - 1}{2x - x^2} = \frac{2x - 1}{-(x^2 - 2x)} = -\frac{2x - 1}{x^2 - 2x}$$

The LCM is $x(x - 2)(x + 3)$.

$$\frac{2x - 1}{2x - x^2} = -\frac{2x - 1}{x(x - 2)} \cdot \frac{x + 3}{x + 3} = -\frac{2x^2 + 5x - 3}{x(x - 2)(x + 3)}$$

$$\frac{x}{x^2 + x - 6} = \frac{x}{(x - 2)(x + 3)} \cdot \frac{x}{x} = \frac{x^2}{x(x - 2)(x + 3)}$$

Example 8

Write the fractions $\frac{x + 4}{x^2 - 3x - 10}$ and $\frac{2x}{25 - x^2}$ in terms of the LCM of the denominators.

Your solution

$$-\frac{2x^2 + 4x}{(x + 2)(x + 5)(x - 5)}$$

Solutions on p. A45

| Objective C | To add or subtract algebraic fractions with like denominators |

When adding algebraic fractions in which the denominators are the same, add the numerators. The denominator of the sum is the common denominator.

$$\frac{a}{b} + \frac{c}{b} = \frac{a+c}{b}$$

$$\frac{5x}{18} + \frac{7x}{18} = \frac{12x}{18} = \frac{2x}{3}$$

$$\frac{x}{x^2-1} + \frac{1}{x^2-1} = \frac{x+1}{x^2-1} = \frac{\overset{1}{(\cancel{x+1})}}{(x-1)\underset{1}{(\cancel{x+1})}} = \frac{1}{x-1}$$

Note that the sum is written in simplest form.

When subtracting algebraic fractions with like denominators, subtract the numerators. The denominator of the difference is the common denominator. Write the answer in simplest form.

$$\frac{a}{b} - \frac{c}{b} = \frac{a-c}{b}$$

$$\frac{2x}{x-2} - \frac{4}{x-2} = \frac{2x-4}{x-2} = \frac{2\overset{1}{(\cancel{x-2})}}{\underset{1}{\cancel{x-2}}} = 2$$

$$\frac{3x-1}{x^2-5x+4} - \frac{2x+3}{x^2-5x+4} = \frac{(3x-1)-(2x+3)}{x^2-5x+4} = \frac{x-4}{x^2-5x+4} = \frac{\overset{1}{(\cancel{x-4})}}{\underset{1}{(\cancel{x-4})}(x-1)} = \frac{1}{x-1}$$

Example 9

Simplify: $\dfrac{7}{x^2} + \dfrac{9}{x^2}$

Solution

$$\frac{7}{x^2} + \frac{9}{x^2} = \frac{7+9}{x^2} = \frac{16}{x^2}$$

Example 10

Simplify: $\dfrac{3}{xy} + \dfrac{12}{xy}$

Your solution

$$\frac{15}{xy}$$

Example 11

Simplify: $\dfrac{3x^2}{x^2-1} - \dfrac{x+4}{x^2-1}$

Solution

$$\frac{3x^2}{x^2-1} - \frac{x+4}{x^2-1} = \frac{3x^2-(x+4)}{x^2-1} = \frac{3x^2-x-4}{x^2-1} =$$

$$\frac{(3x-4)\overset{1}{(\cancel{x+1})}}{(x-1)\underset{1}{(\cancel{x+1})}} = \frac{3x-4}{x-1}$$

Example 12

Simplify: $\dfrac{2x^2}{x^2-x-12} - \dfrac{7x+4}{x^2-x-12}$

Your solution

$$\frac{2x+1}{x+3}$$

Solution on p. A45

Example 13

Simplify:

$$\frac{2x^2 + 5}{x^2 + 2x - 3} - \frac{x^2 - 3x}{x^2 + 2x - 3} + \frac{x - 2}{x^2 + 2x - 3}$$

Solution

$$\frac{2x^2 + 5}{x^2 + 2x - 3} - \frac{x^2 - 3x}{x^2 + 2x - 3} + \frac{x - 2}{x^2 + 2x - 3} =$$

$$\frac{(2x^2 + 5) - (x^2 - 3x) + (x - 2)}{x^2 + 2x - 3} =$$

$$\frac{2x^2 + 5 - x^2 + 3x + x - 2}{x^2 + 2x - 3} =$$

$$\frac{x^2 + 4x + 3}{x^2 + 2x - 3} = \frac{\overset{1}{\cancel{(x + 3)}}(x + 1)}{\underset{1}{\cancel{(x + 3)}}(x - 1)} = \frac{x + 1}{x - 1}$$

Example 14

Simplify:

$$\frac{x^2 - 1}{x^2 - 8x + 12} - \frac{2x + 1}{x^2 - 8x + 12} + \frac{x}{x^2 - 8x + 12}$$

Your solution

$$\frac{x + 1}{x - 6}$$

Copyright © 1989 HMCo

Objective D   ## To add or subtract algebraic fractions with unlike denominators

8
DISK
EIGHT

Reference for Computer Tutor™

Before two fractions with unlike denominators can be added or subtracted, each fraction must be expressed in terms of a common denominator. This common denominator is the LCM of the denominators of the fractions.

Simplify: $\dfrac{x - 3}{x^2 - 2x} + \dfrac{6}{x^2 - 4}$

Find the LCM of the denominators.

Write each fraction in terms of the LCM. Multiply the factors in the numerator.

Add the fractions.

The LCM is $x(x - 2)(x + 2)$.

$$\frac{x - 3}{x^2 - 2x} = \frac{x - 3}{x(x - 2)} \cdot \frac{x + 2}{x + 2} = \frac{x^2 - x - 6}{x(x - 2)(x + 2)}$$

$$\frac{6}{x^2 - 4} = \frac{6}{(x - 2)(x + 2)} \cdot \frac{x}{x} = \frac{6x}{x(x - 2)(x + 2)}$$

$$\frac{x - 3}{x^2 - 2x} + \frac{6}{x^2 - 4} =$$

$$\frac{x^2 - x - 6}{x(x - 2)(x + 2)} + \frac{6x}{x(x - 2)(x + 2)} =$$

$$\frac{x^2 + 5x - 6}{x(x - 2)(x + 2)} =$$

Factor the numerator to determine whether there are common factors in the numerator and denominator.

$$\frac{(x + 6)(x - 1)}{x(x - 2)(x + 2)}$$

Example 15

Simplify: $\frac{y}{x} - \frac{4y}{3x} + \frac{3y}{4x}$

Solution

The LCM of the denominators is 12x.

$\frac{y}{x} = \frac{y}{x} \cdot \frac{12}{12} = \frac{12y}{12x}$ $\frac{4y}{3x} = \frac{4y}{3x} \cdot \frac{4}{4} = \frac{16y}{12x}$

$\frac{3y}{4x} = \frac{3y}{4x} \cdot \frac{3}{3} = \frac{9y}{12x}$

$\frac{y}{x} - \frac{4y}{3x} + \frac{3y}{4x} = \frac{12y}{12x} - \frac{16y}{12x} + \frac{9y}{12x} =$

$\frac{12y - 16y + 9y}{12x} = \frac{5y}{12x}$

Example 16

Simplify: $\frac{z}{8y} - \frac{4z}{3y} + \frac{5z}{4y}$

Your solution

$\frac{z}{24y}$

Example 17

Simplify: $\frac{2x}{x-3} - \frac{5}{3-x}$

Solution

The LCM of $x - 3$ and $3 - x$ is $x - 3$.
Remember: $3 - x = -(x - 3)$

$\frac{2x}{x-3} = \frac{2x}{x-3} \cdot \frac{1}{1} = \frac{2x}{x-3}$

$\frac{5}{3-x} = \frac{5}{-(x-3)} \cdot \frac{-1}{-1} = \frac{-5}{x-3}$

$\frac{2x}{x-3} - \frac{5}{3-x} = \frac{2x}{x-3} - \frac{-5}{x-3} =$

$\frac{2x - (-5)}{x-3)} = \frac{2x+5}{x-3}$

Example 18

Simplify: $\frac{5x}{x-2} - \frac{3}{2-x}$

Your solution

$\frac{5x+3}{x-2}$

Example 19

Simplify: $\frac{2x}{2x-3} - \frac{1}{x+1}$

Solution

The LCM is $(2x - 3)(x + 1)$.

$\frac{2x}{2x-3} = \frac{2x}{2x-3} \cdot \frac{x+1}{x+1} = \frac{2x^2 + 2x}{(2x-3)(x+1)}$

$\frac{1}{x+1} = \frac{1}{x+1} \cdot \frac{2x-3}{2x-3} = \frac{2x-3}{(2x-3)(x+1)}$

$\frac{2x}{2x-3} - \frac{1}{x+1} = \frac{2x^2 + 2x}{(2x-3)(x+1)} - \frac{2x-3}{(2x-3)(x+1)} =$

$\frac{(2x^2 + 2x) - (2x - 3)}{(2x-3)(x+1)} = \frac{2x^2 + 3}{(2x-3)(x+1)}$

Example 20

Simplify: $\frac{4x}{3x-1} - \frac{9}{x+4}$

Your solution

$\frac{4x^2 - 11x + 9}{(3x-1)(x+4)}$

Solutions on p. A45

Example 21

Simplify: $\dfrac{x+3}{x^2-2x-8} + \dfrac{3}{4-x}$

Solution

The LCM is $(x-4)(x+2)$.

$$\dfrac{x+3}{x^2-2x-8} = \dfrac{x+3}{(x-4)(x+2)}$$

$$\dfrac{3}{4-x} = \dfrac{3}{-(x-4)} \cdot \dfrac{-1\cdot(x+2)}{-1\cdot(x+2)} = \dfrac{-3(x+2)}{(x-4)(x+2)}$$

$$\dfrac{x+3}{x^2-2x-8} + \dfrac{3}{4-x} = \dfrac{x+3}{(x-4)(x+2)} + \dfrac{-3(x+2)}{(x-4)(x+2)} =$$

$$\dfrac{(x+3) + (-3)(x+2)}{(x-4)(x+2)} = \dfrac{x+3-3x-6}{(x-4)(x+2)} =$$

$$\dfrac{-2x-3}{(x-4)(x+2)}$$

Example 22

Simplify: $\dfrac{2x-1}{x^2-25} + \dfrac{2}{5-x}$

Your solution

$$-\dfrac{11}{(x+5)(x-5)}$$

Example 23

Simplify: $\dfrac{3x+2}{2x^2-x-1} - \dfrac{3}{2x+1} + \dfrac{4}{x-1}$

Solution

The LCM is $(2x+1)(x-1)$.

$$\dfrac{3x+2}{2x^2-x-1} = \dfrac{3x+2}{(2x+1)(x-1)}$$

$$\dfrac{3}{2x+1} = \dfrac{3}{2x+1} \cdot \dfrac{x-1}{x-1} = \dfrac{3x-3}{(2x+1)(x-1)}$$

$$\dfrac{4}{x-1} = \dfrac{4}{x-1} \cdot \dfrac{2x+1}{2x+1} = \dfrac{8x+4}{(2x+1)(x-1)}$$

$$\dfrac{3x+2}{2x^2-x-1} - \dfrac{3}{2x+1} + \dfrac{4}{x-1} =$$

$$\dfrac{3x+2}{(2x+1)(x-1)} - \dfrac{3x-3}{(2x+1)(x-1)} + \dfrac{8x+4}{(2x+1)(x-1)} =$$

$$\dfrac{(3x+2) - (3x-3) + (8x+4)}{(2x+1)(x-1)} =$$

$$\dfrac{3x+2-3x+3+8x+4}{(2x+1)(x-1)} = \dfrac{8x+9}{(2x+1)(x-1)}$$

Example 24

Simplify: $\dfrac{2x-3}{3x^2-x-2} + \dfrac{5}{3x+2} - \dfrac{1}{x-1}$

Your solution

$$\dfrac{2(2x-5)}{(3x+2)(x-1)}$$

Solutions on p. A46

8.2A Exercises

Find the LCM of the expressions.

1. $8x^3y$
   $12xy^2$
   $24x^3y^2$

2. $6ab^2$
   $18ab^3$
   $18ab^3$

3. $10x^4y^2$
   $15x^3y$
   $30x^4y^2$

4. $12a^2b$
   $18ab^3$
   $36a^2b^3$

5. $8x^2$
   $4x^2 + 8x$
   $8x^2(x+2)$

6. $6y^2$
   $4y + 12$
   $12y^2(y+3)$

7. $2x^2y$
   $3x^2 + 12x$
   $6x^2y(x+4)$

8. $4xy^2$
   $6xy^2 + 12y^2$
   $12xy^2(x+2)$

9. $9x(x + 2)$
   $12(x + 2)^2$
   $36x(x+2)^2$

10. $8x^2(x - 1)^2$
    $10x^3(x - 1)$
    $40x^3(x-1)^2$

11. $3x + 3$
    $2x^2 + 4x + 2$
    $6(x+1)^2$

12. $4x - 12$
    $2x^2 - 12x + 18$
    $4(x-3)^2$

13. $(x - 1)(x + 2)$
    $(x - 1)(x + 3)$
    $(x-1)(x+2)(x+3)$

14. $(2x - 1)(x + 4)$
    $(2x + 1)(x + 4)$
    $(2x-1)(x+4)(2x+1)$

15. $(2x + 3)^2$
    $(2x + 3)(x - 5)$
    $(2x+3)^2(x-5)$

16. $(x - 7)(x + 2)$
    $(x - 7)^2$
    $(x+2)(x-7)^2$

17. $x - 1$
    $x - 2$
    $(x - 1)(x - 2)$
    $(x-1)(x-2)$

18. $(x + 4)(x - 3)$
    $x + 4$
    $x - 3$
    $(x+4)(x-3)$

19. $x^2 - x - 6$
    $x^2 + x - 12$
    $(x-3)(x+2)(x+4)$

20. $x^2 + 3x - 10$
    $x^2 + 5x - 14$
    $(x+5)(x-2)(x+7)$

21. $x^2 + 5x + 4$
    $x^2 - 3x - 28$
    $(x+4)(x+1)(x-7)$

22. $x^2 - 10x + 21$
    $x^2 - 8x + 15$
    $(x-3)(x-7)(x-5)$

23. $x^2 - 2x - 24$
    $x^2 - 36$
    $(x+6)(x-6)(x+4)$

24. $x^2 + 7x + 10$
    $x^2 - 25$
    $(x+2)(x+5)(x-5)$

25. $x^2 - 7x - 30$
    $x^2 - 5x - 24$
    $(x-10)(x-8)(x+3)$

26. $2x^2 - 7x + 3$
    $2x^2 + x - 1$
    $(x-3)(2x-1)(x+1)$

27. $3x^2 - 11x + 6$
    $3x^2 + 4x - 4$
    $(3x-2)(x-3)(x+2)$

28. $2x^2 - 9x + 10$
    $2x^2 + x - 15$
    $(2x-5)(x-2)(x+3)$

29. $6 + x - x^2$
    $x + 2$
    $x - 3$
    $(x+2)(x-3)$

30. $15 + 2x - x^2$
    $x - 5$
    $x + 3$
    $(x-5)(x+3)$

31. $x^2 + 3x - 18$
    $3 - x$
    $x + 6$
    $(x+6)(x-3)$

32. $x^2 - 5x + 6$
    $1 - x$
    $x - 6$
    $(x-1)(x-6)(x-2)(x-3)$

8.2B Exercises

Write each fraction in terms of the LCM of the denominators.

33. $\dfrac{4}{x}, \dfrac{3}{x^2}$

$$\dfrac{4x}{x^2}, \quad \dfrac{3}{x^2}$$

34. $\dfrac{5}{ab^2}, \dfrac{6}{ab}$

$$\dfrac{5}{ab^2}, \quad \dfrac{6b}{ab^2}$$

35. $\dfrac{x}{3y^2}, \dfrac{z}{4y}$

$$\dfrac{4x}{12y^2}, \quad \dfrac{3yz}{12y^2}$$

36. $\dfrac{5y}{6x^2}, \dfrac{7}{9xy}$

$$\dfrac{15y^2}{18x^2y}, \quad \dfrac{14x}{18x^2y}$$

37. $\dfrac{y}{x(x-3)}, \dfrac{6}{x^2}$

$$\dfrac{xy}{x^2(x-3)}, \quad \dfrac{6x-18}{x^2(x-3)}$$

38. $\dfrac{a}{y^2}, \dfrac{6}{y(y+5)}$

$$\dfrac{ay+5a}{y^2(y+5)}, \quad \dfrac{6y}{y^2(y+5)}$$

39. $\dfrac{9}{(x-1)^2}, \dfrac{6}{x(x-1)}$

$$\dfrac{9x}{x(x-1)^2}, \quad \dfrac{6x-6}{x(x-1)^2}$$

40. $\dfrac{a^2}{y(y+7)}, \dfrac{a}{(y+7)^2}$

$$\dfrac{a^2y+7a^2}{y(y+7)^2}, \quad \dfrac{ay}{y(y+7)^2}$$

41. $\dfrac{3}{x-3}, \dfrac{5}{x(3-x)}$

$$\dfrac{3x}{x(x-3)}, \quad -\dfrac{5}{x(x-3)}$$

42. $\dfrac{b}{y(y-4)}, \dfrac{b^2}{4-y}$

$$\dfrac{b}{y(y-4)}, \quad -\dfrac{b^2y}{y(y-4)}$$

43. $\dfrac{3}{(x-5)^2}, \dfrac{2}{5-x}$

$$\dfrac{3}{(x-5)^2}, \quad -\dfrac{2x-10}{(x-5)^2}$$

44. $\dfrac{3}{7-y}, \dfrac{2}{(y-7)^2}$

$$-\dfrac{3y-21}{(y-7)^2}, \quad \dfrac{2}{(y-7)^2}$$

45. $\dfrac{3}{x^2+2x}, \dfrac{4}{x^2}$

$$\dfrac{3x}{x^2(x+2)}, \quad \dfrac{4x+8}{x^2(x+2)}$$

46. $\dfrac{2}{y-3}, \dfrac{3}{y^3-3y^2}$

$$\dfrac{2y^2}{y^2(y-3)}, \quad \dfrac{3}{y^2(y-3)}$$

47. $\dfrac{x-2}{x+3}, \dfrac{x}{x-4}$

$$\dfrac{x^2-6x+8}{(x+3)(x-4)}, \quad \dfrac{x^2+3x}{(x+3)(x-4)}$$

48. $\dfrac{x^2}{2x-1}, \dfrac{x+1}{x+4}$

$$\dfrac{x^3+4x^2}{(2x-1)(x+4)}, \quad \dfrac{2x^2+x-1}{(2x-1)(x+4)}$$

49. $\dfrac{3}{x^2+x-2}, \dfrac{x}{x+2}$

$$\dfrac{3}{(x+2)(x-1)}, \quad \dfrac{x^2-x}{(x+2)(x-1)}$$

50. $\dfrac{3x}{x-5}, \dfrac{4}{x^2-25}$

$$\dfrac{3x^2+15x}{(x+5)(x-5)}, \quad \dfrac{4}{(x+5)(x-5)}$$

51. $\dfrac{5}{2x^2-9x+10}, \dfrac{x-1}{2x-5}$

$$\dfrac{5}{(2x-5)(x-2)}, \quad \dfrac{x^2-3x+2}{(2x-5)(x-2)}$$

52. $\dfrac{x-3}{3x^2+4x-4}, \dfrac{2}{x+2}$

$$\dfrac{x-3}{(3x-2)(x+2)}, \quad \dfrac{6x-4}{(3x-2)(x+2)}$$

53. $\dfrac{x}{x^2+x-6}, \dfrac{2x}{x^2-9}$

$$\dfrac{x^2-3x}{(x+3)(x-3)(x-2)}, \quad \dfrac{2x^2-4x}{(x+3)(x-3)(x-2)}$$

54. $\dfrac{x-1}{x^2+2x-15}, \dfrac{x}{x^2+6x+5}$

$$\dfrac{x^2-1}{(x+5)(x-3)(x+1)}, \quad \dfrac{x^2-3x}{(x+5)(x-3)(x+1)}$$

55. $\dfrac{x}{9-x^2}, \dfrac{x-1}{x^2-6x+9}$

$$-\dfrac{x^2-3x}{(x-3)^2(x+3)}, \quad \dfrac{x^2+2x-3}{(x-3)^2(x+3)}$$

56. $\dfrac{2x}{10+3x-x^2}, \dfrac{x+2}{x^2-8x+15}$

$$-\dfrac{2x^2-6x}{(x-5)(x+2)(x-3)}, \quad \dfrac{x^2+4x+4}{(x-5)(x+2)(x-3)}$$

57. $\dfrac{3x}{x-5}, \dfrac{x}{x+4}, \dfrac{3}{20+x-x^2}$

$$\dfrac{3x^2+12x}{(x-5)(x+4)}, \quad \dfrac{x^2-5x}{(x-5)(x+4)}, \quad -\dfrac{3}{(x-5)(x+4)}$$

58. $\dfrac{x+1}{x+5}, \dfrac{x+2}{x-7}, \dfrac{3}{35+2x-x^2}$

$$\dfrac{x^2-6x-7}{(x+5)(x-7)}, \quad \dfrac{x^2+7x+10}{(x+5)(x-7)}, \quad -\dfrac{3}{(x+5)(x-7)}$$

8.2C Exercises

Simplify.

59. $\dfrac{3}{y^2} + \dfrac{8}{y^2}$

$$\dfrac{11}{y^2}$$

60. $\dfrac{6}{ab} - \dfrac{2}{ab}$

$$\dfrac{4}{ab}$$

61. $\dfrac{3}{x+4} - \dfrac{10}{x+4}$

$$-\dfrac{7}{x+4}$$

62. $\dfrac{x}{x+6} - \dfrac{2}{x+6}$

$$\dfrac{x-2}{x+6}$$

63. $\dfrac{3x}{2x+3} + \dfrac{5x}{2x+3}$

$$\dfrac{8x}{2x+3}$$

64. $\dfrac{6y}{4y+1} - \dfrac{11y}{4y+1}$

$$-\dfrac{5y}{4y+1}$$

65. $\dfrac{2x+1}{x-3} + \dfrac{3x+6}{x-3}$

$$\dfrac{5x+7}{x-3}$$

66. $\dfrac{4x+3}{2x-7} + \dfrac{3x-8}{2x-7}$

$$\dfrac{7x-5}{2x-7}$$

67. $\dfrac{5x-1}{x+9} - \dfrac{3x+4}{x+9}$

$$\dfrac{2x-5}{x+9}$$

68. $\dfrac{6x-5}{x-10} - \dfrac{3x-4}{x-10}$

$$\dfrac{3x-1}{x-10}$$

69. $\dfrac{x-7}{2x+7} - \dfrac{4x-3}{2x+7}$

$$\dfrac{-3x-4}{2x+7}$$

70. $\dfrac{2n}{3n+4} - \dfrac{5n-3}{3n+4}$

$$\dfrac{-3n+3}{3n+4}$$

71. $\dfrac{x}{x^2+2x-15} - \dfrac{3}{x^2+2x-15}$

$$\dfrac{1}{x+5}$$

72. $\dfrac{3x}{x^2+3x-10} - \dfrac{6}{x^2+3x-10}$

$$\dfrac{3}{x+5}$$

73. $\dfrac{2x+3}{x^2-x-30} - \dfrac{x-2}{x^2-x-30}$

$$\dfrac{1}{x-6}$$

74. $\dfrac{3x-1}{x^2+5x-6} - \dfrac{2x-7}{x^2+5x-6}$

$$\dfrac{1}{x-1}$$

75. $\dfrac{4y+7}{2y^2+7y-4} - \dfrac{y-5}{2y^2+7y-4}$

$$\dfrac{3}{2y-1}$$

76. $\dfrac{x+1}{2x^2-5x-12} + \dfrac{x+2}{2x^2-5x-12}$

$$\dfrac{1}{x-4}$$

77. $\dfrac{2x^2+3x}{x^2-9x+20} + \dfrac{2x^2-3}{x^2-9x+20} - \dfrac{4x^2+2x+1}{x^2-9x+20}$

$$\dfrac{1}{x-5}$$

78. $\dfrac{2x^2+3x}{x^2-2x-63} - \dfrac{x^2-3x+21}{x^2-2x-63} - \dfrac{x-7}{x^2-2x-63}$

$$\dfrac{x-2}{x-9}$$

8.2D Exercises

Simplify.

79. $\frac{4}{x} + \frac{5}{y}$

$$\frac{4y + 5x}{xy}$$

80. $\frac{7}{a} + \frac{5}{b}$

$$\frac{7b + 5a}{ab}$$

81. $\frac{12}{x} - \frac{5}{2x}$

$$\frac{19}{2x}$$

82. $\frac{5}{3a} - \frac{3}{4a}$

$$\frac{11}{12a}$$

83. $\frac{1}{2x} - \frac{5}{4x} + \frac{7}{6x}$

$$\frac{5}{12x}$$

84. $\frac{7}{4y} + \frac{11}{6y} - \frac{8}{3y}$

$$\frac{11}{12y}$$

85. $\frac{5}{3x} - \frac{2}{x^2} + \frac{3}{2x}$

$$\frac{19x - 12}{6x^2}$$

86. $\frac{6}{y^2} + \frac{3}{4y} - \frac{2}{5y}$

$$\frac{120 + 7y}{20y^2}$$

87. $\frac{2}{x} - \frac{3}{2y} + \frac{3}{5x} - \frac{1}{4y}$

$$\frac{52y - 35x}{20xy}$$

88. $\frac{5}{2a} + \frac{7}{3b} - \frac{2}{b} - \frac{3}{4a}$

$$\frac{21b + 4a}{12ab}$$

89. $\frac{2x + 1}{3x} + \frac{x - 1}{5x}$

$$\frac{13x + 2}{15x}$$

90. $\frac{4x - 3}{6x} + \frac{2x + 3}{4x}$

$$\frac{14x + 3}{12x}$$

91. $\frac{x - 3}{6x} + \frac{x + 4}{8x}$

$$\frac{7}{24}$$

92. $\frac{2x - 3}{2x} + \frac{x + 3}{3x}$

$$\frac{8x - 3}{6x}$$

93. $\frac{2x + 9}{9x} - \frac{x - 5}{5x}$

$$\frac{x + 90}{45x}$$

94. $\frac{3y - 2}{12y} - \frac{y - 3}{18y}$

$$\frac{7}{36}$$

95. $\frac{x + 4}{2x} - \frac{x - 1}{x^2}$

$$\frac{x^2 + 2x + 2}{2x^2}$$

96. $\frac{x - 2}{3x^2} - \frac{x + 4}{x}$

$$\frac{-3x^2 - 11x - 2}{3x^2}$$

Simplify.

97. $\dfrac{x - 10}{4x^2} + \dfrac{x + 1}{2x}$

$$\dfrac{2x^2 + 3x - 10}{4x^2}$$

98. $\dfrac{x + 5}{3x^2} + \dfrac{2x + 1}{2x}$

$$\dfrac{6x^2 + 5x + 10}{6x^2}$$

99. $\dfrac{2x + 1}{6x^2} - \dfrac{x - 4}{4x}$

$$\dfrac{-3x^2 + 16x + 2}{12x^2}$$

100. $\dfrac{x + 3}{6x} - \dfrac{x - 3}{8x^2}$

$$\dfrac{4x^2 + 9x + 9}{24x^2}$$

101. $\dfrac{x + 2}{xy} - \dfrac{3x - 2}{x^2y}$

$$\dfrac{x^2 - x + 2}{x^2y}$$

102. $\dfrac{3x - 1}{xy^2} - \dfrac{2x + 3}{xy}$

$$\dfrac{3x - 2xy - 3y - 1}{xy^2}$$

103. $\dfrac{4x - 3}{3x^2y} + \dfrac{2x + 1}{4xy^2}$

$$\dfrac{16xy - 12y + 6x^2 + 3x}{12x^2y^2}$$

104. $\dfrac{5x + 7}{6xy^2} - \dfrac{4x - 3}{8x^2y}$

$$\dfrac{20x^2 + 28x - 12xy + 9y}{24x^2y^2}$$

105. $\dfrac{x - 2}{8x^2} - \dfrac{x + 7}{12xy}$

$$\dfrac{3xy - 6y - 2x^2 - 14x}{24x^2y}$$

106. $\dfrac{3x - 1}{6y^2} - \dfrac{x + 5}{9xy}$

$$\dfrac{9x^2 - 3x - 2xy - 10y}{18xy^2}$$

107. $\dfrac{4}{x - 2} + \dfrac{5}{x + 3}$

$$\dfrac{9x + 2}{(x - 2)(x + 3)}$$

108. $\dfrac{2}{x - 3} + \dfrac{5}{x - 4}$

$$\dfrac{7x - 23}{(x - 3)(x - 4)}$$

109. $\dfrac{6}{x - 7} - \dfrac{4}{x + 3}$

$$\dfrac{2(x + 23)}{(x - 7)(x + 3)}$$

110. $\dfrac{3}{y + 6} - \dfrac{4}{y - 3}$

$$\dfrac{-y - 33}{(y + 6)(y - 3)}$$

111. $\dfrac{2x}{x + 1} + \dfrac{1}{x - 3}$

$$\dfrac{2x^2 - 5x + 1}{(x + 1)(x - 3)}$$

112. $\dfrac{3x}{x - 4} + \dfrac{2}{x + 6}$

$$\dfrac{3x^2 + 20x - 8}{(x - 4)(x + 6)}$$

113. $\dfrac{4x}{2x - 1} - \dfrac{5}{x - 6}$

$$\dfrac{4x^2 - 34x + 5}{(2x - 1)(x - 6)}$$

114. $\dfrac{6x}{x + 5} - \dfrac{3}{2x + 3}$

$$\dfrac{3(4x^2 + 5x - 5)}{(x + 5)(2x + 3)}$$

Simplify.

115. $\dfrac{2a}{a-7} + \dfrac{5}{7-a}$

$$\dfrac{2a-5}{a-7}$$

116. $\dfrac{4x}{6-x} + \dfrac{5}{x-6}$

$$\dfrac{-4x+5}{x-6}$$

117. $\dfrac{x}{x^2-9} + \dfrac{3}{x-3}$

$$\dfrac{4x+9}{(x+3)(x-3)}$$

118. $\dfrac{y}{y^2-16} + \dfrac{1}{y-4}$

$$\dfrac{2(y+2)}{(y+4)(y-4)}$$

119. $\dfrac{2x}{x^2-x-6} - \dfrac{3}{x+2}$

$$\dfrac{-x+9}{(x-3)(x+2)}$$

120. $\dfrac{5x}{x^2+2x-8} - \dfrac{2}{x+4}$

$$\dfrac{3x+4}{(x+4)(x-2)}$$

121. $\dfrac{3x-1}{x^2-10x+25} - \dfrac{3}{x-5}$

$$\dfrac{14}{(x-5)(x-5)}$$

122. $\dfrac{2a+3}{a^2-7a+12} - \dfrac{2}{a-3}$

$$\dfrac{11}{(a-3)(a-4)}$$

123. $\dfrac{x+4}{x^2-x-42} + \dfrac{3}{7-x}$

$$\dfrac{-2(x+7)}{(x+6)(x-7)}$$

124. $\dfrac{x+3}{x^2-3x-10} + \dfrac{2}{5-x}$

$$\dfrac{-x-1}{(x+2)(x-5)}$$

125. $\dfrac{1}{x+1} + \dfrac{x}{x-6} - \dfrac{5x-2}{x^2-5x-6}$

$$\dfrac{x-4}{x-6}$$

126. $\dfrac{x}{x-4} + \dfrac{5}{x+5} - \dfrac{11x-8}{x^2+x-20}$

$$\dfrac{x+3}{x+5}$$

127. $\dfrac{3x+1}{x-1} - \dfrac{x-1}{x-3} + \dfrac{x+1}{x^2-4x+3}$

$$\dfrac{2x+1}{x-1}$$

128. $\dfrac{4x+1}{x-8} - \dfrac{3x+2}{x+4} - \dfrac{49x+4}{x^2-4x-32}$

$$\dfrac{x-2}{x+4}$$

129. $\dfrac{2x+9}{3-x} + \dfrac{x+5}{x+7} - \dfrac{2x^2+3x-3}{x^2+4x-21}$

$$\dfrac{-3(x^2+8x+25)}{(x-3)(x+7)}$$

130. $\dfrac{3x+5}{x+5} - \dfrac{x+1}{2-x} - \dfrac{4x^2-3x-1}{x^2+3x-10}$

$$\dfrac{4(2x-1)}{(x+5)(x-2)}$$

Section **3**   Complex Fractions

Objective A   To simplify a complex fraction

A **complex fraction** is a fraction whose numerator or denominator contains one or more fractions. Examples of complex fractions are shown at the right.

$$\dfrac{3}{2 - \dfrac{1}{2}}, \quad \dfrac{4 + \dfrac{1}{x}}{3 + \dfrac{2}{x}}, \quad \dfrac{\dfrac{1}{x - 1} + x + 3}{x - 3 + \dfrac{1}{x + 4}}$$

Simplify: $\dfrac{\dfrac{a^2 b}{c}}{\dfrac{b}{ac^2}}$

Find the LCM of the denominators of the fractions in the numerator and denominator.

The LCM of c and ac^2 is ac^2.

Multiply the numerator and denominator of the complex fraction by the LCM.

$$\dfrac{\dfrac{a^2 b}{c}}{\dfrac{b}{ac^2}} = \dfrac{\dfrac{a^2 b}{c}}{\dfrac{b}{ac^2}} \cdot \dfrac{ac^2}{ac^2}$$

$$= \dfrac{\dfrac{a^2 b}{c}(ac^2)}{\dfrac{b}{ac^2}(ac^2)}$$

Simplify.

$$= \dfrac{a^3 bc}{b} = a^3 c$$

Simplify: $\dfrac{1 - \dfrac{4}{x^2}}{1 + \dfrac{2}{x}}$

Find the LCM of the denominators of the fractions in the numerator and denominator.

The LCM of x^2 and x is x^2.

$$\dfrac{1 - \dfrac{4}{x^2}}{1 + \dfrac{2}{x}} =$$

Multiply the numerator and denominator of the complex fraction by the LCM. Then simplify.

$$\dfrac{1 - \dfrac{4}{x^2}}{1 + \dfrac{2}{x}} \cdot \dfrac{x^2}{x^2} = \dfrac{1 \cdot x^2 - \dfrac{4}{x^2} \cdot x^2}{1 \cdot x^2 + \dfrac{2}{x} \cdot x^2} =$$

$$\dfrac{x^2 - 4}{x^2 + 2x} = \dfrac{(x - 2)(\overset{1}{\cancel{x + 2}})}{x(\underset{1}{\cancel{x + 2}})} =$$

$$\dfrac{x - 2}{x}$$

Example 1

Simplify: $\dfrac{\dfrac{1}{x} + \dfrac{1}{2}}{\dfrac{1}{x^2} - \dfrac{1}{4}}$

Solution

The LCM of x, 2, x^2, and 4 is $4x^2$.

$$\dfrac{\dfrac{1}{x} + \dfrac{1}{2}}{\dfrac{1}{x^2} - \dfrac{1}{4}} = \dfrac{\dfrac{1}{x} + \dfrac{1}{2}}{\dfrac{1}{x^2} - \dfrac{1}{4}} \cdot \dfrac{4x^2}{4x^2} = \dfrac{\dfrac{1}{x} \cdot 4x^2 + \dfrac{1}{2} \cdot 4x^2}{\dfrac{1}{x^2} \cdot 4x^2 - \dfrac{1}{4} \cdot 4x^2} =$$

$$\dfrac{4x + 2x^2}{4 - x^2} = \dfrac{2x(2 \cancel{+ x})^{1}}{(2 - x)\cancel{(2 + x)}_{1}} = \dfrac{2x}{2 - x}$$

Example 2

Simplify: $\dfrac{\dfrac{1}{3} - \dfrac{1}{x}}{\dfrac{1}{9} - \dfrac{1}{x^2}}$

Your solution

$$\dfrac{3x}{x + 3}$$

Example 3

Simplify: $\dfrac{1 - \dfrac{2}{x} - \dfrac{15}{x^2}}{1 - \dfrac{11}{x} + \dfrac{30}{x^2}}$

Solution

The LCM of x and x^2 is x^2.

$$\dfrac{1 - \dfrac{2}{x} - \dfrac{15}{x^2}}{1 - \dfrac{11}{x} + \dfrac{30}{x^2}} = \dfrac{1 - \dfrac{2}{x} - \dfrac{15}{x^2}}{1 - \dfrac{11}{x} + \dfrac{30}{x^2}} \cdot \dfrac{x^2}{x^2} =$$

$$\dfrac{1 \cdot x^2 - \dfrac{2}{x} \cdot x^2 - \dfrac{15}{x^2} \cdot x^2}{1 \cdot x^2 - \dfrac{11}{x} \cdot x^2 + \dfrac{30}{x^2} \cdot x^2} = \dfrac{x^2 - 2x - 15}{x^2 - 11x + 30} =$$

$$\dfrac{\cancel{(x - 5)}^{1}(x + 3)}{\cancel{(x - 5)}_{1}(x - 6)} = \dfrac{x + 3}{x - 6}$$

Example 4

Simplify: $\dfrac{1 + \dfrac{4}{x} + \dfrac{3}{x^2}}{1 + \dfrac{10}{x} + \dfrac{21}{x^2}}$

Your solution

$$\dfrac{x + 1}{x + 7}$$

Solutions on p. A47

8.3A Exercises

Simplify.

1. $\dfrac{\frac{x^3y^4}{z}}{\frac{xy^2}{z^2}}$

   x^2y^2z

2. $\dfrac{\frac{a^4b}{c^2}}{\frac{ab^5}{c}}$

   $\dfrac{a^3}{b^4c}$

3. $\dfrac{\frac{m^2n}{p^2}}{\frac{mn^3}{p^3}}$

   $\dfrac{mp}{n^2}$

4. $\dfrac{\frac{a^2c}{b^3}}{\frac{ac^4}{b^2}}$

   $\dfrac{a}{bc^3}$

5. $\dfrac{a + \frac{2}{a}}{1 - \frac{2}{a}}$

   $\dfrac{a^2+2}{a-2}$

6. $\dfrac{x - \frac{1}{x}}{1 - \frac{1}{x}}$

   $x+1$

7. $\dfrac{1 + \frac{3}{b}}{b - \frac{3}{b}}$

   $\dfrac{b+3}{b^2-3}$

8. $\dfrac{1 - \frac{2}{y}}{y - \frac{4}{y}}$

   $\dfrac{1}{y+2}$

9. $\dfrac{x}{x - \frac{1}{2}}$

   $\dfrac{2x}{2x-1}$

10. $\dfrac{b}{b + \frac{2}{3}}$

    $\dfrac{3b}{3b+2}$

11. $\dfrac{y}{y - \frac{1}{4}}$

    $\dfrac{4y}{4y-1}$

12. $\dfrac{a}{a + \frac{1}{5}}$

    $\dfrac{5a}{5a+1}$

13. $\dfrac{1 - \frac{4}{y^2}}{1 + \frac{2}{y}}$

    $\dfrac{y-2}{y}$

14. $\dfrac{\frac{1}{y^2} - 1}{\frac{1}{y} + 1}$

    $1-y$

15. $\dfrac{1 + \frac{3}{x}}{1 - \frac{9}{x^2}}$

    $\dfrac{x}{x-3}$

16. $\dfrac{1 + \frac{4}{x}}{1 - \frac{16}{x^2}}$

    $\dfrac{x}{x-4}$

17. $\dfrac{\frac{4}{a^2} - 1}{\frac{2}{a} + 1}$

    $\dfrac{2-a}{a}$

18. $\dfrac{\frac{1}{a} + \frac{1}{3}}{\frac{1}{a^2} - \frac{1}{9}}$

    $\dfrac{3a}{3-a}$

19. $\dfrac{\frac{1}{x} - \frac{1}{2}}{\frac{1}{4} - \frac{1}{x^2}}$

    $-\dfrac{2x}{x+2}$

20. $\dfrac{\frac{1}{2} + \frac{1}{a}}{\frac{1}{4} - \frac{1}{a^2}}$

    $\dfrac{2a}{a-2}$

21. $\dfrac{\frac{1}{3} - \frac{1}{y}}{\frac{1}{9} - \frac{1}{y^2}}$

    $\dfrac{3y}{y+3}$

Simplify.

22. $\dfrac{2 - \dfrac{8}{x+4}}{3 - \dfrac{12}{x+4}}$

$\dfrac{2}{3}$

23. $\dfrac{5 - \dfrac{25}{x+5}}{1 - \dfrac{3}{x+5}}$

$\dfrac{5x}{x+2}$

24. $\dfrac{1 + \dfrac{5}{y-2}}{1 - \dfrac{2}{y-2}}$

$\dfrac{y+3}{y-4}$

25. $\dfrac{2 - \dfrac{11}{2x-1}}{3 - \dfrac{17}{2x-1}}$

$\dfrac{4x - 13}{2(3x - 10)}$

26. $\dfrac{4 - \dfrac{2}{x+7}}{5 + \dfrac{1}{x+7}}$

$\dfrac{2(2x + 13)}{5x + 36}$

27. $\dfrac{5 + \dfrac{3}{x-8}}{2 - \dfrac{1}{x-8}}$

$\dfrac{5x - 37}{2x - 17}$

28. $\dfrac{1 - \dfrac{1}{x} - \dfrac{6}{x^2}}{1 - \dfrac{9}{x^2}}$

$\dfrac{x + 2}{x + 3}$

29. $\dfrac{1 + \dfrac{4}{x} + \dfrac{4}{x^2}}{1 - \dfrac{2}{x} - \dfrac{8}{x^2}}$

$\dfrac{x + 2}{x - 4}$

30. $\dfrac{1 - \dfrac{5}{x} - \dfrac{6}{x^2}}{1 + \dfrac{6}{x} + \dfrac{5}{x^2}}$

$\dfrac{x - 6}{x + 5}$

31. $\dfrac{1 - \dfrac{7}{a} + \dfrac{12}{a^2}}{1 + \dfrac{1}{a} - \dfrac{20}{a^2}}$

$\dfrac{a - 3}{a + 5}$

32. $\dfrac{1 - \dfrac{6}{x} + \dfrac{8}{x^2}}{\dfrac{4}{x^2} + \dfrac{3}{x} - 1}$

$-\dfrac{x - 2}{x + 1}$

33. $\dfrac{1 + \dfrac{3}{x} - \dfrac{18}{x^2}}{\dfrac{21}{x^2} - \dfrac{4}{x} - 1}$

$-\dfrac{x + 6}{x + 7}$

34. $\dfrac{x - \dfrac{4}{x+3}}{1 + \dfrac{1}{x+3}}$

$x - 1$

35. $\dfrac{y + \dfrac{1}{y-2}}{1 + \dfrac{1}{y-2}}$

$y - 1$

36. $\dfrac{1 - \dfrac{x}{2x+1}}{x - \dfrac{1}{2x+1}}$

$\dfrac{1}{2x - 1}$

37. $\dfrac{1 - \dfrac{2x-2}{3x-1}}{x - \dfrac{4}{3x-1}}$

$\dfrac{1}{3x - 4}$

38. $\dfrac{\dfrac{1}{x} + \dfrac{2}{x-1}}{\dfrac{3}{x} + \dfrac{1}{x-1}}$

$\dfrac{3x - 1}{4x - 3}$

39. $\dfrac{\dfrac{3}{n+1} + \dfrac{1}{n}}{\dfrac{2}{n+1} + \dfrac{3}{n}}$

$\dfrac{4n + 1}{5n + 3}$

40. $\dfrac{\dfrac{3}{2x-1} - \dfrac{1}{x}}{\dfrac{3}{x} + \dfrac{2}{2x-1}}$

$\dfrac{x + 1}{8x - 3}$

41. $\dfrac{\dfrac{4}{3x+1} + \dfrac{3}{x}}{\dfrac{1}{x} - \dfrac{2}{3x+1}}$

$\dfrac{13x + 3}{x + 1}$

42. $\dfrac{\dfrac{3}{b-4} - \dfrac{2}{b+1}}{\dfrac{5}{b+1} - \dfrac{1}{b-4}}$

$\dfrac{b + 11}{4b - 21}$

<table>
<tr><td>**Section 4**</td><td># Solving Equations Containing Fractions</td></tr>
</table>

Section **4**

Solving Equations Containing Fractions

Objective A   ## To solve an equation containing fractions

8
DISK
EIGHT

Reference for
Computer
Tutor™

To solve an equation containing fractions, **clear denominators** by multiplying each side of the equation by the LCM of the denominators. Then solve for the variable.

Solve: $\frac{3x-1}{4} + \frac{2}{3} = \frac{7}{6}$

The LCM is 12.

Multiply each side of the equation by the LCM of the denominators.

Simplify using the Distributive Property and the Properties of Fractions.

$$\frac{3x-1}{4} + \frac{2}{3} = \frac{7}{6}$$

$$12\left(\frac{3x-1}{4} + \frac{2}{3}\right) = 12 \cdot \frac{7}{6}$$

$$12\left(\frac{3x-1}{4}\right) + 12 \cdot \frac{2}{3} = 12 \cdot \frac{7}{6}$$

$$\frac{\overset{3}{\cancel{12}}}{1}\left(\frac{3x-1}{\underset{1}{\cancel{4}}}\right) + \frac{\overset{4}{\cancel{12}}}{1} \cdot \frac{2}{\underset{1}{\cancel{3}}} = \frac{\overset{2}{\cancel{12}}}{1} \cdot \frac{7}{\underset{1}{\cancel{6}}}$$

Solve for x.

$$9x - 3 + 8 = 14$$
$$9x + 5 = 14$$
$$9x = 9$$
$$x = 1$$

1 checks as a solution.
The solution is 1.

Occasionally, a value of the variable that appears to be a solution will make one of the denominators zero. In this case, the equation has no solution for that value of the variable.

Solve: $\frac{2x}{x-2} = 1 + \frac{4}{x-2}$

The LCM is $x - 2$.

Multiply each side of the equation by the LCM of the denominators.

Simplify using the Distributive Property and Properties of Fractions.

$$\frac{2x}{x-2} = 1 + \frac{4}{x-2}$$

$$(x-2)\frac{2x}{x-2} = (x-2)\left(1 + \frac{4}{x-2}\right)$$

$$(x-2)\left(\frac{2x}{x-2}\right) = (x-2) \cdot 1 + (x-2) \cdot \frac{4}{x-2}$$

$$\frac{\cancel{x-2}}{1} \cdot \frac{2x}{\cancel{x-2}} = (x-2) + \frac{\cancel{x-2}}{1} \cdot \frac{4}{\cancel{x-2}}$$

Solve for x.

$$2x = x - 2 + 4$$
$$2x = x + 2$$
$$x = 2$$

When x is replaced by 2, the denominators of $\frac{2x}{x-2}$ and $\frac{4}{x-2}$ are zero.

The equation has no solution.

Example 1

Solve: $\dfrac{4}{x+4} = \dfrac{2}{x}$

Solution

$$\dfrac{4}{x+4} = \dfrac{2}{x} \quad \text{The LCM is } x(x+4).$$

$$\dfrac{x(x+4)}{1} \cdot \dfrac{4}{x+4} = \dfrac{x(x+4)}{1} \cdot \dfrac{2}{x}$$

$$\dfrac{x\overset{1}{(x+4)}}{1} \cdot \dfrac{4}{\underset{1}{x+4}} = \dfrac{\overset{1}{x}(x+4)}{1} \cdot \dfrac{2}{\underset{1}{x}}$$

$$4x = (x+4)2$$
$$4x = 2x + 8$$
$$2x = 8$$
$$x = 4$$

4 checks as a solution.
The solution is 4.

Example 2

Solve: $\dfrac{2}{x+6} = \dfrac{3}{x}$

Your solution

-18

Example 3

Solve: $\dfrac{3x}{x-4} = 5 + \dfrac{12}{x-4}$

Solution

$$\dfrac{3x}{x-4} = 5 + \dfrac{12}{x-4} \quad \text{The LCM is } x-4.$$

$$\dfrac{(x-4)}{1} \cdot \dfrac{3x}{x-4} = \dfrac{(x-4)}{1}\left(5 + \dfrac{12}{x-4}\right)$$

$$\dfrac{\overset{1}{(x-4)}}{1} \cdot \dfrac{3x}{\underset{1}{x-4}} = \dfrac{(x-4)}{1} \cdot 5 + \dfrac{\overset{1}{(x-4)}}{1} \cdot \dfrac{12}{\underset{1}{x-4}}$$

$$3x = (x-4)5 + 12$$
$$3x = 5x - 20 + 12$$
$$3x = 5x - 8$$
$$-2x = -8$$
$$x = 4$$

4 does not check as a solution.
The equation has no solution.

Example 4

Solve: $\dfrac{5x}{x+2} = 3 - \dfrac{10}{x+2}$

Your solution

no solution

Solutions on p. A47

Objective B

Reference for Computer Tutor™

To solve variation problems

The equation $y = kx$, where k is a constant, is an example of a **direct variation.** The equation $y = kx$ is read "y varies directly as x" or "y is proportional to x." The constant k is called the **constant of variation** or the **constant of proportionality.**

A nurse makes $10 per hour. The nurse's total wage (w) is directly proportional to the number of hours (h) worked. The equation of variation is $w = 10h$. The constant of proportionality is 10.

A direct variation equation can be written in the form $y = kx^n$, where n is a positive number. For example, the equation $y = kx^2$ is read "y varies directly as the square of x."

Given that V varies directly as r and that $V = 20$ when $r = 4$, find the constant of variation and the equation of variation.

Write the basic variation equation. $V = kr$

Replace V and r by the given values. $20 = k \cdot 4$

Solve for the constant of variation. $5 = k$

The constant of variation is 5.

Write the direct variation equation by sub- $V = 5r$
stituting the value of k into the direct variation
equation.

The tension (T) in a spring varies directly as the distance (x) it is stretched. If $T = 8$ lb when $x = 2$ in., find T when $x = 4$ in.

Write the basic direct variation equation. $T = kx$

Replace T and x by the given values. $8 = k \cdot 2$

Solve for the constant of variation. $4 = k$

Write the direct variation equation by sub- $T = 4x$
stituting the value of k into the basic direct
variation equation.

To find T when $x = 4$, substitute 4 for x in $T = 4 \cdot 4 = 16$
the equation and solve for T.

The tension is 16 lb.

The equation $y = \dfrac{k}{x}$, where k is a constant, is an example of an **inverse variation.** The

equation $y = \dfrac{k}{x}$ is read "y varies inversely as x" or "y is inversely proportional to x."

In general, an inverse variation equation can be written $y = \dfrac{k}{x^n}$, where n is a positive number. For example, the equation $y = \dfrac{k}{x^2}$ is read "y varies inversely as the square of x."

Given that P varies inversely as x and that $P = 5$ when $x = 2$, find P when $x = 10$.

Write the basic inverse variation equation.	$P = \dfrac{k}{x}$
Replace P and x by the given values.	$5 = \dfrac{k}{2}$
Solve for the constant of variation.	$10 = k$
Write the inverse variation equation by substituting the value of k into the basic inverse variation equation.	$P = \dfrac{10}{x}$
To find P when $x = 10$, substitute 10 for x in the equation and solve for P.	$P = \dfrac{10}{10}$
	$P = 1$

Example 5

The amount (A) of medication prescribed for a person is directly related to the person's weight (W). For a 50-kilogram person, 2 ml of medication are prescribed. How many milliliters of medication are required for a person who weighs 75 kg?

Strategy

To find the required amount of medication:
▷ Write the basic direct variation equation, replace the variables by the given values, and solve for k.
▷ Write the direct variation equation, replacing k by its value. Substitute 75 for W and solve for A.

Solution

$A = kW$

$2 = k \cdot 50$

$\dfrac{1}{25} = k$

$A = \dfrac{1}{25}W = \dfrac{1}{25} \cdot 75 = 3$

The required amount of medication is 3 ml.

Example 6

A company that produces personal computers has determined that the number of computers it can sell (s) is inversely proportional to the price (P) of the computer. Two thousand computers can be sold when the price is $2500. How many computers can be sold if the price of a computer is $2000?

Your strategy

Your solution

2500 computers

Solution on p. A48

8.4A Exercises

Solve.

1. $\frac{2x}{3} - \frac{5}{2} = -\frac{1}{2}$

    3

2. $\frac{x}{3} - \frac{1}{4} = \frac{1}{12}$

    1

3. $\frac{x}{3} = \frac{x}{6} + 2$

    12

4. $\frac{a}{4} = \frac{a}{2} + 3$

    −12

5. $\frac{x}{2} = 3 + \frac{x}{5}$

    10

6. $\frac{n}{3} = 2 + \frac{n}{4}$

    24

7. $\frac{x}{3} - \frac{1}{4} = \frac{x}{4} - \frac{1}{6}$

    1

8. $\frac{2y}{9} - \frac{1}{6} = \frac{y}{9} + \frac{1}{6}$

    3

9. $\frac{2x - 5}{8} + \frac{1}{4} = \frac{x}{8} + \frac{3}{4}$

    9

10. $\frac{3x + 4}{12} - \frac{1}{3} = \frac{5x + 2}{12} - \frac{1}{2}$

    2

11. $\frac{5x}{3} = 4 + 3x$

    −3

12. $6 = \frac{3x}{2} + 9$

    −2

13. $3 = \frac{4 + a}{a}$

    2

14. $2 = \frac{5 + x}{x}$

    5

15. $\frac{3 + y}{y} = 6$

    $\frac{3}{5}$

16. $\frac{2 + x}{x} = 8$

    $\frac{2}{7}$

17. $\frac{6}{2a + 1} = 2$

    1

18. $\frac{12}{3x - 2} = 3$

    2

19. $\frac{9}{2x - 5} = -2$

    $\frac{1}{4}$

20. $\frac{6}{4 - 3x} = 3$

    $\frac{2}{3}$

21. $\frac{y + 3}{y - 2} = 6$

    3

22. $\frac{x + 4}{x - 1} = 5$

    $\frac{9}{4}$

23. $7 = \frac{a - 2}{a + 1}$

    $-\frac{3}{2}$

24. $4 = \frac{x - 5}{x + 1}$

    −3

Solve.

25. $2 + \frac{5}{x} = 7$

1

26. $3 + \frac{8}{n} = 5$

4

27. $1 - \frac{9}{x} = 4$

-3

28. $3 - \frac{12}{x} = 7$

-3

29. $\frac{2}{y} + 5 = 9$

$\frac{1}{2}$

30. $\frac{6}{x} + 3 = 11$

$\frac{3}{4}$

31. $\frac{3}{x-2} = \frac{4}{x}$

8

32. $\frac{5}{x+3} = \frac{3}{x-1}$

7

33. $\frac{5}{x+2} = \frac{5}{x}$

no solution

34. $\frac{8}{x-3} = \frac{8}{x}$

no solution

35. $\frac{2}{3x-1} = \frac{3}{4x+1}$

5

36. $\frac{5}{3x-4} = \frac{-3}{1-2x}$

-7

37. $\frac{-3}{2x+5} = \frac{2}{x-1}$

-1

38. $\frac{4}{5y-1} = \frac{2}{2y-1}$

-1

39. $\frac{4x}{x-4} + 5 = \frac{5x}{x-4}$

5

40. $\frac{2x}{x+2} - 5 = \frac{7x}{x+2}$

-1

41. $2 + \frac{3}{a-3} = \frac{a}{a-3}$

no solution

42. $\frac{x}{x+4} = 3 - \frac{4}{x+4}$

no solution

43. $\frac{4}{x^2+2x-8} = \frac{2}{x-2} + \frac{2}{x+4}$

0

44. $\frac{2}{x^2+2x-3} = \frac{2}{x+3} + \frac{3}{x-1}$

-1

45. $\frac{10}{x^2-x-6} = \frac{2}{x-3} + \frac{3}{x+2}$

no solution

46. $\frac{15}{x^2-3x-4} = \frac{3}{x-4} + \frac{1}{x+1}$

no solution

8.4B Exercises

Solve.

47. Given that P varies directly as R and $P = 20$ when $R = 5$, find P when $R = 6$.

    24

48. Given that T varies directly as S and $T = 36$ when $S = 9$, find T when $S = 7$.

    28

49. Given that M is directly proportional to P and $M = 15$ when $P = 30$, find M when $P = 20$.

    10

50. Given that A is directly proportional to B and $A = 6$ when $B = 18$, find A when $B = 21$.

    7

51. D varies directly as T and $D = 120$ when $T = 2$. Find T when $D = 300$.

    5

52. P varies directly as x and $P = 68$ when $x = 4$. Find x when $P = 85$.

    5

53. Given that T varies inversely as x and $T = 10$ when $x = 4$, find T when $x = 5$.

    8

54. Given that M varies inversely as Q and $M = 12$ when $Q = 5$, find M when $Q = 6$.

    10

55. C is inversely proportional to H and $C = 8$ when $H = 3$. Find C when $H = 12$.

    2

56. W is inversely proportional to V and $W = 9$ when $V = 1$. Find W when $V = 3$.

    3

57. Given that Y varies inversely as X and $Y = 16$ when $X = 4$, find X when $Y = 12$.

    $\frac{16}{3}$

58. Given that L varies inversely as P and $L = 12$ when $P = 5$, find P when $L = 5$.

    12

59. If A varies directly as the square of r and $A = 3.14$ when $r = 1$, find A when $r = 2$.

    12.56

60. If A varies directly as the square of r and $A = \frac{22}{7}$ when $r = 1$, find A when $r = 7$.

    154

61. If P varies inversely as the square of x and $P = 2$ when $x = 4$, find P when $x = 12$.

    $\frac{2}{9}$

62. If M varies inversely as the square of N and $M = 4$ when $N = 2$, find M when $N = 6$.

    $\frac{4}{9}$

63. The distance (d) a spring will stretch varies directly as the force (f) applied to the spring. If a force of 6 lb is required to stretch the spring 3 in., what force is required to stretch the spring 4 in.?

    8 lb

64. The pressure (p) on a diver in the water varies directly as the depth (d). If the pressure is 4.5 lb per square inch when the depth is 10 ft, what is the pressure per square inch when the depth is 15 ft?

    6.75 pounds per square inch

Solve.

65. The number of bushels of wheat (b) produced by a farm is directly proportional to the number of acres (A) planted in wheat. If a 20-acre farm yields 450 bushels of wheat, what is the yield of a farm that has 30 acres of wheat?

675 bushels

66. The profit (P) realized by a company varies directly as the number of products it sells (s). If a company makes a profit of $4000 on the sale of 250 products, what is the profit when the company sells 5000 products?

$80,000

67. The stopping distance (s) of a car varies directly as the square of its speed (v). If a car traveling 50 mph requires 170 ft to stop, find the stopping distance for a car traveling 60 mph.

244.8 ft

68. The distance (s) a ball will roll down an inclined plane is directly proportional to the square of the time (t). If the ball rolls 6 ft in one second, how far will it roll in 3 seconds?

54 ft

69. The distance (s) a body falls from rest varies directly as the square of the time (t) of the fall. An object falls 64 ft in 2 seconds. How far will it fall in 5 seconds?

400 ft

70. The resistance (R) to the flow of electric current in a wire is inversely proportional to the square of the diameter (d) of a wire. If a wire of diameter 0.01 cm has a resistance of 0.5 ohms, what is the resistance in a wire that is 0.02 cm in diameter?

0.125 ohms

71. The speed (v) of a gear varies inversely as the number of teeth (t). If a gear that has 45 teeth makes 24 revolutions per minute, how many revolutions will a gear that has 36 teeth make?

30 revolutions per minute

72. For a constant temperature, the pressure (P) of a gas varies inversely as the volume (V). If the pressure is 30 lb per square inch when the volume is 500 ft³, find the pressure per square inch when the volume is 200 ft³.

75 pounds per square inch

73. The number of items (n) that can be purchased for a given amount of money is inversely proportional to the cost (C) of an item. If 60 items can be purchased when the cost per item is $.25, how many items can be purchased when the cost per item is $.20?

75 items

74. The length (L) of a rectangle of fixed area varies inversely as the width (w). If the length of a rectangle is 8 ft when the width is 5 ft, find the length of the rectangle when the width is 4 ft.

10 ft

75. The intensity (I) of a light source is inversely proportional to the square of the distance (d) from the source. If the intensity is 12 lumens at a distance of 10 ft, what is the intensity when the distance is 5 ft?

48 lumens

76. The repulsive force (f) between two north poles of a magnet is inversely proportional to the square of the distance (d) between them. If the repulsive force is 20 lb when the distance is 4 in., find the repulsive force when the distance is 2 in.

80 lb

Section 5 Literal Equations

Objective A To solve a literal equation for one of the variables

**Reference for
Computer
Tutor™**

A **literal equation** is an equation that contains more than one variable. Examples of literal equations are shown at the right.

$$2x + 3y = 6$$
$$4w - 2x + z = 0$$

Formulas are used to express a relationship among physical quantities. A **formula** is a literal equation that states rules about measurements. Examples of formulas are shown at the right.

$$\frac{1}{R_1} + \frac{1}{R_2} = \frac{1}{R} \qquad \text{(Physics)}$$
$$s = a + (n - 1)d \qquad \text{(Mathematics)}$$
$$A = P + Prt \qquad \text{(Business)}$$

The Addition and Multiplication Properties can be used to solve a literal equation for one of the variables. The goal is to rewrite the equation so that the letter being solved for is alone on one side of the equation and all the other numbers and variables are on the other side.

Solve $A = P(1 + i)$ for i.

The goal is to rewrite the equation so that i is on one side of the equation and all other variables are on the other side.

Use the Distributive Property to remove parentheses.

$$A = P(1 + i)$$
$$A = P + Pi$$

Add the opposite of P to each side of the equation.

$$A + (-P) = P + (-P) + Pi$$
$$A - P = Pi$$

Multiply each side of the equation by the reciprocal of P.

$$\frac{1}{P}(A - P) = \frac{1}{P}(Pi)$$
$$\frac{A - P}{P} = i$$

Example 1

Solve $3x - 4y = 12$ for y.

Solution

$$3x - 4y = 12$$
$$3x + (-3x) - 4y = -3x + 12$$
$$-4y = -3x + 12$$
$$\left(-\frac{1}{4}\right)(-4y) = \left(-\frac{1}{4}\right)(-3x + 12)$$
$$y = \frac{3}{4}x - 3$$

Example 2

Solve $5x - 2y = 10$ for y.

Your solution

$$y = \frac{5}{2}x - 5$$

Example 3

Solve $i = \dfrac{E}{R + r}$ for R.

Solution

$$i = \frac{E}{R + r}$$

$$(R + r)i = (R + r)\frac{E}{R + r}$$

$$Ri + ri = E$$

$$Ri + ri + (-ri) = E + (-ri)$$

$$Ri = E - ri$$

$$\frac{1}{i}(Ri) = \frac{1}{i}(E - ri)$$

$$R = \frac{E - ri}{i}$$

Example 4

Solve $s = \dfrac{A + L}{2}$ for L.

Your solution

$$L = 2s - A$$

Example 5

Solve $L = a(1 + ct)$ for c.

Solution

$$L = a(1 + ct)$$

$$L = a + act$$

$$L + (-a) = a + (-a) + act$$

$$L - a = act$$

$$\frac{1}{at}(L - a) = \frac{1}{at}(act)$$

$$\frac{L - a}{at} = c$$

Example 6

Solve $S = a + (n - 1)d$ for n.

Your solution

$$n = \frac{S - a + d}{d}$$

Example 7

Solve $S = C - rC$ for C.

Solution

$$S = C - rC$$

$$S = (1 - r)C \qquad \text{Factoring}$$

$$\frac{1}{1 - r} \cdot S = \frac{1}{1 - r}(1 - r)C$$

$$\frac{S}{1 - r} = C$$

Example 8

Solve $S = C + rC$ for C.

Your solution

$$C = \frac{S}{1 + r}$$

Solutions on p. A48

8.5A Exercises

Solve for y.

1. $3x + y = 10$
$y = -3x + 10$

2. $2x + y = 5$
$y = -2x + 5$

3. $4x - y = 3$
$y = 4x - 3$

4. $5x - y = 7$
$y = 5x - 7$

5. $3x + 2y = 6$
$y = -\frac{3}{2}x + 3$

6. $2x + 3y = 9$
$y = -\frac{2}{3}x + 3$

7. $2x - 5y = 10$
$y = \frac{2}{5}x - 2$

8. $5x - 2y = 4$
$y = \frac{5}{2}x - 2$

9. $2x + 7y = 14$
$y = -\frac{2}{7}x + 2$

10. $6x - 5y = 10$
$y = \frac{6}{5}x - 2$

11. $x + 3y = 6$
$y = -\frac{1}{3}x + 2$

12. $x + 2y = 8$
$y = -\frac{1}{2}x + 4$

13. $x - 4y = 12$
$y = \frac{1}{4}x - 3$

14. $x - 3y = 9$
$y = \frac{1}{3}x - 3$

15. $3x - y + 7 = 0$
$y = 3x + 7$

16. $2x - y + 5 = 0$
$y = 2x + 5$

Solve for x.

17. $x + 3y = 6$
$x = -3y + 6$

18. $x + 6y = 10$
$x = -6y + 10$

19. $3x - y = 3$
$x = \frac{1}{3}y + 1$

20. $2x - y = 6$
$x = \frac{1}{2}y + 3$

21. $2x + 5y = 10$
$x = -\frac{5}{2}y + 5$

22. $4x + 3y = 12$
$x = -\frac{3}{4}y + 3$

23. $x - 2y + 1 = 0$
$x = 2y - 1$

24. $x - 4y - 3 = 0$
$x = 4y + 3$

25. $5x + 4y + 20 = 0$
$x = -\frac{4}{5}y - 4$

26. $3x + 5y + 15 = 0$
$x = -\frac{5}{3}y - 5$

27. $3x - 2y - 15 = 0$
$x = \frac{2}{3}y + 5$

28. $5x - 8y + 10 = 0$
$x = \frac{8}{5}y - 2$

29. $2 + 3ax = 4$
$x = \frac{2}{3a}$

30. $5 - 2ax = 1$
$x = \frac{2}{a}$

31. $7 = 4 - 3ax$
$x = -\frac{1}{a}$

32. $6 = 4 - 5ax$
$x = -\frac{2}{5a}$

33. $3ax - 4x = 2$
$x = \frac{2}{3a - 4}$

34. $5x - 2ax = 6$
$x = \frac{6}{5 - 2a}$

35. $8 = 3(1 - 2ax)$
$x = -\frac{5}{6a}$

36. $6 = 4(3 - ax)$
$x = \frac{3}{2a}$

37. $4(2 - 3ax) = 11$
$x = -\frac{1}{4a}$

38. $7(3 - 2ax) = 14$
$x = \frac{1}{2a}$

39. $2(1 - 3ax) = x + 4$
$x = -\frac{2}{6a + 1}$

40. $3(2 + ax) = 4x + 8$
$x = \frac{2}{3a - 4}$

Solve the formula for the given variable.

41. $A = \frac{1}{2}bh$; h (Geometry)

$$h = \frac{2A}{b}$$

42. $P = a + b + c$; b (Geometry)

$$b = P - a - c$$

43. $d = rt$; t (Physics)

$$t = \frac{d}{r}$$

44. $E = IR$; R (Physics)

$$R = \frac{E}{I}$$

45. $PV = nRT$; T (Chemistry)

$$T = \frac{PV}{nR}$$

46. $A = bh$; h (Geometry)

$$h = \frac{A}{b}$$

47. $P = 2L + 2W$; L (Geometry)

$$L = \frac{P - 2W}{2}$$

48. $F = \frac{9}{5}C + 32$; C (Temperature Conversion)

$$C = \frac{5F - 160}{9}$$

49. $A = \frac{1}{2}h(b_1 + b_2)$; b_1 (Geometry)

$$b_1 = \frac{2A - hb_2}{h}$$

50. $C = \frac{5}{9}(F - 32)$; F (Temperature Conversion)

$$F = \frac{9C + 160}{5}$$

51. $V = \frac{1}{3}Ah$; h (Geometry)

$$h = \frac{3V}{A}$$

52. $P = R - C$; C (Business)

$$C = R - P$$

53. $R = \frac{C - S}{t}$; S (Business)

$$S = C - Rt$$

54. $P = \frac{R - C}{n}$; R (Business)

$$R = Pn + C$$

55. $A = P + Prt$; P (Business)

$$P = \frac{A}{1 + rt}$$

56. $T = fm - gm$; m (Engineering)

$$m = \frac{T}{f - g}$$

57. $A = Sw + w$; w (Physics)

$$w = \frac{A}{S + 1}$$

58. $a = S - Sr$; S (Mathematics)

$$S = \frac{a}{1 - r}$$

Section 6 Application Problems

Objective A   To solve work problems

Reference for
Computer
Tutor™

If a painter can paint a room in 4 hours, then in 1 hour the painter can paint $\frac{1}{4}$ of the room. The painter's rate of work is $\frac{1}{4}$ of the room each hour. The **rate of work** is that part of a task that is completed in one unit of time.

A pipe can fill a tank in 30 minutes. This pipe can fill $\frac{1}{30}$ of the tank in 1 minute. The rate of work is $\frac{1}{30}$ of the tank each minute. If a second pipe can fill the tank in x minutes, the rate of work for the second pipe is $\frac{1}{x}$ of the tank each minute.

In solving a work problem, the goal is to determine the time it takes to complete a task. The basic equation that is used to solve work problems is:

Rate of work × time worked = part of task completed

For example, if a faucet can fill a sink in 6 minutes, then in 5 minutes the faucet will fill $\frac{1}{6} \times 5 = \frac{5}{6}$ of the sink. In 5 minutes the faucet completes $\frac{5}{6}$ of the task.

A painter can paint a wall in 20 minutes. The painter's apprentice can paint the same wall in 30 minutes. How long will it take to paint the wall when they work together?

STRATEGY FOR SOLVING A WORK PROBLEM

▷ For each person or machine, write a numerical or variable expression for the rate of work, the time worked, and the part of the task completed. The results can be recorded in a table.

Unknown time to paint the wall working together: t

	Rate of work	·	Time worked	=	Part of task completed
Painter	$\frac{1}{20}$	·	t	=	$\frac{t}{20}$
Apprentice	$\frac{1}{30}$	·	t	=	$\frac{t}{30}$

▷ Determine how the parts of the task completed are related. Use the fact that the sum of the parts of the task completed must equal 1, the complete task.

The sum of the part of the task completed by the painter and the part of the task completed by the apprentice is 1.

$$\frac{t}{20} + \frac{t}{30} = 1$$
$$60\left(\frac{t}{20} + \frac{t}{30}\right) = 60 \cdot 1$$
$$3t + 2t = 60$$
$$5t = 60$$
$$t = 12$$

Working together, they will paint the wall in 12 minutes.

Example 1

A small water pipe takes three times longer to fill a tank than does a large water pipe. With both pipes open it takes 4 hours to fill the tank. Find the time it would take the small pipe working alone to fill the tank.

Strategy

▷ Time for large pipe to fill the tank: t
Time for small pipe to fill the tank: $3t$

	Rate	Time	Part
Small pipe	$\frac{1}{3t}$	4	$\frac{4}{3t}$
Large pipe	$\frac{1}{t}$	4	$\frac{4}{t}$

▷ The sum of the parts of the task completed by each pipe must equal one.

Solution

$$\frac{4}{3t} + \frac{4}{t} = 1$$

$$3t\left(\frac{4}{3t} + \frac{4}{t}\right) = 3t \cdot 1$$

$$4 + 12 = 3t$$

$$16 = 3t$$

$$\frac{16}{3} = t$$

$$3t = 3\left(\frac{16}{3}\right) = 16$$

The small pipe working alone takes 16 hours to fill the tank.

Example 2

Two computer printers that work at the same rate are working together to print the payroll checks for a large corporation. After working together for 2 hours, one of the printers quits. The second requires 3 more hours to complete the payroll checks. Find the time it would take one printer working alone to print the payroll.

Your strategy

Your solution

7 hours

Solution on p. A49

Objective B

To solve uniform motion problems

A car that travels constantly in a straight line at 30 mph is in uniform motion. **Uniform motion** means that the speed of an object does not change.

The basic equation used to solve uniform motion problems is:

Distance = rate × time

An alternate form of this equation can be written by solving the equation for time.

$$\frac{\textbf{Distance}}{\textbf{Rate}} = \textbf{time}$$

This form of the equation is useful when the total time of travel for two objects or the time of travel between two points is known.

The speed of a boat in still water is 20 mph. The boat traveled 75 mi down a river in the same amount of time as it traveled 45 mi up the river. Find the rate of the river's current.

STRATEGY FOR SOLVING A UNIFORM MOTION PROBLEM

▷ For each object, write a numerical or variable expression for the distance, rate, and time. The results can be recorded in a table.

The unknown rate of the river's current: r

	Distance	÷	Rate	=	Time
Down river	75	÷	$20 + r$	=	$\frac{75}{20 + r}$
Up river	45	÷	$20 - r$	=	$\frac{45}{20 - r}$

▷ Determine how the times traveled by each object are related. For example, it may be known that the times are equal or the total time may be known.

The time down the river is equal to the time up the river.

$$\frac{75}{20 + r} = \frac{45}{20 - r}$$

$$(20 + r)(20 - r)\frac{75}{20 + r} = (20 + r)(20 - r)\frac{45}{20 - r}$$

$$(20 - r)75 = (20 + r)45$$

$$1500 - 75r = 900 + 45r$$

$$-120r = -600$$

$$r = 5$$

The rate of the river's current is 5 mph.

Example 3

A jet can fly 600 mph in calm air. Traveling with the wind, the plane can fly 2100 mi in the same amount of time as it flies 1500 mi against the wind. Find the rate of the wind.

Strategy

▷ Rate of wind: r

	Distance	Rate	Time
With wind	2100	$600 + r$	$\dfrac{2100}{600 + r}$
Against wind	1500	$600 - r$	$\dfrac{1500}{600 - r}$

▷ The time spent flying with the wind equals the time spent flying against the wind.

Solution

$$\frac{2100}{600 + r} = \frac{1500}{600 - r}$$

$$(600 + r)(600 - r)\frac{2100}{600 + r} = (600 + r)(600 - r)\frac{1500}{600 - r}$$

$$(600 - r)2100 = (600 + r)1500$$

$$1{,}260{,}000 - 2100r = 900{,}000 + 1500r$$

$$360{,}000 = 3600r$$

$$100 = r$$

The rate of the wind is 100 mph.

Example 4

The total time for a sailboat to sail back and forth across a lake 6 km wide was 2 hours. The rate sailing back was three times the rate sailing across. Find the rate across the lake.

Your strategy

Your solution

4 km/h

Solution on p. A49

8.6A Exercises

Solve.

1. A park has two sprinklers that are used to fill a fountain. One sprinkler can fill the fountain in 3 hours, while the second sprinkler can fill the fountain in 6 hours. How long will it take to fill the fountain with both sprinklers operating?

2 hours

2. A new printing press can complete the weekly edition of a news magazine in 10 hours. An older printing press requires 15 hours to do the same task. How long would it take to print the weekly edition with both presses operating?

6 hours

3. Two farmers are plowing a field. One farmer, using an old tractor and working alone, requires 12 hours to plow the field. A second farmer, using a modern tractor, can plow the same field in 4 hours. How long would it take to plow the field with both tractors working together?

3 hours

4. A small air conditioner will cool a room 5° in 75 minutes. A larger air conditioner will cool the room 5° in 50 minutes. How long would it take to cool the room 5° with both air conditioners operating?

30 minutes

5. A new machine can fill soda bottles three times faster than an old machine. With both machines working together, they can complete the task in 9 hours. How long would it take the new machine working alone to complete the task?

12 hours

6. An experienced painter can paint a fence twice as fast as an inexperienced painter. Working together, the painters require 4 hours to paint the fence. How long would it take the experienced painter working alone to paint the fence?

6 hours

7. A plumber can install a garbage disposal in 45 minutes. With the plumber's assistant helping, the task would take 30 minutes. How long would it take the assistant working alone to complete the task?

90 minutes

8. A mason can construct a retaining wall in 10 hours. With the mason's apprentice assisting, the task would take 6 hours. How long would it take the apprentice working alone to construct the wall?

15 hours

9. An electrician requires 2 hours to install an electrical motor, while an apprentice requires 6 hours to install the motor. The electrician worked for one hour and then stopped. How long would it take the apprentice to complete the installation?

3 hours

10. One member of a telephone repair crew can wire new telephone circuits in 4 hours, while it would take 6 hours for the second member of the crew to do the same job. After working alone for 2 hours, the first crew member quits and the second member completes the task. How long does it take the second member to complete the task?

3 hours

11. One welder requires 2 hours to make the welds on a steel frame, while a second welder requires 4 hours to do the same job. The first welder worked for one hour and then quit. How long would it take the second welder to complete the welds?

2 hours

12. One cement mason can lay a cement foundation in 8 hours, while it takes a second 12 hours to do the same task. After working alone for 4 hours, the first mason quits. How long would it take the second mason to complete the task?

6 hours

8.6B Exercises

Solve.

13. An express train travels 300 mi in the same amount of time that a freight train travels 180 mi. The rate of the express train is 20 mph faster than that of the freight train. Find the rate of each train.

freight train: 30 mph;
express train: 50 mph

14. A postal clerk on vacation took an 8-mile cruise in a sailboat in the same amount of time as a 20-mile cruise on a power boat. The rate of the power boat is 12 mph faster than the rate of the sailboat. Find the rate of each boat.

sailboat: 8 mph;
power boat: 20 mph

15. A twin-engine plane can fly 660 mi in the same amount of time as it takes a single-engine plane to fly 330 mi. The rate of the twin-engine plane is 100 mph faster than that of the single-engine plane. Find the rate of the twin-engine plane.

200 mph

16. The rate of a motorcycle is 36 mph faster than the rate of a bicycle. The motorcycle travels 192 mi in the same amount of time as the bicycle travels 48 mi. Find the rate of the motorcycle.

48 mph

17. A sales accountant traveled 1800 mi by jet and 300 mi on a prop plane. The rate of the jet is four times the rate of the prop plane. The entire trip took a total of 5 hours. Find the rate of each.

prop plane: 150 mph;
jet plane: 600 mph

18. A motorist drove 90 mi before running out of gas and then walking 5 mi to a gas station. The rate of the motorist in the car was nine times the rate walking. The time spent walking and driving was 3 hours. Find the rate at which the motorist walks.

5 mph

19. A computer representative traveled 135 mi by train and then an additional 855 mi by plane. The rate of the plane was three times the rate of the train and the total time for the trip was 6 hours. Find the rate of the plane.

210 mph

20. A marketing manager traveled 1080 mi on a corporate jet and then an additional 180 mi by helicopter. The rate of the jet is four times the rate of the helicopter. The entire trip took 5 hours. Find the rate of the jet.

360 mph

21. A light plane can fly at a rate of 100 mph in calm air. Traveling with the wind, the plane flew 360 mi in the same amount of time as it flew 240 mi against the wind. Find the rate of the wind.

20 mph

22. A tour boat used for river excursions can travel 6 mph in calm water. The amount of time it takes to travel 12 mi against the river's current is the same as the amount of time it takes to travel 24 mi with the current. Find the rate of the current.

2 mph

23. A twin-engine plane can travel 200 mph in calm air. Flying with the wind, the plane can fly 660 mi in the same amount of time as it takes to fly 540 mi against the wind. Find the rate of the wind.

20 mph

24. A rowing team can row 20 mph in calm water. Rowing with the current of a river, the team can row 25 mi in the same amount of time as they row 15 mi against the current. Find the rate of the current.

5 mph

Calculators and Computers

The first two sections of Chapter 8 present operations with algebraic fractions. Many students find performing operations on algebraic fractions difficult. The difficulty often lies in the fact that, in any one problem, there are a number of steps that must be performed, and it is essential that the student understand the function of each step of the process.

In performing operations with algebraic fractions, it is helpful to keep in mind that addition, subtraction, multiplication, and division performed on algebraic fractions involves the same steps as these operations performed on numerical fractions. It is the fractions themselves that make the procedure look more difficult and the greater amount of time that it takes to perform them that makes them seem so much more complicated. Therefore, you are encouraged to practice as much as possible.

Two programs on the Student Disk will provide you with additional practice with algebraic expressions. These programs are entitled SIMPLIFY AN ALGEBRAIC FRACTION and RATIONAL EXPRESSIONS.

The program SIMPLIFY AN ALGEBRAIC FRACTION will allow you to practice writing an algebraic fraction in simplest form. The program allows you to choose one of three levels of difficulty. Level one contains the easiest problems and level three contains the most difficult problems.

After you have chosen a level of difficulty, the program will display a problem. Using paper and pencil, simplify the expression. Then press the RETURN key. The correct solution will be displayed.

After you have completed a problem, you may continue with problems of the same level of difficulty or return to the menu, where you can change the level of difficulty or quit the program.

The program RATIONAL EXPRESSIONS on the Student Disk will give you additional practice in multiplying and dividing rational expressions. There are three levels of difficulty, with the first level being the easiest problems and the third level the most difficult. You may choose the level you wish to practice.

After you choose the level of difficulty, a program will be displayed on the screen. Using paper and pencil, simplify the expression. When you are ready, press the RETURN key. The correct solution will be displayed. Compare this solution with your solution.

After each problem, you have the choice of continuing the same level of problems, returning to the menu to change the level, or quitting the program.

Chapter Summary

KEY WORDS

An **algebraic fraction** is a fraction in which the numerator or denominator is a variable expression.

An algebraic fraction is in **simplest form** when the numerator and denominator have no common factors.

The **reciprocal** of a fraction is the fraction with the numerator and denominator interchanged.

The **least common multiple (LCM)** of two or more numbers is the smallest number that contains the prime factorization of each number.

A **complex fraction** is a fraction whose numerator or denominator contains one or more fractions.

Direct variation can be expressed as the equation $y = kx$, where k is a constant called the **constant of variation** or the **constant of proportionality.** **Inverse variation** can be expressed as the equation $y = \dfrac{k}{x}$, where k is a constant.

A **literal equation** is an equation that contains more than one variable.

A **formula** is a literal equation that states rules about measurements.

ESSENTIAL RULES

To add fractions:	$\dfrac{a}{b} + \dfrac{c}{b} = \dfrac{a + c}{b}$
To subtract fractions:	$\dfrac{a}{b} - \dfrac{c}{b} = \dfrac{a - c}{b}$
To multiply fractions:	$\dfrac{a}{b} \cdot \dfrac{c}{d} = \dfrac{ac}{bd}$
To divide fractions:	$\dfrac{a}{b} \div \dfrac{c}{d} = \dfrac{a}{b} \cdot \dfrac{d}{c} = \dfrac{ad}{bc}$
Equation for work problems:	Rate of work × time worked = part of task completed
Uniform motion equation:	Distance = rate × time or Distance ÷ rate = time

Review/Test

1. Simplify: $\dfrac{16x^5y}{24x^2y^4}$

   $\dfrac{2x^3}{3y^3}$

2. Simplify: $\dfrac{x^2 + 4x - 5}{1 - x^2}$

   $-\dfrac{x+5}{x+1}$

3. Find the LCM of $6x - 3$ and $2x^2 + x - 1$.

   $3(2x-1)(x+1)$

4. Write each fraction in terms of the LCM of the denominators.

   $\dfrac{3}{x^2 - 2x}, \dfrac{x}{x^2 - 4}$ $\dfrac{3x+6}{x(x+2)(x-2)}, \dfrac{x^2}{x(x+2)(x-2)}$

5. Simplify: $\dfrac{2x}{x^2 + 3x - 10} - \dfrac{4}{x^2 + 3x - 10}$

   $\dfrac{2}{x+5}$

6. Simplify: $\dfrac{3x}{x^2 + 5x - 24} - \dfrac{9}{x^2 + 5x - 24}$

   $\dfrac{3}{x+8}$

7. Simplify: $\dfrac{y}{x} - \dfrac{5y}{2x} + \dfrac{3y}{4x}$

   $-\dfrac{3y}{4x}$

8. Simplify: $\dfrac{2}{2x - 1} - \dfrac{1}{x + 1}$

   $\dfrac{3}{(2x-1)(x+1)}$

9. Simplify: $\dfrac{4x - 8}{6x + 18} \cdot \dfrac{2x + 6}{x^2 - 2x}$

   $\dfrac{4}{3x}$

10. Simplify: $\dfrac{x^5y^3}{x^3(x+3)} \cdot \dfrac{x^2 - 9}{x^2y^4}$

    $\dfrac{x^3(x+3)}{y(x+2)}$

11. Simplify: $\dfrac{ab^2 - 2a^2b}{c^2} \div \dfrac{4a^2 - 2ab}{c^3}$

    $-\dfrac{bc}{2}$

12. Simplify: $\dfrac{x^2 - x - 56}{x^2 + 8x + 7} \div \dfrac{x^2 - 13x + 40}{x^2 - 4x - 5}$

    1

13. Simplify: $\dfrac{1 - \dfrac{3}{x}}{2 + \dfrac{3}{x}}$

    $\dfrac{x-3}{2x+3}$

14. Simplify: $\dfrac{1 + \dfrac{1}{x} - \dfrac{12}{x^2}}{1 + \dfrac{2}{x} - \dfrac{8}{x^2}}$

    $\dfrac{x-3}{x-2}$

15. Solve: $\dfrac{6}{x} - 2 = 1$

    2

16. Solve: $\dfrac{2}{x + 1} - 3 = \dfrac{-2}{x + 1}$

    $\dfrac{1}{3}$

17. P varies directly as x and $P = 14$ when $x = 2$. Find P when $x = 5$.

    35

18. W is inversely proportional to V and $W = 6$ when $V = 2$. Find W when $V = 3$.

    4

19. Solve $3x - 8y = 16$ for y.

    $y = \dfrac{3}{8}x - 2$

20. Solve $d = s + rt$ for t.

    $t = \dfrac{d-s}{r}$

21. One water pipe can fill a tank in 9 minutes while a second pipe requires 18 minutes to fill the tank. How long would it take both pipes working together to fill the tank?

    6 minutes

22. The rower of a boat can row at a rate of 5 mph in calm water. Rowing with the current, the boat travels 14 mi in the same amount of time as it travels 6 mi against the current. Find the rate of the current.

    2 mph

23. With cold and hot water running, a bathtub can be filled in 6 minutes. The hot water faucet working alone requires 15 minutes to fill the tub. How long would it take the cold water faucet working alone to fill the tub?

    10 minutes

24. A freight train and a passenger train leave a town at 10 a.m. and head for a town 300 mi away. The rate of the passenger train is twice the rate of the freight train. The passenger train arrives 5 hours ahead of the freight train. Find the rate of each train.

    freight train: 30 mph;
    passenger train: 60 mph

Cumulative Review/Test

1. Simplify: $\dfrac{2}{2x-1} - \dfrac{1}{x+1}$

$$\dfrac{3}{(2x-1)(x+1)}$$

2. Factor $12x^2 - x - 1$.

$$(3x-1)(4x+1)$$

3. Simplify: $\dfrac{15b^4 - 5b^2 + 10b}{5b}$

$$3b^3 - b + 2$$

4. Simplify: $\dfrac{x^2 - 3x - 18}{x^2 + 8x + 15} \div \dfrac{x^2 - 10x + 24}{x^2 + 4x - 5}$

$$\dfrac{x-1}{x-4}$$

5. Solve: $\dfrac{3x}{x-3} - 2 = \dfrac{10}{x-3}$

$$4$$

6. Simplify: $(x^3 - 8) \div (x - 2)$

$$x^2 + 2x + 4$$

7. Simplify $(a - 3b)(a + 4b)$.

$$a^2 + ab - 12b^2$$

8. Factor $y^2 - 7y + 6$.

$$(y-6)(y-1)$$

9. Simplify: $\dfrac{1 - \dfrac{2}{x} - \dfrac{15}{x^2}}{1 - \dfrac{25}{x^2}}$

$$\dfrac{x+3}{x+5}$$

10. Simplify: $\dfrac{12x^4 y^2}{18xy^7}$

$$\dfrac{2x^3}{3y^5}$$

11. Solve the proportion $\dfrac{2}{x+3} = \dfrac{12}{x-2}$.

$$-4$$

12. Simplify $(a^2 b^5)(ab^2)$.

$$a^3 b^7$$

13. Simplify: $\dfrac{3x}{x^2 - 9} - \dfrac{9}{x^2 - 9}$

$$\dfrac{3}{x+3}$$

14. Factor $2a^3 + 7a^2 - 15a$.

$$a(2a-3)(a+5)$$

15. Solve: $4 - \dfrac{2}{3}x = 7$

$$-\dfrac{9}{2}$$

16. M is directly proportional to P and $M = 15$ when $P = 5$. Find M when $P = 7$.

$$21$$

17. Find $16\frac{2}{3}\%$ of 60.

$$10$$

18. Simplify: $\dfrac{3x - 6}{9x + 3} \cdot \dfrac{5x + 10}{x^2 - 4}$

$$\dfrac{5}{3x+1}$$

19. Simplify: $\dfrac{x^2 - 7x + 10}{25 - x^2}$

$$-\dfrac{x-2}{x+5}$$

20. Solve $f = v + at$ for t.

$$t = \dfrac{f-v}{a}$$

21. A silversmith mixes 60 g of an alloy that is 40% silver with 120 g of another silver alloy. The resulting alloy is 60% silver. Find the percent of silver in the 120-gram alloy.

$$70\%$$

22. Two solar heating panels will raise the temperature of water 1° in 60 minutes. One panel, working alone, requires 90 minutes to raise the temperature of the water 1°. How long would it take the second panel working alone to heat the water?

$$180 \text{ minutes}$$

23. A canoeist can paddle at a rate of 7 mph in calm water. Traveling with the current, the canoe traveled 40 mi in the same amount of time as it traveled 16 mi against the current. Find the rate of the current.

$$3 \text{ mph}$$

24. The frequency of vibration (f) in an open pipe organ varies inversely as the length (L) of the pipe. If the air in a pipe 2 m long vibrates 60 times per minute, find the frequency in a pipe that is 1.5 m long.

$$80 \text{ times per minute}$$

chapter 9

Graphs and Linear Equations

Objectives

9.1A   To graph points on a rectangular coordinate system

9.1B   To determine a solution of a linear equation in two variables

9.1C   To graph an equation of the form $y = mx + b$

9.1D   To graph an equation of the form $Ax + By = C$

9.2A   To find the x- and y-intercepts of a straight line

9.2B   To find the slope of a straight line

9.2C   To graph a line using the slope and y-intercept

9.3A   To find the equation of a line using the equation $y = mx + b$

9.3B   To find the equation of a line using the point-slope formula

9.4A   To determine if a given ordered pair is a solution of a system of linear equations

9.4B   To solve a system of linear equations by graphing

9.5A   To solve a system of linear equations by the substitution method

9.5B   To solve a system of linear equations by the addition method

Section 1 Graphs of Straight Lines

Objective A To graph points on a rectangular coordinate system

Reference for
Computer
Tutor™

A **rectangular coordinate system** is formed by two number lines, one horizontal and one vertical, that intersect at the zero point of each line. The point of intersection is called the **origin.** The two lines are called the **coordinate axes,** or simply **axes.**

The axes determine a plane and divide the plane into four regions, called **quadrants.** The quadrants are numbered counterclockwise from I to IV.

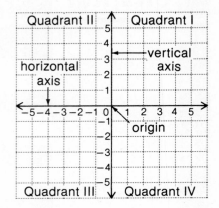

Each point in the plane can be identified by a pair of numbers called an **ordered pair.** The first number of the pair measures a horizontal distance and is called the **abscissa.** The second number of the pair measures a vertical distance and is called the **ordinate.** The **coordinates** of a point are the numbers in the ordered pair associated with the point.

horizontal distance ─────┐   ┌───── vertical distance

ordered pair → (3 , 4)

abscissa ─────┘   └───── ordinate

The **graph of an ordered pair** is a point in the plane. The graphs of the points (2, 3) and (3, 2) are shown at the right. Notice that they are different points. The order in which the numbers in an ordered pair appear *is* important.

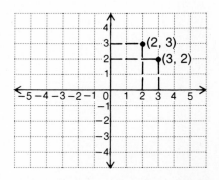

Example 1	Graph the ordered pairs $(-2, -3)$, $(3, -2)$, $(1, 3)$, and $(4, 1)$.	Example 2	Graph the ordered pairs $(-1, 3)$, $(1, 4)$, $(-4, 0)$, and $(-2, -1)$.
Solution	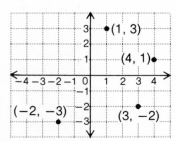	Your solution	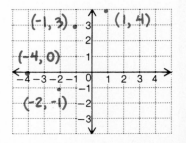

Solution on p. A51

Example 3 Find the coordinates of each of the points.

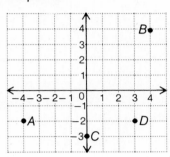

Solution
$A\ (-4,\ -2)$
$B\ (4,\ 4)$
$C\ (0,\ -3)$
$D\ (3,\ -2)$

Example 4 Find the coordinates of each of the points.

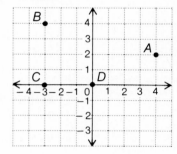

Your solution
A (4, 2)
B (-3, 4)
C (-3, 0)
D (0, 0)

Example 5
a) Name the abscissas of points A and C.
b) Name the ordinates of points B and D.

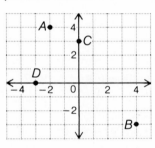

Solution
a) Abscissa of point A: -2
    Abscissa of point C: 0
b) Ordinate of point B: -3
    Ordinate of point D: 0

Example 6
a) Name the abscissas of points A and C.
b) Name the ordinates of points B and D.

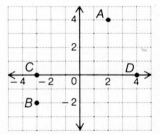

Your solution
a) Abscissa of point A: 2
   Abscissa of point C: -3
b) Ordinate of point B: -2
   Ordinate of point D: 0

Solutions on p. A51

Objective B To determine a solution of a linear equation in two variables

Reference for Computer Tutor™

An equation of the form $y = mx + b$, where m and b are constants, is a **linear equation in two variables.** Examples of linear equations are shown at the right. Note that the exponent of each variable is always one.

$y = 3x + 4$	$(m = 3,\ \ b = 4)$
$y = 2x - 3$	$(m = 2,\ \ b = -3)$
$y = -\frac{2}{3}x + 1$	$(m = -\frac{2}{3}, b = 1)$
$y = -2x$	$(m = -2, b = 0)$
$y = x + 2$	$(m = 1,\ \ b = 2)$

A **solution of an equation in two variables** is an order pair of numbers (x, y) that makes the equation a true statement.

Is $(1, -2)$ a solution of $y = 3x - 5$?

Replace x with 1, the abscissa.
Replace y with -2, the ordinate.

$$
\begin{array}{c|c}
\multicolumn{2}{c}{y = 3x - 5} \\
\hline
-2 & 3(1) - 5 \\
& 3 - 5 \\
\hline
\multicolumn{2}{c}{-2 = -2}
\end{array}
$$

Compare the results. If the results are equal, the given ordered pair is a solution. If the results are not equal, the given ordered pair is not a solution.

Yes, $(1, -2)$ is a solution of the equation $y = 3x - 5$.

Besides the ordered pair $(1, -2)$, there are many other ordered pair solutions of the equation $y = 3x - 5$. For example, the method used above can be used to show that $(2, 1)$, $(-1, -8)$, $\left(\frac{2}{3}, -3\right)$ and $(0, -5)$ are also solutions.

In general, a linear equation in two variables has an infinite number of solutions. By choosing any value for x and substituting that value into the linear equation, a corresponding value of y can be found.

Find the ordered pair solution of $y = 2x - 5$ corresponding to $x = 1$.

Substitute 1 for x.
Solve for y.

$$
\begin{aligned}
y &= 2x - 5 \\
&= 2 \cdot 1 - 5 \\
&= 2 - 5 \\
&= -3
\end{aligned}
$$

The ordered pair solution is $(1, -3)$.

Example 7 Is $(-3, 2)$ a solution of $y = 2x + 2$?

Solution

$$
\begin{array}{c|c}
\multicolumn{2}{c}{y = 2x + 2} \\
\hline
2 & 2(-3) + 2 \\
& -6 + 2 \\
& -4 \\
\hline
\multicolumn{2}{c}{2 \neq -4}
\end{array}
$$

No, $(-3, 2)$ is not a solution of $y = 2x + 2$.

Example 8 Is $(2, -4)$ a solution of $y = -\frac{1}{2}x - 3$?

Your solution

yes

Example 9 Find the ordered pair solution of $y = \frac{2}{3}x - 1$ corresponding to $x = 3$.

Solution

$$
\begin{aligned}
y &= \frac{2}{3}x - 1 \\
&= \frac{2}{3}(3) - 1 \\
&= 2 - 1 \\
&= 1
\end{aligned}
$$

The ordered pair solution is $(3, 1)$.

Example 10 Find the ordered pair solution of $y = -\frac{1}{4}x + 1$ corresponding to $x = 4$.

Your solution

$(4, 0)$

Solutions on p. A51

Objective C

9
DISK
NINE

Reference for
Computer
Tutor™

To graph an equation of the form $y = mx + b$

The **graph of an equation in two variables** is a drawing of the ordered pair solutions of the equation. For a linear equation in two variables, the graph is a straight line.

To graph a linear equation, find ordered pair solutions of the equation. Do this by choosing any value of x and finding the corresponding value of y. Repeat this procedure, choosing different values for x, until you have found the number of solutions desired.

Since the graph of a linear equation in two variables is a straight line, and a straight line is determined by two points, it is necessary to find only two solutions. However, it is recommended that at least three points be used to insure accuracy.

Graph $y = 2x + 1$.

Choose any values of x and then find the corresponding values of y. The numbers $0, 2$, and -1 were chosen arbitrarily for x. It is convenient to record these solutions in a table.

x	$y =$	$2x + 1$	y
0		$2 \cdot 0 + 1$	1
2		$2 \cdot 2 + 1$	5
-1		$2(-1) + 1$	-1

The horizontal axis is the x-axis.
The vertical axis is the y-axis.
Graph the ordered pair solutions $(0, 1), (2, 5)$, and $(-1, -1)$.
Draw a line through the ordered pair solutions.

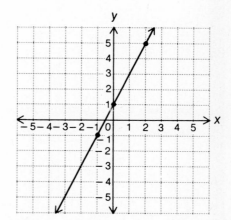

Remember that a graph is a drawing of the ordered pair solutions of the equation. Therefore, every point on the graph is a solution of the equation and every solution of the equation is a point on the graph.

Note that $(-2, -3)$ and $(1, 3)$ are points on the graph and that these points are solutions of the equation $y = 2x + 1$.

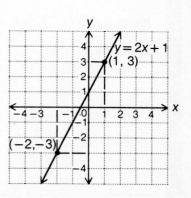

Graph $y = \frac{1}{3}x - 1$.

Step 1 Find at least three solutions.
When *m is a fraction,* choose values of *x* that will simplify the evaluation.
Display the ordered pairs in a table.

x	y
0	−1
3	0
−3	−2

Step 2 Graph the ordered pairs on a rectangular coordinate system and draw a straight line through the points.

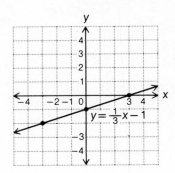

Example 11   Graph $y = 3x - 2$.

Solution

x	y
0	−2
1	1
−1	−5
2	4

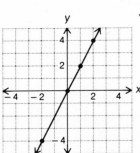

Example 12   Graph $y = 3x + 1$.

Your solution

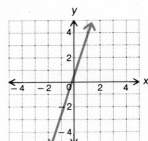

Example 13   Graph $y = 2x$.

Solution

x	y
0	0
2	4
−2	−4
1	2

Example 14   Graph $y = -2x$.

Your solution

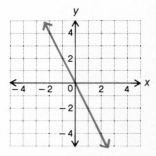

Example 15   Graph $y = \frac{1}{2}x - 1$.

Solution

x	y
0	−1
2	0
−2	−2
4	1

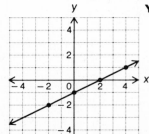

Example 16   Graph $y = \frac{1}{3}x - 3$.

Your solution

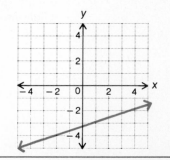

Solutions on p. A51

Objective D	To graph an equation of the form $Ax + By = C$

An equation in the form $Ax + By = C$, where A, B, and C are constants, is also a linear equation. Examples of these equations are shown at the right.

$2x + 3y = 6$ $(A = 2, B = 3, \quad C = 6)$
$x - 2y = -4$ $(A = 1, B = -2, C = -4)$
$2x + y = 0$ $(A = 2, B = 1, \quad C = 0)$
$4x - 5y = 2$ $(A = 4, B = -5, C = 2)$

To graph an equation of the form $Ax + By = C$, first solve the equation for y. Then follow the same procedure used for graphing an equation of the form $y = mx + b$.

Graph $3x + 4y = 12$.

Step 1 Solve the equation for y.

$$3x + 4y = 12$$
$$4y = -3x + 12$$
$$y = -\frac{3}{4}x + 3$$

Step 2 Find at least three solutions. Display the ordered pairs in a table.

x	y
0	3
4	0
-4	6

Step 3 Graph the ordered pairs on a rectangular coordinate system and draw a straight line through the points.

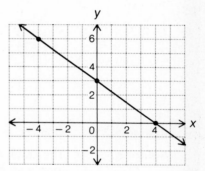

The graph of an equation in which one of the variables is missing is either a horizontal or a vertical line.

The equation $y = 2$ could be written $0 \cdot x + y = 2$. No matter what value of x is chosen, y is always 2. Some solutions to the equation are $(3, 2)$, $(-1, 2)$, $(0, 2)$, and $(-4, 2)$. The graph is shown at the right.

The **graph of $y = b$** is a horizontal line passing through point $(0, b)$.

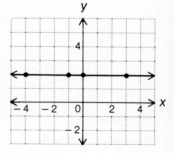

The equation $x = -2$ could be written $x + 0 \cdot y = -2$. No matter what value of y is chosen, x is always -2. Some solutions of the equation are $(-2, 3)$, $(-2, -2)$, $(-2, 0)$, and $(-2, 2)$. The graph is shown at the right.

The **graph of $x = a$** is a vertical line passing through point $(a, 0)$.

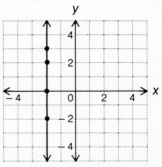

Example 17   Graph $2x - 5y = 10$.

Solution

$2x - 5y = 10$
$\quad -5y = -2x + 10$
$\qquad y = \dfrac{2}{5}x - 2$

x	y
0	-2
5	0
-5	-4

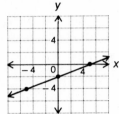

Example 18   Graph $5x - 2y = 10$.

Your solution

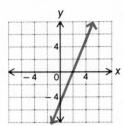

Example 19   Graph $x + 2y = 6$.

Solution

$x + 2y = 6$
$\quad 2y = -x + 6$
$\qquad y = -\dfrac{1}{2}x + 3$

x	y
0	3
2	2
-2	4
4	1

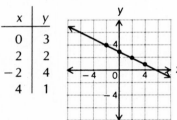

Example 20   Graph $x - 3y = 9$.

Your solution

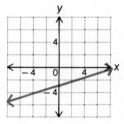

Example 21   Graph $y = -2$.

Solution   The graph of an equation of the form $y = b$ is a horizontal line passing through point $(0, b)$.

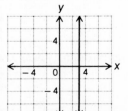

Example 22   Graph $y = 3$.

Your solution

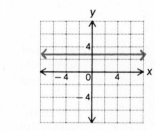

Example 23   Graph $x = 3$.

Solution   The graph of an equation of the form $x = a$ is a vertical line passing through point $(a, 0)$.

Example 24   Graph $x = -4$.

Your solution

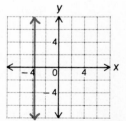

Solutions on pp. A51–52

9.1A Exercises

1. Graph the ordered pairs
   $(-2, 1)$, $(3, -5)$
   $(-2, 4)$, and $(0, 3)$.

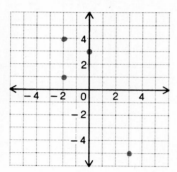

2. Graph the ordered pairs
   $(5, -1)$, $(-3, -3)$,
   $(-1, 0)$, and $(1, -1)$.

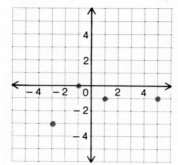

3. Graph the ordered pairs
   $(0, 0)$, $(0, -5)$,
   $(-3, 0)$, and $(0, 2)$.

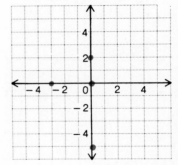

4. Graph the ordered pairs
   $(-4, 5)$, $(-3, 1)$,
   $(3, -4)$, and $(5, 0)$.

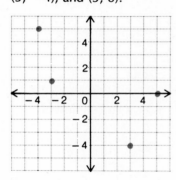

5. Graph the ordered pairs
   $(-1, 4)$, $(-2, -3)$,
   $(0, 2)$, and $(4, 0)$.

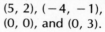
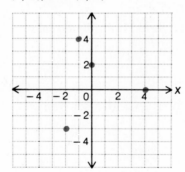

6. Graph the ordered pairs
   $(5, 2)$, $(-4, -1)$,
   $(0, 0)$, and $(0, 3)$.

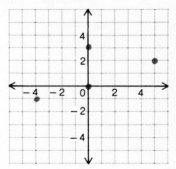

7. Find the coordinates of each
   of the points.

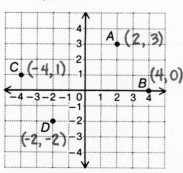

8. Find the coordinates of each
   of the points.

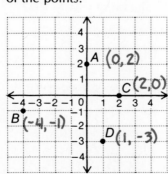

9. Find the coordinates of each
   of the points.

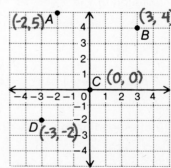

10. Find the coordinates of each of the points.

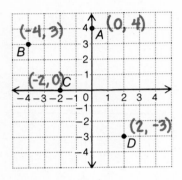

11. a) Name the abscissas of points A and C.   **2 ; -4**
    b) Name the ordinates of points B and D.   **1 ; -3**

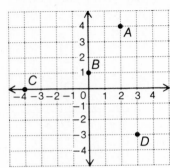

12. a) Name the abscissas of points A and C.   **0 ; 3**
    b) Name the ordinates of points B and D.   **1 ; -1**

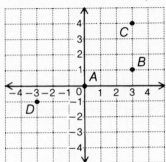

9.1B Exercises

13. Is (3, 4) a solution of
    $y = -x + 7$?
    yes

14. Is (2, −3) a solution of
    $y = x + 5$?
    no

15. Is (−1, 2) a solution of
    $y = \frac{1}{2}x - 1$?
    no

16. Is (1, −3) a solution of
    $y = -2x - 1$?
    yes

17. Is (4, 1) a solution of
    $y = \frac{1}{4}x + 1$?
    no

18. Is (−5, 3) a solution of
    $y = -\frac{2}{5}x + 1$?
    yes

19. Is (0, 4) a solution of
    $y = \frac{3}{4}x + 4$?
    yes

20. Is (−2, 0) a solution of
    $y = -\frac{1}{2}x - 1$?
    yes

21. Is (0, 0) a solution of
    $y = 3x + 2$?
    no

22. Is (0, 0) a solution of
    $y = -\frac{3}{4}x$?
    yes

23. Find the ordered pair solution of $y = 3x - 2$ corresponding to $x = 3$.
    (3, 7)

24. Find the ordered pair solution of $y = 4x + 1$ corresponding to $x = -1$.
    (-1, -3)

25. Find the ordered pair solution of $y = \frac{2}{3}x - 1$ corresponding to $x = 6$.
    (6, 3)

26. Find the ordered pair solution of $y = \frac{3}{4}x - 2$ corresponding to $x = 4$.
    (4, 1)

27. Find the ordered pair solution of $y = -3x + 1$ corresponding to $x = 0$.
    (0, 1)

28. Find the ordered pair solution of $y = \frac{2}{5}x - 5$ corresponding to $x = 0$.
    (0, -5)

29. Find the ordered pair solution of $y = \frac{2}{5}x + 2$ corresponding to $x = -5$.
    (-5, 0)

30. Find the ordered pair solution of $y = -\frac{1}{6}x - 2$ corresponding to $x = 12$.
    (12, -4)

9.1C Exercises

Graph.

31. $y = 2x - 3$

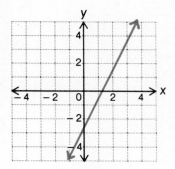

32. $y = -2x + 2$

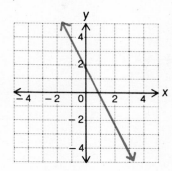

33. $y = \frac{1}{3}x$

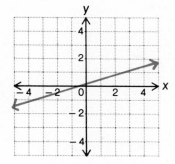

34. $y = -3x$

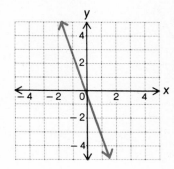

35. $y = \frac{2}{3}x - 1$

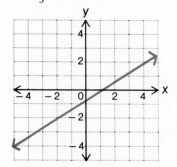

36. $y = \frac{3}{4}x + 2$

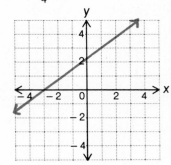

37. $y = -\frac{1}{4}x + 2$

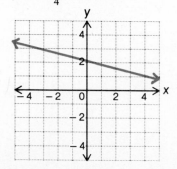

38. $y = -\frac{1}{3}x + 1$

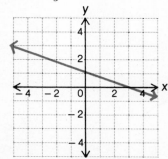

Graph.

39. $y = -\frac{2}{5}x + 1$

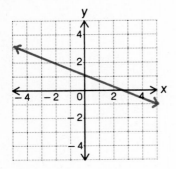

40. $y = -\frac{1}{2}x + 3$

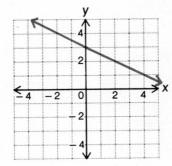

41. $y = 2x - 4$

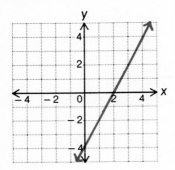

42. $y = 3x - 4$

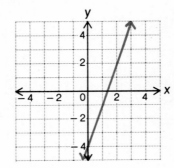

43. $y = -x + 2$

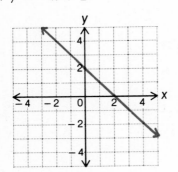

44. $y = -x - 1$

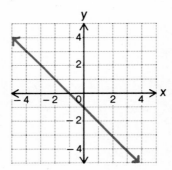

45. $y = -\frac{2}{3}x + 1$

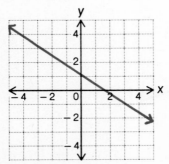

46. $y = 5x - 4$

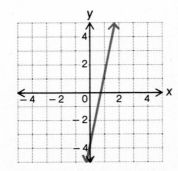

9.1D Exercises

Graph.

47. $3x + y = 3$

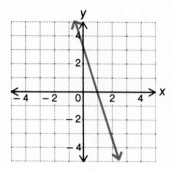

48. $2x + y = 4$

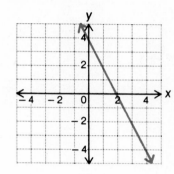

49. $2x + 3y = 6$

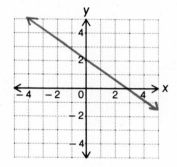

50. $3x + 2y = 4$

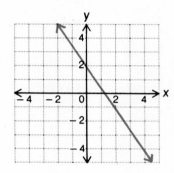

51. $x - 2y = 4$

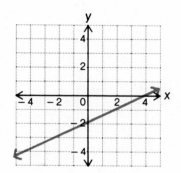

52. $x - 3y = 6$

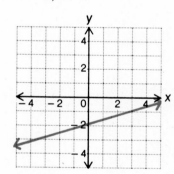

53. $y = 4$

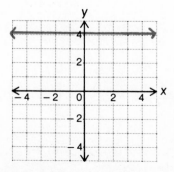

54. $x = -2$

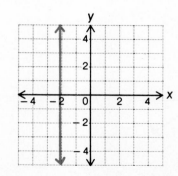

Graph.

55. $2x - 3y = 6$

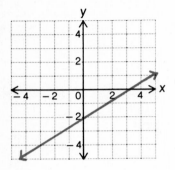

56. $3x - 2y = 8$

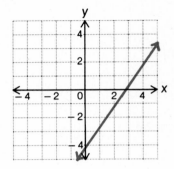

57. $2x + 5y = 10$

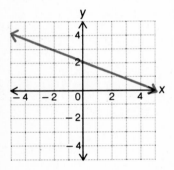

58. $3x + 4y = 12$

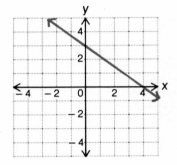

59. $x = 3$

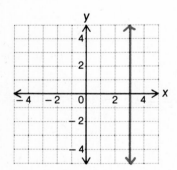

60. $y = -4$

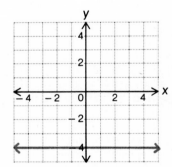

61. $2x + 3y = 3$

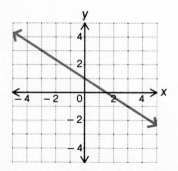

62. $4x - 3y = 12$

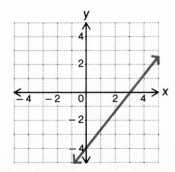

Section 2 Intercepts and Slopes of Straight Lines

Objective A   To find the *x*- and *y*-intercepts of a straight line

Reference for
Computer
Tutor™

The graph of the equation $2x + 3y = 6$ is shown at the right. The graph crosses the *x*-axis at the point (3, 0). This point is called the **x-intercept.** The graph also crosses the *y*-axis at the point (0, 2). This point is called the **y-intercept.**

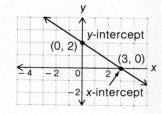

Find the *x*-intercept and the *y*-intercept of the graph of the equation $2x - 3y = 12$.

To find the *x*-intercept, let $y = 0$
(Any point on the *x*-axis has
y-coordinate 0.)

$$2x - 3y = 12$$
$$2x - 3(0) = 12$$
$$2x = 12$$
$$x = 6$$

The *x*-intercept is (6, 0).

To find the *y*-intercept, let $x = 0$
(Any point on the *y*-axis has
x-coordinate 0.)

$$2x - 3y = 12$$
$$2(0) - 3y = 12$$
$$-3y = 12$$
$$y = -4$$

The *y*-intercept is (0, -4).

Find the *y*-intercept of $y = 3x + 4$.

$$y = 3x + 4$$
Let $x = 0$ $\qquad = 3(0) + 4$
$\qquad\qquad\qquad = 4$

The *y*-intercept is (0, 4).

For any equation of the form $y = mx + b$, the *y*-intercept is (0, *b*).

Some linear equations can be graphed by finding the *x*- and *y*-intercepts and then drawing a line through the two points.

Example 1   Find the *x*- and *y*-intercepts for $x - 2y = 4$. Graph the line.

Solution

x-intercept:	*y*-intercept:
$x - 2y = 4$	$x - 2y = 4$
$x - 2(0) = 4$	$0 - 2y = 4$
$x = 4$	$-2y = 4$
	$y = -2$
(4, 0)	(0, -2)

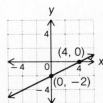

Example 2   Find the *x*- and *y*-intercepts for $4x - y = 4$. Graph the line.

Your solution

x - intercept : (1, 0)
y - intercept : (0, -4)

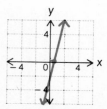

Solution on p. A53

Example 3   Find the x- and y-intercepts for $y = 2x - 4$. Graph the line.

Solution

x-intercept: y-intercept:
$y = 2x - 4$ $(0, b)$
$0 = 2x - 4$ $b = -4$
$-2x = -4$ $(0, -4)$
$x = 2$
$(2, 0)$

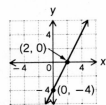

Example 4   Find the x- and y-intercepts for $y = 3x - 6$. Graph the line.

Your solution

x - intercept : (2,0)
y - intercept : (0,-6)

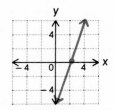

Solution on p. A53

Reference for
Computer
Tutor™

Objective B   To find the slope of a straight line

The graphs of $y = \frac{2}{3}x + 1$ and $y = 2x + 1$ are shown at the right. Each graph crosses the y-axis at the point $(0, 1)$, but the graphs have different slants. The **slope** of a line is a measure of the slant of a line. The symbol for slope is **m**.

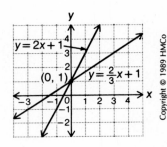

The slope of a line containing two points is the ratio of the change in the y values of the two points to the change in the x values. The line containing the points $(-2, -3)$ and $(6, 1)$ is graphed at the right. The change in the y values is the difference between the two ordinates.

Change in $y = 1 - (-3) = 4$

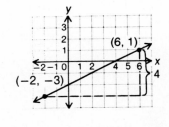

The change in the x values is the difference between the two abscissas.

Change in $x = 6 - (-2) = 8$

Slope $= m = \dfrac{\text{change in } y}{\text{change in } x} = \dfrac{4}{8} = \dfrac{1}{2}$

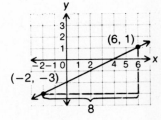

A formula for the slope of a line containing two points, P_1 and P_2, whose coordinates are (x_1, y_1) and (x_2, y_2), is given by:

Slope $= m = \dfrac{y_2 - y_1}{x_2 - x_1}$

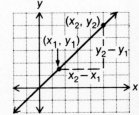

Find the slope of the line containing the points $(-1, 1)$ and $(2, 3)$.

Let $P_1 = (-1, 1)$ and $P_2 = (2, 3)$.
(It does not matter which point is
named P_1 or P_2; the slope will be
the same.)

$$m = \frac{y_2 - y_1}{x_2 - x_1} = \frac{3 - 1}{2 - (-1)} = \frac{2}{3}$$

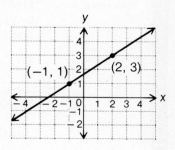

A line that slants upward to the right always has a **positive slope.**

Find the slope of the line containing the points $(-3, 4)$ and $(2, -2)$.

Let $P_1 = (-3, 4)$ and $P_2 = (2, -2)$.

$$m = \frac{y_2 - y_1}{x_2 - x_1} = \frac{-2 - 4}{2 - (-3)} = \frac{-6}{5} = -\frac{6}{5}$$

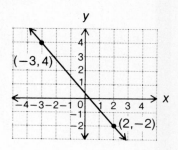

A line that slants downward to the right always has a **negative slope.**

Find the slope of the line containing the points $(-1, 3)$ and $(4, 3)$.

Let $P_1 = (-1, 3)$ and $P_2 = (4, 3)$.

$$m = \frac{y_2 - y_1}{x_2 - x_1} = \frac{3 - 3}{4 - (-1)} = \frac{0}{5} = 0$$

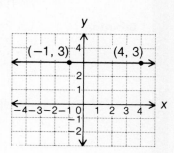

A horizontal line has **zero slope.**

Find the slope of a line containing the points $(2, -2)$ and $(2, 4)$.

Let $P_1 = (2, -2)$ and $P_2 = (2, 4)$.

$$m = \frac{y_2 - y_1}{x_2 - x_1} = \frac{4 - (-2)}{2 - 2} = \frac{6}{0}$$

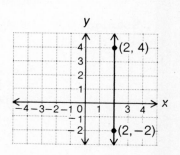

Division by zero is not defined.

A vertical line has **no slope.**

Example 5   Find the slope of the line containing the points $(-2, -1)$ and $(3, 4)$.

Solution   Let $P_1 = (-2, -1)$ and $P_2 = (3, 4)$.

$$m = \frac{y_2 - y_1}{x_2 - x_1} = \frac{4 - (-1)}{3 - (-2)} = \frac{5}{5} = 1$$

The slope is 1.

Example 6   Find the slope of the line containing the points $(-1, 2)$ and $(1, 3)$.

Your solution $\dfrac{1}{2}$

Example 7   Find the slope of the line containing the points $(-3, 1)$ and $(2, -2)$.

Solution   Let $P_1 = (-3, 1)$ and $P_2 = (2, -2)$.

$$m = \frac{y_2 - y_1}{x_2 - x_1} = \frac{-2 - 1}{2 - (-3)} = \frac{-3}{5}$$

The slope is $-\dfrac{3}{5}$.

Example 8   Find the slope of the line containing the points $(1, 2)$ and $(4, -5)$.

Your solution $-\dfrac{7}{3}$

Example 9   Find the slope of the line containing the points $(-1, 4)$ and $(-1, 0)$.

Solution   Let $P_1 = (-1, 4)$ and $P_2 = (-1, 0)$.

$$m = \frac{y_2 - y_1}{x_2 - x_1} = \frac{0 - 4}{-1 - (-1)} = \frac{-4}{0}$$

The line has no slope.

Example 10   Find the slope of the line containing the points $(2, 3)$ and $(2, 7)$.

Your solution   no slope

Example 11   Find the slope of the line containing the points $(-1, 2)$ and $(4, 2)$.

Solution   Let $P_1 = (-1, 2)$ and $P_2 = (4, 2)$.

$$m = \frac{y_2 - y_1}{x_2 - x_1} = \frac{2 - 2}{4 - (-1)} = \frac{0}{5} = 0$$

The line has zero slope.

Example 12   Find the slope of the line containing the points $(1, -3)$ and $(-5, -3)$.

Your solution   zero slope

Solutions on p. A53

Reference for
Computer
Tutor™

Objective C   ## To graph a line using the slope and y-intercept

The graph of the equation $y = \frac{2}{3}x + 1$ is shown at the right. The points $(-3, -1)$ and $(3, 3)$ are on the graph. The slope of the line is:

$$m = \frac{3 - (-1)}{3 - (-3)} = \frac{4}{6} = \frac{2}{3}$$

Note that the slope of the line has the same value as the coefficient of x.

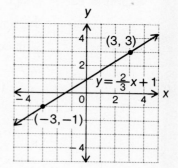

For any equation of the form $y = mx + b$, the slope of the line is m, the coefficient of x. The y-intercept is $(0, b)$. Thus, an equation of the form $y = mx + b$ is called the **slope-intercept form of a straight line.**

Find the slope and the y-intercept of the line $y = -\frac{3}{4}x + 1$.

$$y = \boxed{m}\, x + \boxed{b}$$
$$y = \boxed{-\frac{3}{4}}\, x + \boxed{1}$$

Slope $= m = -\frac{3}{4}$ ———————   ———————y-intercept $= (0, b) = (0, 1)$

The slope is $-\frac{3}{4}$. The y-intercept is $(0, 1)$.

When the equation of a straight line is in the form $y = mx + b$, the graph can be drawn using the slope and y-intercept. First locate the y-intercept. Use the slope to find a second point on the line. Then draw a line through the two points.

Graph $y = 2x - 3$.

$y = 2x + (-3)$

y-intercept $= (0, b) = (0, -3)$

$m = 2 = \frac{2}{1} = \frac{\text{change in } y}{\text{change in } x}$

Beginning at the y-intercept, move right 1 unit (change in x) and then up 2 units (change in y).

$(1, -1)$ is a second point on the graph.

Draw a line through the two points $(0, -3)$ and $(1, -1)$.

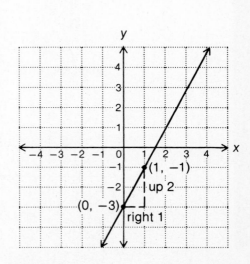

Example 13   Graph $y = -\frac{2}{3}x + 1$ by using the slope and y-intercept.

Solution y-intercept $= (0, b) = (0, 1)$

$m = -\frac{2}{3} = \frac{-2}{3}$ (Move right 3 units, then down 2 units.)

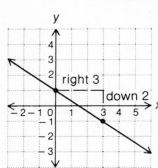

Example 14   Graph $y = -\frac{1}{4}x - 1$ by using the slope and y-intercept.

Your solution

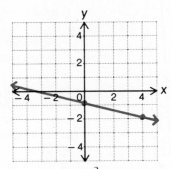

Example 15   Graph $y = -\frac{3}{4}x$ by using the slope and y-intercept.

Solution y-intercept $= (0, b) = (0, 0)$

$m = -\frac{3}{4} = \frac{-3}{4}$

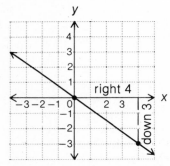

Example 16   Graph $y = -\frac{3}{5}x$ by using the slope and y-intercept.

Your solution

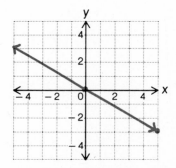

Example 17   Graph $2x - 3y = 6$ by using the slope and y-intercept.

Solution   Solve the equation for y.

$2x - 3y = 6$

$-3y = -2x + 6$

$y = \frac{2}{3}x - 2$

y-intercept $= (0, -2)$ $m = \frac{2}{3}$

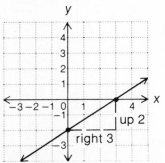

Example 18   Graph $x - 2y = 4$ by using the slope and y-intercept.

Your solution

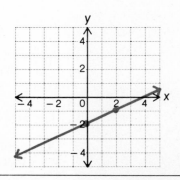

Solutions on p. A53

9.2A Exercises

Find the x- and y-intercepts.

1. $x - y = 3$

(3, 0)
(0, -3)

2. $3x + 4y = 12$

(4, 0)
(0, 3)

3. $y = 3x - 6$

(2, 0)
(0, -6)

4. $y = 2x + 10$

(-5, 0)
(0, 10)

5. $x - 5y = 10$

(10, 0)
(0, -2)

6. $3x + 2y = 12$

(4, 0)
(0, 6)

7. $y = 3x + 12$

(-4, 0)
(0, 12)

8. $y = 5x + 10$

(-2, 0)
(0, 10)

9. $2x - 3y = 0$

(0, 0)
(0, 0)

10. $3x + 4y = 0$

(0, 0)
(0, 0)

11. $y = -\frac{1}{2}x + 3$

(6, 0)
(0, 3)

12. $y = \frac{2}{3}x - 4$

(6, 0)
(0, -4)

Find the x- and y-intercepts and graph.

13. $5x + 2y = 10$ (2, 0)
(0, 5)

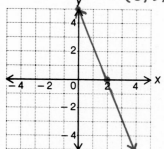

14. $x - 3y = 6$ (6, 0)
(0, -2)

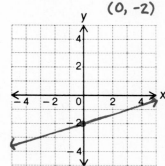

15. $y = \frac{3}{4}x - 3$ (4, 0)
(0, -3)

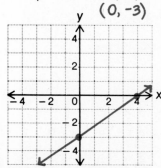

16. $y = \frac{2}{5}x - 2$ (5, 0)
(0, -2)

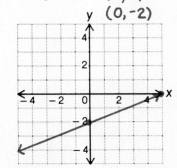

9.2B Exercises

Find the slope of the line containing the points.

17. $P_1(4, 2)$, $P_2(3, 4)$

-2

18. $P_1(2, 1)$, $P_2(3, 4)$

3

19. $P_1(-1, 3)$, $P_2(2, 4)$

$\dfrac{1}{3}$

20. $P_1(-2, 1)$, $P_2(2, 2)$

$\dfrac{1}{4}$

21. $P_1(2, 4)$, $P_2(4, -1)$

$-\dfrac{5}{2}$

22. $P_1(1, 3)$, $P_2(5, -3)$

$-\dfrac{3}{2}$

23. $P_1(-2, 3)$, $P_2(2, 1)$

$-\dfrac{1}{2}$

24. $P_1(5, -2)$, $P_2(1, 0)$

$-\dfrac{1}{2}$

25. $P_1(8, -3)$, $P_2(4, 1)$

-1

26. $P_1(0, 3)$, $P_2(2, -1)$

-2

27. $P_1(3, -4)$, $P_2(3, 5)$

no slope

28. $P_1(-1, 2)$, $P_2(-1, 3)$

no slope

29. $P_1(4, -2)$, $P_2(3, -2)$

0

30. $P_1(5, 1)$, $P_2(-2, 1)$

0

31. $P_1(0, -1)$, $P_2(3, -2)$

$-\dfrac{1}{3}$

32. $P_1(3, 0)$, $P_2(2, -1)$

1

33. $P_1(-2, 3)$, $P_2(1, 3)$

0

34. $P_1(4, -1)$, $P_2(-3, -1)$

0

35. $P_1(-2, 4)$, $P_2(-1, -1)$

-5

36. $P_1(6, -4)$, $P_2(4, -2)$

-1

37. $P_1(-2, -3)$, $P_2(-2, 1)$

no slope

38. $P_1(5, 1)$, $P_2(5, -2)$

no slope

39. $P_1(-1, 5)$, $P_2(5, 1)$

$-\dfrac{2}{3}$

40. $P_1(-1, 5)$, $P_2(7, 1)$

$-\dfrac{1}{2}$

9.2C Exercises

Graph by using the slope and y-intercept.

41. $y = 3x + 1$

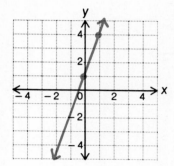

42. $y = -2x - 1$

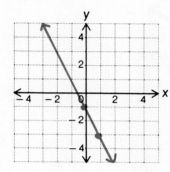

43. $y = \frac{2}{5}x - 2$

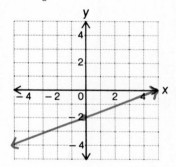

44. $y = \frac{3}{4}x + 1$

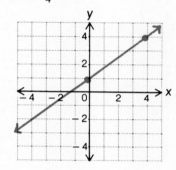

45. $2x + y = 3$

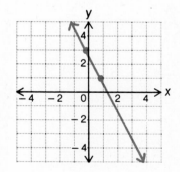

46. $3x - y = 1$

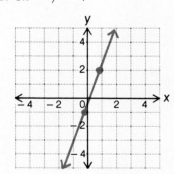

47. $x - 2y = 4$

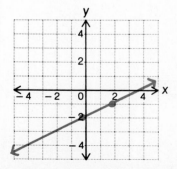

48. $x + 3y = 6$

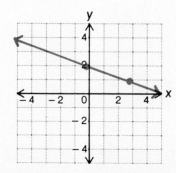

Graph by using the slope and y-intercept.

49. $y = \frac{2}{3}x$

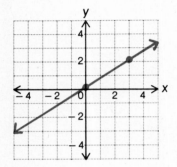

50. $y = \frac{1}{2}x$

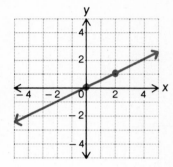

51. $y = -x + 1$

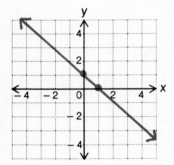

52. $y = -x - 3$

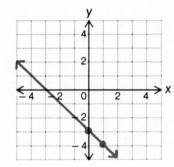

53. $3x - 4y = 12$

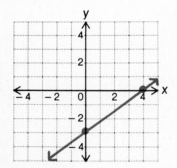

54. $5x - 2y = 10$

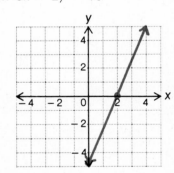

55. $y = -4x + 2$

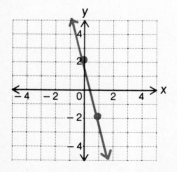

56. $4x - 5y = 20$

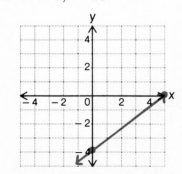

Section 3 · Equations of Straight Lines

Objective A · To find the equation of a line using the equation
$y = mx + b$

Reference for
Computer
Tutor™

When the slope of a line and a point on the line are known, the equation of the line can be written using the slope-intercept form, $y = mx + b$.

Find the equation of the line that has slope 3 and y-intercept $(0, 2)$.

$$y = mx + b$$
The given slope, 3, is m. $$y = 3x + b$$
Replace m with 3.
The given point, $(0, 2)$, is the y-intercept.
Replace b with 2. $$y = 3x + 2$$

Find the equation of the line that has slope $\frac{1}{2}$ and contains point $(-2, 4)$.

$$y = mx + b$$
The given slope, $\frac{1}{2}$, is m. $$y = \frac{1}{2}x + b$$

Replace m with $\frac{1}{2}$.

The given point, $(-2, 4)$ is a solution
of the equation of the line.
Replace x and y in the equation with $$4 = \frac{1}{2}(-2) + b$$
the coordinates of the point.

Solve for b, the y-intercept. $$4 = -1 + b$$
$$5 = b$$

Write the equation of the line by $$y = mx + b$$
replacing m and b in the equation by
their values.
$$y = \frac{1}{2}x + 5$$

Example 1 Find the equation of the line that contains the point $(3, -3)$ and has slope $\frac{2}{3}$.

Example 2 Find the equation of the line that contains the point $(4, -2)$ and has slope $\frac{3}{2}$.

Solution
$$y = \frac{2}{3}x + b$$
$$-3 = \frac{2}{3}(3) + b$$
$$-3 = 2 + b$$
$$-5 = b$$
$$y = \frac{2}{3}x - 5$$

Your solution
$$y = \frac{3}{2}x - 8$$

Solution on p. A54

| Objective B | To find the equation of a line using the point-slope formula |

An alternate method for finding the equation of a line, given the slope and a point on the line, involves use of the point-slope formula. The point-slope formula is derived from the formula for slope.

Let (x_1, y_1) be the given point on the line and (x, y) be any other point on the line.

Formula for slope
$$\frac{y - y_1}{x - x_1} = m$$

Multiply both sides of the equation by $(x - x_1)$.
$$\frac{y - y_1}{x - x_1}(x - x_1) = m(x - x_1)$$

Simplify.
$$y - y_1 = m(x - x_1)$$

The **point-slope formula** is $y - y_1 = m(x - x_1)$.
In this equation, m is the slope and (x_1, y_1) is the given point.

Find the equation of the line that passes through point $(-3, 2)$ and has slope $\frac{2}{3}$.

$(x_1, y_1) = (-3, 2)$ $m = \frac{2}{3}$ $y - y_1 = m(x - x_1)$

$$y - 2 = \frac{2}{3}[x - (-3)]$$

$$y - 2 = \frac{2}{3}(x + 3)$$

$$y - 2 = \frac{2}{3}x + 2$$

$$y = \frac{2}{3}x + 4$$

The equation of the line is $y = \frac{2}{3}x + 4$.

Example 3 Use the point-slope formula to find the equation of the line that passes through point $(-2, -1)$ and has slope $\frac{3}{2}$.

Example 4 Use the point-slope formula to find the equation of the line that passes through point $(4, -2)$ and has slope $\frac{3}{4}$.

Solution $m = \frac{3}{2}$ $(x_1, y_1) = (-2, -1)$

$$y - y_1 = m(x - x_1)$$

$$y - (-1) = \frac{3}{2}[x - (-2)]$$

$$y + 1 = \frac{3}{2}(x + 2)$$

$$y + 1 = \frac{3}{2}x + 3$$

$$y = \frac{3}{2}x + 2$$

The equation of the line is
$y = \frac{3}{2}x + 2$.

Your solution

$$y = \frac{3}{4}x - 5$$

9.3A Exercises

Use the slope-intercept form.

1. Find the equation of the line that contains the point (0, 2) and has slope 2.

$$y = 2x + 2$$

2. Find the equation of the line that contains the point (0, −1) and has slope −2.

$$y = -2x - 1$$

3. Find the equation of the line that contains the point (−1, 2) and has slope −3.

$$y = -3x - 1$$

4. Find the equation of the line that contains the point (2, −3) and has slope 3.

$$y = 3x - 9$$

5. Find the equation of the line that contains the point (3, 1) and has slope $\frac{1}{3}$.

$$y = \frac{1}{3}x$$

6. Find the equation of the line that contains the point (−2, 3) and has slope $\frac{1}{2}$.

$$y = \frac{1}{2}x + 4$$

7. Find the equation of the line that contains the point (4, −2) and has slope $\frac{3}{4}$.

$$y = \frac{3}{4}x - 5$$

8. Find the equation of the line that contains the point (2, 3) and has slope $-\frac{1}{2}$.

$$y = -\frac{1}{2}x + 4$$

9. Find the equation of the line that contains the point (5, −3) and has slope $-\frac{3}{5}$.

$$y = -\frac{3}{5}x$$

10. Find the equation of the line that contains the point (5, −1) and has slope $\frac{1}{5}$.

$$y = \frac{1}{5}x - 2$$

11. Find the equation of the line that contains the point (2, 3) and has slope $\frac{1}{4}$.

$$y = \frac{1}{4}x + \frac{5}{2}$$

12. Find the equation of the line that contains the point (−1, 2) and has slope $-\frac{1}{2}$.

$$y = -\frac{1}{2}x + \frac{3}{2}$$

13. Find the equation of the line that contains the point (3, −2) and has slope $-\frac{3}{4}$.

$$y = -\frac{3}{4}x + \frac{1}{4}$$

14. Find the equation of the line that contains the point (4, −1) and has slope $-\frac{1}{3}$.

$$y = -\frac{1}{3}x + \frac{1}{3}$$

15. Find the equation of the line that contains the point (2, −2) and has slope −1.

$$y = -x$$

16. Find the equation of the line that contains the point (5, −3) and has slope −1.

$$y = -x + 2$$

9.3B Exercises

Use the point-slope formula.

17. Find the equation of the line that passes through point $(1, -1)$ and has slope 2.

$$y = 2x - 3$$

18. Find the equation of the line that passes through point $(2, 3)$ and has slope -1.

$$y = -x + 5$$

19. Find the equation of the line that passes through point $(-2, 1)$ and has slope -2.

$$y = -2x - 3$$

20. Find the equation of the line that passes through point $(-1, -3)$ and has slope -3.

$$y = -3x - 6$$

21. Find the equation of the line that passes through point $(0, 0)$ and has slope $\frac{2}{3}$.

$$y = \frac{2}{3}x$$

22. Find the equation of the line that passes through point $(0, 0)$ and has slope $-\frac{1}{5}$.

$$y = -\frac{1}{5}x$$

23. Find the equation of the line that passes through point $(2, 3)$ and has slope $\frac{1}{2}$.

$$y = \frac{1}{2}x + 2$$

24. Find the equation of the line that passes through point $(3, -1)$ and has slope $\frac{2}{3}$.

$$y = \frac{2}{3}x - 3$$

25. Find the equation of the line that passes through point $(-4, 1)$ and has slope $-\frac{3}{4}$.

$$y = -\frac{3}{4}x - 2$$

26. Find the equation of the line that passes through point $(-5, 0)$ and has slope $-\frac{1}{5}$.

$$y = -\frac{1}{5}x - 1$$

27. Find the equation of the line that passes through point $(-2, 1)$ and has slope $\frac{3}{4}$.

$$y = \frac{3}{4}x + \frac{5}{2}$$

28. Find the equation of the line that passes through point $(3, -2)$ and has slope $\frac{1}{6}$.

$$y = \frac{1}{6}x - \frac{5}{2}$$

29. Find the equation of the line that passes through point $(4, -2)$ and has slope $-\frac{1}{2}$.

$$y = -\frac{1}{2}x$$

30. Find the equation of the line that passes through point $(5, -1)$ and has slope $-\frac{1}{3}$.

$$y = -\frac{1}{3}x + \frac{2}{3}$$

31. Find the equation of the line that passes through point $(2, -1)$ and has slope 1.

$$y = x - 3$$

32. Find the equation of the line that passes through point $(-4, 0)$ and has slope $-\frac{1}{4}$.

$$y = -\frac{1}{4}x - 1$$

Section **4**   Solving Systems of Linear Equations by Graphing

Objective A   To determine if a given ordered pair is a solution of a system of linear equations

Equations considered together are called a **system of equations.** A system of equations is shown at the right.

$$2x + y = 3$$
$$x + y = 1$$

A **solution of a system of equations** is an ordered pair that is a solution of each equation of the system.

Is $(2, -1)$ a solution of the system
$$2x + y = 3$$
$$x + y = 1?$$

$2x + y = 3$	
$2(2) + (-1)$	3
$4 + (-1)$	3
$3 = 3$	

$x + y = 1$	
$2 + (-1)$	1
$1 = 1$	

Yes, since $(2, -1)$ is a solution of each equation, it is the solution of the system of equations.

Example 1   Is $(1, -3)$ a solution of the system
$$3x + 2y = -3$$
$$x - 3y = 6?$$

Solution

$3x + 2y = -3$		$x - 3y = 6$	
$3 \cdot 1 + 2(-3)$	-3	$1 - 3(-3)$	6
$3 + (-6)$	-3	$1 - (-9)$	6
$-3 = -3$		$10 \neq 6$	

No, $(1, -3)$ is not a solution of the system of equations.

Example 2   Is $(-1, -2)$ a solution of the system
$$2x - 5y = 8$$
$$-x + 3y = -5?$$

Your solution

yes

Solution on p. A55

Objective B   To solve a system of linear equations by graphing

The solution of a system of linear equations can be found by graphing the two lines on the same coordinate system. The point of intersection of the lines is the ordered pair that is a solution of each equation of the system. It is the solution of the system of equations.

Solve by graphing: $2x + 3y = 6$
$\qquad\qquad\qquad\qquad 2x + y = -2$

Graph each line.

Find the point of intersection.

$(-3, 4)$ is a solution of each equation.

The solution is $(-3, 4)$.

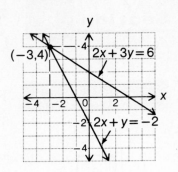

Solve by graphing: $2x - y = 1$
$\qquad\qquad\qquad\qquad 6x - 3y = 12$

Graph each line.

The lines are parallel and therefore do not intersect. The system of equations has no solution.

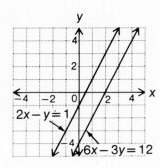

Example 3   Solve by graphing:
$\qquad\qquad\quad x - 2y = 2$
$\qquad\qquad\quad x + y = 5$

Solution

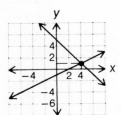

The solution is $(4, 1)$.

Example 4   Solve by graphing:
$\qquad\qquad\quad x + 3y = 3$
$\qquad\qquad\quad -x + y = 5$

Your solution

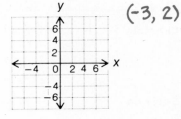

$(-3, 2)$

Example 5   Solve by graphing:
$\qquad\qquad\quad 4x - 2y = 6$
$\qquad\qquad\qquad\quad y = 2x - 3$

Solution

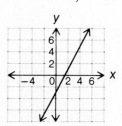

The two equations represent the same line. Any ordered pair that is a solution of one equation is also a solution of the other equation.

Example 6   Solve by graphing:
$\qquad\qquad\qquad\quad y = 3x - 1$
$\qquad\qquad\quad 6x - 2y = -6$

Your solution

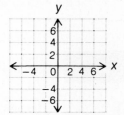

no solution

9.4A Exercises

1. Is (2, 3) a solution of the system
$$3x + 4y = 18$$
$$2x - y = 1?$$

yes

2. Is (2, −1) a solution of the system
$$x - 2y = 4$$
$$2x + y = 3?$$

yes

3. Is (1, −2) a solution of the system
$$3x - y = 5$$
$$2x + 5y = -8?$$

yes

4. Is (−1, −1) a solution of the system
$$x - 4y = 3$$
$$3x + y = 2?$$

no

5. Is (4, 3) a solution of the system
$$5x - 2y = 14$$
$$x + y = 8?$$

no

6. Is (2, 5) a solution of the system
$$3x + 2y = 16$$
$$2x - 3y = 4?$$

no

7. Is (−1, 3) a solution of the system
$$4x - y = -5$$
$$2x + 5y = 13?$$

no

8. Is (4, −1) a solution of the system
$$x - 4y = 9$$
$$2x - 3y = 11?$$

no

9. Is (0, 0) a solution of the system
$$4x + 3y = 0$$
$$2x - y = 1?$$

no

10. Is (2, 0) a solution of the system
$$3x - y = 6$$
$$x + 3y = 2?$$

yes

11. Is (2, −3) a solution of the system
$$y = 2x - 7$$
$$3x - y = 9?$$

yes

12. Is (−1, −2) a solution of the system
$$3x - 4y = 5$$
$$y = x - 1?$$

yes

13. Is (5, 2) a solution of the system
$$y = 2x - 8$$
$$y = 3x - 13?$$

yes

14. Is (−4, 3) a solution of the system
$$y = 2x + 11$$
$$y = 5x - 19?$$

no

15. Is (−2, −3) a solution of the system
$$3x - 4y = 6$$
$$2x - 7y = 17?$$

yes

16. Is (0, 0) a solution of the system
$$y = 2x$$
$$3x + 5y = 0?$$

yes

17. Is (0, −3) a solution of the system
$$4x - 3y = 9$$
$$2x + 5y = 15?$$

no

18. Is (4, 0) a solution of the system
$$2x + 3y = 8$$
$$x - 5y = 4?$$

yes

9.4B Exercises

Solve by graphing.

19. $x - y = 3$
    $x + y = 5$
    (4, 1)

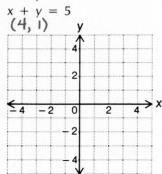

20. $2x - y = 4$
    $x + y = 5$
    (3, 2)

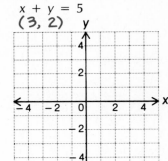

21. $x + 2y = 6$
    $x - y = 3$
    (4, 1)

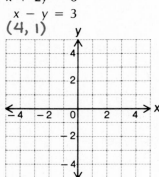

22. $3x - y = 3$
    $2x + v = 2$
    (1, 0)

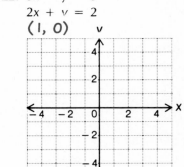

23. $3x - 2y = 6$
    $y = 3$
    (4, 3)

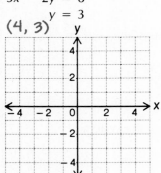

24. $x = 2$
    $3x + 2y = 4$
    (2, -1)

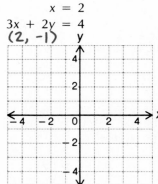

25. $x = 3$
    $y = -2$
    (3, -2)

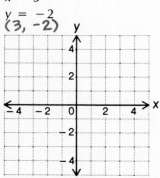

26. $x + 1 = 0$
    $y - 3 = 0$
    (-1, 3)

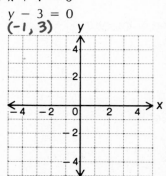

Solve by graphing.

27. $y = 2x - 6$
        $x + y = 0$
(2, -2)
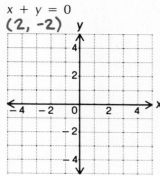

28. $5x - 2y = 11$
        $y = 2x - 5$
(1, -3)
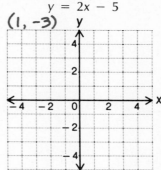

29. $2x + y = -2$
      $6x + 3y = 6$
no solution
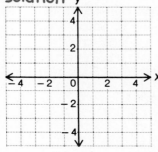

30. $x + y = 5$
        $3x + 3y = 6$
no solution
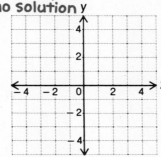

31. $4x - 2y = 4$
        $y = 2x - 2$
Any solution of one equation is a solution of the other equation.
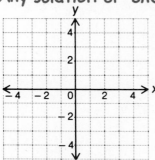

32. $2x + 6y = 6$
        $y = -\frac{1}{3}x + 1$
Any solution of one equation is a solution of the other equation.
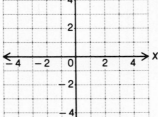

33. $x - y = 5$
      $2x - y = 6$
(1, -4)
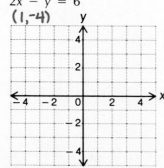

34. $5x - 2y = 10$
        $3x + 2y = 6$
(2, 0)
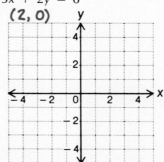

Solve by graphing.

35. $3x + 4y = 0$
    $2x - 5y = 0$
    (0, 0)

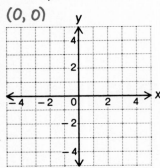

36. $2x - 3y = 0$
    $y = -\frac{1}{3}x$
    (0, 0)

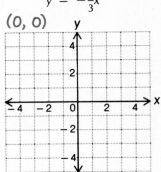

37. $x - 3y = 3$
    $2x - 6y = 12$
    no solution

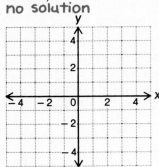

38. $4x + 6y = 12$
    $6x + 9y = 18$
    Any solution of one equation is
    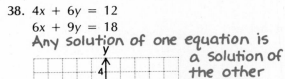 a solution of
    the other
    equation.

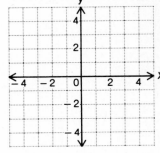

39. $3x + 2y = -4$
    $x = 2y + 4$
    (0, -2)

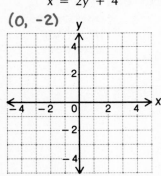

40. $5x + 2y = -14$
    $3x - 4y = 2$
    (-2, -2)

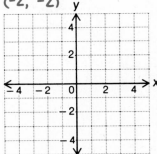

41. $4x - y = 5$
    $3x - 2y = 5$
    (1, -1)

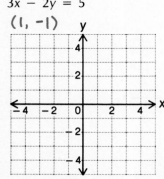

42. $2x - 3y = 9$
    $4x + 3y = -9$
    (0, -3)

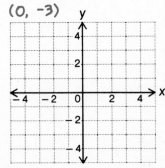

Section 5 Solving Systems of Linear Equations Algebraically

Objective A To solve a system of linear equations by the substitution method

Reference for
Computer
Tutor™

A graphical solution of a system of equations may give only an approximate solution of the system. For example, the point $\left(\frac{1}{4}, \frac{1}{2}\right)$ would be difficult to read from the graph. An algebraic method, called the **substitution method,** can be used to find an exact solution of a system.

In the system of equations at the right, equation (2) states that $y = 3x - 9$. Substitute $3x - 9$ for y in equation (1).

(1) $\quad 2x + 5y = -11$
(2) $\quad\quad\quad y = 3x - 9$

$$2x + 5(3x - 9) = -11$$

Solve for x.

$$2x + 15x - 45 = -11$$
$$17x - 45 = -11$$
$$17x = 34$$
$$x = 2$$

Substitute the value of x into equation (2) and solve for y.

(2)
$$y = 3x - 9$$
$$y = 3 \cdot 2 - 9$$
$$y = 6 - 9$$
$$y = -3$$

The solution is $(2, -3)$.

Solve: $\quad 5x + y = 4$
$\quad\quad\quad 2x - 3y = 5$

(1) $\quad 5x + y = 4$
(2) $\quad 2x - 3y = 5$

Solve equation (1) for y. Equation (1) is chosen because it is the easier equation to solve for one variable in terms of the other.

$$5x + y = 4$$
$$y = -5x + 4$$

Substitute $-5x + 4$ for y in equation (2).

$$2x - 3(-5x + 4) = 5$$

Solve for x.

$$2x + 15x - 12 = 5$$
$$17x - 12 = 5$$
$$17x = 17$$
$$x = 1$$

Substitute the value of x in equation (1) and solve for y.

$$5x + y = 4$$
$$5(1) + y = 4$$
$$5 + y = 4$$
$$y = -1$$

The solution is $(1, -1)$.

Example 1   Solve by substitution:
$$3x + 4y = -2$$
$$-x + 2y = 4$$

Solution   Solve equation (2) for x.
$$-x + 2y = 4$$
$$-x = -2y + 4$$
$$x = 2y - 4$$
Substitutite in equation (1).
$$3(2y - 4) + 4y = -2$$
$$6y - 12 + 4y = -2$$
$$10y - 12 = -2$$
$$10y = 10$$
$$y = 1$$
Substitute in equation (2).
$$-x + 2y = 4$$
$$-x + 2(1) = 4$$
$$-x + 2 = 4$$
$$-x = 2$$
$$x = -2$$

The solution is $(-2, 1)$.

Example 2   Solve by substitution:
$$7x - y = 4$$
$$3x + 2y = 9$$

Your solution

$\langle 1, 3 \rangle$

Example 3   Solve by substitution:
$$4x + 2y = 5$$
$$y = -2x + 1$$

Solution
$$4x + 2y = 5$$
$$4x + 2(-2x + 1) = 5$$
$$4x - 4x + 2 = 5$$
$$2 = 5$$

This is not a true equation. The lines are parallel and therefore do not intersect. The system does not have a solution.

Example 4   Solve by substitution:
$$3x - y = 4$$
$$y = 3x + 2$$

Your solution

no solution

Example 5   Solve by substitution:
$$6x - 2y = 4$$
$$y = 3x - 2$$

Solution
$$6x - 2y = 4$$
$$6x - 2(3x - 2) = 4$$
$$6x - 6x + 4 = 4$$
$$4 = 4$$

This is a true equation. The two equations represent the same line. Any ordered pair that is a solution of one equation is also a solution of the other equation.

Example 6   Solve by substitution:
$$y = -2x + 1$$
$$6x + 3y = 3$$

Your solution

The two equations represent the same line. Any ordered pair that is a solution of one equation is also a solution of the other equation.

Solutions on p. A56

Objective B	To solve a system of linear equations by the addition method

Another algebraic method for solving a system of equations is called the **addition method.** It is based on the Addition Property of Equations.

Note, for the system of equations at the right, the effect of adding equation (2) to equation (1). Since 2y and −2y are opposites, adding the equations results in an equation with only one variable.

$$\begin{aligned}(1)\quad & 3x + 2y = 4\\(2)\quad & 4x - 2y = 10\\& \overline{7x + 0y = 14}\\& 7x = 14\end{aligned}$$

The solution of the resulting equation is the first component of the ordered pair solution of the system.

$$\begin{aligned}7x &= 14\\x &= 2\end{aligned}$$

The second component is found by substituting the value of x into equation (1) or (2) and then solving for y. Equation (1) is used here.

$$\begin{aligned}(1)\quad 3x + 2y &= 4\\3 \cdot 2 + 2y &= 4\\6 + 2y &= 4\\2y &= -2\\y &= -1\end{aligned}$$

The solution is (2, −1).

Sometimes adding the two equations does not eliminate one of the variables. In this case, use the Multiplication Property of Equations to rewrite one or both of the equations, so that when the equations are added, one of the variables is eliminated.

To do this, first choose which variable to eliminate. The coefficients of that variable must be opposites. Multiply each equation by a constant that will produce coefficients that are opposites.

Solve: $3x + 2y = 7$
$\qquad 5x - 4y = 19$

$$\begin{aligned}(1)\quad & 3x + 2y = 7\\(2)\quad & 5x - 4y = 19\end{aligned}$$

Eliminate y. Multiply equation (1) by 2.

$$\begin{aligned}2(3x + 2y) &= 2 \cdot 7\\5x - 4y &= 19\end{aligned}$$

Now the coefficients of the y terms are opposites.

$$\begin{aligned}6x + 4y &= 14\\5x - 4y &= 19\end{aligned}$$

Add the equations.
Solve for x.

$$\begin{aligned}11x + 0y &= 33\\11x &= 33\\x &= 3\end{aligned}$$

Substitute the value of x into one of the equations and solve for y. Equation (2) is used here.

$$\begin{aligned}(2)\quad 5x - 4y &= 19\\5 \cdot 3 - 4y &= 19\\15 - 4y &= 19\\-4y &= 4\\y &= -1\end{aligned}$$

The solution is (3, −1).

Solve: $5x + 6y = 3$
       $2x - 5y = 16$

(1) $5x + 6y = 3$
(2) $2x - 5y = 16$

Eliminate x. Multiply equation (1) by 2 and equation (2) by -5. Note how the constants are selected.

$2 \cdot (5x + 6y) = 2 \cdot 3$
$-5 \cdot (2x - 5y) = -5 \cdot 16$
└──The negative is used so that the coefficients will be opposites.

Now the coefficients of the x terms are opposites.

$10x + 12y = 6$
$-10x + 25y = -80$

Add the equations.
Solve for y.

$0x + 37y = -74$
$37y = -74$
$y = -2$

Substitue the value of y into one of the equations and solve for x. Equation (1) is used here.

(1) $5x + 6y = 3$
$5x + 6(-2) = 3$
$5x - 12 = 3$
$5x = 15$
$x = 3$

The solution is $(3, -2)$.

Solve: $5x = 2y + 19$
       $3x + 4y = 1$

(1) $5x = 2y + 19$
(2) $3x + 4y = 1$

Write equation (1) in the form $Ax + By = C$.

$5x - 2y = 19$
$3x + 4y = 1$

Eliminate y. Multiply equation (1) by 2.

$2(5x - 2y) = 2 \cdot 19$
$3x + 4y = 1$

Now the coefficients of the y terms are opposites.

$10x - 4y = 38$
$3x + 4y = 1$

Add the equations.
Solve for x.

$13x + 0y = 39$
$13x = 39$
$x = 3$

Substitute the value of x into one of the equations and solve for y. Equation (1) is used here.

$5x = 2y + 19$
$5 \cdot 3 = 2y + 19$
$15 = 2y + 19$
$-4 = 2y$
$-2 = y$

The solution is $(3, -2)$.

Solve: $2x + y = 2$ (1) $2x + y = 2$
         $4x + 2y = 5$ (2) $4x + 2y = 5$

Eliminate y. Multiply equation (1) by -2.

$$-2(2x + y) = -2 \cdot 2$$
$$4x + 2y = 5$$

$$-4x - 2y = -4$$
$$4x + 2y = 5$$

Add the equations.

$$0x + 0y = 1$$
$$0 = 1$$

This is not a true equation. The lines are parallel and therefore do not intersect. The system does not have a solution.

Example 7   Solve by the addition method:
$$2x + 4y = 7$$
$$5x - 3y = -2$$

Solution   Eliminate x.

$$5(2x + 4y) = 5 \cdot 7$$
$$-2(5x - 3y) = -2 \cdot (-2)$$

$$10x + 20y = 35$$
$$-10x + 6y = 4$$

Add the equations.

$$26y = 39$$
$$y = \frac{39}{26} = \frac{3}{2}$$

Replace y in equation (1).

$$2x + 4\left(\frac{3}{2}\right) = 7$$
$$2x + 6 = 7$$
$$2x = 1$$
$$x = \frac{1}{2}$$

The solution is $\left(\frac{1}{2}, \frac{3}{2}\right)$.

Example 8   Solve by the addition method:
$$x - 2y = 1$$
$$2x + 4y = 0$$

Your solution

$$\left(\frac{1}{2}, -\frac{1}{4}\right)$$

Solution on p. A56

Example 9   Solve by the addition method:

$$6x + 9y = 15$$
$$4x + 6y = 10$$

Solution   Eliminate x.

$$4(6x + 9y) = 4 \cdot 15$$
$$-6(4x + 6y) = -6 \cdot 10$$

$$24x + 36y = 60$$
$$-24x - 36y = -60$$

Add the equations.

$$0x + 0y = 0$$
$$0 = 0$$

This is a true equation. The two equations represent the same line. Any ordered pair that is a solution of one equation is also a solution of the other equation.

Example 10   Solve by the addition method:

$$2x - 3y = 4$$
$$-4x + 6y = -8$$

Your solution

The two equations represent the same line. Any ordered pair that is a solution of one equation is also a solution of the other equation.

Example 11   Solve by the addition method:

$$2x = y + 8$$
$$3x + 2y = 5$$

Solution   Write equation (1) in the form $Ax + By = C$.

$$2x = y + 8$$
$$2x - y = 8$$

Eliminate y.

$$2(2x - y) = 2 \cdot 8$$
$$3x + 2y = 5$$

$$4x - 2y = 16$$
$$3x + 2y = 5$$

Add the equations.

$$7x = 21$$
$$x = 3$$

Replace x in equation (1).

$$2x = y + 8$$
$$2 \cdot 3 = y + 8$$
$$6 = y + 8$$
$$-2 = y$$

The solution is $(3, -2)$.

Example 12   Solve by the addition method:

$$4x + 5y = 11$$
$$3y = x + 10$$

Your solution

(-1, 3)

Solutions on p. A57

9.5A Exercises

Solve by substitution.

1. $2x + 3y = 7$
   $x = 2$

   (2, 1)

2. $y = 3$
   $3x - 2y = 6$

   (4, 3)

3. $y = x - 3$
   $x + y = 5$

   (4, 1)

4. $y = x + 2$
   $x + y = 6$

   (2, 4)

5. $x = y - 2$
   $x + 3y = 2$

   (-1, 1)

6. $x = y + 1$
   $x + 2y = 7$

   (3, 2)

7. $2x + 3y = 9$
   $y = x - 2$

   (3, 1)

8. $3x + 2y = 11$
   $y = x + 3$

   (1, 4)

9. $3x - y = 2$
   $y = 2x - 1$

   (1, 1)

10. $2x - y = -5$
    $y = x + 4$

    (-1, 3)

11. $x = 2y - 3$
    $2x - 3y = -5$

    (-1, 1)

12. $x = 3y - 1$
    $3x + 4y = 10$

    (2, 1)

13. $y = 4 - 3x$
    $3x + y = 5$

    no solution

14. $y = 2 - 3x$
    $6x + 2y = 7$

    no solution

15. $x = 3y + 3$
    $2x - 6y = 12$

    no solution

16. $x = 2 - y$
    $3x + 3y = 6$

    Any solution of one equation is a solution of the other equation.

17. $3x + 5y = -6$
    $x = 5y + 3$

    $\left(-\frac{3}{4}, -\frac{3}{4}\right)$

18. $y = 2x + 3$
    $4x - 3y = 1$

    (-5, -7)

19. $4x - 3y = -1$
    $y = 2x - 3$

    (5, 7)

20. $3x - 7y = 28$
    $x = 3 - 4y$

    (7, -1)

21. $7x + y = 14$
    $2x - 5y = -33$

    (1, 7)

Solve by substitution.

22. $3x + y = 4$
$4x - 3y = 1$

$(1, 1)$

23. $x - 4y = 9$
$2x - 3y = 11$

$\left(\frac{17}{5}, -\frac{7}{5}\right)$

24. $3x - y = 6$
$x + 3y = 2$

$(2, 0)$

25. $4x - y = -5$
$2x + 5y = 13$

$\left(-\frac{6}{11}, \frac{31}{11}\right)$

26. $3x - y = 5$
$2x + 5y = -8$

$(1, -2)$

27. $3x + 4y = 18$
$2x - y = 1$

$(2, 3)$

28. $4x + 3y = 0$
$2x - y = 0$

$(0, 0)$

29. $5x + 2y = 0$
$x - 3y = 0$

$(0, 0)$

30. $6x - 3y = 6$
$2x - y = 2$

Any solution of one equation is a solution of the other equation.

31. $3x + y = 4$
$9x + 3y = 12$

Any solution of one equation is a solution of the other equation.

32. $x - 5y = 6$
$2x - 7y = 9$

$(1, -1)$

33. $x + 7y = -5$
$2x - 3y = 5$

$\left(\frac{20}{17}, -\frac{15}{17}\right)$

34. $y = 2x + 11$
$y = 5x - 19$

$(10, 31)$

35. $y = 2x - 8$
$y = 3x - 13$

$(5, 2)$

36. $y = -4x + 2$
$y = -3x - 1$

$(3, -10)$

37. $x = 3y + 7$
$x = 2y - 1$

$(-17, -8)$

38. $x = 4y - 2$
$x = 6y + 8$

$(-22, -5)$

39. $x = 3 - 2y$
$x = 5y - 10$

$\left(-\frac{5}{7}, \frac{13}{7}\right)$

40. $y = 2x - 7$
$y = 4x + 5$

$(-6, -19)$

41. $3x - y = 11$
$2x + 5y = -4$

$(3, -2)$

42. $-x + 6y = 8$
$2x + 5y = 1$

$(-2, 1)$

9.5B Exercises

Solve by the addition method.

43. $x + y = 4$
$x - y = 6$
$(5, -1)$

44. $2x + y = 3$
$x - y = 3$
$(2, -1)$

45. $x + y = 4$
$2x + y = 5$
$(1, 3)$

46. $x - 3y = 2$
$x + 2y = -3$
$(-1, -1)$

47. $2x - y = 1$
$x + 3y = 4$
$(1, 1)$

48. $x - 2y = 4$
$3x + 4y = 2$
$(2, -1)$

49. $4x - 5y = 22$
$x + 2y = -1$
$(3, -2)$

50. $3x - y = 11$
$2x + 5y = 13$
$(4, 1)$

51. $2x - y = 1$
$4x - 2y = 2$
Any solution of one equation is a solution of the other equation.

52. $x + 3y = 2$
$3x + 9y = 6$
Any solution of one equation is a solution of the other equation.

53. $4x + 3y = 15$
$2x - 5y = 1$
$(3, 1)$

54. $3x - 7y = 13$
$6x + 5y = 7$
$(2, -1)$

55. $2x - 3y = 1$
$4x - 6y = 2$
Any solution of one equation is a solution of the other equation.

56. $2x + 4y = 6$
$3x + 6y = 9$
Any solution of one equation is a solution of the other equation.

57. $5x - 2y = -1$
$x + 3y = -5$
$\left(-\dfrac{13}{17}, -\dfrac{24}{17}\right)$

58. $4x - 3y = 1$
$8x + 5y = 13$
$(1, 1)$

59. $5x + 7y = 10$
$3x - 14y = 6$
$(2, 0)$

60. $7x + 10y = 13$
$4x + 5y = 6$
$(-1, 2)$

61. $3x - 2y = 0$
$6x + 5y = 0$
$(0, 0)$

62. $5x + 2y = 0$
$3x + 5y = 0$
$(0, 0)$

63. $2x - 3y = 16$
$3x + 4y = 7$
$(5, -2)$

Solve by the addition method.

64. $3x + 4y = 10$
$4x + 3y = 11$
$(2, 1)$

65. $5x + 3y = 7$
$2x + 5y = 1$
$\left(\dfrac{32}{19}, -\dfrac{9}{19}\right)$

66. $-2x + 7y = 9$
$3x + 2y = -1$
$(-1, 1)$

67. $7x - 2y = 13$
$5x + 3y = 27$
$(3, 4)$

68. $12x + 5y = 23$
$2x - 7y = 39$
$\left(\dfrac{178}{47}, -\dfrac{211}{47}\right)$

69. $8x - 3y = 11$
$6x - 5y = 11$
$(1, -1)$

70. $4x - 8y = 36$
$3x - 6y = 27$
Any solution of one equation is a solution of the other equation.

71. $5x + 15y = 20$
$2x + 6y = 8$
Any solution of one equation is a solution of the other equation.

72. $y = 2x - 3$
$3x + 4y = -1$
$(1, -1)$

73. $3x = 2y + 7$
$5x - 2y = 13$
$(3, 1)$

74. $2y = 4 - 9x$
$9x - y = 25$
$(2, -7)$

75. $2x + 9y = 16$
$5x = 1 - 3y$
$(-1, 2)$

76. $3x - 4 = y + 18$
$4x + 5y = -21$
$\left(\dfrac{89}{19}, -\dfrac{151}{19}\right)$

77. $2x + 3y = 7 - 2x$
$7x + 2y = 9$
$(1, 1)$

78. $5x - 3y = 3y + 4$
$4x + 3y = 11$
$(2, 1)$

79. $3x + y = 1$
$5x + y = 2$
$\left(\dfrac{1}{2}, -\dfrac{1}{2}\right)$

80. $2x - y = 1$
$2x - 5y = -1$
$\left(\dfrac{3}{4}, \dfrac{1}{2}\right)$

81. $4x + 3y = 3$
$x + 3y = 1$
$\left(\dfrac{2}{3}, \dfrac{1}{9}\right)$

82. $2x - 5y = 4$
$x + 5y = 1$
$\left(\dfrac{5}{3}, -\dfrac{2}{15}\right)$

83. $3x - 4y = 1$
$4x + 3y = 1$
$\left(\dfrac{7}{25}, -\dfrac{1}{25}\right)$

84. $2x - 7y = -17$
$3x + 5y = 17$
$\left(\dfrac{34}{31}, \dfrac{85}{31}\right)$

Calculators and Computers

The program GRAPHS OF STRAIGHT LINES on the Student Disk graphs lines of the form $y = mx + b$, where m is the slope and b is the y-intercept. After each line is drawn, you will have the option of erasing the line, drawing another line, or quitting the program.

Remember that when entering a fractional slope or y-intercept, enter it as a decimal. For example, to graph $y = \frac{3}{4}x + 2$, enter the slope $\frac{3}{4}$ as 0.75.

The program EQUATION OF A STRAIGHT LINE on the Student Disk can be used to practice finding the equation of a line. You will be asked to find the equation of a line given the slope and a point on the line. Solve the problem using paper and pencil. When you are ready, press the RETURN key and the answer will be displayed. The equation of the line is always given in the form $Ax + By = C$.

In Section 4 of Chapter 9, systems of linear equations were solved by the addition method. By using the addition method, the system of equations $\begin{array}{l} ax + by = c \\ dx + ey = f \end{array}$ can

be solved. The solution is $x = \frac{ce - bf}{ae - bd}$ and $y = \frac{af - cd}{ae - bd}$, $ae - bd \neq 0$.

Using this solution, a system of equations can be solved by using a calculator. Since the denominators for each expression are identical, the denominator is calculated first and then stored in the calculator's memory. For example:

Solve: $3x + 4y = 5$
$\qquad 2x + 5y = 8$

$a = 3, b = 4, c = 5, d = 2, e = 5, f = 8$

Calculate the denominator
$D = ae - bd$.

$3 \boxed{\times} 5 \boxed{-} \boxed{(} 4 \boxed{\times} 2 \boxed{)} \boxed{=}$

Store the result in memory.   Press $\boxed{M+}$.

Calculate x. $x = \frac{ce - bf}{D}$.

$5 \boxed{\times} 5 \boxed{-} \boxed{(} 4 \boxed{\times} 8 \boxed{)} \boxed{=} \boxed{\div} \boxed{MR} \boxed{=}$

The result in the display should be -1.

Calculate y. $y = \frac{af - cd}{D}$.

$3 \boxed{\times} 8 \boxed{-} \boxed{(} 5 \boxed{\times} 2 \boxed{)} \boxed{=} \boxed{\div} \boxed{MR} \boxed{=}$

The result in the display should be 2.

The solution of the system is $(-1, 2)$.

The keys $\boxed{M+}$ (store in memory) and $\boxed{MR}$ (recall from memory) were used for this illustration. Some calculators use the keys $\boxed{STO}$ (store in memory) and $\boxed{RCL}$ (recall from memory). If your calculator has the $\boxed{STO}$ and $\boxed{RCL}$ keys, then use them in place of the keys shown in the example above. Also, if the value of the denominator is zero, then the system is dependent and this calculator method cannot be used.

Chapter Summary

KEY WORDS

A **rectangular coordinate system** is formed by two number lines, one horizontal and one vertical, that intersect at the zero point of each line. The point of intersection is called the **origin.** The two number lines are called the **coordinate axes,** or simply **axes.** A rectangular coordinate system divides the plane into four regions called **quadrants.**

An **ordered pair** (a, b) is used to locate a point in a plane. The first number in an ordered pair measures a horizontal distance and is called the **abscissa.** The second number measures a vertical distance and is called the **ordinate.** The **coordinates** of a point are the numbers in the ordered pair associated with the point.

An equation of the form $y = mx + b$, where m and b are constants, is a **linear equation in two variables.** A **solution of an equation in two variables** is an ordered pair of numbers that makes the equation a true statement.

The **graph of an equation in two variables** is a drawing of the ordered pair solutions of the equation. For a linear equation in two variables, the graph is a straight line.

The **graph of** $y = b$ is a horizontal line passing through point $(0, b)$. The **graph of** $x = a$ is a vertical line passing through point $(a, 0)$.

The point at which a graph crosses the x-axis is called the **x-intercept.** The point at which a graph crosses the y-axis is called the **y-intercept.**

The **slope** of a line is the measure of the slant of a line. The symbol for slope is **m.** A line that slants upward to the right has a **positive slope.** A line that slants downward to the right has a **negative slope.** A horizontal line has **zero slope.** A vertical line has **no slope.**

Equations considered together are called a **system of equations.** A **solution of a system of equations** in two variables is an ordered pair that is a solution of each equation of the system.

ESSENTIAL RULES

Slope of a straight line $\text{slope} = m = \dfrac{y_2 - y_1}{x_2 - x_1}$

Slope-intercept form of a straight line $y = mx + b$

Point-slope form of a straight line $y - y_1 = m(x - x_1)$

A system of equations can be solved by   the graphing method, the substitution method, or the addition method.

Review/Test

1. Graph the ordered pairs $(-3, 1)$ and $(0, 2)$.

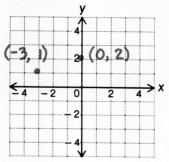

$(-3, 1)$ $(0, 2)$

2. Find the ordered pair solution of
$y = -\frac{2}{3}x + 2$ corresponding to $x = 3$.

$(3, 0)$

3. Graph $y = 3x + 1$.

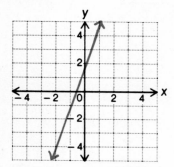

4. Graph $3x - 2y = 6$.

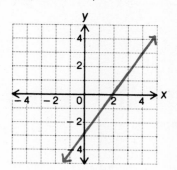

5. Find the x- and y-intercepts for $6x - 4y = 12$.

$(2, 0)$
$(0, -3)$

6. Find the slope of the line containing the points $(2, -3)$ and $(4, 1)$.

2

7. Find the equation of the line that contains the point $(0, -1)$ and has slope 3.

$y = 3x - 1$

8. Find the equation of the line that contains the point $(2, 3)$ and has slope $\frac{1}{2}$.

$y = \frac{1}{2}x + 2$

9. Graph the line that has slope $-\frac{2}{3}$ and y-intercept $(0, 4)$.

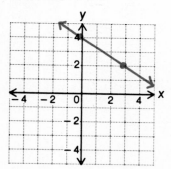

10. Solve by graphing $3x + 2y = 6$
                         $5x + 2y = 2$

$(-2, 6)$

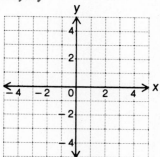

11. Is $(-2, 3)$ a solution of the equation
$2x + 5y = 11$
$x + 3y = 7$?

yes

12. Solve by substitution: $3x + 5y = 1$
                           $2x - y = 5$

$(2, -1)$

13. Solve by the addition method:
$2x - 5y = 6$
$4x + 3y = -1$

$(\frac{1}{2}, -1)$

14. Solve by the addition method:
$5x + 6y = -7$
$3x + 4y = -5$

$(1, -2)$

Cumulative Review/Test

1. Simplify $4(2 - 3x) - 5(x - 4)$.
   $-17x + 28$

3. Simplify $\frac{8.4 \times 10^9}{2.1 \times 10^6}$.

   $4 \times 10^3 = 4000$

5. Graph $y = \frac{1}{2}x - 1$.

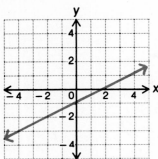

7. Write $6\frac{2}{3}\%$ as a fraction. $\frac{1}{15}$

9. Solve by substitution: $3x - 5y = -23$
   $(-6, 1)$ $x + 2y = -4$

11. Simplify $12 - 18 \div 3 \cdot (-2)^2$.
    -12

13. Find the x- and y-intercept for $2x - 3y = 12$.
    $(6, 0)$
    $(0, -4)$

15. Find the equation of the line that contains the
    point $(2, -1)$ and has slope $\frac{1}{2}$.
    $y = \frac{1}{2}x - 2$

17. Graph $2x - 3y = 6$.

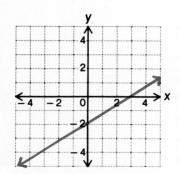

19. Simplify: $\frac{x^5y^3}{x^2 - x - 6} \cdot \frac{x^2 - 9}{x^2y^4}$

    $\frac{x^3(x + 3)}{y(x + 2)}$

21. Simplify $(-2x^2y)^3(2xy^2)^2$.
    $-32x^8y^7$

2. Factor $5x^2 + 15x + 10$.
   $5(x + 2)(x + 1)$

4. Is $(2, 0)$ a solution of the system
   $5x - 3y = 10$
   $4x + 7y = 8$?
   yes

6. Graph the line that has slope $\frac{1}{2}$ and y-intercept 2.

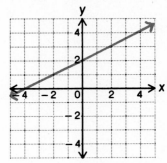

8. Solve: $2x - \frac{2}{3} = \frac{7}{3}$ $\frac{3}{2}$

10. Find the ordered pair solution of $y = 2x - 1$
    corresponding to $x = -2$.
    $(-2, -5)$

12. Solve by the addition method: $5x - 3y = 29$
    $(4, -3)$ $4x + 7y = -5$

14. Evaluate $\frac{a - b}{a^2 - c}$ when $a = -2$, $b = 3$, and
    $c = -4$. $-\frac{5}{8}$

16. Simplify $\frac{-15x^7}{5x^5}$.
    $-3x^2$

18. Solve by graphing $3x + 2y = 6$
    $3x - 2y = 6$

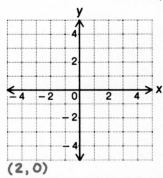

    $(2, 0)$

20. Find the slope of the line containing the points
    $(2, 3)$ and $(-2, 3)$.
    0

22. Solve: $-\frac{4}{7}x > 16$
    $x < -28$

chapter 10 Radical Expressions

Objectives

Section 1   # Addition and Subtraction of Radical Expressions

Objective A   ## To simplify numerical radical expressions

Reference for
Computer
Tutor™

A **square root** of a positive number x is a number whose square is x.

A square root of 16 is 4 since $4^2 = 16$.
A square root of 16 is -4 since $(-4)^2 = 16$.

Every positive number has two square roots, one a positive and one a negative number. The symbol "$\sqrt{}$", called a **radical,** is used to indicate the positive or **principal square root** of a number. For example, $\sqrt{16} = 4$ and $\sqrt{25} = 5$. The number under the radical sign is called the **radicand.**

When the negative square root of a number is to be found, a negative sign is placed in front of the radical. For example, $-\sqrt{16} = -4$ and $-\sqrt{25} = -5$.

The square of an integer is a **perfect square.**

$$7^2 = 49$$
$$9^2 = 81$$
$$12^2 = 144$$

An integer that is a perfect square can be written as the product of prime factors, each of which has an even exponent when expressed in exponential form.

$$49 = 7 \cdot 7 = 7^2$$
$$81 = 3 \cdot 3 \cdot 3 \cdot 3 = 3^4$$
$$144 = 2 \cdot 2 \cdot 2 \cdot 2 \cdot 3 \cdot 3 = 2^4 3^2$$

To find the square root of a perfect square written in exponential form, remove the radical sign and multiply the exponent by $\frac{1}{2}$.

Simplify $\sqrt{625}$.

Write the prime factorization of the radicand in exponential form. $\sqrt{625} = \sqrt{5^4}$

Remove the radical sign and multiply the exponent by $\frac{1}{2}$. $= 5^2$

Simplify. $= 25$

If a number is not a perfect square, its square root can only be approximated, for example, $\sqrt{2}$ and $\sqrt{7}$.

$$\sqrt{2} \approx 1.4142135\ldots$$
$$\sqrt{7} \approx 2.6457513\ldots$$

These numbers are **irrational numbers.** Their decimal representations never terminate or repeat. The rational numbers and the irrational numbers taken together are called the **real numbers.**

The approximate square roots of the positive integers up to 200 can be found in the Appendix on page A3. The square roots have been rounded to the nearest thousandth.

A radical expression is in simplest form when the radicand contains no factor that is a perfect square. The Product Property of Square Roots is used to simplify radical expressions.

> **The Product Property of Square Roots**
> If a and b are positive real numbers, then $\sqrt{ab} = \sqrt{a} \cdot \sqrt{b}$ and $\sqrt{a} \cdot \sqrt{b} = \sqrt{ab}$.

Simplify $\sqrt{96}$.

Write the prime factorization of the radicand in exponential form.

$$\sqrt{96} = \sqrt{2^5 \cdot 3}$$

Write the radicand as a product of a perfect square and factors that do not contain a perfect square.

$$= \sqrt{2^4(2 \cdot 3)}$$

Use the Product Property of Square Roots.

$$= \sqrt{2^4}\sqrt{2 \cdot 3}$$

Simplify.

$$= 2^2\sqrt{2 \cdot 3}$$
$$= 4\sqrt{6}$$

Simplify $\sqrt{-4}$.

The square root of a negative number is not a real number since the square of a real number is always non-negative.

$\sqrt{-4}$ is not a real number.

Simplify $\sqrt{125}$. Then find the decimal approximation. Round to the nearest thousandth.

Write the prime factorization of the radicand in exponential form.

$$\sqrt{125} = \sqrt{5^3}$$

Write the radicand as a product of a perfect square and factors that do not contain a perfect square.

$$= \sqrt{5^2 \cdot 5}$$

Use the Product Property of Square Roots.

$$= \sqrt{5^2}\sqrt{5}$$

Simplify.

$$= 5\sqrt{5}$$

Replace the radical expression by the decimal approximation found on page A3.

$$\approx 5(2.236)$$

Simplify.

$$\approx 11.180$$

Note that in the table on page A3, the decimal approximation of $\sqrt{125}$ is 11.180.

Example 1

Simplify $\sqrt{108}$.

Solution

$\sqrt{108} = \sqrt{2^2 \cdot 3^3} = \sqrt{2^2 \cdot 3^2 \cdot 3} = \sqrt{2^2 \cdot 3^2}\sqrt{3}$
$= 2 \cdot 3\sqrt{3} = 6\sqrt{3}$

Example 2

Simplify $\sqrt{28}$.

Your solution

$2\sqrt{7}$

Solution on p. A59

Example 3

Simplify $3\sqrt{90}$.

Solution

$3\sqrt{90} = 3\sqrt{2 \cdot 3^2 \cdot 5} = 3\sqrt{3^2(2 \cdot 5)} = $
$3\sqrt{3^2}\sqrt{2 \cdot 5} = 3 \cdot 3\sqrt{10} = 9\sqrt{10}$

Example 4

Simplify $-5\sqrt{32}$.

Your solution

$-20\sqrt{2}$

Example 5

Find the decimal approximation of $\sqrt{252}$. Use the table on page A3.

Solution

$\sqrt{252} = \sqrt{2^2 \cdot 3^2 \cdot 7} = \sqrt{2^2 \cdot 3^2}\sqrt{7} = 2 \cdot 3\sqrt{7} = $
$6\sqrt{7} \approx 6(2.646) \approx 15.876$

Example 6

Find the decimal approximation of $\sqrt{216}$. Use the table on page A3.

Your solution

14.694

Objective B   To simplify variable radical expressions

Reference for Computer Tutor™

Variable expressions that contain radicals do not always represent real numbers.

The variable expression at the right does not represent a real number when x is a negative number, for example, when x is -4.

$\sqrt{x^3}$

$\sqrt{(-4)^3} = \sqrt{-64}$ Not a real number

For this reason, the variables in this chapter will represent non-negative numbers unless otherwise stated.

A variable or a product of variables written in exponential form is a **perfect square** when each exponent is an even number.

To find the square root of a perfect square, remove the radical sign and multiply each exponent by $\frac{1}{2}$.

Simplify $\sqrt{a^6}$.

Remove the radical sign and multiply the exponent by $\frac{1}{2}$. $\sqrt{a^6} = a^3$

A variable radical expression is in simplest form when the radicand contains no factor that is a perfect square.

Simplify $\sqrt{x^7}$.

Write x^7 as the product of x and a perfect square.

$$\sqrt{x^7} = \sqrt{x^6 \cdot x}$$

Use the Product Property of Square Roots.

$$= \sqrt{x^6}\sqrt{x}$$

Simplify the perfect square.

$$= x^3\sqrt{x}$$

Simplify $3x\sqrt{8x^3y^{13}}$.

Write the prime factorization of the coefficient of the radicand in exponential form.

$$3x\sqrt{8x^3y^{13}} = 3x\sqrt{2^3x^3y^{13}}$$

Write the radicand as a product of a perfect square and factors that do not contain a perfect square.

$$= 3x\sqrt{2^2x^2y^{12}(2xy)}$$

Use the Product Property of Square Roots.

$$= 3x\sqrt{2^2x^2y^{12}}\sqrt{2xy}$$

Simplify.

$$= 3x \cdot 2xy^6\sqrt{2xy}$$
$$= 6x^2y^6\sqrt{2xy}$$

Simplify $\sqrt{25(x + 2)^2}$.

Write the prime factorization of the coefficient in exponential form.

$$\sqrt{25(x + 2)^2} = \sqrt{5^2(x + 2)^2}$$

Simplify.

$$= 5(x + 2)$$
$$= 5x + 10$$

Example 7

Simplify $\sqrt{b^{15}}$.

Solution

$$\sqrt{b^{15}} = \sqrt{b^{14} \cdot b} = \sqrt{b^{14}} \cdot \sqrt{b} = b^7\sqrt{b}$$

Example 8

Simplify $\sqrt{y^{19}}$.

Your solution

$$y^9\sqrt{y}$$

Example 9

Simplify $\sqrt{24x^5}$.

Solution

$$\sqrt{24x^5} = \sqrt{2^3 \cdot 3 \cdot x^5} = \sqrt{2^2x^4(2 \cdot 3x)} =$$
$$\sqrt{2^2 \cdot x^4}\sqrt{2 \cdot 3x} = 2x^2\sqrt{6x}$$

Example 10

Simplify $\sqrt{45b^7}$.

Your solution

$$3b^3\sqrt{5b}$$

Solutions on p. A59

Example 11

Simplify $2a\sqrt{18a^3b^{10}}$.

Solution

$2a\sqrt{18a^3b^{10}} = 2a\sqrt{2 \cdot 3^2 \cdot a^3 \cdot b^{10}} =$
$2a\sqrt{3^2a^2b^{10}(2a)} = 2a\sqrt{3^2a^2b^{10}}\sqrt{2a} =$
$2a \cdot 3 \cdot a \cdot b^5\sqrt{2a} = 6a^2b^5\sqrt{2a}$

Example 12

Simplify $3a\sqrt{28a^9b^{18}}$.

Your solution

$6a^5b^9\sqrt{7a}$

Example 13

Simplify $\sqrt{16(x + 5)^2}$.

Solution

$\sqrt{16(x + 5)^2} = \sqrt{2^4(x + 5)^2} = 2^2(x + 5) =$
$4(x + 5) = 4x + 20$

Example 14

Simplify $\sqrt{25(a + 3)^2}$.

Your solution

$5a + 15$

Example 15

Simplify $\sqrt{x^2 + 10x + 25}$.

Solution

$\sqrt{x^2 + 10x + 25} = \sqrt{(x + 5)^2} = x + 5$

Example 16

Simplify $\sqrt{x^2 + 14x + 49}$.

Your solution

$x + 7$

Solutions on p. A59

Objective C   # To add and subtract radical expressions

Reference for Computer Tutor™

The Distributive Property is used to simplify the sum or difference of radical expressions with like radicands.

$5\sqrt{2} + 3\sqrt{2} = (5 + 3)\sqrt{2} = 8\sqrt{2}$
$6\sqrt{2x} - 4\sqrt{2x} = (6 - 4)\sqrt{2x} = 2\sqrt{2x}$

Radical expressions that are in simplest form and have unlike radicands cannot be simplified by the Distributive Property.

$2\sqrt{3} + 4\sqrt{2}$ cannot be simplified by the Distributive Property.

Simplify $4\sqrt{8} - 10\sqrt{2}$.

Simplify each term.
$$4\sqrt{8} - 10\sqrt{2} = 4\sqrt{2^3} - 10\sqrt{2}$$

$$\boxed{= 4\sqrt{2^2 \cdot 2} - 10\sqrt{2}}$$ Do this step mentally.

$$= 4\sqrt{2^2}\sqrt{2} - 10\sqrt{2}$$
$$= 4 \cdot 2\sqrt{2} - 10\sqrt{2}$$
$$= 8\sqrt{2} - 10\sqrt{2}$$

Simplify the expression by using the Distributive Property.

$$\boxed{= (8 - 10)\sqrt{2}}$$ Do this step mentally.

$$= -2\sqrt{2}$$

Simplify $8\sqrt{18x} - 2\sqrt{32x}$.

Simplify each term.
$$8\sqrt{18x} - 2\sqrt{32x} = 8\sqrt{2 \cdot 3^2 x} - 2\sqrt{2^5 x}$$

$$\boxed{= 8\sqrt{3^2 \cdot 2x} - 2\sqrt{2^4 \cdot 2x}}$$ Do this step mentally.

$$= 8\sqrt{3^2}\sqrt{2x} - 2\sqrt{2^4}\sqrt{2x}$$
$$= 8 \cdot 3\sqrt{2x} - 2 \cdot 2^2\sqrt{2x}$$
$$= 24\sqrt{2x} - 8\sqrt{2x}$$

Simplify the expression by using the Distributive Property.

$$\boxed{= (24 - 8)\sqrt{2x}}$$ Do this step mentally.

$$= 16\sqrt{2x}$$

Example 17

Simplify $5\sqrt{2} - 3\sqrt{2} + 12\sqrt{2}$.

Solution

$$5\sqrt{2} - 3\sqrt{2} + 12\sqrt{2} = 14\sqrt{2}$$

Example 18

Simplify $9\sqrt{3} + 3\sqrt{3} - 18\sqrt{3}$.

Your solution

$$-6\sqrt{3}$$

Example 19

Simplify $2\sqrt{8a} + 2\sqrt{18a} - 2\sqrt{32a}$.

Solution

$$2\sqrt{8a} + 2\sqrt{18a} - 2\sqrt{32a} =$$
$$2\sqrt{2^3 a} + 2\sqrt{2 \cdot 3^2 a} - 2\sqrt{2^5 a} =$$
$$2\sqrt{2^2}\sqrt{2a} + 2\sqrt{3^2}\sqrt{2a} - 2\sqrt{2^4}\sqrt{2a} =$$
$$2 \cdot 2\sqrt{2a} + 2 \cdot 3\sqrt{2a} - 2 \cdot 2^2\sqrt{2a} =$$
$$4\sqrt{2a} + 6\sqrt{2a} - 8\sqrt{2a} = 2\sqrt{2a}$$

Example 20

Simplify $\sqrt{27b} - 2\sqrt{12b} + 7\sqrt{3b}$.

Your solution

$$6\sqrt{3b}$$

Solutions on p. A59

370 **Chapter 10 / Radical Expressions**

Example 21

Simplify $3\sqrt{12} - 5\sqrt{27}$.

Solution

$3\sqrt{12} - 5\sqrt{27} = 3\sqrt{2^2 \cdot 3} - 5\sqrt{3^3} =$
$3\sqrt{2^2}\sqrt{3} - 5\sqrt{3^2}\sqrt{3} =$
$3 \cdot 2\sqrt{3} - 5 \cdot 3\sqrt{3} = 6\sqrt{3} - 15\sqrt{3} = -9\sqrt{3}$

Example 22

Simplify $2\sqrt{50} - 5\sqrt{32}$.

Your solution

$-10\sqrt{2}$

Example 23

Simplify $3\sqrt{12x^3} - 2x\sqrt{3x}$.

Solution

$3\sqrt{12x^3} - 2x\sqrt{3x} = 3\sqrt{2^2 \cdot 3 \cdot x^3} - 2x\sqrt{3x} =$
$3\sqrt{2^2 \cdot x^2}\sqrt{3x} - 2x\sqrt{3x} =$
$3 \cdot 2 \cdot x\sqrt{3x} - 2x\sqrt{3x} =$
$6x\sqrt{3x} - 2x\sqrt{3x} =$
$4x\sqrt{3x}$

Example 24

Simplify $y\sqrt{28y} + 7\sqrt{63y^3}$.

Your solution

$23y\sqrt{7y}$

Example 25

Simplify $2x\sqrt{8y} - 3\sqrt{2x^2y} + 2\sqrt{32x^2y}$.

Solution

$2x\sqrt{8y} - 3\sqrt{2x^2y} + 2\sqrt{32x^2y} =$
$2x\sqrt{2^3y} - 3\sqrt{2x^2y} + 2\sqrt{2^5x^2y} =$
$2x\sqrt{2^2}\sqrt{2y} - 3\sqrt{x^2}\sqrt{2y} + 2\sqrt{2^4x^2}\sqrt{2y} =$
$2x \cdot 2\sqrt{2y} - 3 \cdot x\sqrt{2y} + 2 \cdot 2^2 \cdot x\sqrt{2y} =$
$4x\sqrt{2y} - 3x\sqrt{2y} + 8x\sqrt{2y} = 9x\sqrt{2y}$

Example 26

Simplify $2\sqrt{27a^5} - 4a\sqrt{12a^3} + a^2\sqrt{75a}$.

Your solution

$3a^2\sqrt{3a}$

Simplify.

1. $\sqrt{16}$
  4

2. $\sqrt{64}$
  8

3. $\sqrt{49}$
  7

4. $\sqrt{144}$
  12

5. $\sqrt{32}$
  $4\sqrt{2}$

6. $\sqrt{50}$
  $5\sqrt{2}$

7. $\sqrt{8}$
  $2\sqrt{2}$

8. $\sqrt{12}$
  $2\sqrt{3}$

9. $6\sqrt{18}$
  $18\sqrt{2}$

10. $-3\sqrt{48}$
  $-12\sqrt{3}$

11. $5\sqrt{40}$
  $10\sqrt{10}$

12. $2\sqrt{28}$
  $4\sqrt{7}$

13. $\sqrt{15}$
  $\sqrt{15}$

14. $\sqrt{21}$
  $\sqrt{21}$

15. $\sqrt{29}$
  $\sqrt{29}$

16. $\sqrt{13}$
  $\sqrt{13}$

17. $-9\sqrt{72}$
  $-54\sqrt{2}$

18. $11\sqrt{80}$
  $44\sqrt{5}$

19. $\sqrt{45}$
  $3\sqrt{5}$

20. $\sqrt{225}$
  15

21. $\sqrt{0}$
  0

22. $\sqrt{210}$
  $\sqrt{210}$

23. $6\sqrt{128}$
  $48\sqrt{2}$

24. $9\sqrt{288}$
  $108\sqrt{2}$

25. $\sqrt{105}$
  $\sqrt{105}$

26. $\sqrt{55}$
  $\sqrt{55}$

27. $\sqrt{900}$
  30

28. $\sqrt{300}$
  $10\sqrt{3}$

29. $5\sqrt{180}$
  $30\sqrt{5}$

30. $7\sqrt{98}$
  $49\sqrt{2}$

31. $\sqrt{250}$
  $5\sqrt{10}$

32. $\sqrt{120}$
  $2\sqrt{30}$

33. $\sqrt{96}$
  $4\sqrt{6}$

34. $\sqrt{160}$
  $4\sqrt{10}$

35. $\sqrt{324}$
  18

36. $\sqrt{444}$
  $2\sqrt{111}$

Find the decimal approximation. Use the table on page A3 and a calculator.

37. $\sqrt{240}$
  15.492

38. $\sqrt{300}$
  17.32

39. $\sqrt{288}$
  16.968

40. $\sqrt{600}$
  24.49

41. $\sqrt{256}$
  16

42. $\sqrt{729}$
  27

43. $\sqrt{275}$
  16.585

44. $\sqrt{450}$
  21.21

45. $\sqrt{245}$
  15.652

46. $\sqrt{525}$
  22.915

47. $\sqrt{352}$
  18.76

48. $\sqrt{363}$
  19.052

10.1B Exercises

Simplify.

49. $\sqrt{x^6}$
x^3

50. $\sqrt{x^{12}}$
x^6

51. $\sqrt{y^{15}}$
$y^7\sqrt{y}$

52. $\sqrt{y^{11}}$
$y^5\sqrt{y}$

53. $\sqrt{a^{20}}$
a^{10}

54. $\sqrt{a^{16}}$
a^8

55. $\sqrt{x^4y^4}$
x^2y^2

56. $\sqrt{x^{12}y^8}$
x^6y^4

57. $\sqrt{4x^4}$
$2x^2$

58. $\sqrt{25y^8}$
$5y^4$

59. $\sqrt{24x^2}$
$2x\sqrt{6}$

60. $\sqrt{x^3y^{15}}$
$xy^7\sqrt{xy}$

61. $\sqrt{x^3y^7}$
$xy^3\sqrt{xy}$

62. $\sqrt{a^{15}b^5}$
$a^7b^2\sqrt{ab}$

63. $\sqrt{a^3b^{11}}$
$ab^5\sqrt{ab}$

64. $\sqrt{24y^7}$
$2y^3\sqrt{6y}$

65. $\sqrt{60x^5}$
$2x^2\sqrt{15x}$

66. $\sqrt{72y^7}$
$6y^3\sqrt{2y}$

67. $\sqrt{49a^4b^8}$
$7a^2b^4$

68. $\sqrt{144x^2y^8}$
$12xy^4$

69. $\sqrt{18x^5y^7}$
$3x^2y^3\sqrt{2xy}$

70. $\sqrt{32a^5b^{15}}$
$4a^2b^7\sqrt{2ab}$

71. $\sqrt{40x^{11}y^7}$
$2x^5y^3\sqrt{10xy}$

72. $\sqrt{72x^9y^3}$
$6x^4y\sqrt{2xy}$

73. $\sqrt{80a^9b^{10}}$
$4a^4b^5\sqrt{5a}$

74. $\sqrt{96a^5b^7}$
$4a^2b^3\sqrt{6ab}$

75. $2\sqrt{16a^2b^3}$
$8ab\sqrt{b}$

76. $5\sqrt{25a^4b^7}$
$25a^2b^3\sqrt{b}$

77. $x\sqrt{x^4y^2}$
x^3y

78. $y\sqrt{x^3y^6}$
$xy^4\sqrt{x}$

79. $4\sqrt{20a^4b^7}$
$8a^2b^3\sqrt{5b}$

80. $5\sqrt{12a^3b^4}$
$10ab^2\sqrt{3a}$

81. $3x\sqrt{12x^2y^7}$
$6x^2y^3\sqrt{3y}$

82. $4y\sqrt{18x^5y^4}$
$12x^2y^3\sqrt{2x}$

83. $2x^2\sqrt{8x^2y^3}$
$4x^3y\sqrt{2y}$

84. $3y^2\sqrt{27x^4y^3}$
$9x^2y^3\sqrt{3y}$

85. $\sqrt{25(a+4)^2}$
$5a+20$

86. $\sqrt{81(x+y)^4}$
$9x^2+18xy+9y^2$

87. $\sqrt{4(x+2)^4}$
$2x^2+8x+8$

88. $\sqrt{9(x+2)^8}$
$3(x+2)^4$

89. $\sqrt{x^2+4x+4}$
$x+2$

90. $\sqrt{b^2+8b+16}$
$b+4$

91. $\sqrt{y^2+2y+1}$
$y+1$

92. $\sqrt{a^2+6a+9}$
$a+3$

10.1C Exercises

Simplify.

93. $2\sqrt{2} + \sqrt{2}$
$3\sqrt{2}$

94. $3\sqrt{5} + 8\sqrt{5}$
$11\sqrt{5}$

95. $-3\sqrt{7} + 2\sqrt{7}$
$-\sqrt{7}$

96. $4\sqrt{5} - 10\sqrt{5}$
$-6\sqrt{5}$

97. $-3\sqrt{11} - 8\sqrt{11}$
$-11\sqrt{11}$

98. $-3\sqrt{3} - 5\sqrt{3}$
$-8\sqrt{3}$

99. $2\sqrt{x} + 8\sqrt{x}$
$10\sqrt{x}$

100. $3\sqrt{y} + 2\sqrt{y}$
$5\sqrt{y}$

101. $8\sqrt{y} - 10\sqrt{y}$
$-2\sqrt{y}$

102. $-5\sqrt{2a} + 2\sqrt{2a}$
$-3\sqrt{2a}$

103. $-2\sqrt{3b} - 9\sqrt{3b}$
$-11\sqrt{3b}$

104. $-7\sqrt{5a} - 5\sqrt{5a}$
$-12\sqrt{5a}$

105. $3x\sqrt{2} - x\sqrt{2}$
$2x\sqrt{2}$

106. $2y\sqrt{3} - 9y\sqrt{3}$
$-7y\sqrt{3}$

107. $2a\sqrt{3a} - 5a\sqrt{3a}$
$-3a\sqrt{3a}$

108. $-5b\sqrt{3x} - 2b\sqrt{3x}$
$-7b\sqrt{3x}$

109. $3\sqrt{xy} - 8\sqrt{xy}$
$-5\sqrt{xy}$

110. $-4\sqrt{xy} + 6\sqrt{xy}$
$2\sqrt{xy}$

111. $\sqrt{45} + \sqrt{125}$
$8\sqrt{5}$

112. $\sqrt{32} - \sqrt{98}$
$-3\sqrt{2}$

113. $2\sqrt{2} + 3\sqrt{8}$
$8\sqrt{2}$

114. $4\sqrt{128} - 3\sqrt{32}$
$20\sqrt{2}$

115. $5\sqrt{18} - 2\sqrt{75}$
$15\sqrt{2} - 10\sqrt{3}$

116. $5\sqrt{75} - 2\sqrt{18}$
$25\sqrt{3} - 6\sqrt{2}$

117. $5\sqrt{4x} - 3\sqrt{9x}$
$\sqrt{x}$

118. $-3\sqrt{25y} + 8\sqrt{49y}$
$41\sqrt{y}$

119. $3\sqrt{3x^2} - 5\sqrt{27x^2}$
$-12x\sqrt{3}$

120. $-2\sqrt{8y^2} + 5\sqrt{32y^2}$
$16y\sqrt{2}$

121. $2x\sqrt{xy^2} - 3y\sqrt{x^2y}$
$2xy\sqrt{x} - 3xy\sqrt{y}$

122. $4a\sqrt{b^2a} - 3b\sqrt{a^2b}$
$4ab\sqrt{a} - 3ab\sqrt{b}$

123. $3x\sqrt{12x} - 5\sqrt{27x^3}$
$-9x\sqrt{3x}$

124. $2a\sqrt{50a} + 7\sqrt{32a^3}$
$38a\sqrt{2a}$

125. $4y\sqrt{8y^3} - 7\sqrt{18y^5}$
$-13y^2\sqrt{2y}$

126. $2a\sqrt{8ab^2} - 2b\sqrt{2a^3}$
$2ab\sqrt{2a}$

127. $b^2\sqrt{a^5b} + 3a^2\sqrt{ab^5}$
$4a^2b^2\sqrt{ab}$

128. $y^2\sqrt{x^5y} + x\sqrt{x^3y^5}$
$2x^2y^2\sqrt{xy}$

Simplify.

129. $4\sqrt{2} - 5\sqrt{2} + 8\sqrt{2}$

$7\sqrt{2}$

130. $3\sqrt{3} + 8\sqrt{3} - 16\sqrt{3}$

$-5\sqrt{3}$

131. $5\sqrt{x} - 8\sqrt{x} + 9\sqrt{x}$

$6\sqrt{x}$

132. $\sqrt{x} - 7\sqrt{x} + 6\sqrt{x}$

0

133. $8\sqrt{2} - 3\sqrt{y} - 8\sqrt{2}$

$-3\sqrt{y}$

134. $8\sqrt{3} - 5\sqrt{2} - 5\sqrt{3}$

$3\sqrt{3} - 5\sqrt{2}$

135. $8\sqrt{8} - 4\sqrt{32} - 9\sqrt{50}$

$-45\sqrt{2}$

136. $2\sqrt{12} - 4\sqrt{27} + \sqrt{75}$

$-3\sqrt{3}$

137. $-2\sqrt{3} + 5\sqrt{27} - 4\sqrt{45}$

$13\sqrt{3} - 12\sqrt{5}$

138. $-2\sqrt{8} - 3\sqrt{27} + 3\sqrt{50}$

$11\sqrt{2} - 9\sqrt{3}$

139. $4\sqrt{75} + 3\sqrt{48} - \sqrt{99}$

$32\sqrt{3} - 3\sqrt{11}$

140. $2\sqrt{75} - 5\sqrt{20} + 2\sqrt{45}$

$10\sqrt{3} - 4\sqrt{5}$

141. $\sqrt{25x} - \sqrt{9x} + \sqrt{16x}$

$6\sqrt{x}$

142. $\sqrt{4x} - \sqrt{100x} - \sqrt{49x}$

$-15\sqrt{x}$

143. $3\sqrt{3x} + \sqrt{27x} - 8\sqrt{75x}$

$-34\sqrt{3x}$

144. $5\sqrt{5x} + 2\sqrt{45x} - 3\sqrt{80x}$

$-\sqrt{5x}$

145. $2a\sqrt{75b} - a\sqrt{20b} + 4a\sqrt{45b}$

$10a\sqrt{3b} + 10a\sqrt{5b}$

146. $2b\sqrt{75a} - 5b\sqrt{27a} + 2b\sqrt{20a}$

$-5b\sqrt{3a} + 4b\sqrt{5a}$

147. $x\sqrt{3y^2} - 2y\sqrt{12x^2} + xy\sqrt{3}$

$-2xy\sqrt{3}$

148. $a\sqrt{27b^2} + 3b\sqrt{147a^2} - ab\sqrt{3}$

$23ab\sqrt{3}$

149. $3\sqrt{ab^3} + 4a\sqrt{ab} - 5b\sqrt{4ab}$

$-7b\sqrt{ab} + 4a\sqrt{ab}$

150. $5\sqrt{a^3b} + a\sqrt{4ab} - 3\sqrt{49a^3b}$

$-14a\sqrt{ab}$

151. $3a\sqrt{2ab^2} - \sqrt{a^2b^2} + 4b\sqrt{3a^2b}$

$3ab\sqrt{2a} - ab + 4ab\sqrt{3b}$

152. $2\sqrt{4a^2b^2} - 3a\sqrt{9ab^2} + 4b\sqrt{a^2b}$

$4ab - 9ab\sqrt{a} + 4ab\sqrt{b}$

Section 2 **Multiplication and Division of Radical Expressions**

Objective A To multiply radical expressions

Reference for
Computer
Tutor™

The Product Property of Square Roots can also be used to multiply variable radical expressions.

$$\sqrt{2x}\sqrt{3y} = \sqrt{2x \cdot 3y} = \sqrt{6xy}$$

Simplify $(\sqrt{x})^2$.

Multipy the radicands.　　　　　$(\sqrt{x})^2 = \sqrt{x}\sqrt{x}\ \boxed{= \sqrt{x \cdot x}}$　　Do this step
mentally.

Simplify.　　　　　　　　　　　　　　$= \sqrt{x^2}$
　　　　　　　　　　　　　　　　　　$= x$

Note: For $a > 0$, $(\sqrt{a})^2 = \sqrt{a^2} = a$

Simplify $\sqrt{2x^2}\sqrt{32x^5}$.

Use the Product Property of　　　$\sqrt{2x^2}\sqrt{32x^5}\ \boxed{= \sqrt{2x^2 \cdot 32x^5}}$　　Do this step
Square Roots.　　　　　　　　　　　　　　　　　　　　　　　　　　　mentally.
Multiply the radicands.
Simplify.　　　　　　　　　　　　　　　$= \sqrt{64x^7}$
　　　　　　　　　　　　　　　　　　　$= \sqrt{2^6 x^7}$
　　　　　　　　　　　　　　　　　　　$= \sqrt{2^6 x^6}\sqrt{x}$
　　　　　　　　　　　　　　　　　　　$= 2^3 x^3 \sqrt{x}$
　　　　　　　　　　　　　　　　　　　$= 8x^3 \sqrt{x}$

Simplify $\sqrt{2x}(x + \sqrt{2x})$.

Use the Distributive　　$\sqrt{2x}(x + \sqrt{2x})\ \boxed{= \sqrt{2x}(x) + \sqrt{2x}\sqrt{2x}}$　　Do this step
Property to remove　　　　　　　　　　　　　　　　　　　　　　　　　　mentally.
parentheses.

　　　　　　　　　　　　　$= x\sqrt{2x} + \sqrt{4x^2}$
　　　　　　　　　　　　　$= x\sqrt{2x} + \sqrt{2^2 x^2}$
　　　　　　　　　　　　　$= x\sqrt{2x} + 2x$

Simplify $(\sqrt{2} - 3x)(\sqrt{2} + x)$.

Use the FOIL　　　　　$(\sqrt{2} - 3x)(\sqrt{2} + x) = \sqrt{2 \cdot 2} + x\sqrt{2} - 3x\sqrt{2} - 3x^2$
method to remove　　　　　　　　　　　　　　　　$= \sqrt{2^2} + (x - 3x)\sqrt{2} - 3x^2$
parentheses.　　　　　　　　　　　　　　　　　　$= 2 - 2x\sqrt{2} - 3x^2$

The expressions $a + b$ and $a - b$, which are the sum and difference of two terms, are called **conjugates** of each other. Conjugates differ only in the sign of one of the terms.

Simplify $(2 + \sqrt{7})(2 - \sqrt{7})$.

The product of conjugates of the form　　　$(2 + \sqrt{7})(2 - \sqrt{7}) = 2^2 - \sqrt{7^2}$
$(a + b)(a - b) = a^2 - b^2$.　　　　　　　　　　　　　　　　$= 4 - 7$
　　　　　　　　　　　　　　　　　　　　　　　　　　　　$= -3$

Simplify $(3 + \sqrt{y})(3 - \sqrt{y})$.

The product of conjugates of the form　　　$(3 + \sqrt{y})(3 - \sqrt{y}) = 3^2 - \sqrt{y^2}$
$(a + b)(a - b) = a^2 - b^2$.　　　　　　　　　　　　　　　　$= 9 - y$

Example 1

Simplify $\sqrt{3x^4}\sqrt{2x^2y}\sqrt{6xy^2}$.

Solution

$\sqrt{3x^4}\sqrt{2x^2y}\sqrt{6xy^2} = \sqrt{36x^7y^3} = $
$\sqrt{2^23^2x^7y^3} = \sqrt{2^23^2x^6y^2}\sqrt{xy} = $
$2 \cdot 3x^3y\sqrt{xy} = 6x^3y\sqrt{xy}$

Example 2

Simplify $\sqrt{5a}\sqrt{15a^3b^4}\sqrt{3b^5}$.

Your solution

$15a^2b^4\sqrt{b}$

Example 3

Simplify $\sqrt{3ab}(\sqrt{3a} + \sqrt{9b})$.

Solution

$\sqrt{3ab}(\sqrt{3a} + \sqrt{9b}) = \sqrt{3^2a^2b} + \sqrt{3^3ab^2} = $
$\sqrt{3^2a^2}\sqrt{b} + \sqrt{3^2b^2}\sqrt{3a} = 3a\sqrt{b} + 3b\sqrt{3a}$

Example 4

Simplify $\sqrt{5x}(\sqrt{5x} - \sqrt{25y})$.

Your solution

$5x - 5\sqrt{5xy}$

Example 5

Simplify $(\sqrt{a} - \sqrt{b})(\sqrt{a} + \sqrt{b})$.

Solution

$(\sqrt{a} - \sqrt{b})(\sqrt{a} + \sqrt{b}) = \sqrt{a^2} - \sqrt{b^2} = a - b$

Example 6

Simplify $(2\sqrt{x} + 7)(2\sqrt{x} - 7)$.

Your solution

$4x - 49$

Example 7

Simplify $(2\sqrt{x} - \sqrt{y})(5\sqrt{x} - 2\sqrt{y})$.

Solution

$(2\sqrt{x} - \sqrt{y})(5\sqrt{x} - 2\sqrt{y}) = $
$10\sqrt{x^2} - 4\sqrt{xy} - 5\sqrt{xy} + 2\sqrt{y^2} = $
$10x - 9\sqrt{xy} + 2y$

Example 8

Simplify $(3\sqrt{x} - \sqrt{y})(5\sqrt{x} - 2\sqrt{y})$.

Your solution

$15x - 11\sqrt{xy} + 2y$

Solutions on p. A60

| Objective B | To divide radical expressions |

Reference for Computer Tutor™

The Quotient Property of Square Roots
The square root of a quotient is equal
to the quotient of the square roots.

If a and b are positive real numbers,
then $\sqrt{\dfrac{a}{b}} = \dfrac{\sqrt{a}}{\sqrt{b}}$ and $\dfrac{\sqrt{a}}{\sqrt{b}} = \sqrt{\dfrac{a}{b}}$.

Simplify $\sqrt{\dfrac{4x^2}{z^6}}$.

Rewrite the radical expression as the
quotient of the square roots.

$\sqrt{\dfrac{4x^2}{z^6}} \;\middle|\; = \dfrac{\sqrt{4x^2}}{\sqrt{z^6}}$ Do this step
mentally.

Simplify.

$= \dfrac{\sqrt{2^2x^2}}{\sqrt{z^6}} = \dfrac{2x}{z^3}$

Simplify $\sqrt{\dfrac{24x^3y^7}{3x^7y^2}}$.

Simplify the radicand.

$\sqrt{\dfrac{24x^3y^7}{3x^7y^2}} = \sqrt{\dfrac{8y^5}{x^4}}$

Rewrite the radical expression as the quotient of the square roots.

$= \dfrac{\sqrt{8y^5}}{\sqrt{x^4}}$ Do this step mentally.

Simplify.

$= \dfrac{\sqrt{2^3y^5}}{\sqrt{x^4}}$

$= \dfrac{\sqrt{2^2y^4}\sqrt{2y}}{\sqrt{x^4}}$

$= \dfrac{2y^2\sqrt{2y}}{x^2}$

Simplify $\dfrac{\sqrt{4x^2y}}{\sqrt{xy}}$.

Use the Quotient Property of Square Roots.

$\dfrac{\sqrt{4x^2y}}{\sqrt{xy}} = \sqrt{\dfrac{4x^2y}{xy}}$

Simplify the radicand.

$= \sqrt{4x}$

Simplify the radical expression.

$= \sqrt{2^2}\sqrt{x}$

$= 2\sqrt{x}$

A radical expression is not considered to be in simplest form if a radical remains in the denominator. The procedure used to remove a radical from the denominator is called **rationalizing the denominator.**

Simplify $\dfrac{2}{\sqrt{3}}$.

Multiply the expression by 1 in the form $\dfrac{\sqrt{3}}{\sqrt{3}}$

$\dfrac{2}{\sqrt{3}} = \dfrac{2}{\sqrt{3}} \cdot \dfrac{\sqrt{3}}{\sqrt{3}}$

The radicand in the denominator is a perfect square.

$= \dfrac{2\sqrt{3}}{\sqrt{3^2}}$ Do this step mentally.

Simplify.
The radical has been removed from the denominator.

$= \dfrac{2\sqrt{3}}{3}$

When the denominator is a binomial expression with a radical, multiply the numerator and denominator by the conjugate of the denominator.

Simplify $\dfrac{1}{\sqrt{y}+3}$.

Multiply the numerator and denominator by $\sqrt{y}-3$, the conjugate of $\sqrt{y}+3$.

$\dfrac{1}{\sqrt{y}+3} = \dfrac{1}{\sqrt{y}+3} \cdot \dfrac{\sqrt{y}-3}{\sqrt{y}-3}$

Simplify.

$= \dfrac{\sqrt{y}-3}{\sqrt{y^2}-3^2}$ Do this step mentally.

$= \dfrac{\sqrt{y}-3}{y-9}$

Simplify $\dfrac{\sqrt{2} + \sqrt{18y^2}}{\sqrt{2}}$.

Divide each term in the numerator by the denominator.

$$\dfrac{\sqrt{2} + \sqrt{18y^2}}{\sqrt{2}} = \dfrac{\sqrt{2}}{\sqrt{2}} + \dfrac{\sqrt{18y^2}}{\sqrt{2}}$$

Use the Quotient Property of Square Roots.

$$= 1 + \sqrt{\dfrac{18y^2}{2}}$$

Simplify.

$$= 1 + \sqrt{9y^2}$$
$$= 1 + \sqrt{3^2 y^2}$$
$$= 1 + 3y$$

Example 9

Simplify $\dfrac{\sqrt{4x^2y^5}}{\sqrt{3x^4y}}$.

Solution

$\dfrac{\sqrt{4x^2y^5}}{\sqrt{3x^4y}} = \sqrt{\dfrac{2^2x^2y^5}{3x^4y}} = \sqrt{\dfrac{2^2y^4}{3x^2}} = \dfrac{2y^2}{x\sqrt{3}} =$

$\dfrac{2y^2}{x\sqrt{3}} \cdot \dfrac{\sqrt{3}}{\sqrt{3}} = \dfrac{2y^2\sqrt{3}}{3x}$

Example 10

Simplify $\dfrac{\sqrt{15x^6y^7}}{\sqrt{3x^7y^9}}$.

Your solution

$$\dfrac{\sqrt{5x}}{xy}$$

Example 11

Simplify $\dfrac{\sqrt{2}}{\sqrt{2} - \sqrt{x}}$.

Solution

$\dfrac{\sqrt{2}}{\sqrt{2} - \sqrt{x}} = \dfrac{\sqrt{2}}{\sqrt{2} - \sqrt{x}} \cdot \dfrac{\sqrt{2} + \sqrt{x}}{\sqrt{2} + \sqrt{x}} = \dfrac{2 + \sqrt{2x}}{2 - x}$

Example 12

Simplify $\dfrac{\sqrt{y}}{\sqrt{y} + 3}$.

Your solution

$$\dfrac{y - 3\sqrt{y}}{y - 9}$$

Example 13

Simplify $\dfrac{\sqrt{20} - 2\sqrt{125}}{\sqrt{5}}$.

Solution

$\dfrac{\sqrt{20} - 2\sqrt{125}}{\sqrt{5}} = \dfrac{\sqrt{20}}{\sqrt{5}} - \dfrac{2\sqrt{125}}{\sqrt{5}} =$

$\sqrt{\dfrac{20}{5}} - 2\sqrt{\dfrac{125}{5}} = \sqrt{4} - 2\sqrt{25} =$

$\sqrt{2^2} - 2\sqrt{5^2} = 2 - 2 \cdot 5 = 2 - 10 = -8$

Example 14

Simplify $\dfrac{\sqrt{27x^3} - 3\sqrt{12x}}{\sqrt{3x}}$.

Your solution

$$3x - 6$$

10.2A Exercises

Simplify.

1. $\sqrt{5} \cdot \sqrt{5}$
   5

2. $\sqrt{11} \cdot \sqrt{11}$
   11

3. $\sqrt{3} \cdot \sqrt{12}$
   6

4. $\sqrt{2} \cdot \sqrt{8}$
   4

5. $\sqrt{x} \cdot \sqrt{x}$
   x

6. $\sqrt{y} \cdot \sqrt{y}$
   y

7. $\sqrt{xy^3} \cdot \sqrt{x^5y}$
   x^3y^2

8. $\sqrt{a^3b^5} \cdot \sqrt{ab^5}$
   a^2b^5

9. $\sqrt{3a^2b^5} \cdot \sqrt{6ab^7}$
   $3ab^6\sqrt{2a}$

10. $\sqrt{5x^3y} \cdot \sqrt{10x^2y}$
    $5x^2y\sqrt{2x}$

11. $\sqrt{6a^3b^2} \cdot \sqrt{24a^5b}$
    $12a^4b\sqrt{b}$

12. $\sqrt{8ab^5} \cdot \sqrt{12a^7b}$
    $4a^4b^3\sqrt{6}$

13. $\sqrt{2}(\sqrt{2} - \sqrt{3})$
    $2 - \sqrt{6}$

14. $3(\sqrt{12} - \sqrt{3})$
    $3\sqrt{3}$

15. $\sqrt{x}(\sqrt{x} - \sqrt{y})$
    $x - \sqrt{xy}$

16. $\sqrt{b}(\sqrt{a} - \sqrt{b})$
    $\sqrt{ab} - b$

17. $\sqrt{5}(\sqrt{10} - \sqrt{x})$
    $5\sqrt{2} - \sqrt{5x}$

18. $\sqrt{6}(\sqrt{y} - \sqrt{18})$
    $\sqrt{6y} - 6\sqrt{3}$

19. $\sqrt{8}(\sqrt{2} - \sqrt{5})$
    $4 - 2\sqrt{10}$

20. $\sqrt{10}(\sqrt{20} - \sqrt{a})$
    $10\sqrt{2} - \sqrt{10a}$

21. $(\sqrt{x} - 3)^2$
    $x - 6\sqrt{x} + 9$

22. $(2\sqrt{a} - y)^2$
    $4a - 4y\sqrt{a} + y^2$

23. $\sqrt{3a}(\sqrt{3a} - \sqrt{3b})$
    $3a - 3\sqrt{ab}$

24. $\sqrt{5x}(\sqrt{10x} - \sqrt{x})$
    $5x\sqrt{2} - x\sqrt{5}$

25. $\sqrt{2ac} \cdot \sqrt{5ab} \cdot \sqrt{10cb}$
    $10abc$

26. $\sqrt{3xy} \cdot \sqrt{6x^3y} \cdot \sqrt{2y^2}$
    $6x^2y^2$

27. $(3\sqrt{x} - 2y)(5\sqrt{x} - 4y)$
    $15x - 22y\sqrt{x} + 8y^2$

28. $(5\sqrt{x} + 2\sqrt{y})(3\sqrt{x} - \sqrt{y})$
    $15x + \sqrt{xy} - 2y$

29. $(\sqrt{x} - \sqrt{y})(\sqrt{x} + \sqrt{y})$
    $x - y$

30. $(\sqrt{3x} + y)(\sqrt{3x} - y)$
    $3x - y^2$

31. $(2\sqrt{x} + \sqrt{y})(5\sqrt{x} + 4\sqrt{y})$
    $10x + 13\sqrt{xy} + 4y$

32. $(5\sqrt{x} - 2\sqrt{y})(3\sqrt{x} - 4\sqrt{y})$
    $15x - 26\sqrt{xy} + 8y$

10.2B Exercises

Simplify.

33. $\dfrac{\sqrt{32}}{\sqrt{2}}$

4

34. $\dfrac{\sqrt{45}}{\sqrt{5}}$

3

35. $\dfrac{\sqrt{98}}{\sqrt{2}}$

7

36. $\dfrac{\sqrt{48}}{\sqrt{3}}$

4

37. $\dfrac{\sqrt{27a}}{\sqrt{3a}}$

3

38. $\dfrac{\sqrt{72x^5}}{\sqrt{2x}}$

$6x^2$

39. $\dfrac{\sqrt{15x^3y}}{\sqrt{3xy}}$

$x\sqrt{5}$

40. $\dfrac{\sqrt{40x^5y^2}}{\sqrt{5xy}}$

$2x^2\sqrt{2y}$

41. $\dfrac{\sqrt{2a^5b^4}}{\sqrt{98ab^4}}$

$\dfrac{a^2}{7}$

42. $\dfrac{\sqrt{48x^5y^2}}{\sqrt{3x^3y}}$

$4x\sqrt{y}$

43. $\dfrac{1}{\sqrt{3}}$

$\dfrac{\sqrt{3}}{3}$

44. $\dfrac{1}{\sqrt{8}}$

$\dfrac{\sqrt{2}}{4}$

45. $\dfrac{3}{\sqrt{x}}$

$\dfrac{3\sqrt{x}}{x}$

46. $\dfrac{4}{\sqrt{2x}}$

$\dfrac{2\sqrt{2x}}{x}$

47. $\dfrac{\sqrt{8x^2y}}{\sqrt{2x^4y^2}}$

$\dfrac{2\sqrt{y}}{xy}$

48. $\dfrac{\sqrt{9xy^2}}{\sqrt{27x}}$

$\dfrac{y\sqrt{3}}{3}$

49. $\dfrac{\sqrt{4x^2y}}{\sqrt{3xy^3}}$

$\dfrac{2\sqrt{3x}}{3y}$

50. $\dfrac{\sqrt{16x^3y^2}}{\sqrt{8x^3y}}$

$\sqrt{2y}$

51. $\dfrac{1}{\sqrt{2}-3}$

$-\dfrac{\sqrt{2}+3}{7}$

52. $\dfrac{5}{\sqrt{7}-3}$

$-\dfrac{5\sqrt{7}+15}{2}$

53. $\dfrac{3}{5+\sqrt{5}}$

$\dfrac{15-3\sqrt{5}}{20}$

54. $\dfrac{7}{\sqrt{2}-7}$

$-\dfrac{7\sqrt{2}+49}{47}$

55. $\dfrac{\sqrt{xy}}{\sqrt{x}-\sqrt{y}}$

$\dfrac{x\sqrt{y}+y\sqrt{x}}{x-y}$

56. $\dfrac{\sqrt{x}}{\sqrt{x}-\sqrt{y}}$

$\dfrac{x+\sqrt{xy}}{x-y}$

57. $\dfrac{3\sqrt{2}-8\sqrt{2}}{\sqrt{2}}$

-5

58. $\dfrac{5\sqrt{3}-2\sqrt{3}}{2\sqrt{3}}$

$\dfrac{3}{2}$

59. $\dfrac{2\sqrt{8}+3\sqrt{2}}{\sqrt{32}}$

$\dfrac{7}{4}$

60. $\dfrac{6x\sqrt{5}-3\sqrt{125}}{\sqrt{45}}$

$2x-5$

61. $\dfrac{3x\sqrt{x^3}-4\sqrt{x^5}}{\sqrt{x}}$

$-x^2$

62. $\dfrac{7a\sqrt{a^5}+5a^3\sqrt{a}}{\sqrt{9a}}$

$4a^3$

Section 3 Solving Equations Containing Radical Expressions

Objective A To solve an equation containing one or more radical expressions

Reference for Computer Tutor™

An equation that contains a variable expression in a radicand is a **radical equation.**

$$\sqrt{x} = 4$$
$$\sqrt{x + 2} = \sqrt{x - 7}$$ } Radical Equations

The following property of equality is used to solve radical equations.

Property of Squaring Both Sides of an Equation
If two numbers are equal, then the squares of the numbers are equal.	If a and b are real numbers and $a = b$, then $a^2 = b^2$.

Solve $\sqrt{x - 2} - 7 = 0$.

Rewrite the equation with the radical on one side of the equation and the constant on the other side.

$$\sqrt{x - 2} - 7 = 0$$
$$\sqrt{x - 2} = 7$$

Square both sides of the equation.

$$(\sqrt{x - 2})^2 = 7^2$$

Solve the resulting equation.

$$x - 2 = 49$$
$$x = 51$$

Check the solution.
When squaring both sides of an equation, the resulting equation may have a solution that is not a solution of the original equation.

Check: $\sqrt{x - 2} - 7 = 0$
$\sqrt{51 - 2} - 7 = 0$
$\sqrt{49} - 7 = 0$
$\sqrt{7^2} - 7 = 0$
$7 - 7 = 0$
$0 = 0$ A true equation

The solution is 51.

Example 1

Solve: $\sqrt{3x} + 2 = 5$

Solution

$\sqrt{3x} + 2 = 5$ Check: $\sqrt{3x} + 2 = 5$
$\sqrt{3x} = 3$ $\sqrt{3 \cdot 3} + 2 = 5$
$(\sqrt{3x})^2 = 3^2$ $\sqrt{3^2} + 2 = 5$
$3x = 9$ $3 + 2 = 5$
$x = 3$ $5 = 5$

The solution is 3.

Example 2

Solve: $\sqrt{4x} + 3 = 7$

Your solution

4

Solution on p. A60

Example 3

Solve: $0 = 3 - \sqrt{2x - 3}$

Solution

$$
\begin{aligned}
0 &= 3 - \sqrt{2x - 3} \\
-3 &= -\sqrt{2x - 3} \\
(-3)^2 &= (-\sqrt{2x - 3})^2 \\
9 &= 2x - 3 \\
12 &= 2x \\
6 &= x
\end{aligned}
$$

Check:
$$
\begin{aligned}
0 &= 3 - \sqrt{2x - 3} \\
0 &= 3 - \sqrt{2 \cdot 6 - 3} \\
0 &= 3 - \sqrt{12 - 3} \\
0 &= 3 - \sqrt{9} \\
0 &= 3 - \sqrt{3^2} \\
0 &= 3 - 3 \\
0 &= 0
\end{aligned}
$$

The solution is 6.

Example 4

Solve: $\sqrt{3x - 2} - 5 = 0$

Your solution

9

Example 5

Solve: $\sqrt{2x + 1} = \sqrt{3x - 4}$

Solution

$$
\begin{aligned}
\sqrt{2x + 1} &= \sqrt{3x - 4} \\
(\sqrt{2x + 1})^2 &= (\sqrt{3x - 4})^2 \\
2x + 1 &= 3x - 4 \\
2x &= 3x - 5 \\
-x &= -5 \\
x &= 5
\end{aligned}
$$

Check:
$$
\begin{aligned}
\sqrt{2x + 1} &= \sqrt{3x - 4} \\
\sqrt{2 \cdot 5 + 1} &= \sqrt{3 \cdot 5 - 4} \\
\sqrt{10 + 1} &= \sqrt{15 - 4} \\
\sqrt{11} &= \sqrt{11}
\end{aligned}
$$

The solution is 5.

Example 6

Solve: $\sqrt{4x + 3} = \sqrt{x + 12}$

Your solution

3

Solutions on pp. A60–A61

10.3A Exercises

Solve and check.

1. $\sqrt{x} = 5$
   25

2. $\sqrt{y} = 7$
   49

3. $\sqrt{a} = 12$
   144

4. $\sqrt{a} = 9$
   81

5. $\sqrt{b} = -8$
   no solution

6. $\sqrt{y} = -6$
   no solution

7. $\sqrt{5x} = 5$
   5

8. $\sqrt{3x} = 4$
   $\frac{16}{3}$

9. $\sqrt{4x} = 8$
   16

10. $\sqrt{6x} = 3$
    $\frac{3}{2}$

11. $\sqrt{2x} - 4 = 0$
    8

12. $3 - \sqrt{5x} = 0$
    $\frac{9}{5}$

13. $\sqrt{4x} + 5 = 2$
    no solution

14. $\sqrt{3x} + 9 = 4$
    no solution

15. $\sqrt{3x} - 6 = 0$
    12

16. $8 - \sqrt{4x} = 0$
    16

17. $\sqrt{2x} + 7 = 8$
    $\frac{1}{2}$

18. $6 + \sqrt{3x} = 18$
    48

19. $\sqrt{3x - 2} = 4$
    6

20. $\sqrt{5x + 6} = 1$
    -1

21. $\sqrt{2x + 1} = 7$
    24

22. $\sqrt{5x + 4} = 3$
    1

23. $\sqrt{3x + 3} = 3$
    2

24. $3 = \sqrt{5 - 2x}$
    -2

25. $\sqrt{12 - x} = 4$
    -4

26. $\sqrt{4x + 8} = 2$
    -1

27. $0 = 2 - \sqrt{3 - x}$
    -1

28. $0 = 5 - \sqrt{10 + x}$
    15

29. $0 = 4 - \sqrt{7x + 2}$
    2

30. $0 = 3 - \sqrt{4x + 1}$
    2

31. $\sqrt{5x + 2} = 0$
    $-\frac{2}{5}$

32. $\sqrt{3x - 7} = 0$
    $\frac{7}{3}$

33. $\sqrt{4x + 9} = 0$
    $-\frac{9}{4}$

Solve and check.

34. $\sqrt{6x - 8} = 0$
$\dfrac{4}{3}$

35. $\sqrt{3x} - 6 = -4$
$\dfrac{4}{3}$

36. $\sqrt{5x} + 8 = 23$
45

37. $\sqrt{4x} - 9 = 1$
25

38. $\sqrt{2x} + 5 = 11$
18

39. $\sqrt{6x} + 7 = 2$
no solution

40. $\sqrt{3x} + 8 = 4$
no solution

41. $8 - \sqrt{5x} = 3$
5

42. $6 - \sqrt{9x} = 6$
0

43. $0 = \sqrt{3x - 9} - 6$
15

44. $0 = \sqrt{2x + 7} - 3$
1

45. $\sqrt{2x} = \sqrt{3x - 4}$
4

46. $\sqrt{3x} = \sqrt{2x + 5}$
5

47. $\sqrt{5x - 1} = \sqrt{3x + 9}$
5

48. $\sqrt{3x + 4} = \sqrt{12x - 14}$
2

49. $\sqrt{5x - 3} = \sqrt{4x - 2}$
1

50. $\sqrt{5x - 9} = \sqrt{2x - 3}$
2

51. $\sqrt{3x + 2} = \sqrt{5x - 8}$
5

52. $\sqrt{4 - 3x} = \sqrt{8 - 2x}$
-4

53. $\sqrt{5 - 2x} = \sqrt{6 - 5x}$
$\dfrac{1}{3}$

54. $\sqrt{3 - 7x} = \sqrt{6 - 4x}$
-1

55. $\sqrt{3x - 5} - \sqrt{x + 7} = 0$
6

56. $\sqrt{2x + 8} - \sqrt{6x + 8} = 0$
0

57. $\sqrt{4x - 3} - \sqrt{2x + 5} = 0$
4

58. $\sqrt{5x + 1} - \sqrt{3x + 7} = 0$
3

59. $\sqrt{x^2 - 5x + 6} = \sqrt{x^2 - 8x + 9}$
1

60. $\sqrt{x^2 - 4x + 4} = \sqrt{x^2 - 6x + 8}$
2

61. $\sqrt{x^2 + 3x - 3} = \sqrt{x^2 - x + 2}$
$\dfrac{5}{4}$

62. $\sqrt{x^2 - 2x + 4} = \sqrt{x^2 + 5x - 12}$
$\dfrac{16}{7}$

Calculators and Computers

The square root of a perfect square can be found using the $\boxed{\sqrt{x}}$ key on a calculator. For example, to find

$$\sqrt{7225}$$

using a calculator, enter 7225 and press the $\boxed{\sqrt{x}}$ key. The display should read 85.

If a number is not a perfect square, its square root can be approximated using a calculator. On page 365, the decimal approximation of $\sqrt{125}$ was found to be 11.180, rounded to the nearest thousandth. To calculate

$$\sqrt{125}$$

using a calculator, enter 125 and press the $\boxed{\sqrt{x}}$ key. The display should read 11.18034.

If the $\boxed{\sqrt{x}}$ key is pressed when a negative number is in the display, an error message will appear in the display of the calculator. For example, enter 4 and press $\boxed{+/-}$ $\boxed{\sqrt{x}}$. The error message appears because $\sqrt{-4}$ is not a real number.

Use your calculator to simplify the numerical radical expressions given at the bottom of this page.

Chapter 10 presents simplification of numerical and variable radical expressions. As shown above, a calculator can be used to find the square root of a perfect square or to approximate the square root of a number that is not a perfect square. A computer program can be used to simplify variable radical expressions. One such program is on the Student Disk.

The program RADICAL EXPRESSIONS on the Student Disk will allow you to practice simplifying radical expressions. The program will display a radical expression. Then, using pencil and paper, simplify the expression. When you are finished, press the RETURN key. The correct solution will be displayed on the screen.

After you complete a problem, you have the opportunity to continue to practice or to quit the program. Press the letter "C" to continue or the letter "Q" to quit.

Simplify. Round to the nearest thousandth.

1. $\sqrt{234}$ 2. $\sqrt{296}$ 3. $\sqrt{348}$ 4. $\sqrt{410}$

5. $\sqrt{573}$ 6. $\sqrt{625}$ 7. $\sqrt{1444}$ 8. $\sqrt{1700}$

ANSWERS: **1.** 15.297 **2.** 17.205 **3.** 18.655 **4.** 20.248 **5.** 23.937 **6.** 25 **7.** 38 **8.** 41.231

Chapter Summary

KEY WORDS

A **square root** of a positive number x is a number whose square is x. Every positive number has two square roots, one a positive and one a negative number. The **principal square root** of a number is the positive square root of the number.

The symbol "$\sqrt{\ }$" is called a **radical** and is used to indicate the principal square root of a number. The **radicand** is the number under the radical sign.

A number that is the square of an integer is a **perfect square.**

A variable or a product of variables written in exponential notation is a **perfect square** when each exponent is an even number.

If a number is not a perfect square, its square root can only be approximated. These numbers are **irrational numbers.** Their decimal representations never terminate or repeat.

Conjugates are binomial expressions that differ only in the sign of the second term. The expressions $a + b$ and $a - b$ are conjugates.

Rationalizing the denominator is the procedure used to remove a radical from the denominator of a fraction.

A **radical equation** is an equation that contains a variable expression in a radicand.

ESSENTIAL RULES

The Product Property of Square Roots

If a and b are positive real numbers, then $\sqrt{ab} = \sqrt{a} \cdot \sqrt{b}$ and $\sqrt{a} \cdot \sqrt{b} = \sqrt{ab}$.

The Quotient Property of Square Roots

If a and b are positive real numbers, then $\sqrt{\dfrac{a}{b}} = \dfrac{\sqrt{a}}{\sqrt{b}}$ and $\dfrac{\sqrt{a}}{\sqrt{b}} = \sqrt{\dfrac{a}{b}}$.

Property of Squaring Both Sides of an Equation

If a and b are real numbers and $a = b$, then $a^2 = b^2$.

Review/Test

1. Simplify $\sqrt{45}$.
$3\sqrt{5}$

2. Simplify $\sqrt{75}$.
$5\sqrt{3}$

3. Simplify $-2\sqrt{80}$.
$-8\sqrt{5}$

4. Find the decimal representation of $\sqrt{175}$. Use the table on page A3.
13.230

5. Simplify $\sqrt{121x^8y^2}$.
$11x^4y$

6. Simplify $\sqrt{72x^7y^2}$.
$6x^3y\sqrt{2x}$

7. Simplify $\sqrt{32a^5b^{11}}$.
$4a^2b^5\sqrt{2ab}$

8. Simplify $\sqrt{x^2 + 4x + 4}$.
$x + 2$

9. Simplify $8\sqrt{y} - 3\sqrt{y}$.
$5\sqrt{y}$

10. Simplify $5\sqrt{8} - 3\sqrt{50}$.
$-5\sqrt{2}$

11. Simplify $3\sqrt{8y} - 2\sqrt{72x} + 5\sqrt{18y}$.
$21\sqrt{2y} - 12\sqrt{2x}$

12. Simplify $2x\sqrt{3xy^3} - 2y\sqrt{12x^3y} - 3xy\sqrt{xy}$.
$-2xy\sqrt{3xy} - 3xy\sqrt{xy}$

13. Simplify $\sqrt{8x^3y}\sqrt{10xy^4}$.
$4x^2y^2\sqrt{5y}$

14. Simplify $\sqrt{3x^2y}\sqrt{6xy^2}\sqrt{2x}$.
$6x^2y\sqrt{y}$

15. Simplify $\sqrt{a}(\sqrt{a} - \sqrt{b})$.
$a - \sqrt{ab}$

16. Simplify $(\sqrt{y} - 3)(\sqrt{y} + 5)$.
$y + 2\sqrt{y} - 15$

17. Simplify $\frac{\sqrt{162}}{\sqrt{2}}$.
9

18. Simplify $\frac{\sqrt{98a^6b^4}}{\sqrt{2a^3b^2}}$.
$7ab\sqrt{a}$

19. Simplify $\frac{2}{\sqrt{3} - 1}$.
$\sqrt{3} + 1$

20. Simplify $\frac{3\sqrt{x^3} - 4\sqrt{9x}}{3\sqrt{x}}$.
$x - 4$

21. Solve: $\sqrt{5x - 6} = 7$
11

22. Solve: $\sqrt{9x} + 3 = 18$
25

23. Solve: $\sqrt{5x} = \sqrt{2x + 9}$
3

24. Solve: $\sqrt{8x - 3} = \sqrt{4x + 5}$
2

Cumulative Review/Test

1. Solve: $3(x - 7) \geq 5x - 12$

   $x \leq -\dfrac{9}{2}$

2. Simplify: $\dfrac{\sqrt{320}}{\sqrt{5}}$

   8

3. Simplify: $2a\sqrt{2ab^3} + b\sqrt{8a^3b} - 5ab\sqrt{ab}$

   $4ab\sqrt{2ab} - 5ab\sqrt{ab}$

4. Solve by substitution: $4x - 3y = 1$
   $2x + y = 3$

   $(1, 1)$

5. Find the equation of the line that contains the point $(-2, -3)$ and has slope $\frac{1}{2}$.

   $y = \frac{1}{2}x - 2$

6. Simplify: $\left(\frac{2}{3}\right)^2 \cdot \left(\frac{3}{4} - \frac{3}{2}\right) + \left(\frac{1}{2}\right)^2$

   $-\dfrac{1}{12}$

7. Simplify: $\dfrac{3}{2 - \sqrt{5}}$

   $-6 - 3\sqrt{5}$

8. Simplify: $\sqrt{108}$

   $6\sqrt{3}$

9. Factor $2a^3 - 16a^2 + 30a$.

   $2a(a - 5)(a - 3)$

10. Solve: $\sqrt{3x - 2} - 4 = 0$

    6

11. Simplify: $\dfrac{3x^3 - 6x^2}{4x^2 + 4x} \cdot \dfrac{3x - 9}{9x^3 - 45x^2 + 54x}$

    $\dfrac{1}{4(x+1)}$

12. Simplify: $\dfrac{x + 2}{x - 4} - \dfrac{6}{x^2 - 7x + 12}$

    $\dfrac{x + 3}{x - 3}$

13. Simplify: $3\sqrt{32} - 2\sqrt{128}$

    $-4\sqrt{2}$

14. Solve: $\dfrac{x}{2x - 5} - 2 = \dfrac{3x}{2x - 5}$

    $\dfrac{5}{3}$

15. Simplify: $(-3x^2y)(-2x^3y^4)$

    $6x^5y^5$

16. Simplify: $\sqrt{3}(\sqrt{6} - \sqrt{x^2})$

    $3\sqrt{2} - x\sqrt{3}$

17. Factor $12x^3y^2 - 9x^2y^3$.

    $3x^2y^2(4x - 3y)$

18. Solve: $2x - 4[3x - 2(1 - 3x)] = 2(3 - 4x)$

    $\dfrac{1}{13}$

19. Simplify: $\sqrt{2a^9b}\sqrt{98ab^3}\sqrt{2a}$

    $14a^5b^2\sqrt{2a}$

20. 28% of what number is 210?

    750

21. In a lake, 100 fish are caught, tagged, and then released. Later 150 fish are caught. Three of the fish are found to have tags. Estimate the number of fish in the lake.

    5000 fish

22. Three-fifths of a number is less than negative fifteen. Find the largest integer that will satisfy the inequality.

    -26

23. A small water pipe takes twice as long to fill a tank as does a larger water pipe. With both pipes open, it takes 16 hours to fill the tank. Find the time it would take the small pipe working alone to fill the tank.

    48 hours

24. How many ounces of pure water must be added to 40 oz of a 12% salt solution to make a salt solution that is 5% salt?

    56 oz

chapter 11

Quadratic Equations

Objectives

11.1A To solve a quadratic equation by factoring

11.1B To solve a quadratic equation by taking square roots

11.2A To solve a quadratic equation by completing the square

11.3A To solve a quadratic equation by using the quadratic formula

Section 1 Solving Quadratic Equations by Factoring or by Taking Square Roots

Objective A   To solve a quadratic equation by factoring

Reference for
Computer
Tutor™

An equation of the form $ax^2 + bx + c = 0$, where a, b, and c are constants and $a \neq 0$, is a **quadratic equation.**

$4x^2 - 3x + 1 = 0$, $a = 4$, $b = -3$, $c = 1$
$3x^2 - 4 = 0$, $a = 3$, $b = 0$, $c = -4$

A quadratic equation is also called a **second-degree equation.**

A quadratic equation is in **standard form** when the polynomial is in descending order and equal to zero.

Quadratic equations sometimes can be solved by using the Principle of Zero Products.

> **The Principle of Zero Products**
> If the product of two factors is zero, then at least one of the factors must be zero.
>
> If $ab = 0$, then $a = 0$ or $b = 0$.

Solve: $(x - 3)(x + 5) = 0$

	$(x - 3)(x + 5) = 0$
Use the Principle of Zero Products. Let each factor equal zero.	$x - 3 = 0 \qquad x + 5 = 0$
Rewrite each equation in the form *variable = constant*.	$x = 3 \qquad\qquad x = -5$
Write the solutions.	The solutions are 3 and -5.

Solve by factoring: $2x^2 - x = 1$

	$2x^2 - x = 1$
Write the equation in standard form.	$2x^2 - x - 1 = 0$
Factor.	$(2x + 1)(x - 1) = 0$
Let each factor equal zero.	$2x + 1 = 0 \qquad x - 1 = 0$
Rewrite each equation in the form *variable = constant*.	$2x = -1 \qquad\qquad x = 1$
	$x = -\dfrac{1}{2}$
Write the solutions.	The solutions are $-\dfrac{1}{2}$ and 1.

Check:

$$2x^2 - x = 1 \qquad\qquad 2x^2 - x = 1$$
$$2\left(-\tfrac{1}{2}\right)^2 - \left(-\tfrac{1}{2}\right) = 1 \qquad 2(1)^2 - 1 = 1$$
$$2 \cdot \tfrac{1}{4} + \tfrac{1}{2} = 1 \qquad 2 \cdot 1 - 1 = 1$$
$$\tfrac{1}{2} + \tfrac{1}{2} = 1 \qquad\qquad 2 - 1 = 1$$
$$1 = 1 \qquad\qquad\qquad 1 = 1$$

Example 1   Solve by factoring:
$x^2 + 10x + 25 = 0$

Solution
$x^2 + 10x + 25 = 0$
$(x + 5)(x + 5) = 0$
$x + 5 = 0 \qquad x + 5 = 0$
$\quad x = -5 \qquad \quad x = -5$

-5 is a double root of the equation.

The solution is -5.

Example 2   Solve by factoring:
$x^2 + 2x - 8 = 0$

Your solution

-4 and 2

Example 3   Solve by factoring:
$4x^2 = (x + 1)(x + 6)$

Solution
$$4x^2 = (x + 1)(x + 6)$$
$$4x^2 = x^2 + 7x + 6$$
$$3x^2 - 7x - 6 = 0$$
$$(3x + 2)(x - 3) = 0$$

$3x + 2 = 0 \qquad x - 3 = 0$
$\quad 3x = -2 \qquad \quad x = 3$
$\quad\; x = -\dfrac{2}{3}$

The solutions are $-\dfrac{2}{3}$ and 3.

Example 4   Solve by factoring:
$2x^2 = (x + 2)(x + 3)$

Your solution

-1 and 6

Solutions on p. A62

Objective B   To solve a quadratic equation by taking square roots

Reference for Computer Tutor™

The quadratic equation $x^2 = 25$ can be read "the square of a number equals 25." The solution is the positive or the negative square root of 25, 5 or -5.

$$\begin{array}{c|c} x^2 & = 25 \\ \hline 5^2 & 25 \\ 25 & = 25 \end{array} \qquad \begin{array}{c|c} x^2 & = 25 \\ \hline (-5)^2 & 25 \\ 25 & = 25 \end{array}$$
5 is a solution. -5 is a solution.

The solution can be found by taking the square root of each side of the equation and writing the positive and the negative square roots of the number.
$x = \pm 5$ means $x = 5$ or $x = -5$.

$$x^2 = 25$$
$$\sqrt{x^2} = \sqrt{25}$$
$$x = \pm\sqrt{25} = \pm 5$$
The solutions are 5 and -5.

Solve by taking square roots: $3x^2 = 36$

$$3x^2 = 36$$

Solve for x^2.

$$x^2 = 12$$

Take the square root of each side of the equation.

$$\sqrt{x^2} = \sqrt{12}$$

Simplify.

$$x = \pm\sqrt{12} = \pm 2\sqrt{3}$$

Write the solutions.

The solutions are $2\sqrt{3}$ and $-2\sqrt{3}$.

Check:

$3x^2 = 36$	$3x^2 = 36$
$3(2\sqrt{3})^2 = 36$	$3(-2\sqrt{3})^2 = 36$
$3(12) = 36$	$3(12) = 36$
$36 = 36$	$36 = 36$

An equation containing the square of a binomial can be solved by taking square roots.

Solve by taking square roots: $2(x - 1)^2 - 36 = 0$

$$2(x - 1)^2 - 36 = 0$$

Solve for $(x - 1)^2$.

$$2(x - 1)^2 = 36$$
$$(x - 1)^2 = 18$$

Take the square root of each side of the equation.

$$\sqrt{(x - 1)^2} = \sqrt{18}$$

Simplify.

$$x - 1 = \pm\sqrt{18} = \pm 3\sqrt{2}$$

Solve for x.

$$x - 1 = 3\sqrt{2} \qquad x - 1 = -3\sqrt{2}$$
$$x = 1 + 3\sqrt{2} \qquad x = 1 - 3\sqrt{2}$$

Write the solutions.

The solutions are $1 + 3\sqrt{2}$ and $1 - 3\sqrt{2}$.

$1 + 3\sqrt{2}$ and $1 - 3\sqrt{2}$ check as solutions.

Example 5 Solve by taking square roots: $x^2 + 16 = 0$

Solution
$$x^2 + 16 = 0$$
$$x^2 = -16$$
$$\sqrt{x^2} = \sqrt{-16}$$

$\sqrt{-16}$ is not a real number.

The equation has no real number solution.

Example 6 Solve by taking square roots: $x^2 + 81 = 0$

Your solution

no real number solution

Example 7 Solve by taking square roots: $2(x - 4)^2 = 8$

Solution
$$2(x - 4)^2 = 8$$
$$(x - 4)^2 = 4$$
$$\sqrt{(x - 4)^2} = \sqrt{4}$$
$$x - 4 = \pm\sqrt{4} = \pm 2$$

$$x - 4 = 2 \qquad x - 4 = -2$$
$$x = 6 \qquad x = 2$$

The solutions are 2 and 6.

Example 8 Solve by taking square roots: $4(x + 2)^2 = 9$

Your solution

$-\dfrac{1}{2}$ and $-\dfrac{7}{2}$

Solutions on p. A62

11.1A Exercises

Solve.

1. $(x - 5)(x + 3) = 0$
5 and -3

2. $(x - 2)(x + 6) = 0$
2 and -6

3. $(x + 7)(x - 8) = 0$
-7 and 8

4. $(2x - 3)(x + 7) = 0$
$\frac{3}{2}$ and -7

5. $(3x + 5)(x - 4) = 0$
$-\frac{5}{3}$ and 4

6. $(4x - 1)(3x + 5) = 0$
$\frac{1}{4}$ and $-\frac{5}{3}$

Solve by factoring.

7. $x^2 + 2x - 15 = 0$
-5 and 3

8. $t^2 + 3t - 10 = 0$
-5 and 2

9. $z^2 - 4z + 3 = 0$
1 and 3

10. $s^2 - 5s + 4 = 0$
1 and 4

11. $p^2 + 3p + 2 = 0$
-1 and -2

12. $v^2 + 6v + 5 = 0$
-1 and -5

13. $x^2 - 6x + 9 = 0$
3

14. $y^2 - 8y + 16 = 0$
4

15. $12y^2 + 8y = 0$
0 and $-\frac{2}{3}$

16. $6x^2 - 9x = 0$
0 and $\frac{3}{2}$

17. $r^2 - 10 = 3r$
-2 and 5

18. $t^2 - 12 = 4t$
6 and -2

19. $3v^2 - 5v + 2 = 0$
$\frac{2}{3}$ and 1

20. $2p^2 - 3p - 2 = 0$
2 and $-\frac{1}{2}$

21. $3s^2 + 8s = 3$
$\frac{1}{3}$ and -3

22. $3x^2 + 5x = 12$
$\frac{4}{3}$ and -3

23. $9z^2 = 12z - 4$
$\frac{2}{3}$

24. $6r^2 = 12 - r$
$-\frac{3}{2}$ and $\frac{4}{3}$

25. $4t^2 = 4t + 3$
$-\frac{1}{2}$ and $\frac{3}{2}$

26. $5y^2 + 11y = 12$
$\frac{4}{5}$ and -3

27. $4v^2 - 4v + 1 = 0$
$\frac{1}{2}$

28. $9s^2 - 6s + 1 = 0$
$\frac{1}{3}$

29. $x^2 - 9 = 0$
-3 and 3

30. $t^2 - 16 = 0$
-4 and 4

31. $4y^2 - 1 = 0$
$-\frac{1}{2}$ and $\frac{1}{2}$

32. $9z^2 - 4 = 0$
$-\frac{2}{3}$ and $\frac{2}{3}$

33. $x + 15 = x(x - 1)$
-3 and 5

Solve by factoring.

34. $p + 18 = p(p - 2)$

   6 and -3

35. $r^2 - r - 2 = (2r - 1)(r - 3)$

   1 and 5

36. $s^2 + 5s - 4 = (2s + 1)(s - 4)$

   0 and 12

37. $x^2 + x + 5 = (3x + 2)(x - 4)$

   -1 and $\frac{13}{2}$

11.1B Exercises

Solve by taking square roots.

38. $x^2 = 36$

   -6 and 6

39. $y^2 = 49$

   -7 and 7

40. $v^2 - 1 = 0$

   -1 and 1

41. $z^2 - 64 = 0$

   -8 and 8

42. $4x^2 - 49 = 0$

   $-\frac{7}{2}$ and $\frac{7}{2}$

43. $9w^2 - 64 = 0$

   $-\frac{8}{3}$ and $\frac{8}{3}$

44. $9y^2 = 4$

   $-\frac{2}{3}$ and $\frac{2}{3}$

45. $4z^2 = 25$

   $-\frac{5}{2}$ and $\frac{5}{2}$

46. $16y^2 - 9 = 0$

   $-\frac{3}{4}$ and $\frac{3}{4}$

47. $25x^2 - 64 = 0$

   $-\frac{8}{5}$ and $\frac{8}{5}$

48. $y^2 + 81 = 0$

   no real number solution

49. $z^2 + 49 = 0$

   no real number solution

50. $w^2 - 24 = 0$

   $-2\sqrt{6}$ and $2\sqrt{6}$

51. $v^2 - 48 = 0$

   $-4\sqrt{3}$ and $4\sqrt{3}$

52. $(x - 1)^2 = 36$

   7 and -5

53. $(y + 2)^2 = 49$

   -9 and 5

54. $2(x + 5)^2 = 8$

   -3 and -7

55. $4(z - 3)^2 = 100$

   -2 and 8

56. $9(x - 1)^2 - 16 = 0$

   $\frac{7}{3}$ and $-\frac{1}{3}$

57. $4(y + 3)^2 - 81 = 0$

   $-\frac{15}{2}$ and $\frac{3}{2}$

58. $49(v + 1)^2 - 25 = 0$

   $-\frac{2}{7}$ and $-\frac{12}{7}$

59. $81(y - 2)^2 - 64 = 0$

   $\frac{26}{9}$ and $\frac{10}{9}$

60. $(x - 4)^2 - 20 = 0$

   $4 + 2\sqrt{5}$ and $4 - 2\sqrt{5}$

61. $(y + 5)^2 - 50 = 0$

   $-5 + 5\sqrt{2}$ and $-5 - 5\sqrt{2}$

62. $(x + 1)^2 + 36 = 0$

   no real number solution

63. $(y - 7)^2 + 49 = 0$

   no real number solution

64. $2\left(z - \frac{1}{2}\right)^2 = 12$

   $\frac{1}{2} + \sqrt{6}$ and $\frac{1}{2} - \sqrt{6}$

65. $3\left(v + \frac{3}{4}\right)^2 = 36$

   $-\frac{3}{4} + 2\sqrt{3}$ and $-\frac{3}{4} - 2\sqrt{3}$

Section 2 Solving Quadratic Equations by Completing the Square

Objective A To solve a quadratic equation by completing the square

11
DISK ELEVEN

Reference for Computer Tutor™

Recall that a perfect square trinomial is the square of a binomial.

Perfect Square Trinomial		Square of a Binomial
$x^2 + 6x + 9$	$=$	$(x + 3)^2$
$x^2 - 10x + 25$	$=$	$(x - 5)^2$
$x^2 + 8x + 16$	$=$	$(x + 4)^2$

For each perfect square trinomial, the square of $\frac{1}{2}$ of the coefficient of x equals the constant term.

$x^2 + 6x + 9, \quad \left(\frac{1}{2} \cdot 6\right)^2 = 9$

$x^2 - 10x + 25, \quad \left[\frac{1}{2}(-10)\right]^2 = 25$

$x^2 + 8x + 16, \quad \left(\frac{1}{2} \cdot 8\right)^2 = 16$

$$\left(\frac{1}{2} \text{ coefficient of } x\right)^2 = \text{constant term}$$

This relationship can be used to write the constant term for a perfect square trinomial. Adding to a binomial the constant term that makes it a perfect square trinomial is called **completing the square.**

Complete the square on $x^2 - 8x$. Write the resulting perfect square trinomial as the square of a binomial.

Find the constant term.

$\left[\frac{1}{2}(-8)\right]^2 = 16$

Complete the square on $x^2 - 8x$ by adding the constant term.

$x^2 - 8x + 16$

Write the resulting perfect square trinomial as the square of a binomial.

$x^2 - 8x + 16 = (x - 4)^2$

Complete the square on $y^2 + 5y$. Write the resulting perfect square trinomial as the square of a binomial.

Find the constant term.

$\left(\frac{1}{2} \cdot 5\right)^2 = \left(\frac{5}{2}\right)^2 = \frac{25}{4}$

Complete the square on $y^2 + 5y$ by adding the constant term.

$y^2 + 5y + \frac{25}{4}$

Write the resulting perfect square trinomial as the square of a binomial.

$y^2 + 5y + \frac{25}{4} = \left(y + \frac{5}{2}\right)^2$

A quadratic equation that cannot be solved by factoring can be solved by completing the square. Add to both sides of the equation the term that completes the square. Rewrite the quadratic equation in the form $(x + a)^2 = b$. Take the square root of each side of the equation and then solve for x.

Solve by completing the square: $x^2 - 6x - 3 = 0$

$$x^2 - 6x - 3 = 0$$

Add the opposite of the constant term to each side of the equation.

$$x^2 - 6x = 3$$

Find the constant term that completes the square on $x^2 - 6x$.

$$\left[\frac{1}{2}(-6)\right]^2 = 9$$ Do this step mentally.

Add this term to each side of the equation.

$$x^2 - 6x + 9 = 3 + 9$$

Factor the perfect square trinomial.

$$(x - 3)^2 = 12$$

Take the square root of each side of the equation.

$$\sqrt{(x - 3)^2} = \sqrt{12}$$

Simplify.

$$x - 3 = \pm\sqrt{12} = \pm 2\sqrt{3}$$

Solve for x.

$$x - 3 = 2\sqrt{3} \qquad x - 3 = -2\sqrt{3}$$
$$x = 3 + 2\sqrt{3} \qquad x = 3 - 2\sqrt{3}$$

Write the solution.

The solutions are $3 + 2\sqrt{3}$ and $3 - 2\sqrt{3}$.

Check:

$$x^2 - 6x - 3 = 0$$
$$(3 + 2\sqrt{3})^2 - 6(3 + 2\sqrt{3}) - 3 = 0$$
$$9 + 12\sqrt{3} + 12 - 18 - 12\sqrt{3} - 3 = 0$$
$$0 = 0$$

$$x^2 - 6x - 3 = 0$$
$$(3 - 2\sqrt{3})^2 - 6(3 - 2\sqrt{3}) - 3 = 0$$
$$9 - 12\sqrt{3} + 12 - 18 + 12\sqrt{3} - 3 = 0$$
$$0 = 0$$

Solve by completing the square: $2x^2 - x - 1 = 0$

$$2x^2 - x - 1 = 0$$
$$2x^2 - x = 1$$

Add the opposite of the constant term to each side of the equation.

To complete the square, the coefficient of the x^2 term must be 1. Multiply each term by the reciprocal of the coefficient of x^2.

$$\frac{1}{2}(2x^2 - x) = \frac{1}{2} \cdot 1$$

$$x^2 - \frac{1}{2}x = \frac{1}{2}$$

Find the term that completes the square on $x^2 - \frac{1}{2}x$.

$$\left[\frac{1}{2}\left(-\frac{1}{2}\right)\right]^2 = \left(-\frac{1}{4}\right)^2 = \frac{1}{16}$$ Do this step mentally.

Add this term to each side of the equation.

$$x^2 - \frac{1}{2}x + \frac{1}{16} = \frac{1}{2} + \frac{1}{16}$$

Factor the perfect square trinomial.

$$\left(x - \frac{1}{4}\right)^2 = \frac{9}{16}$$

Take the square root of each side of the equation.

$$\sqrt{\left(x - \frac{1}{4}\right)^2} = \sqrt{\frac{9}{16}}$$

Simplify.

$$x - \frac{1}{4} = \pm\frac{3}{4}$$

Solve for x.

$$x - \frac{1}{4} = \frac{3}{4} \qquad x - \frac{1}{4} = -\frac{3}{4}$$
$$x = 1 \qquad x = -\frac{1}{2}$$

The solutions are 1 and $-\frac{1}{2}$.

1 and $-\frac{1}{2}$ check as solutions.

Example 1 Solve by completing the square: $2x^2 - 4x - 1 = 0$

Solution
$$2x^2 - 4x - 1 = 0$$
$$2x^2 - 4x = 1$$
$$\frac{1}{2}(2x^2 - 4x) = \frac{1}{2} \cdot 1$$
$$x^2 - 2x = \frac{1}{2}$$
$$x^2 - 2x + 1 = \frac{1}{2} + 1 \qquad \text{Complete the square.}$$
$$(x - 1)^2 = \frac{3}{2}$$
$$\sqrt{(x - 1)^2} = \sqrt{\frac{3}{2}}$$
$$x - 1 = \pm\sqrt{\frac{3}{2}} = \pm\frac{\sqrt{6}}{2}$$
$$x - 1 = \frac{\sqrt{6}}{2} \qquad x - 1 = -\frac{\sqrt{6}}{2}$$
$$x = 1 + \frac{\sqrt{6}}{2} \qquad x = 1 - \frac{\sqrt{6}}{2}$$
$$= \frac{2 + \sqrt{6}}{2} \qquad = \frac{2 - \sqrt{6}}{2}$$

The solutions are $\frac{2 + \sqrt{6}}{2}$ and $\frac{2 - \sqrt{6}}{2}$.

Example 2 Solve by completing the square: $3x^2 - 6x - 2 = 0$

Your solution

$$\frac{3 + \sqrt{15}}{3} \quad \text{and} \quad \frac{3 - \sqrt{15}}{3}$$

Solution on p. A63

Example 3

Solve by completing the square:
$x^2 + 4x + 5 = 0$

Solution

$x^2 + 4x + 5 = 0$
$\quad x^2 + 4x = -5$

Complete the square.

$x^2 + 4x + 4 = -5 + 4$
$\quad\quad (x + 2)^2 = -1$
$\quad \sqrt{(x + 2)^2} = \sqrt{-1}$

$\sqrt{-1}$ is not a real number.

The quadratic equation has no real number solution.

Example 4

Solve by completing the square:
$x^2 + 6x + 12 = 0$

Your solution

no real number solution

Example 5

Solve by completing the square:
$x^2 + 6x + 4 = 0$

Approximate the solutions. Use the Table of Square Roots on page A3.

Solution

$x^2 + 6x + 4 = 0$
$\quad x^2 + 6x = -4$

Complete the square.

$x^2 + 6x + 9 = -4 + 9$
$\quad\quad (x + 3)^2 = 5$
$\quad \sqrt{(x + 3)^2} = \sqrt{5}$
$\quad\quad\quad x + 3 = \pm\sqrt{5}$

$\begin{aligned} x + 3 &= \sqrt{5} & x + 3 &= -\sqrt{5} \\ x &= -3 + \sqrt{5} & x &= -3 - \sqrt{5} \\ &\approx -3 + 2.236 & &\approx -3 - 2.236 \\ &\approx -0.764 & &\approx -5.236 \end{aligned}$

The solutions are approximately -0.764 and -5.236.

Example 6

Solve by completing the square:
$x^2 + 8x + 8 = 0$

Approximate the solutions. Use the Table of Square Roots on page A3.

Your solution

−1.172 and −6.828

Solutions on p. A63

11.2A Exercises

Solve by completing the square.

1. $x^2 + 2x - 3 = 0$

   1 and -3

2. $y^2 + 4y - 5 = 0$

   1 and -5

3. $z^2 - 6z - 16 = 0$

   8 and -2

4. $w^2 + 8w - 9 = 0$

   1 and -9

5. $x^2 = 4x - 4$

   2

6. $z^2 = 8z - 16$

   4

7. $v^2 - 6v + 13 = 0$

   no real number solution

8. $x^2 + 4x + 13 = 0$

   no real number solution

9. $y^2 + 5y + 4 = 0$

   -1 and -4

10. $v^2 - 5v - 6 = 0$

    6 and -1

11. $w^2 + 7w = 8$

    -8 and 1

12. $y^2 + 5y = -4$

    -4 and -1

13. $v^2 + 4v + 1 = 0$

    $-2 + \sqrt{3}$ and $-2 - \sqrt{3}$

14. $y^2 - 2y - 5 = 0$

    $1 + \sqrt{6}$ and $1 - \sqrt{6}$

15. $x^2 + 6x = 5$

    $-3 + \sqrt{14}$ and $-3 - \sqrt{14}$

16. $w^2 - 8w = 3$

    $4 + \sqrt{19}$ and $4 - \sqrt{19}$

17. $z^2 = 2z + 1$

    $1 + \sqrt{2}$ and $1 - \sqrt{2}$

18. $y^2 = 10y - 20$

    $5 + \sqrt{5}$ and $5 - \sqrt{5}$

19. $p^2 + 3p = 1$

    $\dfrac{-3 + \sqrt{13}}{2}$ and $\dfrac{-3 - \sqrt{13}}{2}$

20. $r^2 + 5r = 2$

    $\dfrac{-5 + \sqrt{33}}{2}$ and $\dfrac{-5 - \sqrt{33}}{2}$

21. $t^2 - 3t = -2$

    2 and 1

22. $z^2 - 5z = -3$

    $\dfrac{5 + \sqrt{13}}{2}$ and $\dfrac{5 - \sqrt{13}}{2}$

23. $v^2 + v - 3 = 0$

    $\dfrac{-1 + \sqrt{13}}{2}$ and $\dfrac{-1 - \sqrt{13}}{2}$

24. $x^2 - x = 1$

    $\dfrac{1 + \sqrt{5}}{2}$ and $\dfrac{1 - \sqrt{5}}{2}$

25. $y^2 = 7 - 10y$

    $-5 + 4\sqrt{2}$ and $-5 - 4\sqrt{2}$

26. $v^2 = 14 + 16v$

    $8 + \sqrt{78}$ and $8 - \sqrt{78}$

27. $r^2 - 3r = 5$

    $\dfrac{3 + \sqrt{29}}{2}$ and $\dfrac{3 - \sqrt{29}}{2}$

28. $s^2 + 3s = -1$

    $\dfrac{-3 + \sqrt{5}}{2}$ and $\dfrac{-3 - \sqrt{5}}{2}$

29. $t^2 - t = 4$

    $\dfrac{1 + \sqrt{17}}{2}$ and $\dfrac{1 - \sqrt{17}}{2}$

30. $y^2 + y - 4 = 0$

    $\dfrac{-1 + \sqrt{17}}{2}$ and $\dfrac{-1 - \sqrt{17}}{2}$

31. $x^2 - 3x + 5 = 0$

    no real number solution

32. $z^2 + 5z + 7 = 0$

    no real number solution

33. $2t^2 - 3t + 1 = 0$

    1 and $\frac{1}{2}$

34. $2x^2 - 7x + 3 = 0$

    3 and $\frac{1}{2}$

35. $2r^2 + 5r = 3$

    -3 and $\frac{1}{2}$

36. $2y^2 - 3y = 9$

    3 and $-\frac{3}{2}$

Solve by completing the square.

37. $2s^2 = 7s - 6$

  2 and $\frac{3}{2}$

38. $2x^2 = 3x + 20$

  4 and $-\frac{5}{2}$

39. $2v^2 = v + 1$

  1 and $-\frac{1}{2}$

40. $2z^2 = z + 3$

  $\frac{3}{2}$ and -1

41. $3r^2 + 5r = 2$

  -2 and $\frac{1}{3}$

42. $3t^2 - 8t = 3$

  3 and $-\frac{1}{3}$

43. $3y^2 + 8y + 4 = 0$

  -2 and $-\frac{2}{3}$

44. $3z^2 - 10z - 8 = 0$

  4 and $-\frac{2}{3}$

45. $4x^2 + 4x - 3 = 0$

  $\frac{1}{2}$ and $-\frac{3}{2}$

46. $4v^2 + 4v - 15 = 0$

  $\frac{3}{2}$ and $-\frac{5}{2}$

47. $6s^2 + 7s = 3$

  $\frac{1}{3}$ and $-\frac{3}{2}$

48. $6z^2 = z + 2$

  $\frac{2}{3}$ and $-\frac{1}{2}$

49. $6p^2 = 5p + 4$

  $-\frac{1}{2}$ and $\frac{4}{3}$

50. $6t^2 = t - 2$

  no real number solution

51. $4v^2 - 4v - 1 = 0$

  $\dfrac{1+\sqrt{2}}{2}$ and $\dfrac{1-\sqrt{2}}{2}$

52. $2s^2 - 4s - 1 = 0$

  $\dfrac{2+\sqrt{6}}{2}$ and $\dfrac{2-\sqrt{6}}{2}$

53. $4z^2 - 8z = 1$

  $\dfrac{2+\sqrt{5}}{2}$ and $\dfrac{2-\sqrt{5}}{2}$

54. $3r^2 - 2r = 2$

  $\dfrac{1+\sqrt{7}}{3}$ and $\dfrac{1-\sqrt{7}}{3}$

55. $3y - 6 = (y - 1)(y - 2)$

  2 and 4

56. $7s + 55 = (s + 5)(s + 4)$

  5 and -7

57. $4p + 2 = (p - 1)(p + 3)$

  $1 + \sqrt{6}$ and $1 - \sqrt{6}$

58. $v - 10 = (v + 3)(v - 4)$

  $1 + \sqrt{3}$ and $1 - \sqrt{3}$

Solve by completing the square. Approximate the solutions to the nearest thousandth. Use the Table of Square Roots on page A3 and a calculator.

59. $y^2 + 3y = 5$

  -4.193 and 1.193

60. $w^2 + 5w = 2$

  0.373 and -5.373

61. $2z^2 - 3z = 7$

  2.766 and -1.266

62. $2x^2 + 3x = 11$

  1.712 and -3.212

63. $4x^2 + 6x - 1 = 0$

  -1.652 and 0.152

64. $4x^2 + 2x - 3 = 0$

  0.652 and -1.152

Section 3 Solving Quadratic Equations by Using the Quadratic Formula

Objective A To solve a quadratic equation by using the quadratic formula

11
DISK ELEVEN

Reference for
Computer
Tutor™

Any quadratic equation can be solved by completing the square. Applying this method to the standard form of a quadratic equation produces a formula that can be used to solve any quadratic equation.

Solve $ax^2 + bx + c = 0$ by completing the square.

$$ax^2 + bx + c = 0$$

Add the opposite of the constant term to each side of the equation.
$$ax^2 + bx + c + (-c) = 0 + (-c)$$

$$ax^2 + bx = -c$$

Multiply each side of the equation by the reciprocal of a, the coefficient of x^2.
$$\frac{1}{a}(ax^2 + bx) = \frac{1}{a}(-c)$$

$$x^2 + \frac{b}{a}x = -\frac{c}{a}$$

Complete the square by adding $\left(\frac{1}{2} \cdot \frac{b}{a}\right)^2$ to each side of the equation.
$$x^2 + \frac{b}{a}x + \left(\frac{1}{2} \cdot \frac{b}{a}\right)^2 = \left(\frac{1}{2} \cdot \frac{b}{a}\right)^2 - \frac{c}{a}$$

$$x^2 + \frac{b}{a}x + \frac{b^2}{4a^2} = \frac{b^2}{4a^2} - \frac{c}{a}$$

Simplify the right side of the equation.
$$x^2 + \frac{b}{a}x + \frac{b^2}{4a^2} = \frac{b^2}{4a^2} - \left(\frac{c}{a} \cdot \frac{4a}{4a}\right)$$

$$x^2 + \frac{b}{a}x + \frac{b^2}{4a^2} = \frac{b^2}{4a^2} - \frac{4ac}{4a^2}$$

$$x^2 + \frac{b}{a}x + \frac{b^2}{4a^2} = \frac{b^2 - 4ac}{4a^2}$$

Factor the perfect square trinomial on the left side of the equation.
$$\left(x + \frac{b}{2a}\right)^2 = \frac{b^2 - 4ac}{4a^2}$$

Take the square root of each side of the equation.
$$\sqrt{\left(x + \frac{b}{2a}\right)^2} = \sqrt{\frac{b^2 - 4ac}{4a^2}}$$

$$\left(x + \frac{b}{2a}\right) = \pm\frac{\sqrt{b^2 - 4ac}}{2a}$$

Solve for x.

$$x + \frac{b}{2a} = \frac{\sqrt{b^2 - 4ac}}{2a} \qquad x + \frac{b}{2a} = -\frac{\sqrt{b^2 - 4ac}}{2a}$$

$$x = -\frac{b}{2a} + \frac{\sqrt{b^2 - 4ac}}{2a} \qquad x = -\frac{b}{2a} - \frac{\sqrt{b^2 - 4ac}}{2a}$$

$$= \frac{-b + \sqrt{b^2 - 4ac}}{2a} \qquad = \frac{-b - \sqrt{b^2 - 4ac}}{2a}$$

The Quadratic Formula

The solution of $ax^2 + bx + c = 0$ is $x = \dfrac{-b + \sqrt{b^2 - 4ac}}{2a}$ or $x = \dfrac{-b - \sqrt{b^2 - 4ac}}{2a}$.

The quadratic formula is frequently written in the form $\boldsymbol{x = \dfrac{-b \pm \sqrt{b^2 - 4ac}}{2a}}$.

Solve by using the quadratic formula: $2x^2 = 4x - 1$

Write the equation in standard form.
$a = 2$, $b = -4$, and $c = 1$.

$$2x^2 = 4x - 1$$
$$2x^2 - 4x + 1 = 0$$

Replace a, b, and c in the quadratic formula by their values.

$$x = \frac{-b \pm \sqrt{b^2 - 4ac}}{2a}$$

$$= \frac{-(-4) \pm \sqrt{(-4)^2 - 4 \cdot 2 \cdot 1}}{2 \cdot 2}$$

Simplify.

$$= \frac{4 \pm \sqrt{16 - 8}}{4} = \frac{4 \pm \sqrt{8}}{4}$$

$$= \frac{4 \pm 2\sqrt{2}}{4} = \frac{2 \pm \sqrt{2}}{2}$$

Write the solutions.

The solutions are $\frac{2 + \sqrt{2}}{2}$ and $\frac{2 - \sqrt{2}}{2}$.

$\frac{2 + \sqrt{2}}{2}$ and $\frac{2 - \sqrt{2}}{2}$ check as solutions.

Example 1   Solve by using the quadratic formula: $2x^2 - 3x + 1 = 0$

Solution
$$2x^2 - 3x + 1 = 0$$
$$a = 2, b = -3, c = 1$$
$$x = \frac{-(-3) \pm \sqrt{(-3)^2 - 4(2)(1)}}{2 \cdot 2}$$
$$= \frac{3 \pm \sqrt{9 - 8}}{4} = \frac{3 \pm \sqrt{1}}{4} = \frac{3 \pm 1}{4}$$
$$x = \frac{3 + 1}{4} \qquad x = \frac{3 - 1}{4}$$
$$= \frac{4}{4} = 1 \qquad = \frac{2}{4} = \frac{1}{2}$$

The solutions are 1 and $\frac{1}{2}$.

Example 2   Solve by using the quadratic formula: $3x^2 + 4x - 4 = 0$

Your solution

$\frac{2}{3}$ and -2

Example 3   Solve by using the quadratic formula: $2x^2 = 8x - 5$

Solution
$$2x^2 = 8x - 5$$
$$2x^2 - 8x + 5 = 0$$
$$a = 2, b = -8, c = 5$$
$$x = \frac{-(-8) \pm \sqrt{(-8)^2 - 4(2)(5)}}{2 \cdot 2}$$
$$= \frac{8 \pm \sqrt{64 - 40}}{4} = \frac{8 \pm \sqrt{24}}{4}$$
$$= \frac{8 \pm 2\sqrt{6}}{4} = \frac{4 \pm \sqrt{6}}{2}$$

The solutions are $\frac{4 + \sqrt{6}}{2}$ and $\frac{4 - \sqrt{6}}{2}$.

Example 4   Solve by using the quadratic formula: $x^2 + 2x = 1$

Your solution

$-1 + \sqrt{2}$ and $-1 - \sqrt{2}$

Solutions on p. A64

11.3A Exercises

Solve by using the quadratic formula.

1. $x^2 - 4x - 5 = 0$
   5 and -1

2. $y^2 + 3y + 2 = 0$
   -2 and -1

3. $z^2 - 2z - 15 = 0$
   -3 and 5

4. $v^2 + 5v + 4 = 0$
   -1 and -4

5. $z^2 + 6z - 7 = 0$
   -7 and 1

6. $s^2 + 3s - 10 = 0$
   -5 and 2

7. $t^2 + t - 6 = 0$
   2 and -3

8. $x^2 - x - 2 = 0$
   2 and -1

9. $y^2 = 2y + 3$
   3 and -1

10. $w^2 = 3w + 18$
    6 and -3

11. $r^2 = 5 - 4r$
    -5 and 1

12. $z^2 = 3 - 2z$
    1 and -3

13. $2y^2 - y - 1 = 0$
    $-\frac{1}{2}$ and 1

14. $2t^2 - 5t + 3 = 0$
    1 and $\frac{3}{2}$

15. $w^2 + 3w + 5 = 0$
    no real number solution

16. $x^2 - 2x + 6 = 0$
    no real number solution

17. $p^2 - p = 0$
    0 and 1

18. $2v^2 + v = 0$
    0 and $-\frac{1}{2}$

19. $4t^2 - 9 = 0$
    $\frac{3}{2}$ and $-\frac{3}{2}$

20. $4s^2 - 25 = 0$
    $\frac{5}{2}$ and $-\frac{5}{2}$

21. $4y^2 + 4y = 15$
    $\frac{3}{2}$ and $-\frac{5}{2}$

22. $4r^2 + 4r = 3$
    $\frac{1}{2}$ and $-\frac{3}{2}$

23. $3t^2 = 7t + 6$
    3 and $-\frac{2}{3}$

24. $3x^2 = 10x + 8$
    4 and $-\frac{2}{3}$

25. $5z^2 + 11z = 12$
    -3 and $\frac{4}{5}$

26. $4v^2 = v + 3$
    $-\frac{3}{4}$ and 1

27. $6s^2 - s - 2 = 0$
    $-\frac{1}{2}$ and $\frac{2}{3}$

28. $6y^2 + 5y - 4 = 0$
    $-\frac{4}{3}$ and $\frac{1}{2}$

29. $2x^2 + x + 1 = 0$
    no real number solution

30. $3r^2 - r + 2 = 0$
    no real number solution

31. $t^2 - 2t = 5$
    $1 + \sqrt{6}$ and $1 - \sqrt{6}$

32. $y^2 - 4y = 6$
    $2 + \sqrt{10}$ and $2 - \sqrt{10}$

33. $t^2 + 6t - 1 = 0$
    $-3 + \sqrt{10}$ and $-3 - \sqrt{10}$

Solve by using the quadratic formula.

34. $z^2 + 4z + 1 = 0$
$-2 + \sqrt{3}$ and $-2 - \sqrt{3}$

35. $w^2 = 4w + 9$
$2 + \sqrt{13}$ and $2 - \sqrt{13}$

36. $y^2 = 8y + 3$
$4 + \sqrt{19}$ and $4 - \sqrt{19}$

37. $4t^2 - 4t - 1 = 0$
$\dfrac{1 + \sqrt{2}}{2}$ and $\dfrac{1 - \sqrt{2}}{2}$

38. $4x^2 - 8x - 1 = 0$
$\dfrac{2 + \sqrt{5}}{2}$ and $\dfrac{2 - \sqrt{5}}{2}$

39. $v^2 + 6v + 1 = 0$
$-3 + 2\sqrt{2}$ and $-3 - 2\sqrt{2}$

40. $s^2 + 4s - 8 = 0$
$-2 + 2\sqrt{3}$ and $-2 - 2\sqrt{3}$

41. $4t^2 - 12t - 15 = 0$
$\dfrac{3 + 2\sqrt{6}}{2}$ and $\dfrac{3 - 2\sqrt{6}}{2}$

42. $4w^2 - 20w + 5 = 0$
$\dfrac{5 + 2\sqrt{5}}{2}$ and $\dfrac{5 - 2\sqrt{5}}{2}$

43. $9y^2 + 6y - 1 = 0$
$\dfrac{-1 + \sqrt{2}}{3}$ and $\dfrac{-1 - \sqrt{2}}{3}$

44. $9s^2 - 6s - 2 = 0$
$\dfrac{1 + \sqrt{3}}{3}$ and $\dfrac{1 - \sqrt{3}}{3}$

45. $4p^2 + 4p + 1 = 0$
$-\dfrac{1}{2}$

46. $9z^2 + 12z + 4 = 0$
$-\dfrac{2}{3}$

47. $2x^2 = 4x - 5$
no real number solution

48. $3r^2 = 5r - 6$
no real number solution

49. $4p^2 + 16p = -11$
$\dfrac{-4 + \sqrt{5}}{2}$ and $\dfrac{-4 - \sqrt{5}}{2}$

50. $4y^2 - 12y = -1$
$\dfrac{3 + 2\sqrt{2}}{2}$ and $\dfrac{3 - 2\sqrt{2}}{2}$

51. $4x^2 = 4x + 11$
$\dfrac{1 + 2\sqrt{3}}{2}$ and $\dfrac{1 - 2\sqrt{3}}{2}$

52. $4s^2 + 12s = 3$
$\dfrac{-3 + 2\sqrt{3}}{2}$ and $\dfrac{-3 - 2\sqrt{3}}{2}$

53. $9v^2 = -30v - 23$
$\dfrac{-5 + \sqrt{2}}{3}$ and $\dfrac{-5 - \sqrt{2}}{3}$

54. $9t^2 = 30t + 17$
$\dfrac{5 + \sqrt{42}}{3}$ and $\dfrac{5 - \sqrt{42}}{3}$

Solve by using the quadratic formula. Approximate the solutions to the nearest thousandth. Use the Table of Square Roots on page A3 and a calculator.

55. $x^2 - 2x - 21 = 0$
5.690 and -3.690

56. $y^2 + 4y - 11 = 0$
1.873 and -5.873

57. $s^2 - 6s - 13 = 0$
7.690 and -1.690

58. $w^2 + 8w - 15 = 0$
1.568 and -9.568

59. $2p^2 - 7p - 10 = 0$
4.590 and -1.090

60. $3t^2 - 8t - 1 = 0$
2.786 and -0.120

61. $4z^2 + 8z - 1 = 0$
0.118 and -2.118

62. $4x^2 + 7x + 1 = 0$
-0.157 and -1.593

63. $5v^2 - v - 5 = 0$
1.105 and -0.905

Calculators and Computers

A calculator can be used to check solutions to quadratic equations.

The solutions to the equation

$$x^2 - 6x - 16 = 0$$

can be found by factoring. The solutions are 8 and -2.

To check the solutions, $\qquad$ $8^2 - 6 \cdot 8 - 16 \overset{?}{=} 0$
replace x by 8.

Enter the following keystrokes: $\qquad$ 8 $\boxed{x^2}$ $\boxed{-}$ $\boxed{(}$ 6 $\boxed{\times}$ 8 $\boxed{)}$ $\boxed{-}$ 16 $\boxed{=}$

Note the use of parentheses to ensure that multiplication is completed before subtraction.

The result in the display should be 0. The solution 8 is correct.
The solution -2 can be checked in a similar manner.

The solutions to the equation

$$2x^2 - x - 9 = 0$$

can be found using the quadratic formula. The solutions are $\dfrac{1 + \sqrt{73}}{4}$ and $\dfrac{1 - \sqrt{73}}{4}$.

To check the solutions, first
evaluate the expression $\dfrac{1 + \sqrt{73}}{4}$
and store the result in memory.

Replace x by the solution. The
$\boxed{MR}$ key recalls the solution from
memory.

Is the result in the display zero? Probably not! However, the answer is very close to zero. The result in our display was $9.000000 - 10$. The -10 at the end of the display means that the decimal point should be moved ten places to the left. That makes the number 0.0000000009, which is indeed close to zero. The reason the answer is not exactly zero is that $\sqrt{73}$ is an irrational number and therefore has an infinitely long decimal representation. The calculator, on the other hand, can store only 8 or 9 digits. Therefore, the calculator is using only an approximation of $\sqrt{73}$ in its calculations.

The solution $\dfrac{1 - \sqrt{73}}{4}$ can be checked in a similar manner.

Check the solutions to the quadratic equation. Each of the given solutions should check.

1. $x^2 + 5x - 36 = 0$; solutions: 4 and -9

2. $8x^2 - 10x - 3 = 0$; solutions: $\dfrac{3}{2}$ and $-\dfrac{1}{4}$

3. $x^2 - 6x - 4 = 0$;
   solutions: $3 + \sqrt{13}$ and $3 - \sqrt{13}$

4. $3x^2 - 6x + 2 = 0$;
   solutions: $\dfrac{3 + \sqrt{3}}{3}$ and $\dfrac{3 - \sqrt{3}}{3}$

Chapter Summary

KEY WORDS

A **quadratic equation** is an equation that can be written in the form $ax^2 + bx + c = 0$, where a, b, and c are constants and $a \neq 0$. A quadratic equation is also called a **second-degree equation.**

Adding to a binomial the constant term that makes it a perfect square trinomial is called **completing the square.**

A quadratic equation is in **standard form** when the polynomial is in descending order and equal to zero.

ESSENTIAL RULES

The Quadratic Formula

$$x = \frac{-b \pm \sqrt{b^2 - 4ac}}{2a}$$

The Principle of Zero Products   **If $ab = 0$, then $a = 0$ or $b = 0$.**

For a perfect square trinomial, $\left(\dfrac{1}{2}\textbf{ the coefficient of } x\right)^2 = \textbf{ the constant term.}$

Some quadratic equations can be solved by   factoring or taking square roots.

Any quadratic equation can be solved by   completing the square or using the quadratic formula.

Review/Test

1. Solve: $(x - 5)(x + 6) = 0$
   5 and -6

2. Solve: $(3x + 1)(x - 8) = 0$
   $-\frac{1}{3}$ and 8

3. Solve by factoring: $2x^2 - 5x - 12 = 0$
   $-\frac{3}{2}$ and 4

4. Solve by factoring: $3x^2 + 7x = 20$
   -4 and $\frac{5}{3}$

5. Solve by factoring: $6x^2 - 17x = -5$
   $\frac{5}{2}$ and $\frac{1}{3}$

6. Solve by factoring: $2x = (x + 5)(x - 4)$
   -4 and 5

7. Solve by taking square roots: $x^2 - 81 = 0$
   -9 and 9

8. Solve by taking square roots: $16x^2 = 25$
   $-\frac{5}{4}$ and $\frac{5}{4}$

9. Solve by taking square roots: $9x^2 - 36 = 0$
   -2 and 2

10. Solve by taking square roots: $(x - 6)^2 = 81$
    -3 and 15

11. Solve by taking square roots:
    $2(x - 5)^2 = 36$
    $5 + 3\sqrt{2}$ and $5 - 3\sqrt{2}$

12. Solve by taking square roots:
    $3(x + 4)^2 - 60 = 0$
    $-4 + 2\sqrt{5}$ and $-4 - 2\sqrt{5}$

13. Solve by completing the square:
    $x^2 + 4x - 16 = 0$
    $-2 + 2\sqrt{5}$ and $-2 - 2\sqrt{5}$

14. Solve by completing the square:
    $x^2 - 6x - 5 = 0$
    $3 + \sqrt{14}$ and $3 - \sqrt{14}$

15. Solve by completing the square: $x^2 - 5x = 2$
    $\dfrac{5 + \sqrt{33}}{2}$ and $\dfrac{5 - \sqrt{33}}{2}$

16. Solve by completing the square: $x^2 + 3x = 8$
    $\dfrac{-3 + \sqrt{41}}{2}$ and $\dfrac{-3 - \sqrt{41}}{2}$

17. Solve by completing the square:
    $2x^2 - 6x + 1 = 0$
    $\dfrac{3 + \sqrt{7}}{2}$ and $\dfrac{3 - \sqrt{7}}{2}$

18. Solve by completing the square:
    $2x^2 + 8x = 3$
    $\dfrac{-4 + \sqrt{22}}{2}$ and $\dfrac{-4 - \sqrt{22}}{2}$

19. Solve by using the quadratic formula:
    $x^2 + 4x + 2 = 0$
    $-2 + \sqrt{2}$ and $-2 - \sqrt{2}$

20. Solve by using the quadratic formula:
    $x^2 + 3x - 7 = 0$
    $\dfrac{-3 + \sqrt{37}}{2}$ and $\dfrac{-3 - \sqrt{37}}{2}$

21. Solve by using the quadratic formula:
    $x^2 - 3x = 6$
    $\dfrac{3 + \sqrt{33}}{2}$ and $\dfrac{3 - \sqrt{33}}{2}$

22. Solve by using the quadratic formula:
    $x^2 - 5x = 1$
    $\dfrac{5 + \sqrt{29}}{2}$ and $\dfrac{5 - \sqrt{29}}{2}$

23. Solve by using the quadratic formula:
    $2x^2 - 5x - 3 = 0$
    $-\frac{1}{2}$ and 3

24. Solve by using the quadratic formula:
    $3x^2 - x = 1$
    $\dfrac{1 + \sqrt{13}}{6}$ and $\dfrac{1 - \sqrt{13}}{6}$

Cumulative Review/Test

1. Simplify: $\dfrac{x}{2x-2} - \dfrac{1}{x^2-1}$

   $\dfrac{x+2}{2(x+1)}$

2. Find the equation of the line that contains the point $(-3, 2)$ and has slope $-\dfrac{4}{3}$.

   $y = -\dfrac{4}{3}x - 2$

3. Factor $3x^3 + 2x^2 - 8x$.

   $x(3x-4)(x+2)$

4. Solve by using the quadratic formula:
   $2x^2 - 3x - 2 = 0$

   2 and $-\dfrac{1}{2}$

5. Solve by the addition method: $3x + 2y = 2$
   $\qquad\qquad\qquad\qquad\qquad 5x - 2y = 14$

   $(2, -2)$

6. Simplify: $(\sqrt{a} - \sqrt{2})(\sqrt{a} + \sqrt{2})$

   $a - 2$

7. Simplify: $(2a^2b)^2(-3a^4b^2)$

   $-12a^8b^4$

8. Simplify: $2x - 3[2x - 4(3 - 2x) + 2] - 3$

   $-28x + 27$

9. Solve by factoring: $6x^2 + x = 2$

   $\dfrac{1}{2}$ and $-\dfrac{2}{3}$

10. Solve: $-\dfrac{3}{5}x = -\dfrac{9}{10}$

    $\dfrac{3}{2}$

11. Simplify: $(x^2 - 8) \div (x - 2)$

    $x + 2 - \dfrac{4}{x-2}$

12. Simplify: $\dfrac{3x^2 - 6x}{4x - 6} \div \dfrac{2x^2 + x - 6}{6x^3 - 24x}$

    $\dfrac{9x^2(x-2)^2}{(2x-3)^2}$

13. Simplify: $\dfrac{1 - \dfrac{7}{x} + \dfrac{12}{x^2}}{2 - \dfrac{1}{x} - \dfrac{15}{x^2}}$

    $\dfrac{x-4}{2x+5}$

14. Simplify: $\dfrac{\sqrt{108a^7b^3}}{\sqrt{3a^4b}}$

    $6ab\sqrt{a}$

15. Solve: $2x - 3(4x - 5) = 3x - 6$

    $\dfrac{21}{13}$

16. Solve by taking square roots: $2(x - 5)^2 = 36$

    $5 + 3\sqrt{2}$ and $5 - 3\sqrt{2}$

17. Solve: $2x - 3(2 - 3x) > 2x - 5$

    $x > \dfrac{1}{9}$

18. Find the x- and y-intercepts for the line $4x - 3y = 12$.

    $(3, 0)$
    $(0, -4)$

19. Solve by completing the square:
    $3x^2 + 7x = -3$

    $\dfrac{-7 + \sqrt{13}}{6}$ and $\dfrac{-7 - \sqrt{13}}{6}$

20. Simplify: $\dfrac{\sqrt{12x^2} - \sqrt{27}}{\sqrt{3}}$

    $2x - 3$

21. Find the cost per pound of a mixture made from 20 lb of cashews that cost $3.50 per pound and 50 lb of peanuts that cost $1.75 per pound.

    $2.25 per pound

22. A stock dividend of 100 shares paid $215. At this rate, how many additional shares are required to earn a dividend of $752.50?

    250 additional shares

23. A student received 70, 91, 85, and 77 on four tests in a math class. What scores on the last test will enable the student to receive a minimum of 400 points?

    77 or better

24. A plane can fly 160 mph in calm air. Flying with the wind, the plane can fly 570 mi in the same amount of time as it takes to fly 390 mi against the wind. Find the rate of the wind.

    30 mph

chapter 12 Applied Geometry

Objectives

12.1A To solve problems involving lines and angles

12.1B To solve problems involving angles formed by intersecting lines

12.1C To solve problems involving the angles of a triangle

12.2A To find the perimeter of a geometric figure

12.2B To find the area of a geometric figure

12.3A To solve right triangles

12.3B To solve similar triangles

12.4A To find the volume of a geometric solid

Section **1**   # Lines and Angles

Objective A   ## To solve problems involving lines and angles

Reference for
Computer
Tutor™

The word *geometry* comes from the Greek words for "earth" (geo) and "measure." The original purpose of geometry was to measure land. Today geometry is used in many fields, such as physics, chemistry, and geology. Geometry is used in applied fields such as mechanical drawing and astronomy. Geometric form is used in art and design.

Two basic geometric concepts are plane and space.

A **plane** is a flat surface and can be pictured as a table top or a blackboard. Figures that can lie totally in a plane are called **plane figures.**

Plane

Space extends in all directions. Objects in space, such as trees, ice cubes, doors, or basketballs, are called **solids.**

Space

A **line** extends indefinitely in two directions in a plane. A line has no width. Line ℓ is shown at the right.

ℓ

A **line segment** is part of a line and has two end points. The line segment *AB* is shown at the right.

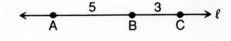

Line Segment

The **length** of a line segment is the distance between the endpoints of the line segment. The length can be expressed as an equation. For the line segment at the right, $AB = 5$, $BC = 3$, and $AC = AB + BC = 5 + 3 = 8$. When no units of measure, such as feet or meters, are given for the length, the distances are assumed to be in the same units of length.

Given $AB = 22$ and $AC = 31$, find the length of *BC*.

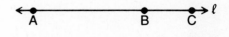

Write an equation for the lengths of the line segments.

$$AB + BC = AC$$

Substitute the lengths of *AB* and *AC* into the equation. Solve for *BC*.

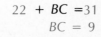

$$22 + BC = 31$$
$$BC = 9$$

Lines in a plane can be parallel or intersecting. **Parallel lines** never meet. The distance between them is always the same. **Intersecting lines** cross at a point in the plane.

Parallel Lines

Intersecting Lines

The symbol "∥" means "is parallel to." In the figure at the right, $AB \parallel CD$ and $p \parallel q$. Note that line p contains line segment AB and line q contains line segment CD. Parallel lines contain parallel line segments.

A **ray** starts at a point and extends indefinitely in one direction.

Ray

An **angle** is formed when two rays start from the same point. Rays r_1 and r_2 start from point B. The common endpoint is called the **vertex** of the angle.

Angle

If A and C are points on rays r_1 and r_2, respectively, then the angle is called $\angle B$ or $\angle ABC$, where "$\angle$" is the symbol for angle. Note that the angle is named by the vertex or the vertex is the second point listed when the angle is named by giving three points.

An angle can also be named by a variable written between the rays close to the vertex. In the figure at the right, $\angle x = \angle QRS = \angle SRQ$ and $\angle y = \angle SRT = \angle TRS$. Note that in this figure more than two rays meet at the vertex. In this case, the vertex cannot be used to name the angle.

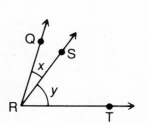

An angle is measured in **degrees.** The symbol for degree is °.

One complete revolution is 360° (360 degrees).

$\frac{1}{4}$ of a revolution is 90°. A 90° angle is called a **right angle.** The symbol "∟" represents a right angle.

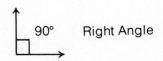

90°   Right Angle

Perpendicular lines are intersecting lines that form right angles.

The symbol "⊥" means "is perpendicular to." In the figure at the right, $AB \perp CD$ and $p \perp q$. Note that line p contains line segment AB and line q contains line segment CD. Perpendicular lines contain perpendicular line segments.

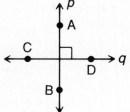

Complementary angles are two angles whose sum is 90°.

$\angle A + \angle B = 70° + 20° = 90°$
$\angle A$ and $\angle B$ are complementary angles.

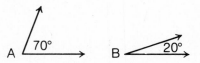

$\frac{1}{2}$ of a revolution is 180°. A 180° angle is called a **straight angle.** $\angle AOB$ is a straight angle.

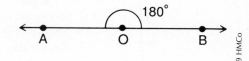

Supplementary angles are two angles whose sum is 180°.

$\angle A + \angle B = 130° + 50° = 180°$
$\angle A$ and $\angle B$ are supplementary angles.

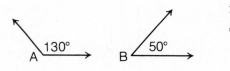

An **acute angle** is an angle whose measure is between 0° and 90°. $\angle B$ above is an acute angle. An **obtuse angle** is an angle whose measure is between 90° and 180°. $\angle A$ above is an obtuse angle.

In the figure at the right, $\angle DAC = 45°$ and $\angle CAB = 55°$.

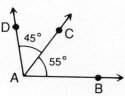

$\angle DAB = \angle DAC + \angle CAB = 45° + 55° = 100°$

In the figure at the right, $\angle EDG = 80°$. $\angle FDG$ is three times the measure of $\angle EDF$. Find the measure of $\angle EDF$.

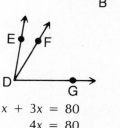

Let x = the measure of $\angle EDF$.
Then $3x$ = the measure of $\angle FDG$.
Write an equation and solve for x.

$$x + 3x = 80$$
$$4x = 80$$
$$x = 20$$

$$\angle EDF = 20°$$

Example 1

Given $MN = 15$, $NO = 18$, and $MP = 48$, find the length of OP.

Solution

$MN + NO + OP = MP$
$15 + 18 + OP = 48$
$33 + OP = 48$
$OP = 15$

Example 2

Given $QR = 24$, $ST = 17$, and $QT = 62$, find the length of RS.

Your solution

21

Example 3

Given $XY = 9$ and YZ is twice the length of XY, find the length of XZ.

Solution

$XZ = XY + YZ$
$XZ = XY + 2(XY)$
$XZ = 9 + 2(9)$
$XZ = 9 + 18$
$XZ = 27$

Example 4

Given $BC = 16$ and AB is $\frac{1}{4}$ the length of BC, find the length of AC.

Your solution

20

Example 5

The difference between two complementary angles is 30°. Find the larger of the two angles.

Strategy

To find the larger angle, write and solve a system of equations, using x to represent one angle and y to represent the other angle.

Solution

$x + y = 90°$
$x - y = 30°$
$2x = 120°$
$x = 60°$

The larger of the two angles is 60°.

Example 6

The difference between two supplementary angles is 40°. Find the larger of the two angles.

Your strategy

Your solution

110°

Solutions on p. A65

Example 7

Find the measure of ∠x.

Solution

$47° + x = 90°$

$\qquad\qquad x = 43°$

$\angle x = 43°$

Example 8

Find the measure of ∠a.

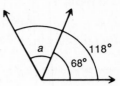

Your solution

50°

Solution on p. A65

| **Objective B** | To solve problems involving angles formed by intersecting lines |

Reference for Computer Tutor™

Four angles are formed by the intersection of two lines. If the two lines are perpendicular, each of the four angles is a right angle. If the two lines are not perpendicular, then two of the angles formed are acute angles and two of the angles are obtuse angles. The two acute angles are always opposite each other and the two obtuse angles are always opposite each other.

In the figure at the right, ∠w and ∠y are acute angles. ∠x and ∠z are obtuse angles. Two angles that are on opposite sides of the intersection of two lines are called **vertical angles.** Vertical angles have the same measure. ∠w and ∠y are vertical angles. ∠x and ∠z are vertical angles.

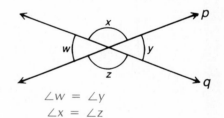

$\angle w = \angle y$
$\angle x = \angle z$

Two angles that share a common side are called **adjacent angles.** For the figure above, ∠x and ∠y are adjacent angles, as are ∠y and ∠z, ∠w and ∠x, and ∠w and ∠z. Adjacent angles of intersecting lines are supplementary angles.

$\angle x + \angle y = 180°$
$\angle y + \angle z = 180°$
$\angle z + \angle w = 180°$
$\angle w + \angle x = 180°$

Given that ∠c = 65°, find the measure of angles a, b, and d.

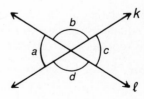

∠c = ∠a because ∠c and ∠a are vertical angles.

$\angle a = 65°$

∠c is supplementary to ∠b because ∠c and ∠b are adjacent angles.

$65° + \angle b = 180°$
$\qquad\qquad \angle b = 115°$

∠b = ∠d because ∠b and ∠d are vertical angles.

$\angle d = 115°$

A line that intersects two other lines at two different points is called a **transversal.**

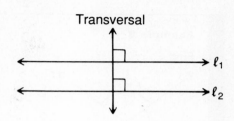

Transversal

If the lines cut by a transversal are parallel lines and the transversal is perpendicular to the parallel lines, all eight angles formed are right angles.

If the lines cut by a transversal are parallel lines and the transversal is not perpendicular to the parallel lines, all four acute angles have the same measure and all four obtuse angles have the same measure. For the figure at the right:

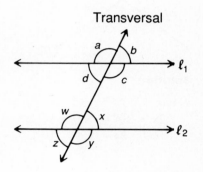

Transversal

$\angle a = \angle c = \angle w = \angle y$ and

$\angle b = \angle d = \angle x = \angle z.$

Alternate interior angles are two angles that are on opposite sides of the transversal and between the parallel lines. $\angle c$ and $\angle w$ are alternate interior angles. $\angle d$ and $\angle x$ are alternate interior angles. Alternate interior angles have the same measure.

Alternate exterior angles are two angles that are on opposite sides of the transversal and outside the parallel lines. $\angle a$ and $\angle y$ are alternate exterior angles. $\angle b$ and $\angle z$ are alternate exterior angles. Alternate exterior angles have the same measure.

Corresponding angles are two angles that are on the same side of the transversal and are both acute angles or are both obtuse angles. For the figure above, the following pairs of angles are corresponding angles: $\angle a$ and $\angle w$, $\angle d$ and $\angle z$, $\angle b$ and $\angle x$, $\angle c$ and $\angle y$. Corresponding angles have the same measure.

Given that $\ell_1 \parallel \ell_2$ and $\angle c = 58°$, find the measures of $\angle f$, $\angle h$, and $\angle g$.

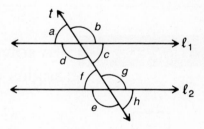

$\angle c$ and $\angle f$ are alternate interior angles.

$\angle f = \angle c = 58°$

$\angle c$ and $\angle h$ are corresponding angles.

$\angle h = \angle c = 58°$

$\angle g$ is supplementary to $\angle h$.

$\angle g + \angle h = 180°$
$\angle g + 58° = 180°$
$\angle g = 122°$

Example 9

Find x.

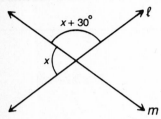

Solution

$x + (x + 30°) = 180°$
$2x + 30° = 180°$
$2x = 150°$
$x = 75°$

Example 10

Find x.

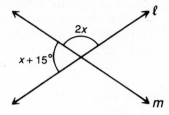

Your solution

55°

Example 11

Given $\ell_1 \parallel \ell_2$, find x.

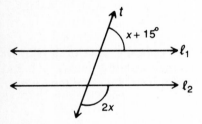

Solution

$(x + 15°) + 2x = 180°$
$3x + 15° = 180°$
$3x = 165°$
$x = 55°$

Example 12

Given $\ell_1 \parallel \ell_2$, find x.

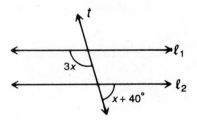

Your solution

35°

Copyright © 1989 HMCo

Solutions on p. A65

Objective C   To solve problems involving the angles of a triangle

12
DISK
TWELVE

Reference for
Computer
Tutor™

If the lines cut by a transversal are nonparallel lines, the three lines will intersect at three points. In the figure at the right, the transversal *t* intersects lines *p* and *q*. The three lines intersect at points *A, B,* and *C.* These three points define three line segments, *AB, BC,* and *AC.* The plane figure formed by these three line segments is called a **triangle.**

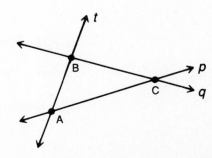

Each of the three points of intersection is the vertex of four angles. The angles within the region enclosed by the triangle are called **interior angles.** In the figure at the right, angles *a*, *b*, and *c* are interior angles. The sum of the measures of the interior angles is $180°$.

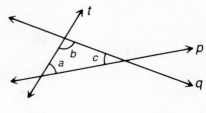

$$\angle a + \angle b + \angle c = 180°$$

An angle adjacent to an interior angle is called an **exterior angle.** The sum of an interior angle and an adjacent exterior angle is 180°.

Given that $\angle c = 40°$ and $\angle g = 100°$, find the measures of angles *a*, *b*, *d*, *e*, *f*, *h*, *w*, *x*, *y*, and *z*.

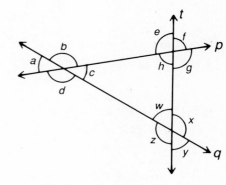

$\angle a$ and $\angle c$ are vertical angles.	$\angle a = \angle c = 40°$
$\angle b$ and $\angle c$ are supplementary angles.	$\angle b + \angle c = 180°$ $\angle b + 40° = 180°$ $\angle b = 140°$
$\angle d$ and $\angle b$ are vertical angles.	$\angle d = \angle b = 140°$
$\angle e$ and $\angle g$ are vertical angles.	$\angle e = \angle g = 100°$
$\angle f$ and $\angle g$ are supplementary angles.	$\angle f + \angle g = 180°$ $\angle f + 100° = 180°$ $\angle f = 80°$
$\angle h$ and $\angle f$ are vertical angles.	$\angle h = \angle f = 80°$
The sum of the measures of the interior angles is 180°.	$\angle c + \angle h + \angle w = 180°$ $40° + 80° + \angle w = 180°$ $120° + \angle w = 180°$ $\angle w = 60°$
$\angle x$ and $\angle w$ are supplementary angles.	$\angle x + \angle w = 180°$ $\angle x + 60° = 180°$ $\angle x = 120°$
$\angle y$ and $\angle w$ are vertical angles.	$\angle y = \angle w = 60°$
$\angle z$ and $\angle x$ are vertical angles.	$\angle z = \angle x = 120°$

Example 13

Given that ∠y = 55°, find the measures of angles a, b, and d.

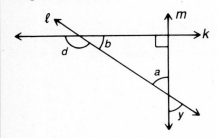

Solution

∠a = ∠y = 55°

∠a + ∠b + 90° = 180°
55° + ∠b + 90° = 180°
     ∠b + 145° = 180°
          ∠b = 35°

∠d + ∠b = 180°
∠d + 35° = 180°
     ∠d = 145°

Example 14

Given that ∠a = 45° and ∠x = 100°, find the measures of angles b, c, and y.

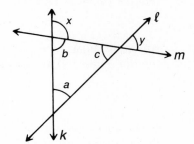

Your solution

∠b = 80°

∠c = 55°

∠y = 55°

Example 15

In a triangle, the measure of one angle is twice the measure of the second angle. The measure of the third angle is 4° less than the measure of the second angle. Find the measure of each angle.

Strategy

To find the measure of each angle:
▷ Let x = the measure of the second angle.
  Then 2x = the measure of the first angle and
  x − 4° = the measure of the third angle.
  The sum of the angles of a triangle is 180°.
▷ Substitute the value of x into the variable
  expressions for the first and third angles.

Solution

2x + x + (x − 4°) = 180°
          4x − 4° = 180°
              4x = 184°
               x = 46°

2x = 2(46°) = 92°   x − 4° = 46° − 4° = 42°

The angles measure 42°, 46°, and 92°.

Example 16

One angle of a triangle is a right angle and one angle is 3° less than twice the measure of the smallest angle. Find the measure of each angle.

Your strategy

Your solution

31°, 59°, and 90°

12.1A Exercises

Solve.

1. Find the complement of a 62° angle.

    28°

2. Find the complement of a 31° angle.

    59°

3. Find the supplement of a 162° angle.

    18°

4. Find the supplement of a 72° angle.

    108°

5. The difference between two complementary angles is 10°. Find the measures of the two angles.

    40° and 50°

6. The difference between two complementary angles is 40°. Find the measures of the two angles.

    25° and 65°

7. The difference between two supplementary angles is 20°. Find the measures of the two angles.

    80° and 100°

8. The difference between two supplementary angles is 80°. Find the measures of the two angles.

    50° and 130°

9. Given $AB = 12$, $CD = 9$, and $AD = 35$, find the length of BC.

    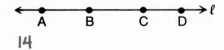

    14

10. Given $AB = 21$, $BC = 14$, and $AD = 54$, find the length of CD.

    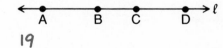

    19

11. Given $QR = 7$ and RS is three times the length of QR, find the length of QS.

    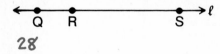

    28

12. Given $QR = 15$ and RS is twice the length of QR, find the length of QS.

    45

13. Given $EF = 20$ and FG is $\frac{1}{2}$ the length of EF, find the length of EG.

    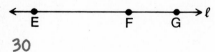

    30

14. Given $EF = 18$ and FG is $\frac{1}{3}$ the length of EF, find the length of EG.

    24

15. Find the measure of $\angle x$.

    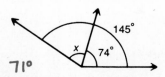

    71°

16. Find the measure of $\angle x$.

    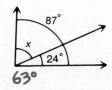

    63°

Solve.

17. Given ∠LOM = 53° and ∠LON = 139°, find the measure of ∠MON.

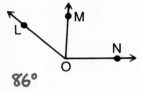

86°

18. Given ∠MON = 38° and ∠LON = 85°, find the measure of ∠LOM.

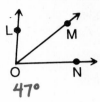

47°

19. Given ∠LON is a right angle, find the measure of ∠x.

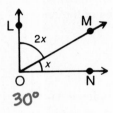

30°

20. Given ∠LON is a right angle, find the measure of ∠x.

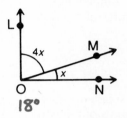

18°

21. Given ∠LON is a right angle, find the measure of ∠x.

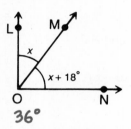

36°

22. Given ∠LON is a right angle, find the measure of ∠x.

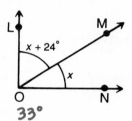

33°

23. Find the measure of ∠a.

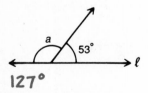

127°

24. Find the measure of ∠a.

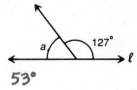

53°

25. Find the measure of ∠a.

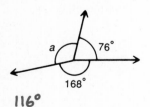

116°

26. Find the measure of ∠a.

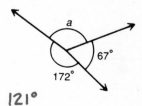

121°

27. Find x.

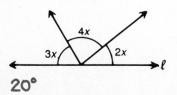

20°

28. Find x.

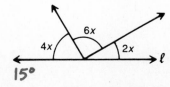

15°

Solve.

29. Find x.

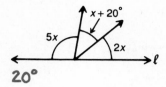

20°

30. Find x.

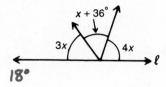

18°

31. Find x.

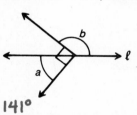

20°

32. Find x.

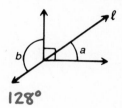

45°

33. Given ∠a = 51°, find the measure of ∠b.

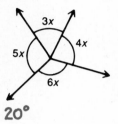

141°

34. Given ∠a = 38°, find the measure of ∠b.

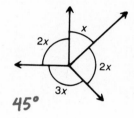

128°

12.1B Exercises

Solve.

35. Find the measure of ∠x.

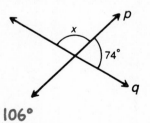

106°

36. Find the measure of ∠x.

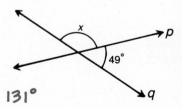

131°

37. Find the measure of ∠x.

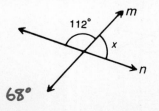

68°

38. Find the measure of ∠x.

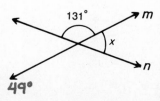

49°

Solve.

39. Given that $\ell_1 \parallel \ell_2$, find the measures of angles a and b.

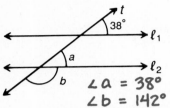

∠a = 38°
∠b = 142°

40. Given that $\ell_1 \parallel \ell_2$, find the measures of angles a and b.

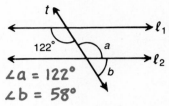

∠a = 122°
∠b = 58°

41. Given that $\ell_1 \parallel \ell_2$, find the measures of angles a and b.

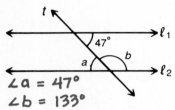

∠a = 47°
∠b = 133°

42. Given that $\ell_1 \parallel \ell_2$, find the measures of angles a and b.

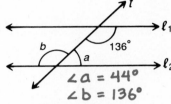

∠a = 44°
∠b = 136°

43. Given that $\ell_1 \parallel \ell_2$, find x.

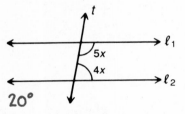

20°

44. Given that $\ell_1 \parallel \ell_2$, find x.

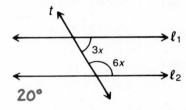

20°

45. Given that $\ell_1 \parallel \ell_2$, find x.

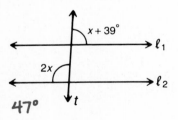

47°

46. Given that $\ell_1 \parallel \ell_2$, find x.

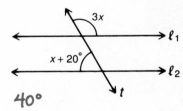

40°

Copyright © 1989 HMCo

12.1C Exercises

Solve.

47. Given that $\angle a = 95°$ and $\angle b = 70°$, find the measures of angles x and y.

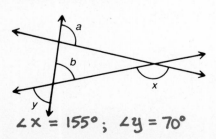

∠x = 155°; ∠y = 70°

48. Given that $\angle a = 35°$ and $\angle b = 55°$, find the measures of angles x and y.

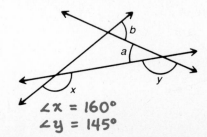

∠x = 160°
∠y = 145°

Solve.

49. Given that ∠y = 45°, find the measures of angles *a* and *b*.

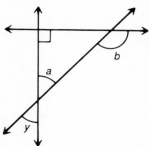

∠a = 45°
∠b = 135°

50. Given that ∠y = 130°, find the measures of angles *a* and *b*.

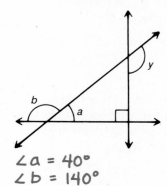

∠a = 40°
∠b = 140°

51. Given that *AO* ⊥ *OB*, express in terms of *x* the number of degrees in ∠*BOC*.

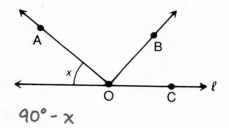

90° – x

52. Given that *AO* ⊥ *OB*, express in terms of *x* the number of degrees in ∠*AOC*.

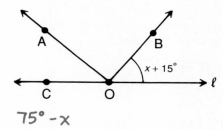

75° – x

53. One angle in a triangle is a right angle, and one angle is equal to 30°. Find the measure of the other angle.

60°

54. A triangle has one right angle and one equal to 7°. Find the measure of the other angle.

83°

55. Two angles of a triangle measure 42° and 103°. Find the measure of the third angle.

35°

56. Two angles of a triangle measure 62° and 45°. Find the measure of the third angle.

73°

57. A triangle has a 13° angle and a 65° angle. Find the measure of the other angle.

102°

58. A triangle has a 105° angle and a 32° angle. Find the measure of the other angle.

43°

59. A triangle has a 45° angle and a right angle. Find the measure of the other angle.

45°

60. A triangle has a 62° angle and a right angle. Find the measure of the other angle.

28°

61. A triangle has a 62° angle and a 104° angle. Find the measure of the other angle.

14°

62. A triangle has a 30° angle and a 45° angle. Find the measure of the other angle.

105°

Solve.

63. In a triangle, one angle is twice the measure of the second angle. The third angle is three times the measure of the second angle. Find the measure of each angle.

30°, 60°, and 90°

64. In a triangle, one angle is 5° more than the measure of the second angle. The third angle is 10° more than the measure of the second angle. Find the measure of each angle.

55°, 60°, and 65°

65. One angle of a triangle is three times the measure of the third angle. The second angle is 5° less than the measure of the third angle. Find the measure of each angle.

32°, 37°, and 111°

66. One angle of a triangle is twice the measure of the second angle. The third angle is three times the measure of the first angle. Find the measure of each angle.

20°, 40°, and 120°

67. The first angle of a triangle is twice the measure of the second angle. The third angle is 10° less than the measure of the first angle. Find the measure of each angle.

38°, 66°, and 76°

68. The first angle of a triangle is three times the measure of the second angle. The third angle is 33° more than the measure of the first angle. Find the measure of each angle.

21°, 63°, and 96°

69. The difference between the measures of the two acute angles in a triangle that has a right angle is 40°. Find the measures of the two acute angles.

25° and 65°

70. The difference between the measures of the two acute angles in a triangle that has a right angle is 32°. Find the measures of the two acute angles.

29° and 61°

71. The sum of the measures of two angles of a triangle is 132° and their difference is 38°. Find the measure of each angle.

47° and 85°

72. The sum of the measures of two angles of a triangle is 128° and their difference is 8°. Find the measure of each angle.

60° and 68°

73. One angle in a triangle is three times as large as the second angle. The exterior angle at the third angle is 120°. Find the measure of the second angle.

30°

74. One angle in a triangle is four times as large as the second angle. The exterior angle at the third angle is 70°. Find the measure of the second angle.

14°

75. One angle in a triangle is 30° larger than the second angle. The exterior angle at the third angle is 110°. Find the measure of the second angle.

40°

76. One angle in a triangle is 15° larger than the second angle. The exterior angle at the third angle is 105°. Find the measure of the second angle.

45°

Section 2 Perimeter and Area

Objective A To find the perimeter of a geometric figure

12
DISK
TWELVE

Reference for
Computer
Tutor™

The **perimeter** of a plane geometric figure is a measure of the distance around the figure. Perimeter is used in buying fencing for a lawn or determining how much baseboard is needed for a room.

A **triangle** is a three-sided plane figure. Using a, b, and c to represent the lengths of the three sides of a triangle, the formula for the perimeter, P, of a triangle is:

$$P = a + b + c$$

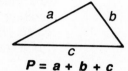

An **isosceles triangle** has two sides of equal length. The angles opposite the equal sides are of equal measure. In the figure at the right, $AC = BC$ and $\angle A = \angle B$

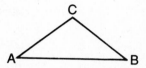

The three sides of an **equilateral triangle** are of equal length. Each of the three angles are of equal measure. Each angle measures 60°. In the figure at the right,

$$AB = BC = CA$$
and
$$\angle A = \angle B = \angle C$$

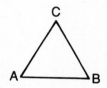

A **quadrilateral** is a four-sided plane figure. Three quadrilaterals with special characteristics are the parallelogram, the rectangle, and the square.

A **parallelogram** is a quadrilateral in which opposite sides are parallel and equal. In the figure at the right, $AD \parallel BC$, $AB \parallel CD$, $AD = BC$, and $AB = CD$ The perimeter of a parallelogram is the sum of the lengths of the four sides.

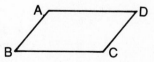

A **rectangle** is a parallelogram that has four right angles. Usually the length, *L*, of a rectangle refers to the length of one of the longer sides of the rectangle and the width, *W*, refers to the length of one of the shorter sides. The formula for the perimeter, *P*, of a rectangle is $P = 2L + 2W$.

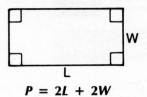

$P = 2L + 2W$

A **square** is a rectangle that has four equal sides. The variable *s* is used to represent the length of a side of a square. The formula for the perimeter, *P*, of a square is $P = 4s$.

$P = 4s$

A **circle** is a plane figure in which all points are the same distance from point *O*, called the **center** of the circle.

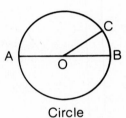

Circle

The **diameter** of a circle is a line segment across the circle going through point *O*. *AB* is a diameter of the circle. The variable *d* is used to designate the diameter of a circle.

The **radius** of a circle is a line segment from the center of the circle to a point on the circle. *OC* is a radius of the circle. The variable *r* is used to designate the radius of a circle.

The length of the diameter is twice the length of the radius.

$$d = 2r \quad \text{or} \quad r = \frac{1}{2}d$$

The distance around a circle is called the **circumference.** The formula for the circumference, *C*, of a circle is:

$$C = \pi d \quad \text{or} \quad C = 2\pi r$$

The number π (pi) is an irrational number and cannot be represented exactly by a fraction or by a terminating or repeating decimal. Note that if the equation $C = \pi d$ is solved for π, the resulting equation is $\pi = \frac{C}{d}$. Therefore, π is the ratio of the circumference to the length of the diameter of a circle.

$$\pi \approx 3.14 \quad \text{or} \quad \frac{22}{7}$$

The length of a side of a square is $3x + 5$. Find the perimeter of the square in terms of the variable x.

Use the equation for the perimeter of a square.

$P = 4s$
$P = 4(3x + 5)$
$P = 12x + 20$

The perimeter is $12x + 20$.

The circumference of a circle is 10 cm. Find the length of a diameter of the circle. Use 3.14 for π. Round to the nearest hundredth.

Use the equation for the circumference of a circle.

$C = \pi d$
$10 = 3.14d$
$3.18 \approx d$

The diameter is 3.18 cm.

Composite geometric figures are figures made from two or more geometric figures. The following composite is made from part of a rectangle and part of a circle.

Composite figure $= 3$ sides of a rectangle $+ \frac{1}{2}$ the circumference of a circle

Perimeter $=$　$2L + W$　$+$　$\frac{1}{2}\pi d$

Find the perimeter of the composite figure shown above if the width of the rectangle is 4 m and the length of the rectangle is 8 m. Use 3.14 for π.

The perimeter equals 2 lengths of a rectangle plus 1 width plus one-half the circumference of a circle. The diameter of the circle equals the width of the rectangle.

$P = 2L + W + \frac{1}{2}\pi d$

$P = 2(8) + 4 + \frac{1}{2}(3.14)(4)$

$P = 16 + 4 + 6.28$
$P = 26.28$

The perimeter is 26.28 m.

Example 1

The perimeter of a rectangle is 34 m. The width is 3 m less than the length. Find the length of the rectangle.

Strategy

To find the perimeter, use the equation for the perimeter of a rectangle. Let L = the length. Then $L - 3$ = the width.

Solution

$P = 2L + 2W$
$34 = 2L + 2(L - 3)$
$34 = 2L + 2L - 6$
$34 = 4L - 6$
$40 = 4L$
$10 = L$

The length of the rectangle is 10 m.

Example 2

In an isosceles triangle, one side is 50% of the length of one of the two equal sides. Find the length of each side if the perimeter is 125 ft.

Your strategy

Your solution

50 ft, 50 ft, and 25 ft

Example 3

The width of a rectangle is $3x$. The length is $4x - 1$. Find the perimeter of the rectangle in terms of the variable x.

Strategy

To find the perimeter, use the equation for the perimeter of a rectangle.

Solution

$P = 2L + 2W$
$P = 2(4x - 1) + 2(3x)$
$P = 8x - 2 + 6x$
$P = 14x - 2$

The perimeter is $14x - 2$.

Example 4

Each of two sides of a parallelogram have a length of $3x + 1$. Each of the other two sides have a length of $2x - 5$. Find the perimeter of the parallelogram in terms of the variable x.

Your strategy

Your solution

$10x - 8$

Solutions on p. A66

Example 5

Find the perimeter of the figure. Use 3.14 for π.

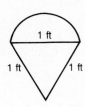

1 ft

1 ft   1 ft

Example 6

The circumference of the circle in the figure is 6π cm. Find the perimeter of square *ABCD*.

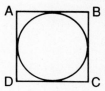

Strategy

The perimeter is equal to 2 sides of a triangle plus $\frac{1}{2}$ the circumference of a circle.

Your strategy

Solution

$P = a + b + \frac{1}{2}\pi d$

$P = 1 + 1 + \frac{1}{2}(3.14)(1)$

$P = 1 + 1 + 1.57$

$P = 3.57$

The perimeter is 3.57 ft.

Your solution

24 cm

Solution on p. A67

To find the area of a geometric figure

Reference for Computer Tutor™

Area is a measure of the amount of surface in a region. Area can be used to describe the size of a rug, a parking lot, a farm, or a national park.

Area is measured in square units.

A square that is 1 ft on each side has an area of 1 square foot, written 1 ft².

1 ft

1 ft

A square that is 1 cm on each side has an area of 1 square centimeter, written 1 cm².

1 cm

1 cm

Figure *ABC* is a triangle. *AB* is the **base.** The line *CD*, perpendicular to the base, is the **height.**

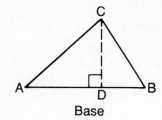

Base

Any side of a triangle can be designated as the base. The corresponding height is found by drawing a line segment perpendicular to the base from the vertex opposite the base. The variable *b* is used to denote the length of the base of a triangle. The variable *h* is used to denote the length of the corresponding height of the triangle.

The formula for the area, *A*, of a triangle is: $A = \frac{1}{2}bh$

Figure *ABCD* is a parallelogram. *BC* is the **base** of the parallelogram. The line *AE*, perpendicular to the base, is the **height.**

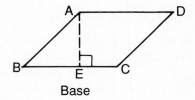

Base

Any side of a parallelogram can be designated as the base. The corresponding height is found by drawing a line segment perpendicular to the base from the opposite side. The variable *b* is used to denote the length of the base of a parallelogram. The variable *h* is used to denote the length of the corresponding height of the parallelogram.

The formula for the area, *A*, of a parallelogram is: $A = bh$

The area of a rectangle is found by multiplying the length by the width.

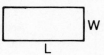

The formula for the area, *A*, of a rectangle is: $A = LW$

The area of a square is found by squaring the length of a side of the square.

The formula for the area, *A*, of a square is: $A = s^2$

The area of a circle is the product of π and the square of the radius.

The formula for the area, A, of a circle is:

$$A = \pi r^2$$

The height of a parallelogram is 2 cm more than twice the length of the base. The area of the parallelogram is 24 cm². Find the height of the parallelogram.

Use the equation for the area of a parallelogram. Let b = the base. Then $2b + 2$ = the height.

$$A = bh$$

$$24 = b(2b + 2)$$

Solve for b.

$$24 = 2b^2 + 2b$$
$$0 = 2b^2 + 2b - 24$$
$$0 = b^2 + b - 12$$
$$0 = (b + 4)(b - 3)$$

$$b + 4 = 0 \qquad b - 3 = 0$$
$$b = -4 \qquad b = 3$$

The base cannot be a negative number. The base is 3 cm.

Substitute the value of b into the variable expression for the height.

$$h = 2b + 2 = 2(3) + 2 = 8$$

The height is 8 cm.

Example 7

The length of the base of a triangle is $2x$. The height is $x - 6$. Find the area of the triangle in terms of the variable x.

Strategy

To find the area, use the equation for the area of a triangle.

Solution

$A = \frac{1}{2}bh$

$A = \frac{1}{2}(2x)(x - 6)$

$A = x(x - 6)$

$A = x^2 - 6x$

The area is $x^2 - 6x$.

Example 8

The width of a rectangle is $2x - 1$. The length is $x + 4$. Find the area of the rectangle in terms of the variable x.

Your strategy

Your solution

$$2x^2 + 7x - 4$$

Solution on p. A67

Example 9

Find the area of a square that has a perimeter of 32 cm.

Strategy

To find the area:
▷ Use the equation for the perimeter of a square to find the length of a side.
▷ Use the equation for the area of a square.

Solution

$P = 4s$
$32 = 4s$
$8 = s$

$A = s^2$
$A = 8^2$
$A = 64$

The area is 64 cm².

Example 10

A rectangle has a perimeter of 54 in. The width of the rectangle is 6 in. Find the area.

Your strategy

Your solution

126 in²

Example 11

Find the area of the shaded portion of the figure. Use 3.14 for π.

8 m

8 m

Strategy

The area is equal to the area of the square minus the area of the circle.

Solution

$A = s^2 - \pi r^2$
$A = 8^2 - 3.14(4^2)$
$A = 64 - 50.24$
$A = 13.76$

The area is 13.76 m².

Example 12

Find the area of the composite figure.

6 in.

10 in.

4 in.

Your strategy

Your solution

48 in²

Solutions on p. A67

12.2A Exercises

Solve. Use 3.14 for π. Round to the nearest hundredth.

1. The lengths of the three sides of a triangle are 3.8 cm, 5.2 cm, and 8.4 cm. Find the perimeter of the triangle.

   17.4 cm

2. The length of each side of an equilateral triangle is $5\frac{1}{2}$ in. Find the perimeter of the triangle.

   $16\frac{1}{2}$ in.

3. Each of two sides of a parallelogram have a length of 4.3 m. Each of the other two sides has a length of 3.7 m. Find the perimeter of the parallelogram.

   16 m

4. Each of two sides of a parallelogram have a length of 3.5 ft. Each of the other two sides has a length of 2.25 ft. Find the perimeter of the parallelogram.

   11.5 ft

5. The length of a rectangular park is 55 yd. The width is 47 yd. How many yards of fencing are needed to surround the park?

   204 yd

6. The width of a rectangular garden is 21 ft and the length is 32 ft. How many feet of fencing are needed to surround the garden?

   106 ft

7. The length of each side of a square is 12.2 cm. Find the perimeter of the square.

   48.8 cm

8. Find the perimeter of a square that is 0.35 m on each side.

   1.4 m

9. The radius of a circle is 4.5 in. Find the length of a diameter of the circle.

   9 in.

10. Find the length of a radius of a circle that has a diameter of length 0.84 m.

    0.42 m

11. Find the circumference of a circle that has a diameter of length 1.5 in.

    4.71 in.

12. The radius of a circle is 2.3 cm. Find the circumference of the circle.

    14.44 cm

13. The length of each side of a square is $3x + 2$. Find the perimeter of the square in terms of the variable x.

    $12x + 8$

14. The length of each side of a square is $5x - 1$. Find the perimeter of the square in terms of the variable x.

    $20x - 4$

Solve. Use 3.14 for π. Round to the nearest hundredth.

15. The width of a rectangle is $2x$. The length is $3x - 4$. Find the perimeter of the rectangle in terms of the variable x.

10x − 8

16. The length of a rectangle is $4x - 1$. The width is $2x$. Find the perimeter of the rectangle in terms of the variable x.

12x − 2

17. Each of two sides of a parallelogram have a length of $x + 5$. Each of the other two sides has a length of $2x - 1$. Find the perimeter of the parallelogram in terms of the variable x.

6x + 8

18. Each of two sides of a parallelogram have a length of $2x + 7$. Each of the other two sides has a length of $3x - 2$. Find the perimeter of the parallelogram in terms of the variable x.

10x + 10

19. The lengths of the sides of a triangle measure $3x - 2$, $2x + 3$, and $x + 6$. Find the perimeter of the triangle in terms of the variable x.

6x + 7

20. The length of each side of an equilateral triangle measures $4x - 7$. Find the perimeter of the triangle in terms of the variable x.

12x − 21

21. A rectangular playground has a perimeter of 440 ft. The width of the playground is 20 ft less than the length. Find the length and width of the playground.

length : 120 ft ;
width : 100 ft

22. A rectangular garden has a perimeter of 64 ft. The length of the garden is 8 ft more than the width. Find the length and width of the garden.

length : 20 ft ;
width : 12 ft

23. The perimeter of a rectangle is 50 m. The width of the rectangle is 5 m less than the length. Find the length and width of the rectangle.

length : 15 m ;
width : 10 m

24. The perimeter of a rectangle is 120 ft. The length of the rectangle is twice the width. Find the length and width of the rectangle.

length : 40 ft ;
width : 20 ft

25. The perimeter of a triangle is 20 ft. The first side is 1 ft less than twice the second side. The third side is 1 ft more than twice the second side. Find the measure of each side.

4 ft, 7 ft, and 9 ft

26. The perimeter of an isosceles triangle is 25 cm. One side is 2 cm less than the length of one of the equal sides. Find the measure of each side.

9 cm, 9 cm, and 7 cm

27. The circumference of a circle is 8 cm. Find the length of a diameter of the circle.

2.55 cm

28. The circumference of a circle is 12 cm. Find the length of a diameter of the circle.

3.82 cm

Solve. Use 3.14 for π. Round to the nearest hundredth.

29. The circumference of a circle is 20 m. Find the length of a radius of the circle.

3.18 m

30. The circumference of a circle is 9 m. Find the length of a radius of the circle.

1.43 m

31. The length of a side of a square is 2 in. less than the measure of one side of an equilateral triangle. The perimeter of the square is equal to the perimeter of the triangle. Find the length of a side of the triangle.

8 in.

32. The length of a side of a square is 4 cm less than the measure of one side of an equilateral triangle. The perimeter of the square is equal to the perimeter of the triangle. Find the length of a side of the triangle.

16 cm

33. A bicycle tire has a diameter of 24 in. How many feet does the bicycle travel if the wheel makes 5 revolutions?

31.4 ft

34. A tricycle tire has a diameter of 12 in. How many feet does the tricycle travel if the wheel makes 8 revolutions?

25.12 ft

Find the perimeter of the composite figure. Use 3.14 for π.

35.

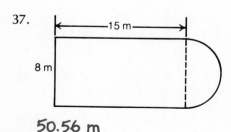

6 cm

40.26 cm

36.

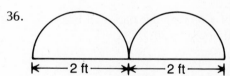

2 ft   2 ft

10.28 ft

37.

15 m

8 m

50.56 m

38.

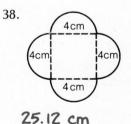

4cm

4cm   4cm

4cm

25.12 cm

39.

5 cm   5 cm

5 cm   5 cm

7 cm

30.99 cm

40.

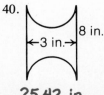

8 in.

3 in.

25.42 in.

12.2B Exercises

Solve. Use 3.14 for π. Round to the nearest hundredth.

41. The length of the base of a triangle is 2.4 cm. The height is 3.5 cm. Find the area of the triangle.

    4.2 cm²

42. The height of a triangle is $2\frac{1}{2}$ in. The length of the base is $4\frac{1}{4}$ in. Find the area of the triangle.

    $5\frac{5}{16}$ in²

43. The height of a parallelogram is 0.4 m. The length of the base is 0.8 m. Find the area of the parallelogram.

    0.32 m²

44. The length of the base of a parallelogram is 3.7 cm and the height is 6.2 cm. Find the area of the parallelogram.

    22.94 cm²

45. The length of a side of a square is $3\frac{1}{2}$ in. Find the area of the square.

    $12\frac{1}{4}$ in²

46. Find the area of a square that is 2.5 ft on each side.

    6.25 ft²

47. Find the area of a rectangular park that has a length of 54 yd and a width of 32 yd.

    1728 yd²

48. A rectangular garden has a length of 17 ft and a width of 12 ft. Find the area of the garden.

    204 ft²

49. The radius of a circle is 8.5 cm. Find the area of the circle.

    226.87 cm²

50. Find the area of a circle that has a radius of length 2.5 in.

    19.63 in²

51. The length of a rectangle is $x + 7$. The width is $x - 4$. Find the area of the rectangle in terms of the variable x.

    $x^2 + 3x - 28$

52. The width of a rectangle is $x - 1$. The length is $2x + 1$. Find the area of the rectangle in terms of the variable x.

    $2x^2 - x - 1$

53. The length of a side of a square is $x + 2$. Find the area of the square in terms of the variable x.

    $x^2 + 4x + 4$

54. The length of a side of a square is $2x - 1$. Find the area of the square in terms of the variable x.

    $4x^2 - 4x + 1$

Solve. Use 3.14 for π. Round to the nearest hundredth.

55. The length of the base of a triangle is $3x - 4$. The height is $4x$. Find the area of the triangle in terms of the variable x.

$6x^2 - 8x$

56. The length of the base of a triangle is $5x + 2$. The height is $6x$. Find the area of the triangle in terms of the variable x.

$15x^2 + 6x$

57. The radius of a circle is $x + 3$. Find the area of the circle in terms of π and the variable x.

$\pi x^2 + 6\pi x + 9\pi$

58. The radius of a circle is $x - 2$. Find the area of the circle in terms of π and the variable x.

$\pi x^2 - 4\pi x + 4\pi$

59. The length of the base of a triangle is four times the height. The area of the triangle is 50 ft². Find the base and height of the triangle.

base: 20 ft;
height: 5 ft

60. The height of a triangle is 3 m more than twice the length of the base. The area of the triangle is 76 m². Find the height of the triangle.

19 m

61. The length of a rectangle is three times the width. The area is 300 in². Find the length and width of the rectangle.

length: 30 in.;
width: 10 in.

62. The length of a rectangle is 2 ft more than twice the width. The area is 312 ft². Find the length and width of the rectangle.

length: 26 ft;
width: 12 ft

63. The height of a triangle is four times the length of the base. The area of the triangle is 18 m². Find the base and height of the triangle.

base: 3 m;
height: 12 m

64. The height of a triangle is 2 m more than twice the length of the base. The area of the triangle is 20 m². Find the base and height of the triangle.

base: 4 m;
height: 10 m

65. The length of a rectangle is 5 in. more than twice the width. The area is 75 in². Find the length and width of the rectangle.

length: 15 in.;
width: 5 in.

66. The width of a rectangle is 5 ft less than the length. The area of the rectangle is 176 ft². Find the length and width of the rectangle.

length: 16 ft;
width: 11 ft

67. The length of each side of a square is extended 2 in. The area of the resulting square is 144 in². Find the length of a side of the original square.

10 in.

68. The length of each side of a square is extended 5 in. The area of the resulting square is 64 in². Find the length of a side of the original square.

3 in.

Solve. Use 3.14 for π. Round to the nearest hundredth.

69. A circle has a radius of 8 in. Find the increase in area when the radius is increased by 2 in.

    113.04 in²

70. A circle has a radius of 5 cm. Find the increase in area when the radius is doubled.

    235.5 cm²

71. A rectangle is 8 ft wide and $(3x - 2)$ ft long. Express as an integer the minimum length of the rectangle when the area is greater than 104 ft².

    14 ft

72. The base of a triangle is 10 in. and the height is $(2x - 4)$ in. Express as an integer the maximum height of the triangle when the area is less than 80 in².

    15 in.

73. What is the number of square units in the area of a triangle whose vertices have coordinates $(4, -3)$, $(4, 2)$, and $(8, -1)$?

    10 square units

74. What is the number of square units in the area of a triangle whose vertices have coordinates $(-2, 2)$, $(1, -3)$, and $(4, 2)$?

    15 square units

75. Find the area of the figure.

    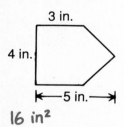

    16 in²

76. Find the area of the figure.

    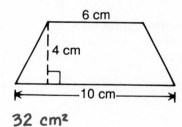

    32 cm²

77. The circumference of the circle in the figure is 10π cm. Find the area of square $ABCD$.

    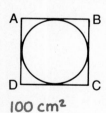

    100 cm²

78. Find the area of the concrete driveway.

    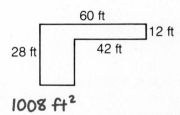

    1008 ft²

79. How much hardwood flooring is needed to cover the roller rink?

    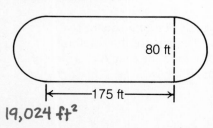

    19,024 ft²

80. Find the area of the 2-meter boundary around the swimming pool.

    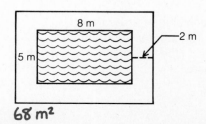

    68 m²

Section **3** Triangles

Objective A To solve right triangles

Reference for
Computer
Tutor™

A **right triangle** contains one right angle. The side opposite the right angle is called the **hypotenuse.** The other two sides are called **legs.**

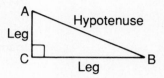

Pythagorus, a Greek mathematician, discovered that the square of the hypotenuse of a right triangle is equal to the sum of the squares of the two legs. This is called the **Pythagorean Theorem.**

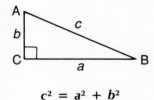

$$c^2 = a^2 + b^2$$

If the lengths of two sides of a right triangle are known, the Pythagorean Theorem can be used to find the length of the third side.

Find the hypotenuse of a right triangle with legs that measure 3 in. and 4 in.

Use the Pythagorean Theorem.
$a = 3, b = 4$

$$c^2 = a^2 + b^2$$
$$c^2 = 3^2 + 4^2$$
$$c^2 = 9 + 16$$
$$c^2 = 25$$

Take the principal square root of both sides of the equation.

$$\sqrt{c^2} = \sqrt{25}$$
$$c = 5$$

The hypotenuse is 5 in.

The length of one leg of a right triangle is 5 cm. The hypotenuse is 8 cm. Find the length of the other leg. Round to the nearest hundredth.

Use the Pythagorean Theorem.
$a = 5, c = 8$

$$a^2 + b^2 = c^2$$
$$5^2 + b^2 = 8^2$$
$$25 + b^2 = 64$$
$$b^2 = 39$$

Take the principal square root of both sides of the equation.

$$\sqrt{b^2} = \sqrt{39}$$
$$b \approx 6.24$$

The length of the leg is 6.24 cm.

The Pythagorean Theorem can be used to find a relationship among the sides of two special right triangles.

Recall that an isosceles triangle has two equal angles. In an **isosceles right triangle,** $\angle A$ and $\angle B$ both measure 45°. For this reason, an isosceles right triangle is also called a **45°-45°-90° triangle.**

Find the hypotenuse of an isosceles right triangle if the length of one of the legs measures 1 unit.

Use the Pythagorean Theorem. In an isosceles right triangle, both legs are of equal length.
$a = 1, b = 1$

$$c^2 = a^2 + b^2$$
$$c^2 = 1^2 + 1^2$$
$$c^2 = 1 + 1$$
$$c^2 = 2$$

Take the principal square root of both sides of the equation.

$$\sqrt{c^2} = \sqrt{2}$$
$$c = \sqrt{2}$$

The hypotenuse is $\sqrt{2}$ units.

The figure corresponding to this example is shown at the right.

For any isosceles right triangle, the hypotenuse, c, equals $\sqrt{2}$ times the length of a leg.

$$c = \sqrt{2} \text{ (length of a leg)}$$

For example, if the length of one of the legs in a 45°-45°-90° triangle is $4\sqrt{2}$ m, then the hypotenuse is

$$c = \sqrt{2}(4\sqrt{2}) = 4 \cdot 2 = 8 \text{ m}$$

A leg of an isosceles right triangle has a length of 4 m. Find the perimeter of the triangle. Round to the nearest hundredth.

Find the hypotenuse.

$$c = \sqrt{2}(4) = 4\sqrt{2}$$

Find the perimeter.
An isosceles right triangle has 2 equal legs.
$a = 4, b = 4, c = 4\sqrt{2}$

$$P = a + b + c$$
$$P = 4 + 4 + 4\sqrt{2}$$
$$P = 8 + 4\sqrt{2}$$
$$P \approx 8 + 4(1.414)$$
$$P \approx 8 + 5.656$$
$$P \approx 13.656$$

The perimeter is 13.66 m.

The second special right triangle is the
30°-60°-90° triangle. The acute angles
in a 30°-60°-90° triangle measure 30°
and 60°.

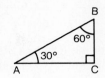

If two 30°-60°-90° triangles, each with a
hypotenuse of 2 units, are positioned so
that the longer legs of each triangle lie on
the same line segment, then an equilateral
triangle is formed and the shorter leg of
each triangle is 1 unit.

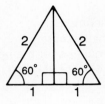

Using the Pythagorean Theorem, the length of
the longer leg can be found. $a = 1, c = 2$

$$a^2 + b^2 = c^2$$
$$1^2 + b^2 = 2^2$$
$$1 + b^2 = 4$$
$$b^2 = 3$$

Take the principal square root
of both sides of the equation.

$$\sqrt{b^2} = \sqrt{3}$$
$$b = \sqrt{3}$$

The relationship among the sides of
a 30°-60°-90° triangle is shown in
the figure at the right.

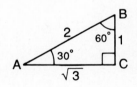

For any 30°-60°-90° triangle, the hypotenuse, c, equals twice the length
of the shorter leg, or the leg opposite
the 30° angle.

$c = 2$(length of shorter leg)

For example, if the shorter leg in a
30°-60°-90° triangle measures 2.4
in., then the hypotenuse is

$$c = 2(2.4) = 4.8 \text{ in.}$$

The **diagonal** of a quadrilateral is a
line segment drawn from one vertex
to the opposite vertex.

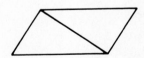

Find the width of rectangle $ABCD$ if
the length of diagonal AC is 12 in.

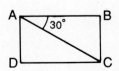

Triangle ABC is a 30°-60°-90° triangle with hypotenuse AC and shorter
leg BC.

$$c = 2(\text{length of shorter leg})$$
$$AC = 2(BC)$$
$$12 = 2(BC)$$
$$6 = BC$$

The width of rectangle $ABCD$ is 6 in.

Example 1

The lengths of the legs of a 30°-60°-90° triangle measure 4 cm and $4\sqrt{3}$ cm. Find the perimeter of the triangle. Round to the nearest tenth.

Strategy

To find the perimeter:
▷ Find the hypotenuse.
▷ Use the equation for the perimeter of a triangle. $4\sqrt{3} \approx 4(1.732) = 6.928$

Solution

$c = 2(\text{length of the shorter leg}) = 2(4) = 8$

$P = a + b + c$
$P \approx 4 + 6.928 + 8 = 18.928$

The perimeter is 18.9 cm.

Example 2

Find the perimeter of a right triangle with legs that measure 4 in. and 8 in. Round to the nearest tenth.

Your strategy

Your solution

20.9 in.

Example 3

Find the area of triangle ABC.

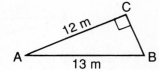

Strategy

To find the area:
▷ Use the Pythagorean Theorem to find the length of side BC.
▷ Use the equation for the area of a triangle. Let BC = the base and AC = the height.

Solution

$$c^2 = a^2 + b^2$$
$$13^2 = a^2 + 12^2$$
$$169 = a^2 + 144$$
$$25 = a^2$$
$$\sqrt{25} = \sqrt{a^2}$$
$$5 = a \qquad \text{Side } BC = 5 \text{ m}$$

$A = \frac{1}{2}bh = \frac{1}{2}(5)(12) = 30$

The area is 30 m².

Example 4

The length of a side of a square is 5 cm. Find the length of the diagonal of the square. Round to the nearest tenth.

Your strategy

Your solution

7.1 cm

Objective B

Reference for
Computer
Tutor™

To solve similar triangles

Similar objects have the same shape but not necessarily the same size. A baseball is similar to a basketball. A model airplane is similar to an actual airplane.

Similar objects have corresponding parts; for example, the propellers on the model airplane correspond to the propellers on the actual airplane. The relationship between the sizes of each of the corresponding parts can be written as a ratio, and each ratio will be the same. If the propellers on the model plane are $\frac{1}{50}$ the size of the propellers on the actual plane, then the model wing is $\frac{1}{50}$ the size of the actual wing, the model fuselage is $\frac{1}{50}$ the size of the actual fuselage, and so on.

The two triangles *ABC* and *DEF* are similar. The ratios of corresponding sides are equal.

$$\frac{AB}{DE} = \frac{2}{6} = \frac{1}{3}, \frac{BC}{EF} = \frac{3}{9} = \frac{1}{3}, \text{ and } \frac{AC}{DF} = \frac{4}{12} = \frac{1}{3}$$

The ratio of corresponding sides $= \frac{1}{3}$.

Since the ratios of corresponding sides are equal, three proportions can be formed.

$$\frac{AB}{DE} = \frac{BC}{EF}, \frac{AB}{DE} = \frac{AC}{DF}, \text{ and } \frac{BC}{EF} = \frac{AC}{DF}.$$

The ratio of corresponding heights equals the ratio of corresponding sides.

 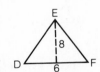

Ratio of corresponding sides $= \frac{1.5}{6} = \frac{1}{4}$.

Ratio of heights $= \frac{2}{8} = \frac{1}{4}$.

Congruent objects have the same shape *and* the same size.

The two triangles at the right are congruent. They have exactly the same size.

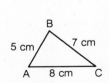

For triangles, congruent means that the corresponding sides *and* angles of the triangle must be equal, unlike similar triangles that just have corresponding angles equal but not necessarily the corresponding sides.

Example 5

Triangles *ABC* and *DEF* are similar. Find *FG*, the height of triangle *DEF*.

 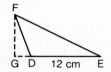

Strategy

To find *FG*, solve a proportion to find the height.

Solution

$$\frac{AB}{DE} = \frac{CH}{FG}$$

$$\frac{8}{12} = \frac{4}{FG}$$

$8(FG) = 12(4)$

$8(FG) = 48$

$FG = 6$

The height *FG* of triangle *DEF* is 6 cm.

Example 6

Triangles *ABC* and *DEF* are similar. Find *FG*, the height of triangle *DEF*.

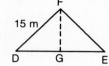

Your strategy

Your solution

10.5 m

Example 7

Triangles *ABC* and *DEF* are similar. Find the area of triangle *DEF*.

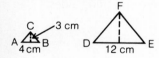

Strategy

To find the area of triangle *DEF*:
▷ Solve a proportion to find the height of triangle *DEF*. Let *h* represent the height.
▷ Use the equation for the area of a triangle.

Solution

$$\frac{AB}{DE} = \frac{\text{height of triangle } ABC}{h}$$

$$\frac{4}{12} = \frac{3}{h}$$

$4 \cdot h = 12 \cdot 3$

$4h = 36$

$h = 9$

$A = \frac{1}{2}bh = \frac{1}{2}(12)(9) = 54$

The area of triangle *DEF* is 54 cm².

Example 8

Triangles *ABC* and *DEF* are similar. Find the perimeter of triangle *ABC*.

 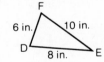

Your strategy

Your solution

12 in.

12.3A Exercises

Find the unknown side of the triangle. Round to the nearest tenth.

1.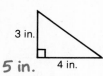

   5 in.

2.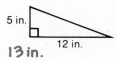

   13 in.

3.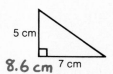

   8.6 cm

4.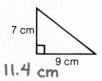

   11.4 cm

5.

   11.2 ft

6.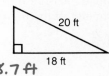

   8.7 ft

7.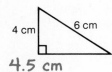

   4.5 cm

8.

   7.9 m

9.

   12.7 yd

Find the lengths of the two legs. Round to the nearest tenth.

10.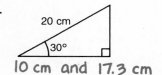

    10 cm and 17.3 cm

11.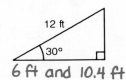

    6 ft and 10.4 ft

12.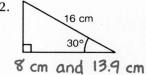

    8 cm and 13.9 cm

Find the hypotenuse of the right triangle. Round to the nearest tenth.

13.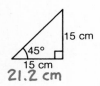

    21.2 cm

14.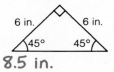

    8.5 in.

15.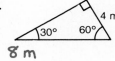

    8 m

16.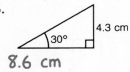

    8.6 cm

17.

    11.3 yd

18.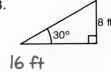

    16 ft

Solve. Round to the nearest tenth.

19. A ladder 8 m long is leaning against a building. How high on the building will the ladder reach when the bottom of the ladder is 3 m from the building?

    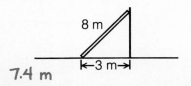

    7.4 m

20. Find the distance between the centers of the holes in the metal plate.

    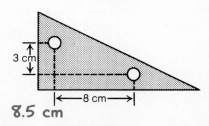

    8.5 cm

Solve. Round to the nearest tenth.

21. Find the perimeter of a right triangle with legs that measure 5 cm and 9 cm.

    24.3 cm

22. Find the perimeter of a right triangle with legs that measure 6 in. and 8 in.

    24 in.

23. The lengths of the legs of a 30°-60°-90° triangle measure 6 m and $6\sqrt{3}$ m. Find the perimeter of the triangle.

    28.4 m

24. The lengths of the legs of a 30°-60°-90° triangle measure 3 ft and $3\sqrt{3}$ ft. Find the perimeter of the triangle.

    14.2 ft

25. The length of a leg of an isosceles right triangle is 3 cm. Find the perimeter of the triangle.

    10.2 cm

26. The length of a leg of an isosceles right triangle is 5 in. Find the perimeter of the triangle.

    17.1 in.

27. Find the area of triangle *ABC*.

    40 in²

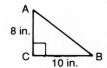

28. Find the area of triangle *ABC*.

    35.7 cm²

29. Find the area of triangle *ABC*.

    16 m²

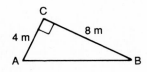

30. Find the area of triangle *ABC*.

    12.5 ft²

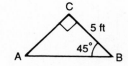

31. The length of a side of a square is 8 m. Find the length of the diagonal of the square.

    11.3 m

32. The length of a side of a square is 6 in. Find the length of the diagonal of the square.

    8.5 in.

33. Find the perimeter of rectangle *ABCD* if the length of diagonal *AC* is 6 m.

    16.4 m

34. Find the perimeter of rectangle *ABCD* if the length of diagonal *AC* is 4 cm.

    10.9 cm

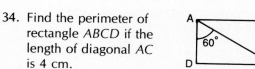

12.3B Exercises

Solve. Round to the nearest tenth.

Triangles *ABC* and *DEF* are congruent.

35. Find the measure of ∠*E*.

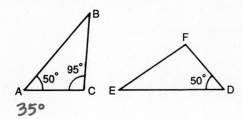

35°

36. Find the measure of ∠*E*.

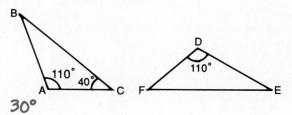

30°

Triangles *ABC* and *DEF* are similar. Find the indicated distance.

37. Find side *DE*.

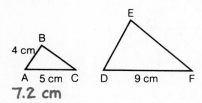

7.2 cm

38. Find side *DE*.

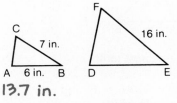

13.7 in.

39. Find the height of triangle *DEF*.

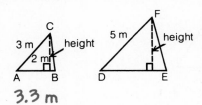

3.3 m

40. Find the height of triangle *ABC*.

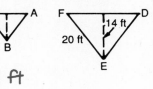

4.9 ft

The sun's rays, objects on Earth, and the shadows cast by them form similar triangles.

41. Find the height of the flagpole.

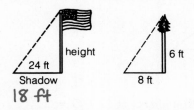

18 ft

42. Find the height of the flagpole.

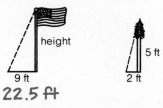

22.5 ft

43. Find the height of the building.

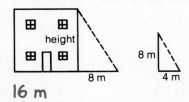

16 m

44. Find the height of the building.

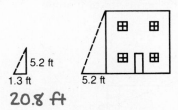

20.8 ft

Solve. Triangles *ABC* and *DEF* are similar. Round to the nearest tenth.

45. Find the perimeter of triangle *ABC*.

12 m

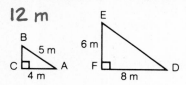

46. Find the perimeter of triangle *DEF*.

38 cm

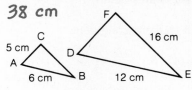

47. Find the perimeter of triangle *ABC*.

12 in.

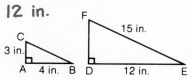

48. Find the area of triangle *DEF*.

45 cm²

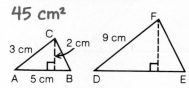

49. Find the area of triangle *ABC*.

56.3 cm²

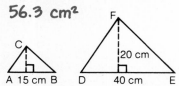

50. Find the area of triangle *DEF*.

49 m²

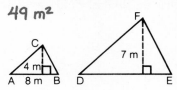

Solve. Round to the nearest tenth.

51. Given *BD* ∥ *AE*, *BD* = 5, *AE* = 8, and *AC* = 10, find the length of *BC*.

6.3

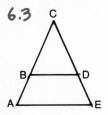

52. Given *AC* ∥ *DE*, *BD* = 8, *AD* = 12, and *BE* = 6, find the length of *BC*.

15

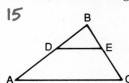

53. Given *DE* ∥ *AC*, *DE* = 6, *AC* = 10, and *AB* = 15, find the length of *DA*.

6

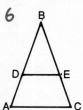

54. Given *AE* ∥ *BD*, *AB* = 3, *ED* = 4, and *BC* = 3, find the length of *CE*.

8

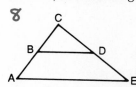

55. Given *MP* and *NQ* intersect at *O*, *NO* = 24, *MN* = 10, and the length of *MO* is twice the length of *OP*, find the perimeter of triangle *OPQ*.

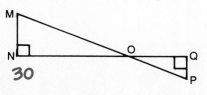

30

56. Given *MP* and *NQ* intersect at *O*, *NO* = 12, *MN* = 9, and the length of *MO* is three times the length of *OP*, find the perimeter of *OPQ*.

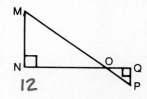

12

Section 4 Volume

To find the volume of a geometric solid

Volume is a measure of the amount of space inside a figure in space. Volume can be used to describe the amount of heating gas used for cooking, the amount of sand and concrete delivered, and the amount of water in storage for a city's water supply.

Volume is measured in cubic units.

A solid 1 ft long, 1 ft wide, and 1 ft high has a volume of 1 cubic foot, written 1 ft³.

Geometric solids are figures in space. Four common geometric solids are the rectangular solid, the cube, the sphere, and the cylinder.

A **rectangular solid** is a solid in which all six faces are rectangles. The variable L is used to represent the length of a rectangular solid, W its width, and H its height.

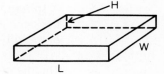

The volume of a rectangular solid equals the area of the base times the height. Since the area of the base equals the length times the width, the formula for the volume, V, of a rectangular solid is:

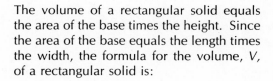

$$V = LWH$$

A **cube** is a rectangular solid in which all six faces are squares. The variable s is used to represent the length of a side of one square.

The volume of a cube equals the area of the base times the height. The area of the base is s^2. The height of the cube is s. Therefore, the volume, V, of a cube is:

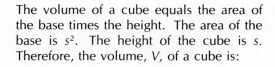

$$V = s^3$$

The most common cylinder is one in which the bases are circles and are perpendicular to the height of the cylinder. This is called a **right circular cylinder.** In this text, the word *cylinder* will mean a right circular cylinder. The variable *r* is used to represent the radius of the base of a cylinder. The variable *h* is used to represent the height of a cylinder.

The volume of a cylinder equals the area of the base times the height. Since the base of a cylinder is a circle and the area of a circle is equal to πr^2, the formula for the volume, *V*, of a cylinder is:

$$V = \pi r^2 h$$

A **sphere** is a solid in which all points are the same distance from point *O*, the **center** of the sphere.

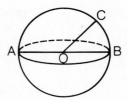

The **diameter** of the sphere is a line across the sphere going through point *O*. *AB* is a diameter of the sphere. The variable *d* is used to represent the diameter of a sphere.

The **radius** of the sphere is a line from the center to a point on the sphere. *OC* is a radius of the sphere. The variable *r* is used to represent the radius of a sphere.

$$d = 2r \quad \text{or} \quad r = \tfrac{1}{2}d$$

The formula for the volume, *V*, of a sphere is:

$$V = \tfrac{4}{3}\pi r^3$$

Find the volume of a sphere with a diameter of 12 in. Use 3.14 for π.

Find the radius of the sphere.

$$r = \tfrac{1}{2}d = \tfrac{1}{2}(12) = 6$$

Use the equation for the volume of a sphere.

$$V = \tfrac{4}{3}\pi r^3$$

$$V = \tfrac{4}{3}(3.14)(6)^3$$

$$V = 904.32$$

The volume is 904.32 in³.

Composite geometric solids are solids made from two or more geometric solids. The following solid is made from a cylinder and one-half of a sphere.

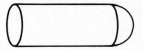 = +

Volume of the composite solid $=$ $\qquad$ $\pi r^2 h$ $\qquad$ + $\qquad$ $\frac{1}{2} \cdot \frac{4}{3}\pi r^3$

Find the volume of the solid shown above if the radius of the base of the cylinder is 3 in. and the height of the cylinder is 10 in. Use 3.14 for π.

The volume equals the volume of a cylinder plus one-half the volume of a sphere. The radius of the sphere equals the radius of the base of the cylinder.

$$V = \pi r^2 h + \frac{1}{2} \cdot \frac{4}{3}\pi r^3$$

$$V = 3.14(3)^2(10) + \frac{2}{3}(3.14)(3)^3$$

$$V = 282.6 + 56.52$$

$$V = 339.12$$

The volume is 339.12 in³.

Example 1

The volume of a cylinder with a height of 14 cm is 176 cm³. Find the radius of the base of the cylinder. Use $\frac{22}{7}$ for π.

Strategy

To find the radius of the base, use the equation for the volume of a cylinder.

Solution

$$V = \pi r^2 h$$

$$176 = \frac{22}{7}(r^2)(14)$$

$$176 = 44r^2$$

$$4 = r^2$$

$$\sqrt{4} = \sqrt{r^2}$$

$$2 = r$$

The radius of the base is 2 cm.

Example 2

The volume of a rectangular solid with a length of 2.1 m and a height of 5.5 m is 111 m³. Find the width of the rectangular solid. Round to the nearest tenth.

Your strategy

Your solution

9.6 m

Solution on p. A69

Example 3

Find the volume of the solid. Use 3.14 for π.

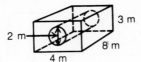

Strategy

To find the volume, subtract the volume of the cylinder from the volume of the rectangular solid. The radius of the base of the

cylinder $= \frac{1}{2}d = \frac{1}{2}(2) = 1$.

Solution

$V = LWH - \pi r^2 h$

$V = 4(8)(3) - 3.14(1)^2(8)$

$V = 96 - 25.12$

$V = 70.88$

The volume is 70.88 m³.

Example 4

Find the volume of the solid. Use 3.14 for π.

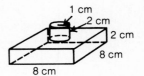

Your strategy

Your solution

134.28 cm^3

Example 5

The height of a cylindrical tank is 20 m. The diameter of the base is 14 m. If only one-fourth of the tank is filled with water, how many cubic meters of water does the tank contain? Use $\frac{22}{7}$ for π.

Strategy

To find the number of cubic meters of water in the tank:
▷ Use the equation for the volume of a cylinder to find the volume of the tank. The radius of the base of the tank $= \frac{1}{2}d = \frac{1}{2}(14) = 7$.

▷ Find $\frac{1}{4}$ of the volume of the tank.

Solution

$V = \pi r^2 h$

$V = \frac{22}{7}(7)^2(20)$

$V = 3080$

$\frac{1}{4}V = \frac{1}{4}(3080) = 770$

The tank contains 770 m³ of water.

Example 6

A spherical globe with a radius of 5 in. is to be packaged in a rectangular cardboard box. Find the volume of the smallest box that can be used for packaging the globe.

Your strategy

Your solution

1000 in^3

Solutions on p. A69

12.4A Exercises

Solve. Use 3.14 for π. Round to the nearest hundredth.

1. The height of a cylinder is 8.4 in. The radius of the base is 2.5 in. Find the volume of the cylinder.

    164.85 in³

2. A rectangular solid has a length of 6.8 m, a width of 2.5 m, and a height of 3 m. Find the volume of the rectangular solid.

    51 m³

3. The diameter of a sphere is 12 cm. Find the volume of the sphere.

    904.32 cm³

4. Find the volume of a sphere with a diameter of 6 m.

    113.04 m³

5. The length of each side of a cube is $(x + 2)$ cm. Express the volume of the cube in terms of the variable x.

    $(x^3 + 6x^2 + 12x + 8)$ cm³

6. The length of a rectangular solid is twice the width. The height is 5 m more than the width. Express the volume of the rectangular solid in terms of the variable x, where x equals the width.

    $(2x^3 + 10x^2)$ m³

7. The radius of the base of a cylinder is $(x - 2)$ cm. The height is $(x + 5)$ cm. Express the volume of the cylinder in terms of π and the variable x.

    $(\pi x^3 + \pi x^2 - 16\pi x + 20\pi)$ cm³

8. The radius of a sphere is $(x + 1)$ mm. Express the volume of the sphere in terms of π and the variable x.

    $\left(\frac{4}{3}\pi x^3 + 4\pi x^2 + 4\pi x + \frac{4}{3}\pi\right)$ mm³

9. The volume of a freezer with a length of 7 ft and a height of 3 ft is 52.5 ft³. Find the width of the freezer.

    2.5 ft

10. The length of an aquarium is 28 in. and the width is 14 in. If the volume of the aquarium is 627.2 in³, find the height.

    1.6 in.

11. The volume of a cylinder with a height of 10 in. is 502.4 in³. Find the radius of the base of the cylinder.

    4 in.

12. The diameter of the base of a cylinder is 14 cm. If the volume of the cylinder is 2310 cm³, find the height of the cylinder.

    15.01 cm

13. A rectangular solid has a square base and a height of 5 in. If the volume of the solid is 125 in³, what are the length and width?

    length : 5 in.;
    width: 5 in.

14. The volume of a rectangular solid is 864 m³. The rectangular solid has a square base and a height of 6 m. Find the dimensions of the solid.

    length: 12 m;
    width: 12 m

Find the volume of the solid. Use 3.14 for π.

15.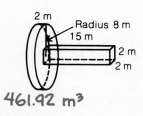

    461.92 m³

16.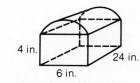

    915.12 in³

Find the volume of the solid. Use 3.14 for π.

17.

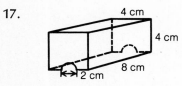

115.44 cm³

18.

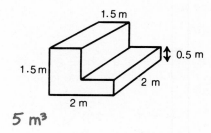

272 ft³

19.

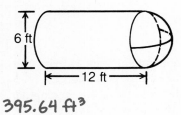

395.64 ft³

20.

1.5 m

1.5 m

0.5 m

2 m

2 m

5 m³

Solve. Use 3.14 for π. Round to the nearest hundredth.

21. An oil storage tank, which is in the shape of a cylinder, is 4 m high and has a 6 m diameter. The oil tank is two-thirds full. Find the number of cubic meters of oil in the tank.

75.36 m³

22. A silo, which is in the shape of a cylinder, is 16 ft in diameter and has a height of 30 ft. The silo is three-fourths full. Find the volume of the portion of the silo that is not being used for storage.

1507.2 ft³

23. What is the effect on the volume of a rectangular solid if both the length and width are doubled?

quadrupled

24. What is the effect on the volume of a cube if the length of each side of the cube is doubled?

multiplied by 8

25. A globe with a radius of 9 in. is to be packaged in a rectangular cardboard box. Find the volume of the smallest box that can be used for packaging the globe.

5832 in³

26. Four cans of juice, which are in the shape of cylinders, are to be packaged in a rectangular box for shipping. The diameter of each can is $4\frac{1}{4}$ in. and the height is 7 in. Find the volume of the smallest box that can be used for packaging the cans.

505.75 in³

27. A set of blocks, which are in the shape of cubes each 3 in. on a side, are to be put in a rectangular box that is 1 ft wide, 1.5 ft long, and 6 in. deep. What is the maximum number of blocks that will fit in the box?

48 blocks

28. A set of building blocks, which are in the shape of cubes each 4 in. on a side, are to be put in a rectangular box that is 1 ft wide, 1.5 ft long, and 8 in. deep. What is the maximum number of blocks that will fit in the box?

24 blocks

Calculators and Computers

Your calculator can be used to solve many geometry problems. The keys $\boxed{\pi}$ and $\boxed{y^x}$ will be used in the calculations.

Press the $\boxed{\pi}$ key on your calculator. The number 3.1415927 should be displayed. This is a closer approximation to π than 3.14 and will therefore give closer approximations to the true circumference and area of a circle or the volume of a cylinder or sphere when used to calculate these measures.

The $\boxed{y^x}$ key is used to calculate powers of a number. For example, to calculate 9^3, press the keys shown at the right. The number 729 should be displayed.

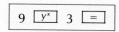

The radius of a circle is 5.5 cm. Find the circumference of the circle.

Use the equation $C = 2\pi r$.

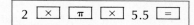

The number 34.557519 should be displayed.
The circumference is 34.56 cm, rounded to the nearest hundredth.

The length of each side of a cube is 3.5 in. Find the volume of the cube.

Use the equation $V = s^3$.

The number 42.875 should be displayed.
The volume is 42.875 in³.

The radius of a sphere is 4.8 cm. Find the volume of the sphere.

Use the equation $V = \frac{4}{3}\pi r^3$.

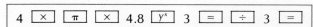

The number 463.24669 should be displayed.
The volume is 463.25, rounded to the nearest hundredth.

The area of a circle is 12 in³. Find the length of a radius of the circle.

Use the equation $A = \pi r^2$.

The number 1.95441 should be displayed.
The radius is 1.95 in., rounded to the nearest hundredth.

Solve. Round to the nearest hundredth.

1. Find the circumference of a circle that has a diameter of 1.4 in.
2. The length of a side of a cube is 5.6 cm. Find the volume of the cube.
3. The radius of the base of a cylinder is 2.3 cm. The height is 7.8 cm. Find the cylinder's volume.
4. The circumference of a circle is 18 cm. Find the length of a radius of the circle.
5. The area of a circle is 78 m². Find the length of a radius of the circle.

ANSWERS: **1.** 4.40 in. **2.** 175.62 cm³ **3.** 129.63 cm³ **4.** 2.86 cm **5.** 4.98 m

Chapter Summary

KEY WORDS

A **line** extends indefinitely in two directions in a plane. A **line segment** is part of a line and has two endpoints. **Parallel lines** never meet; the distance between them is always the same. **Perpendicular lines** are intersecting lines that form right angles.

A **ray** starts at a point and extends indefinitely in one direction. An **angle** is formed when two rays start from the same point. The common endpoint is called the **vertex** of the angle. An angle is measured in **degrees**. A 90° angle is a **right angle**. A 180° angle is a **straight angle**. **Complementary angles** are two angles whose sum is 90°. **Supplementary angles** are two angles whose sum is 180°. An **acute angle** is an angle whose measure is between 0° and 90°. An **obtuse angle** is an angle whose measure is between 90° and 180°.

Two angles that are on opposite sides of the intersection of two lines are **vertical angles.** Two angles that share a common side are **adjacent angles.**

A line that intersects two other lines at two different points is a **transversal.** If the lines cut by a transversal are parallel lines, sets of equal angles are formed: **alternate interior angles, alternate exterior angles,** and **corresponding angles.**

The **perimeter** of a geometric figure is a measure of the distance around the figure. **Area** is a measure of the amount of surface in a region. **Volume** is a measure of the amount of space inside a figure in space.

A **triangle** is a three-sided plane figure. An **isosceles triangle** has two sides of equal length. An **equilateral triangle** has three sides of equal length. A **right triangle** contains one right angle. The side opposite the right angle is the **hypotenuse.** The other two sides are called **legs. 45°-45°-90° triangles** and **30°-60°-90° triangles** are special right triangles.

A **diagonal** of a quadrilateral is a line segment drawn from one vertex to the opposite vertex.

Similar objects have the same shape but not necessarily the same size. The ratios of corresponding sides of similar triangles are equal. **Congruent objects** have the same shape and the same size.

ESSENTIAL RULES

Perimeter Equations

Triangle:	$P = a + b + c$
Rectangle:	$P = 2L + 2W$
Square:	$P = 4s$
Circle:	$C = \pi d$ or $C = 2\pi r$

Area Equations

Triangle:	$A = \frac{1}{2}bh$
Parallelogram:	$A = bh$
Rectangle:	$A = LW$
Square:	$A = s^2$
Circle	$A = \pi r^2$

Volume Equations

Rectangular solid:	$V = LWH$
Cube:	$V = s^3$
Cylinder:	$V = \pi r^2 h$
Sphere:	$V = \frac{4}{3}\pi r^3$

Pythagorean Theorem $c^2 = a^2 + b^2$

Review/Test

Solve. Use 3.14 for π. Round to the nearest hundredth.

1. The difference between two supplementary angles is 30°. Find the measures of the two angles.

    75° and 105°

2. Find x.

    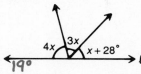

    19°

3. Find the measure of $\angle x$.

    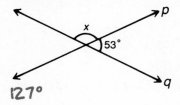

    127°

4. Given that $\ell_1 \parallel \ell_2$, find the measures of angles a and b.

    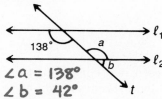

    $\angle a$ = 138°
    $\angle b$ = 42°

5. Given that $\angle a = 74°$ and $\angle b = 52°$, find the measures of angles x and y.

    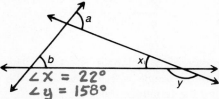

    $\angle X$ = 22°
    $\angle y$ = 158°

6. The difference between the measures of the two acute angles in a right triangle is 20°. Find the measures of the two acute angles.

    35° and 55°

7. The perimeter of an isosceles triangle is 32 cm. One side is 4 cm less than the length of one of the equal sides. Find the measure of each side.

    12 cm, 12 cm, and 8 cm

8. The circumference of a circle is 6 m. Find the length of a radius of the circle.

    0.96 m

9. The width of a rectangle is 4 ft less than the length. The area of the rectangle is 117 ft². Find the length and width of the rectangle.

    length : 13 ft;
    width: 9 ft

10. Find the perimeter of the figure.

    9.14 cm

    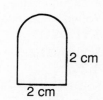

    2 cm

    2 cm

11. Find the area of the figure.

    40 m²

    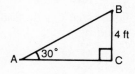
    8 m
    4 m
    12 m

12. Find the unknown sides of the triangle.

    AB = 8 ft;
    AC = 6.93 ft

    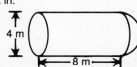
    B
    4 ft
    30°
    A   C

13. Find the perimeter of a right triangle with legs that measure 7 cm and 10 cm.

    29.21 cm

14. Triangles *ABC* and *DEF* are similar. Find the perimeter of triangle *ABC*.

    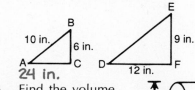

    10 in.   B   6 in.
    A   C   D   12 in.   F
    E
    9 in.

    24 in.

15. The length of a rectangular solid is 18 in. and the width is 14 in. If the volume of the solid is 2520 in³, find the height.

    10 in.

16. Find the volume of the solid.

    117. 23 m³

    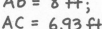
    4 m
    8 m

Cumulative Review/Test

1. A sales executive's paychecks for the last three months were $3480, $3690, and $3210. Find the executive's average monthly paycheck for the three-month period.
   $3460

2. The length of each side of a cube is $(x + 4)$ cm. Express the volume of the cube in terms of the variable x.
   $(x^3 + 12x^2 + 48x + 64)$ cm³

3. Solve: $5x - 7 = 3x + 9$
   8

4. Write 0.068 as a percent.
   6.8%

5. A right triangle has a 53° angle. Find the measures of the other two angles.
   90° and 37°

6. Find the perimeter of a right triangle with legs that measure 5 in. and 7 in. Round to the nearest tenth.
   20.6 in.

7. Simplify: $\frac{27a^3b^2}{(-3ab^2)^3}$
   $-\frac{1}{b^4}$

8. Factor $6x^2 - 5x - 4$.
   $(2x + 1)(3x - 4)$

9. The difference between two complementary angles is 16°. Find the measures of the two angles.
   37° and 53°

10. Triangles ABC and DEF are similar. Find side DE.
    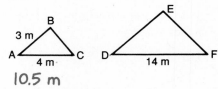
    10.5 m

11. Solve and graph the solution set of $x + 5 \geq 7$.

    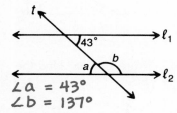 **$x \geq 2$**

12. The perimeter of a rectangle is 64 m. The length of the rectangle is 8 m more than the width. Find the length of the rectangle.
    20 m

13. Find the length of a radius of a circle that has a circumference of 12 in. Use 3.14 for π. Round to the nearest hundredth.
    1.91 in.

14. The height of a triangle is four times the length of the base. The area of the triangle is 50 m². Find the height of the triangle.
    20 m

15. Simplify $(1.2)^2 - 0.4(0.3)$.
    1.32

16. Simplify: $-3[x - 2(3 - 2x) - 5] + 2x$
    $-13x + 33$

17. Solve $R = \frac{C - S}{t}$ for C.
    $C = Rt + S$

18. Solve: $\frac{5y}{6} - \frac{5}{9} = \frac{y}{3} - \frac{5}{6}$
    $-\frac{5}{9}$

19. Given that $\ell_1 \parallel \ell_2$, find the measures of angles a and b.

    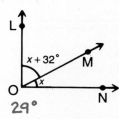

    $\angle a = 43°$
    $\angle b = 137°$

20. Given $\angle LON$ is a right angle, find the measure of $\angle x$.

    29°

21. Simplify: $\frac{x^{-4}y^{-3}}{xy^2}$
    $\frac{1}{x^5y^5}$

22. Find the slope of the line containing the points $(2, -3)$ and $(-1, 4)$.
    $-\frac{7}{3}$

23. Solve: $\sqrt{2x - 3} - 5 = 0$
    14

24. Solve: $2x^2 - 4x - 5 = 0$
    $\frac{2 + \sqrt{14}}{2}$ and $\frac{2 - \sqrt{14}}{2}$

Cumulative Review/Final Exam

1. Simplify: $4^2(3^2)$

    144

2. Simplify: $12 \div (6 - 3) \cdot 4 + 3^2$

    25

3. Subtract: $6\frac{1}{4} - 3\frac{5}{8}$

    $2\frac{5}{8}$

4. Subtract: $90.001 - 29.796$

    60.205

5. Divide: $0.0426 \div 0.062$
   Round to the nearest hundredth.

    0.69

6. Evaluate: $-|-3.8|$

    -3.8

7. Multiply: $\left(2\frac{1}{2}\right)\left(-\frac{1}{5}\right)$

    $-\frac{1}{2}$

8. Evaluate $\frac{-a^2 - b}{a - b}$ when $a = 2$ and $b = -3$.

    $-\frac{1}{5}$

9. Simplify: $3x - 3(2x - 4) - 1$

    $-3x + 11$

10. Solve: $3x - 5 = 10$

     5

11. Solve: $3x - 2(4 - 3x) = -3(2 - x)$

     $\frac{1}{3}$

12. Solve: $-\frac{2}{3}x < -\frac{4}{9}$

     $x > \frac{2}{3}$

13. Solve: $3(3y - 2) + 2 < -3(1 - 2y)$

     $y < \frac{1}{3}$

14. Write "323.4 mi on 13.2 gal of gasoline" as a unit rate.

     24.5 mi/gal

15. Solve the proportion $\frac{5}{4} = \frac{n}{18}$.

     $\frac{45}{2}$

16. Write $\frac{3}{8}$ as a percent.

     37.5 %

17. 22% of what number is 9.9?

     45

18. Simplify: $(3x^2 - 2x + 4) - (5x^2 - 4x - 8)$

     $-2x^2 + 2x + 12$

19. Simplify: $(-2x^2y)^5$

     $-32x^{10}y^5$

20. Simplify: $(-2x^2 + 2x - 1)(x - 3)$

     $-2x^3 + 8x^2 - 7x + 3$

21. Simplify: $\frac{(3xy^4)^2}{12x^3y^3}$

     $\frac{3y^5}{4x}$

22. Simplify: $(x^3 + 5x^2 + 2x - 8) \div (x + 2)$

     $x^2 + 3x - 4$

23. Simplify: $(-2x^{-2}y^4)(3xy^{-1})^2$

$-18y^2$

24. Write 0.00000473 in scientific notation.

4.73×10^{-6}

25. Factor: $-3y^4 + 6y^3 - 21y^2$

$-3y^2(y^2 - 2y + 7)$

26. Factor: $x^2 - 8x - 9$

$(x - 9)(x + 1)$

27. Factor: $6x^2 - x - 12$

$(3x + 4)(2x - 3)$

28. Factor: $-6x^3 - 21x^2 - 18x$

$-3x(2x + 3)(x + 2)$

29. Factor: $49y^2 - 1$

$(7y + 1)(7y - 1)$

30. Factor: $x(y - 1) - 2(y - 1)$

$(y - 1)(x - 2)$

31. Factor: $12x^2 - 27x^2y^2$

$3x^2(2 - 3y)(2 + 3y)$

32. Simplify: $\dfrac{6 - 9x}{3x^2 - 2x}$

$-\dfrac{3}{x}$

33. Simplify: $\dfrac{x^2 - 7x + 12}{x^2 - 4x} \div \dfrac{2x^2 - 5x - 3}{2x^2 + x}$

1

34. Simplify: $\dfrac{3y}{y - 2} - \dfrac{6}{y - 2}$

3

35. Simplify: $\dfrac{3}{x + 5} + \dfrac{7}{x - 1}$

$\dfrac{10x + 32}{(x + 5)(x - 1)}$

36. Simplify: $\dfrac{\frac{1}{2} + \frac{1}{a}}{\frac{1}{4} - \frac{1}{a^2}}$

$\dfrac{2a}{a - 2}$

37. Solve: $\dfrac{3x}{2x - 3} - 4 = \dfrac{2}{2x - 3}$

2

38. W is inversely proportional to V and $W = 8$ when $V = 2$. Find W when $V = 4$.

4

39. Solve $L = a(1 + ct)$ for t.

$t = \dfrac{L - a}{ac}$

40. Graph $2x - 3y = 3$.

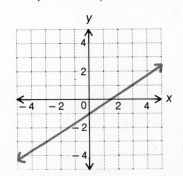

41. Find the slope of the line containing the points $(-2, 4)$ and $(-1, 1)$.

    -3

42. Find the equation of the line that contains the point $(4, -4)$ and has slope $-\frac{3}{4}$.

    $y = -\frac{3}{4}x - 1$

43. Solve: $2x - 3y = 7$
    $\quad\quad\quad 3x + y = 5$

    $(2, -1)$

44. Simplify: $4\sqrt{32}$

    $16\sqrt{2}$

45. Simplify: $a\sqrt{81a^4}$

    $9a^3$

46. Simplify: $2\sqrt{27y} + 8\sqrt{48y}$

    $38\sqrt{3y}$

47. Simplify: $\sqrt{3x}(\sqrt{6x} - \sqrt{x})$

    $3x\sqrt{2} - x\sqrt{3}$

48. Simplify: $\dfrac{3}{\sqrt{2} - 1}$

    $3\sqrt{2} + 3$

49. Solve: $\sqrt{3x} - 2 = 1$

    3

50. Solve: $2x^2 - x = 3$

    $\frac{3}{2}$ and -1

51. Solve: $4(x - 1)^2 = 12$

    $1 + \sqrt{3}$ and $1 - \sqrt{3}$

52. Solve: $3x^2 - 2x = 3$

    $\dfrac{1 + \sqrt{10}}{3}$ and $\dfrac{1 - \sqrt{10}}{3}$

53. Given that $\ell_1 \parallel \ell_2$, find x.

    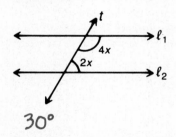

    $30°$

54. Given $AC \parallel DE$, $BE = 8$, $CE = 4$, and $BD = 10$, find the length of AB.

    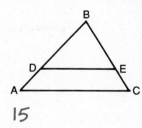

    15

55. One acute angle of a right triangle is twice the measure of the other acute angle. Find the measure of each angle of the triangle.

    $30°, 60°,$ and $90°$

56. The perimeter of a rectangle is 36 m. The length of the rectangle is twice the width. Find the length of the rectangle.

    12 m

57. The length of each side of a square is extended by 3 cm. The area of the resulting square is 121 cm². Find the length of a side of the original square.

    8 cm

58. Find the perimeter of a right triangle with legs that measure 5 in. and 8 in. Round to the nearest tenth.

    22.4 in.

59. The volume of an aquarium is 2304 in³. If the length of the aquarium is 16 in. and the width is 12 in., find the height.

    12 in.

60. A compact car gets 30 mi on each gallon of gasoline. How many miles can the car travel on $4\frac{3}{10}$ gal of gasoline?

    129 mi

61. The monthly utility bills for five homes are $93.46, $72.85, $89.32, $68.71, and $84.19. Find the average utility bill. Round to the nearest cent.

    $81.71

62. The sum of three consecutive odd integers is 105. Find the integers.

    33, 35, and 37

63. The sum of the ages of two coins is 97 years. Two years ago the age of the older coin was twice the age the newer coin was then. Find the present age of the older coin.

    64 years

64. A pre-election survey showed that 4 out of 7 voters would vote in an election. At this rate, how many people would be expected to vote in a city of 133,000?

    76,000 people

65. A city has a population of 72,000. This is 180% of the city's population 5 years ago. What was the city's population 5 years ago?

    40,000 people

66. An investment of $6000 is made at an annual simple interest rate of 7.5%. How much additional money must be invested at 9.5% so that the total interest earned is $735?

    $3000

67. Find the cost per pound of a mixture of coffee made from 60 lb of coffee that cost $3.20 per pound and 20 lb of coffee that cost $8.40 per pound.

    $4.50/lb

68. Eight grams of sugar are added to a 60-gram serving of a breakfast cereal that is 15% sugar. What is the percent concentration of the resulting mixture?

    25%

69. An old pump requires 6 hours longer to empty a pool than does a new pump. With both pumps operating, the pool can be emptied in 4 hours. Find the time required for the new pump working alone to empty the pool.

    6 hours

70. The rate of a motorcycle is 38 mph faster than the rate of a bicycle. The motorcycle travels 165 mi in the same amount of time as the bicycle travels 51 mi. Find the rate of the bicycle.

    17 mph

Appendix

Addition Table

+	0	1	2	3	4	5	6	7	8	9	10	11	12
0	0	1	2	3	4	5	6	7	8	9	10	11	12
1	1	2	3	4	5	6	7	8	9	10	11	12	13
2	2	3	4	5	6	7	8	9	10	11	12	13	14
3	3	4	5	6	7	8	9	10	11	12	13	14	15
4	4	5	6	7	8	9	10	11	12	13	14	15	16
5	5	6	7	8	9	10	11	12	13	14	15	16	17
6	6	7	8	9	10	11	12	13	14	15	16	17	18
7	7	8	9	10	11	12	13	14	15	16	17	18	19
8	8	9	10	11	12	13	14	15	16	17	18	19	20
9	9	10	11	12	13	14	15	16	17	18	19	20	21
10	10	11	12	13	14	15	16	17	18	19	20	21	22
11	11	12	13	14	15	16	17	18	19	20	21	22	23
12	12	13	14	15	16	17	18	19	20	21	22	23	24

Multiplication Table

×	0	1	2	3	4	5	6	7	8	9	10	11	12
0	0	0	0	0	0	0	0	0	0	0	0	0	0
1	0	1	2	3	4	5	6	7	8	9	10	11	12
2	0	2	4	6	8	10	12	14	16	18	20	22	24
3	0	3	6	9	12	15	18	21	24	27	30	33	36
4	0	4	8	12	16	20	24	28	32	36	40	44	48
5	0	5	10	15	20	25	30	35	40	45	50	55	60
6	0	6	12	18	24	30	36	42	48	54	60	66	72
7	0	7	14	21	28	35	42	49	56	63	70	77	84
8	0	8	16	24	32	40	48	56	64	72	80	88	96
9	0	9	18	27	36	45	54	63	72	81	90	99	108
10	0	10	20	30	40	50	60	70	80	90	100	110	120
11	0	11	22	33	44	55	66	77	88	99	110	121	132
12	0	12	24	36	48	60	72	84	96	108	120	132	144

Table of Square Roots

Decimal approximations have been rounded to the nearest thousandth.

Number	Square Root	Number	Square Root	Number	Square Root	Number	Square Root
1	1	51	7.141	101	10.050	151	12.288
2	1.414	52	7.211	102	10.100	152	12.329
3	1.732	53	7.280	103	10.149	153	12.369
4	2	54	7.348	104	10.198	154	12.410
5	2.236	55	7.416	105	10.247	155	12.450
6	2.449	56	7.483	106	10.296	156	12.490
7	2.646	57	7.550	107	10.344	157	12.530
8	2.828	58	7.616	108	10.392	158	12.570
9	3	59	7.681	109	10.440	159	12.610
10	3.162	60	7.746	110	10.488	160	12.649
11	3.317	61	7.810	111	10.536	161	12.689
12	3.464	62	7.874	112	10.583	162	12.728
13	3.606	63	7.937	113	10.630	163	12.767
14	3.742	64	8	114	10.677	164	12.806
15	3.873	65	8.062	115	10.724	165	12.845
16	4	66	8.124	116	10.770	166	12.884
17	4.123	67	8.185	117	10.817	167	12.923
18	4.243	68	8.246	118	10.863	168	12.961
19	4.359	69	8.307	119	10.909	169	13
20	4.472	70	8.367	120	10.954	170	13.038
21	4.583	71	8.426	121	11	171	13.077
22	4.690	72	8.485	122	11.045	172	13.115
23	4.796	73	8.544	123	11.091	173	13.153
24	4.899	74	8.602	124	11.136	174	13.191
25	5	75	8.660	125	11.180	175	13.229
26	5.099	76	8.718	126	11.225	176	13.267
27	5.196	77	8.775	127	11.269	177	13.304
28	5.292	78	8.832	128	11.314	178	13.342
29	5.385	79	8.888	129	11.358	179	13.379
30	5.477	80	8.944	130	11.402	180	13.416
31	5.568	81	9	131	11.446	181	13.454
32	5.657	82	9.055	132	11.489	182	13.491
33	5.745	83	9.110	133	11.533	183	13.528
34	5.831	84	9.165	134	11.576	184	13.565
35	5.916	85	9.220	135	11.619	185	13.601
36	6	86	9.274	136	11.662	186	13.638
37	6.083	87	9.327	137	11.705	187	13.675
38	6.164	88	9.381	138	11.747	188	13.711
39	6.245	89	9.434	139	11.790	189	13.748
40	6.325	90	9.487	140	11.832	190	13.784
41	6.403	91	9.539	141	11.874	191	13.820
42	6.481	92	9.592	142	11.916	192	13.856
43	6.557	93	9.644	143	11.958	193	13.892
44	6.633	94	9.695	144	12	194	13.928
45	6.708	95	9.747	145	12.042	195	13.964
46	6.782	96	9.798	146	12.083	196	14
47	6.856	97	9.849	147	12.124	197	14.036
48	6.928	98	9.899	148	12.166	198	14.071
59	7	99	9.950	149	12.207	199	14.107
50	7.071	100	10	150	12.247	200	14.142

Table of Properties

PROPERTIES OF REAL NUMBERS

Associative Property of Addition
If a, b, and c are real numbers, then
$(a + b) + c = a + (b + c)$.

Associative Property of Multiplication
If a, b, and c are real numbers, then
$(a \cdot b) \cdot c = a \cdot (b \cdot c)$.

Commutative Property of Addition
If a and b are real numbers, then $a + b = b + a$.

Commutative Property of Multiplication
If a and b are real numbers, then $a \cdot b = b \cdot a$.

Addition Property of Zero
If a is a real number, then $a + 0 = 0 + a = a$.

Multiplication Property of One
If a is a real number, then $a \cdot 1 = 1 \cdot a = a$.

Inverse Property of Addition
If a is a real number, then
$a + (-a) = (-a) + a = 0$.

Inverse Property of Multiplication
If a is a real number and $a \neq 0$, then
$a \cdot \dfrac{1}{a} = \dfrac{1}{a} \cdot a = 1$.

DISTRIBUTIVE PROPERTY

If a, b, and c are real numbers, then $a(b + c) = ab + ac$.

PROPERTIES OF EQUATIONS

Addition Property of Equations
If $a = b$, then $a + c = b + c$.

Multiplication Property of Equations
If $a = b$ and $c \neq 0$, then $a \cdot c = b \cdot c$.

PROPERTIES OF EXPONENTS

If m and n are integers, then
$x^m \cdot x^n = x^{m+n}$.

If m and n are integers and $x \neq 0$, then
$\dfrac{x^m}{x^n} = x^{m-n}$.

If m and n are integers, then
$(x^m)^n = x^{m \cdot n}$.

If m, n, and p are integers, then
$(x^m \cdot y^n)^p = x^{m \cdot p} y^{n \cdot p}$.

If x is a real number and $x \neq 0$, then $x^0 = 1$.

If n is a positive integer and $x \neq 0$, then
$x^{-n} = \dfrac{1}{x^n}$.

PRINCIPLE OF ZERO PRODUCTS

If $a \cdot b = 0$, then $a = 0$ or $b = 0$.

PROPERTIES OF RADICAL EXPRESSIONS

If a and b are positive real numbers,
then $\sqrt{ab} = \sqrt{a} \cdot \sqrt{b}$.

If a and b are positive real numbers,
then $\sqrt{\dfrac{a}{b}} = \dfrac{\sqrt{a}}{\sqrt{b}}$.

PROPERTIES OF INEQUALITIES

Addition Properties of Inequalities
If $a > b$, then $a + c > b + c$.
If $a < b$, then $a + c < b + c$.

Multiplication Properties of Inequalities
If $a > b$ and $c > 0$, then $ac > bc$.
If $a < b$ and $c > 0$, then $ac < bc$.
If $a > b$ and $c < 0$, then $ac < bc$.
If $a < b$ and $c < 0$, then $ac > bc$.

PROPERTY OF SQUARING BOTH SIDES OF AN EQUATION

If a and b are real numbers and $a = b$, then $a^2 = b^2$.

Table of Symbols

$+$	add		$<$	is less than
$-$	subtract		$\leq$	is less than or equal to
$\cdot$, x, $(a)(b)$	multiply		$>$	is greater than
$\frac{a}{b}$, $\div$	divide		$\geq$	is greater than or equal to
$(\ )$	parentheses, a grouping symbol		(a, b)	an ordered pair whose first component is a and whose second component is b
$[\ ]$	brackets, a grouping symbol		$^\circ$	degree (for angles)
π	pi, a number approximately equal to $\frac{22}{7}$ or 3.14		$\sqrt{a}$	the principal square root of a
$-a$	the opposite, or additive inverse, of a		$|a|$	the absolute value of a
$\frac{1}{a}$	the reciprocal, or multiplicative inverse, of a		$|\ |$	is parallel to
$=$	is equal to		$\angle$	angle
$\approx$	is approximately equal to		∟	right angle
$\neq$	is not equal to		$\perp$	is perpendicular to

Table of Measurement Abbreviations

U.S. CUSTOMARY SYSTEM

Length
in. inches
ft feet
yd yards
mi miles

Capacity
oz ounces
qt quarts
gal gallons

Weight
oz ounces
lb pounds

Area
in^2 square inches
ft^2 square feet

Volume
in^3 cubic inches
ft^3 cubic feet

Speed
mph miles per hour
mi/s miles per second

METRIC SYSTEM

Length
cm centimeters
m meters
km kilometers

Capacity
ml milliliters
L liters

Weight
g grams
kg kilograms

Area
cm^2 square centimeters
m^2 square meters

Volume
cm^3 cubic centimeters
m^3 cubic meters

Speed
km/h kilometers per hour
m/s meters per second
km/s kilometers per second

Table of Equations

The Uniform Motion Equation	$D = r \cdot t$	
The Basic Percent Equation	$P \cdot B = A$	
The Annual Simple Interest Equation	$I = P \cdot r$	
The Value Mixture Equation	$V = A \cdot C$	
The Percent Mixture Equation	$Q = A \cdot r$	
The Quadratic Formula	$x = \dfrac{-b \pm \sqrt{b^2 - 4ac}}{2a}$	
The Pythagorean Theorem	$c^2 = a^2 + b^2$	
Perimeter Equations	Triangle:	$P = a + b + c$
	Rectangle:	$P = 2L + 2W$
	Square:	$P = 4s$
	Circle:	$C = \pi d$ or $C = 2\pi r$
Area Equations	Triangle:	$A = \frac{1}{2}bh$
	Parallelogram:	$A = bh$
	Rectangle:	$A = LW$
	Square:	$A = s^2$
	Circle:	$A = \pi r^2$
Volume Equations	Rectangular solid:	$V = LWH$
	Cube:	$V = s^3$
	Cylinder:	$V = \pi r^2 h$
	Sphere:	$V = \frac{4}{3}\pi r^3$

Student Disk Documentation

The Student Exercise Disk is intended for student use in the computer center, at home, or in a learning center. The disk contains nine programs that allow the student to practice topics covered in the textbook.

The program provides the student with a menu from which any of the nine programs can be selected. A sample menu is shown below.

```
                      MAIN MENU

     <1>  Add or Subtract Fractions
     <2>  Solve a First-Degree Equation
     <3>  First-Degree Inequalities
     <4>  Factoring
     <5>  Algebraic Fractions
     <6>  Rational Expressions
     <7>  Equation of a Straight Line
     <8>  Graphs of Straight Lines
     <9>  Radical Expressions
     <Q>  Quit

     Your selection -->
     Press Enter after you make your selection.
```

The following is a short description of each program.

Add or Subtract Fractions: This program allows you to practice adding or subtracting numerical fractions.

Solve a First-Degree Equation: This program presents the student with a first-degree equation to solve. By tapping a key, the complete solution to the problem is displayed.

First-Degree Inequalities: This program presents the student with a first-degree inequality to solve. By tapping a key, the complete solution to the problem is displayed.

Factoring: This program provides factoring practice for polynomials of the form $x^2 + bx + c$ or $ax^2 + bx + c$.

Algebraic Fractions: This program provides practice at simplifying rational expressions. By tapping a key, the complete solution is presented to the student.

Rational Expressions: This program provides practice at multiplying and dividing rational expressions. By tapping a key, the complete solution is presented to the student.

Equation of a Straight Line: This program gives the student a slope and a point and asks the student to find the equation of the line. By tapping a key, the complete solution is presented to the student.

Graphs of Straight Lines: This program allows the student to enter the equation of a straight line and then see the graph. Multiple graphs can be placed on one coordinate grid.

Radical Expressions: This program gives the student a square root radical expression containing a constant and up to three variables. The simplified radical expression can be seen by tapping a key.

This disk is currently available for an IBM or IBM compatible computer and for the Apple IIe, IIc, IIgs, or Apple II Plus with 64K memory. Make a back-up copy of this disk before using it.

IBM Back-up

Prepare a label for the back-up disk and place it on a blank disk before inserting it into the disk drive. Place a DOS disk in drive A and turn on the computer. If the computer is already on, press the Ctrl, Alt, and Del keys simultaneously.

Type: format b: /s
Press: Enter

Note: When formating with the system, be careful to format on the same type of computer you plan to use. (You can format a disk without the system by not using the /s in the format statement used above.)

Place your blank disk in drive B and press any key. After a few moments the message "Format another (y)es or (n)o?" will appear.

Type: n

Remove the DOS disk from drive A and insert the Student Disk.

Type: copy a:*.* b:
Press: Enter

When the DOS command line prompt (A >) appears, the back-up is complete and the disk in drive B is ready to use.

To use this disk, place the disk in drive A and turn on the computer. If the computer is already on, press the keys Ctrl, Alt, and Del simultaneously. After a copyright notice, the main menu will appear. Select the program you wish to run from this menu.

Apple Back-up

Turn the computer off. The switch is on the back left side of the computer. Place an Apple System Disk in Drive 1 and turn on the computer.

Type: RUN COPYA
Press: Return

Remove the Apple System Disk from Drive 1 and replace it with the Student Disk. Prepare a label for the back-up disk and place it on a blank disk before inserting it into Drive 2.

A series of messages, five in all, will appear on the screen. Just press RETURN as each message appears.

When the copy procedure is complete, the message

    DO YOU WISH TO MAKE ANOTHER COPY?

will appear.

Type: N
Press: Return

The disk in Drive 2 is now ready for use. Place it in Drive 1. Turn off the computer, wait 10 seconds, and then turn on the computer. You will be ready to use the program.

Reminder: The Student Disk is designed to run on an Apple IIe, IIc, IIgs, or an Apple II Plus with 64K memory.

Answers to Chapter 1

Section 1   Pages 2–4

Example 2   **Example 4**   **a.** $45 > 29$ **b.** $27 > 0$

Example 6 $100{,}000 + 9000 + 200 + 7$ **Example 8** $370{,}000$

Exercises   Pages 5–6

1.   3.

5.   7.

9. $37 < 49$ **11.** $101 > 87$ **13.** $245 > 158$ **15.** $3521 > 3512$ **17.** $0 < 45$ **19.** $815 < 928$

21. $2400 < 24{,}000$ **23.** $7003 < 7020$ **25.** $18{,}020 > 18{,}002$ **27.** $5000 + 200 + 80 + 7$

29. $50{,}000 + 8000 + 900 + 40 + 3$ **31.** $200{,}000 + 10{,}000 + 7000 + 500 + 80 + 6$

33. $50{,}000 + 900 + 40 + 3$ **35.** $200{,}000 + 500 + 80 + 3$ **37.** $400{,}000 + 3000 + 700 + 5$

39. $90{,}000 + 3000 + 200 + 70 + 7$ **41.** $30{,}000 + 5000 + 6$ **43.** 930 **45.** $1{,}400$ **47.** $35{,}700$ **49.** 7000

51. $44{,}000$ **53.** $650{,}000$

Section 2   Pages 7–12

Example 2
```
   3,508
 +92,170
  95,678
```

Example 4
```
   102
  7351
  1024
 + 410
  8887
```

Example 6
```
   2
  95
  88
 +67
 250
```

Example 8
```
 1 1  2 1
     392
   4,079
  89,035
 + 4,992
  98,498
```

Example 10
```
  8925
 -6413
  2512
```

Example 12
```
  17,504
 - 9,302
   8,202
```

Example 14
```
 2 14 7 11
 3  4 8 7
 -   8 6 5
   2 6 1 6
```

Example 16
```
            15
         4 8 12
 5 4, 3 6 2
 -1 4, 4 8 5
   4 0, 0 7 7
```

Example 18
```
       9
     8 10 14
  5 9 0 4
 -2 3 5 7
  3 5 4 7
```

Example 20
```
        13 9 9
   5 3 10 10 13
   6 4, 0 0 3
 -5 4, 9 3 6
    9, 0 6 7
```

Exercises Pages 13–16

1. 729 **3.** 1489 **5.** 14,399 **7.** 15,865 **9.** 156,499 **11.** 14,395 **13.** 1,786,688 **15.** 1,394,799
17. 16,776 **19.** 149,999 **21.** 168,574 **23.** 129,843 **25.** 1584 **27.** 1219 **29.** 11,066
31. 5143 **33.** 102,317 **35.** 79,326 **37.** 1804 **39.** 1579 **41.** 1342 **43.** 1063 **45.** 19,740
47. 7420 **49.** 120,570 **51.** 207,453 **53.** 1888 **55.** 1769 **57.** 309,172 **59.** 343,263
61. 86,170 **63.** 4004 **65.** 71,102 **67.** 6087 **69.** 29,829 **71.** 9707 **73.** 93,695 **75.** 60
77. 66 **79.** 33 **81.** 501 **83.** 962 **85.** 5002 **87.** 1513 **89.** 1244 **91.** 823 **93.** 4401
95. 2201 **97.** 1000 **99.** 4275 **101.** 53 **103.** 29 **105.** 4 **107.** 23 **109.** 9 **111.** 18
113. 456 **115.** 58 **117.** 574 **119.** 375 **121.** 19 **123.** 209 **125.** 113 **127.** 3545
129. 5258 **131.** 4887 **133.** 2571 **135.** 889 **137.** 71,129 **139.** 718 **141.** 29,405
143. 49,624 **145.** 7575 **147.** 1344 **149.** 5048 **151.** 3278 **153.** 479 **155.** 628 **157.** 6532
159. 4286 **161.** 4042 **163.** 5209 **165.** 17,378

Section 3 Pages 17–26

Example 2
$$\begin{array}{r} ^4 \\ 78 \\ \times\ 6 \\ \hline 468 \end{array}$$

Example 4
$$\begin{array}{r} ^{3\,5} \\ 648 \\ \times\ \ 7 \\ \hline 4536 \end{array}$$

Example 6
$$\begin{array}{r} 97 \\ \times 38 \\ \hline 776 \\ 291 \\ \hline 3686 \end{array}$$

Example 8
$$\begin{array}{r} 756 \\ \times 305 \\ \hline 3780 \\ 22680 \\ \hline 230{,}580 \end{array}$$

Example 10 $2^4 \cdot 3^3$

Example 12 10^7

Example 14 $(2 \cdot 2 \cdot 2) \cdot (5 \cdot 5) = 8 \cdot 25 = 200$

Example 16
$$\begin{array}{r} 7 \\ 9\overline{)63} \end{array}$$

Check: $7 \times 9 = 63$

Example 18
$$\begin{array}{r} 705 \\ 9\overline{)\ 6345} \\ -63 \\ \hline 04 \\ -\ 0 \\ \hline 45 \\ -45 \\ \hline 0 \end{array}$$

Check: $705 \times 9 = 6345$

Example 20
$$\begin{array}{r} 870\ r5 \\ 6\overline{)\ 5225} \\ -48 \\ \hline 42 \\ -42 \\ \hline 05 \\ -\ 0 \\ \hline 5 \end{array}$$

Check: $(870 \times 6) + 5 =$
$5220 + 5 = 5225$

Example 22
$$\begin{array}{r} 470\ r29 \\ 39\overline{)\ 18{,}359} \\ -15\ 6 \\ \hline 2\ 75 \\ -2\ 73 \\ \hline 29 \\ -\ 0 \\ \hline 29 \end{array}$$

Check: $(470 \times 39) + 29 =$
$18{,}330 + 29 = 18{,}359$

Example 24
$$\begin{array}{r} 62\ r111 \\ 534\overline{)\ 33{,}219} \\ -32\ 04 \\ \hline 1\ 179 \\ -1\ 068 \\ \hline 111 \end{array}$$

Check: $(62 \times 534) + 111 =$
$33{,}108 + 111 = 33{,}219$

Example 26 1, 2, 4, 5, 8, 10, 20 and 40 are
factors of 40.

Example 28

Strategy   To find the amount that remains to be paid, subtract the down payment ($675) from the cost ($3250).

Solution

$$\begin{array}{r} \overset{11\ 14}{} \\ \overset{2\ \ \cancel{7}\ \ \cancel{4}\ \ 10}{\$\cancel{3}\ \cancel{2}\ \cancel{3}\ \cancel{0}} \\ -\ \ 6\ 7\ 5 \\ \hline \$2\ 5\ 7\ 5 \end{array}$$

$2575 remains to be paid.

Example 30

Strategy   To find the number of cases produced in 8 hours:
▷ Find the number of cases produced in one hour by dividing the number of cans produced (12,600) by the number of cans to a case (24).
▷ Multiply the number of cases produced in one hour by 8.

Solution

$$\begin{array}{r} 525 \\ 24\overline{)\ 12{,}600} \\ -12\ 0 \\ \hline 60 \\ -48 \\ \hline 120 \\ -120 \\ \hline 0 \end{array}$$ cases produced in one hour

$$\begin{array}{r} 525 \\ \times\ \ \ 8 \\ \hline 4200 \end{array}$$

In 8 hours, 4200 cases are produced.

Exercises   Pages 27–32

1. 54   **3.** 328   **5.** 220   **7.** 623   **9.** 711   **11.** 405   **13.** 280   **15.** 1143   **17.** 4010   **19.** 1500
21. 7248   **23.** 635   **25.** 2236   **27.** 5460   **29.** 1860   **31.** 1101   **33.** 1685   **35.** 46,963
37. 59,976   **39.** 19,120   **41.** 19,790   **43.** 144,759   **45.** 560,399   **47.** 651,000   **49.** 559,542
51. 336   **53.** 910   **55.** 640   **57.** 800   **59.** 1794   **61.** 1541   **63.** 63,063   **65.** 33,520
67. 66,866   **69.** 44,100   **71.** 380,834   **73.** 541,164   **75.** 400,995   **77.** 105,315   **79.** 66,000
81. 115,623   **83.** 132,238   **85.** 550,281   **87.** 428,770   **89.** 260,000   **91.** 344,463   **93.** 41,808
95. 189,500   **97.** 401,880   **99.** 225,036   **101.** 292,974   **103.** 1,052,763   **105.** 4,198,388
107. 1,232,000   **109.** 1,302,725   **111.** 2^3 **113.** $6^3 \cdot 7^4$ **115.** $6^3 \cdot 11^4$ **117.** $3 \cdot 10^4$ **119.** $2^2 \cdot 3^3 \cdot 5^4$
121. $5 \cdot 7^2 \cdot 9^2 \cdot 11$ **123.** 200   **125.** 900   **127.** 972   **129.** 120   **131.** 360   **133.** 0   **135.** 90,000
137. 540   **139.** 25,920   **141.** 4,320,000   **143.** 5   **145.** 16   **147.** 80   **149.** 210   **151.** 44
153. 206   **155.** 530   **157.** 902   **159.** 390   **161.** 1056   **163.** 2607   **165.** 9800   **167.** 21,560
169. 3580   **171.** 2 r1   **173.** 5 r2   **175.** 13 r1   **177.** 10 r3   **179.** 90 r2   **181.** 230 r1   **183.** 204 r3
185. 1347 r3   **187.** 778 r2   **189.** 391 r4   **191.** 2417 r1   **193.** 461 r8   **195.** 1160 r4   **197.** 708 r2
199. 3825   **201.** 9044 r2   **203.** 3 r15   **205.** 2 r3   **207.** 21 r36   **209.** 34 r2   **211.** 19 r20
213. 21 r12   **215.** 8 r8   **217.** 4 r49   **219.** 200 r25   **221.** 203 r2   **223.** 33 r33   **225.** 810 r3
227. 185 r2   **229.** 67 r70   **231.** 601 r8   **233.** 200 r9   **235.** 35 r47   **237.** 271   **239.** 4484 r6
241. 608   **243.** 708   **245.** 468 r60   **247.** 15 r7   **249.** 1 r563   **251.** 50 r92   **253.** 1, 2, 5, 10
255. 1, 5   **257.** 1, 2, 3, 4, 6, 12   **259.** 1, 2, 4, 8   **261.** 1, 13   **263.** 1, 2, 3, 6, 9, 18   **265.** 1, 2, 4, 7, 14, 28
267. 1, 29   **269.** 1, 2, 11, 22   **271.** 1, 2, 4, 11, 22, 44   **273.** 1, 7, 49   **275.** 1, 3, 19, 57
277. 1, 2, 3, 4, 6, 8, 12, 16, 24, 48   **279.** 1, 3, 29, 87   **281.** 1, 2, 23, 46   **283.** $315   **285.** $74
287. 432 mi   **289.** 73,964 gal   **291.** $36,995   **293.** 3250 boxes   **295.** 720 boxes

Section 4   Pages 33–36

Example 2 $44 = 2 \cdot 2 \cdot 11$ **Example 4** $177 = 3 \cdot 59$

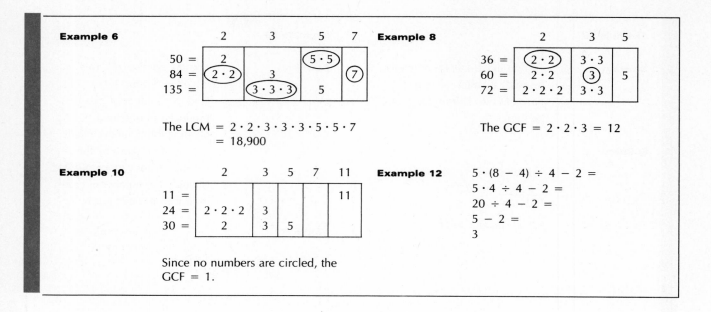

Example 6

	2	3	5	7
50 =	2		5 · 5	
84 =	2 · 2	3		7
135 =		3 · 3 · 3	5	

The LCM = 2 · 2 · 3 · 3 · 3 · 5 · 5 · 7
       = 18,900

Example 8

	2	3	5
36 =	2 · 2	3 · 3	
60 =	2 · 2	3	5
72 =	2 · 2 · 2	3 · 3	

The GCF = 2 · 2 · 3 = 12

Example 10

	2	3	5	7	11
11 =					11
24 =	2 · 2 · 2	3			
30 =	2	3	5		

Since no numbers are circled, the
GCF = 1.

Example 12

$5 \cdot (8 - 4) \div 4 - 2 =$
$5 \cdot 4 \div 4 - 2 =$
$20 \div 4 - 2 =$
$5 - 2 =$
3

Exercises   Pages 37–40

1. 2 · 3   **3.** prime   **5.** 2 · 2 · 2 · 2   **7.** 2 · 2 · 3   **9.** 3 · 3   **11.** 2 · 2 · 3 · 3   **13.** 5 · 13
15. 2 · 2 · 2 · 2 · 5   **17.** 2 · 3 · 3   **19.** 2 · 2 · 7   **21.** prime   **23.** 2 · 3 · 7   **25.** 3 · 3 · 3 · 3   **27.** 5 · 19
29. 2 · 2 · 2 · 3 · 5   **31.** 2 · 5 · 5   **33.** 2 · 11   **35.** 2 · 5 · 7   **37.** 2 · 37   **39.** prime   **41.** 2 · 61
43. 40   **45.** 24   **47.** 30   **49.** 12   **51.** 24   **53.** 60   **55.** 18   **57.** 20   **59.** 42   **61.** 21
63. 24   **65.** 40   **67.** 180   **69.** 72   **71.** 180   **73.** 72   **75.** 120   **77.** 240   **79.** 1   **81.** 6
83. 7   **85.** 25   **87.** 1   **89.** 4   **91.** 4   **93.** 6   **95.** 4   **97.** 2   **99.** 2   **101.** 1   **103.** 2
105. 3   **107.** 5   **109.** 14   **111.** 7   **113.** 5   **115.** 4   **117.** 9   **119.** 10   **121.** 47   **123.** 8
125. 5   **127.** 8   **129.** 27   **131.** 9   **133.** 15   **135.** 30   **137.** 17   **139.** 18   **141.** 6
143. 143   **145.** 44   **147.** 19   **149.** 135   **151.** 2   **153.** 42   **155.** 8   **157.** 16   **159.** 6   **161.** 8
163. 3   **165.** 18   **167.** 11   **169.** 8   **171.** 4

Review/Test   Page 43

1. ⊢+⬥+⊢+⊢+⊢+⊢+⊢+⊢+⊢+⊢+⊢+⊢→ (1.1A)   **2.** 21 > 19 (1.1A)   **3.** 900,000 + 6000 + 300 + 70 + 8 (1.1B)
  0 1 2 3 4 5 6 7 8 9 10 11 12
4. 75,000 (1.1C)   **5.** 96,798 (1.2A)   **6.** 135,915 (1.2A)   **7.** 9333 (1.2B)   **8.** 10,882 (1.2B)
9. 726,104 (1.3A)   **10.** 6,854,144 (1.3A)   **11.** $3^3 \cdot 7^2$ (1.3B)   **12.** 432 (1.3B)   **13.** 703 (1.3C)
14. 8710 r2 (1.3C)   **15.** 1121 r27 (1.3C)   **16.** 1, 2, 3, 4, 6, 9, 12, 18, 36 (1.3D)   **17.** 2 · 2 · 3 · 7 (1.4A)
18. 210 (1.4B)   **19.** 20 (1.4C)   **20.** 9 (1.4D)   **21.** 4430 students (1.3E)   **22.** $1502 (1.3E)
23. $5375 (1.3E)   **24.** 3000 boxes (1.3E)

Cumulative Review/Test   Page 44

1. 100,332 (1.2A)   **2.** 4122 (1.3A)   **3.** 33 r366 (1.3C)   **4.** 2 · 2 · 5 · 11 (1.4A)   **5.** 60,000 + 700 + 5 (1.1B)
6. 1685 (1.2B)   **7.** 402 r3 (1.3C)   **8.** 2 (1.4D)   **9.** 37 > 16 (1.1A)   **10.** 9,799,412 (1.2A)
11. 1,222,832 (1.3A)   **12.** $5^3 \cdot 7^2$ (1.3B)   **13.** 789,000 (1.1C)   **14.** 82,524 (1.2B)   **15.** 209 r11 (1.3C)
16. 1, 2, 3, 6, 9, 18 (1.3D)   **17.** 36 (1.4B)   **18.** 4 (1.4C)   **19.** $999 (1.3E)   **20.** $920 (1.3E)
21. 4400 calculators (1.3E)   **22.** $788 (1.3E)   **23.** $2065 (1.3E)   **24.** $181 (1.3E)

Note: The reference in parentheses following the answers in the Review/Tests and Cumulative Review/Tests refer to the objective which corresponds with that problem. The first number of the reference indicates the chapter, the second number indicates the section, and the letter indicates the objective. For example, the reference (1.2A) stands for Chapter 1, Section 2, Objective A. This notation will be used for all review tests throughout the text.

Answers to Chapter 2

Section 1   Pages 46–50

Example 2	$\frac{17}{4}$; $4\frac{1}{4}$	**Example 4**	$5\overline{)22}^{\,4}$ $\frac{22}{5} = 4\frac{2}{5}$ $\underline{-20}$ $\quad\;2$

Example 6 $7\overline{)28}^{\,4}$ $\frac{28}{7} = 4$

Example 8 $14\frac{5}{8} = \frac{112+5}{8} = \frac{117}{8}$

Example 10 $45 \div 5 = 9$ $\frac{3\cdot 9}{5\cdot 9} = \frac{27}{45}$

$\frac{27}{45}$ is equivalent to $\frac{3}{5}$.

Example 12   Write 6 as $\frac{6}{1}$.

$18 \div 1 = 18$ $\frac{6\cdot 18}{1\cdot 18} = \frac{108}{18}$

$\frac{108}{18}$ is equivalent to 6.

Example 14 $\frac{16}{24} = \dfrac{\overset{1}{2}\cdot\overset{1}{2}\cdot\overset{1}{2}\cdot 2}{\underset{1}{2}\cdot\underset{1}{2}\cdot\underset{1}{2}\cdot 3} = \frac{2}{3}$

Example 16 $\frac{8}{56} = \dfrac{\overset{1}{2}\cdot\overset{1}{2}\cdot\overset{1}{2}}{\underset{1}{2}\cdot\underset{1}{2}\cdot\underset{1}{2}\cdot 7} = \frac{1}{7}$

Example 18 $\frac{15}{32} = \frac{3\cdot 5}{2\cdot 2\cdot 2\cdot 2\cdot 2} = \frac{15}{32}$

Example 20 $\frac{48}{36} = \dfrac{\overset{1}{2}\cdot\overset{1}{2}\cdot 2\cdot 2\cdot\overset{1}{3}}{\underset{1}{2}\cdot\underset{1}{2}\cdot\underset{1}{3}\cdot 3} = \frac{4}{3} = 1\frac{1}{3}$

Example 22 $\frac{4}{15} < \frac{11}{15}$

Example 24 $\frac{9}{14} = \frac{27}{42}$ $\frac{13}{21} = \frac{26}{42}$

$\frac{9}{14} > \frac{13}{21}$

Exercises   Pages 51–52

1. $\frac{5}{4}$; $1\frac{1}{4}$ **3.** $\frac{8}{3}$; $2\frac{2}{3}$ **5.** $\frac{20}{8}$; $2\frac{4}{8}$ **7.** $2\frac{3}{4}$ **9.** 5 **11.** $1\frac{1}{8}$ **13.** $2\frac{3}{10}$ **15.** 3 **17.** $1\frac{1}{7}$ **19.** $2\frac{1}{3}$

21. 16 **23.** $2\frac{1}{8}$ **25.** 1 **27.** $\frac{7}{3}$ **29.** $\frac{13}{2}$ **31.** $\frac{41}{6}$ **33.** $\frac{37}{4}$ **35.** $\frac{21}{2}$ **37.** $\frac{73}{9}$ **39.** $\frac{58}{11}$

41. $\frac{21}{8}$ **43.** $\frac{13}{8}$ **45.** $\frac{100}{9}$ **47.** $\frac{9}{48}$ **49.** $\frac{12}{32}$ **51.** $\frac{9}{51}$ **53.** $\frac{12}{16}$ **55.** $\frac{27}{9}$ **57.** $\frac{3}{48}$ **59.** $\frac{12}{18}$

61. $\frac{28}{32}$ **63.** $\frac{35}{45}$ **65.** $\frac{60}{64}$ **67.** $\frac{1}{3}$ **69.** $\frac{1}{2}$ **71.** $\frac{1}{6}$ **73.** $\frac{2}{3}$ **75.** $1\frac{1}{2}$ **77.** $\frac{2}{5}$ **79.** $\frac{2}{15}$ **81.** $\frac{14}{45}$

83. $\frac{12}{35}$ **85.** $\frac{7}{11}$ **87.** $\frac{11}{40} < \frac{19}{40}$ **89.** $\frac{2}{3} < \frac{5}{7}$ **91.** $\frac{5}{8} > \frac{7}{12}$ **93.** $\frac{7}{9} < \frac{11}{12}$ **95.** $\frac{13}{14} > \frac{19}{21}$ **97.** $\frac{7}{24} < \frac{11}{30}$

Section 2   Pages 53–56

Example 2
$$\frac{7}{8} = \frac{105}{120}$$
$$+\frac{11}{15} = \frac{88}{120}$$
$$\frac{193}{120} = 1\frac{73}{120}$$

Example 4
$$\frac{3}{4} = \frac{30}{40}$$
$$\frac{4}{5} = \frac{32}{40}$$
$$+\frac{5}{8} = \frac{25}{40}$$
$$\frac{87}{40} = 2\frac{7}{40}$$

Example 6
$$7\frac{4}{5} = 7\frac{24}{30}$$
$$6\frac{7}{10} = 6\frac{21}{30}$$
$$+13\frac{11}{15} = 13\frac{22}{30}$$
$$26\frac{67}{30} = 28\frac{7}{30}$$

Example 8
$$17\frac{5}{9} = 17\frac{20}{36}$$
$$-11\frac{5}{12} = 11\frac{15}{36}$$
$$6\frac{5}{36}$$

Example 10
$$21\frac{7}{9} = 21\frac{28}{36} = 20\frac{64}{36}$$
$$-7\frac{11}{12} = 7\frac{33}{36} = 7\frac{33}{36}$$
$$13\frac{31}{36}$$

Exercises   Pages 57–60

1. 1 **3.** $1\frac{4}{11}$ **5.** $2\frac{4}{5}$ **7.** $2\frac{1}{4}$ **9.** $1\frac{1}{6}$ **11.** $\frac{13}{14}$ **13.** $1\frac{1}{45}$ **15.** $\frac{17}{18}$ **17.** $\frac{35}{48}$ **19.** $\frac{23}{60}$ **21.** $\frac{13}{21}$

23. $\frac{37}{56}$ **25.** $\frac{33}{98}$ **27.** $5\frac{7}{10}$ **29.** $5\frac{11}{16}$ **31.** $8\frac{23}{60}$ **33.** $18\frac{8}{9}$ **35.** $11\frac{1}{36}$ **37.** $24\frac{11}{12}$ **39.** $12\frac{17}{22}$

41. $1\frac{17}{18}$ **43.** $1\frac{11}{48}$ **45.** $1\frac{9}{20}$ **47.** $1\frac{109}{180}$ **49.** $1\frac{91}{144}$ **51.** $2\frac{5}{72}$ **53.** $1\frac{20}{33}$ **55.** $2\frac{11}{24}$ **57.** $6\frac{33}{40}$

59. $11\frac{19}{24}$ **61.** $16\frac{29}{120}$ **63.** $24\frac{29}{40}$ **65.** $33\frac{7}{24}$ **67.** $10\frac{5}{36}$ **69.** $10\frac{5}{12}$ **71.** $14\frac{73}{90}$ **73.** $10\frac{13}{48}$

75. $14\frac{19}{24}$ **77.** $\frac{1}{4}$ **79.** $\frac{2}{7}$ **81.** $\frac{1}{2}$ **83.** $\frac{19}{56}$ **85.** $\frac{1}{2}$ **87.** $\frac{4}{45}$ **89.** $\frac{11}{18}$ **91.** $\frac{5}{48}$ **93.** $\frac{1}{12}$ **95.** $\frac{20}{57}$

97. $\frac{17}{36}$ **99.** $\frac{37}{51}$ **101.** $\frac{17}{70}$ **103.** $\frac{49}{120}$ **105.** $\frac{25}{126}$ **107.** $\frac{11}{48}$ **109.** $\frac{23}{72}$ **111.** $\frac{81}{232}$ **113.** $3\frac{1}{6}$

115. $56\frac{4}{23}$ **117.** $4\frac{1}{3}$ **119.** $3\frac{2}{3}$ **121.** $1\frac{3}{5}$ **123.** $8\frac{2}{3}$ **125.** $7\frac{43}{45}$ **127.** $1\frac{2}{5}$ **129.** $14\frac{4}{5}$ **131.** $20\frac{17}{24}$

133. $3\frac{1}{8}$ **135.** $25\frac{8}{15}$ **137.** $6\frac{32}{45}$ **139.** $2\frac{1}{160}$ **141.** $1\frac{169}{200}$ **143.** $48\frac{31}{70}$ **145.** $85\frac{2}{9}$ **147.** $9\frac{5}{13}$

149. $10\frac{169}{180}$ **151.** $32\frac{43}{63}$ **153.** $68\frac{1}{60}$ **155.** $6\frac{83}{100}$

Section 3   Pages 61–66

Example 2

$$5\tfrac{2}{5} \times \tfrac{5}{9} = \tfrac{27}{5} \times \tfrac{5}{9} = \tfrac{27 \cdot 5}{5 \cdot 9} =$$

$$\frac{\overset{1}{\cancel{3}} \cdot \overset{1}{\cancel{3}} \cdot 3 \cdot \overset{1}{\cancel{5}}}{\underset{1}{\cancel{5}} \cdot \underset{1}{\cancel{3}} \cdot \underset{1}{\cancel{3}}} = 3$$

Example 4

$$3\tfrac{2}{5} \times 6\tfrac{1}{4} = \tfrac{17}{5} \times \tfrac{25}{4} = \tfrac{17 \cdot 25}{5 \cdot 4} =$$

$$\frac{17 \cdot \overset{1}{\cancel{5}} \cdot 5}{\underset{1}{\cancel{5}} \cdot 2 \cdot 2} = \tfrac{85}{4} = 21\tfrac{1}{4}$$

Example 6

$$3\tfrac{2}{7} \times 6 = \tfrac{23}{7} \times \tfrac{6}{1} = \tfrac{23 \cdot 6}{7 \cdot 1} =$$

$$\tfrac{23 \cdot 3 \cdot 2}{7 \cdot 1} = \tfrac{138}{7} = 19\tfrac{5}{7}$$

Example 8

$$12\tfrac{3}{5} \div 7 = \tfrac{63}{5} \div \tfrac{7}{1} = \tfrac{63}{5} \times \tfrac{1}{7} =$$

$$\frac{63 \cdot 1}{5 \cdot 7} = \frac{3 \cdot 3 \cdot \overset{1}{\cancel{7}}}{5 \cdot \underset{1}{\cancel{7}}} = \tfrac{9}{5} = 1\tfrac{4}{5}$$

Example 10

$$2\tfrac{5}{6} \div 8\tfrac{1}{2} = \tfrac{17}{6} \div \tfrac{17}{2} = \tfrac{17}{6} \times \tfrac{2}{17} =$$

$$\frac{17 \cdot 2}{6 \cdot 17} = \frac{\overset{1}{\cancel{17}} \cdot \overset{1}{\cancel{2}}}{2 \cdot 3 \cdot \underset{1}{\cancel{17}}} = \tfrac{1}{3}$$

Example 12

$$6\tfrac{2}{5} \div 4 = \tfrac{32}{5} \div \tfrac{4}{1} = \tfrac{32}{5} \times \tfrac{1}{4} =$$

$$\frac{32 \cdot 1}{5 \cdot 4} = \frac{2 \cdot 2 \cdot 2 \cdot \overset{1}{\cancel{2}} \cdot \overset{1}{\cancel{2}}}{5 \cdot \underset{1}{\cancel{2}} \cdot \underset{1}{\cancel{2}}} = \tfrac{8}{5} = 1\tfrac{3}{5}$$

Example 14

Strategy

To find the price of one ounce of gold, divide the total price of the coin ($1275) by the number of ounces $\left(2\tfrac{1}{2}\right)$.

Solution

$$1275 \div 2\tfrac{1}{2} = \tfrac{1275}{1} \div \tfrac{5}{2} = \tfrac{1275}{1} \times \tfrac{2}{5} =$$

$$\tfrac{1275 \cdot 2}{1 \cdot 5} = 510$$

The price of one ounce of gold is $510.

Example 16

Strategy

To find the value of the building:
▷ Find the value of the land $\left(\tfrac{1}{4} \times \$120{,}000\right)$.
▷ Subtract the value of the land from the total value.

Solution

$$\tfrac{1}{4} \times 120{,}000 = \tfrac{120{,}000}{4} = 30{,}000$$

$$\begin{array}{r} 120{,}000 \\ -\ \ 30{,}000 \\ \hline 90{,}000 \end{array}$$

The value of the building is $90,000.

Example 18

Strategy

To find how much of the job remains to be done:
▷ Find the total amount of the house already stained $\left(\tfrac{1}{3} + \tfrac{1}{4}\right)$.
▷ Subtract the amount already stained from 1, which represents the complete job.

Solution

$$\begin{array}{ll} \tfrac{1}{3} = \tfrac{4}{12} & \qquad 1 = \tfrac{12}{12} \\[4pt] +\tfrac{1}{4} = \tfrac{3}{12} & \qquad -\tfrac{7}{12} = \tfrac{7}{12} \\[4pt] \hline \qquad \tfrac{7}{12}\ \text{already} & \qquad\qquad \tfrac{5}{12} \\ \qquad \quad \text{stained} \end{array}$$

$\tfrac{5}{12}$ of the house remains to be stained.

Exercises   Pages 67–72

1. $\frac{7}{12}$ **3.** $\frac{7}{48}$ **5.** $\frac{5}{12}$ **7.** $\frac{1}{3}$ **9.** $\frac{11}{20}$ **11.** $\frac{1}{7}$ **13.** $\frac{1}{8}$ **15.** $\frac{5}{12}$ **17.** $\frac{9}{50}$ **19.** $\frac{5}{32}$ **21.** 6   **23.** $\frac{2}{3}$

25. $\frac{15}{44}$ **27.** $\frac{5}{14}$ **29.** 10   **31.** $\frac{1}{15}$ **33.** $\frac{7}{26}$ **35.** $1\frac{3}{4}$ **37.** 9   **39.** $1\frac{1}{2}$ **41.** 4   **43.** $\frac{4}{9}$ **45.** $\frac{1}{2}$

47. 10   **49.** $6\frac{3}{7}$ **51.** $18\frac{1}{3}$ **53.** $1\frac{5}{7}$ **55.** $3\frac{1}{2}$ **57.** 16   **59.** $8\frac{1}{4}$ **61.** $27\frac{1}{2}$ **63.** 7   **65.** $24\frac{1}{2}$

67. 19   **69.** $27\frac{2}{3}$ **71.** $7\frac{7}{9}$ **73.** 0   **75.** $1\frac{1}{2}$ **77.** $19\frac{1}{2}$ **79.** 7   **81.** $7\frac{2}{5}$ **83.** 16   **85.** $32\frac{4}{5}$

87. $28\frac{1}{2}$ **89.** 18   **91.** $8\frac{8}{15}$ **93.** $34\frac{2}{5}$ **95.** 519   **97.** 270   **99.** $80\frac{1}{3}$ **101.** $\frac{5}{6}$ **103.** 0

105. $1\frac{1}{3}$ **107.** $8\frac{4}{5}$ **109.** $\frac{2}{9}$ **111.** $3\frac{17}{75}$ **113.** $\frac{1}{6}$ **115.** $\frac{7}{10}$ **117.** $1\frac{5}{27}$ **119.** 3   **121.** $\frac{1}{6}$ **123.** 6

125. $\frac{1}{15}$ **127.** 2   **129.** $2\frac{1}{2}$ **131.** 3   **133.** 6   **135.** $\frac{1}{2}$ **137.** 6   **139.** $\frac{1}{30}$ **141.** $1\frac{4}{5}$ **143.** $8\frac{8}{9}$

145. $\frac{1}{6}$ **147.** $1\frac{1}{11}$ **149.** $\frac{16}{21}$ **151.** $\frac{7}{11}$ **153.** $2\frac{13}{16}$ **155.** $\frac{1}{9}$ **157.** 8   **159.** $\frac{11}{28}$ **161.** 72

163. $\frac{3}{22}$ **165.** $4\frac{4}{5}$ **167.** $\frac{35}{47}$ **169.** $9\frac{39}{40}$ **171.** $\frac{12}{53}$ **173.** $2\frac{6}{43}$ **175.** $1\frac{15}{26}$ **177.** $1\frac{4}{15}$ **179.** $\frac{1}{144}$

181. 39   **183.** $2\frac{8}{39}$ **185.** $13\frac{25}{49}$ **187.** $3\frac{1}{25}$ **189.** 0   **191.** 6   **193.** $3\frac{13}{49}$ **195.** 4   **197.** $1\frac{61}{62}$

199. $\frac{1}{2}$ **201.** $1\frac{1}{16}$ in.   **203.** $\$43\frac{1}{8}$ **205.** $\frac{13}{24}$ in.   **207.** $\frac{11}{12}$ ft   **209.** \$484   **211.** \$264   **213.** 16 portions

215. \$14,000   **217.** $\$30\frac{5}{8}$ **219.** $4\frac{7}{24}$ mi   **221.** \$2160   **223.** 33 parcels

Section 4   Pages 73–80

Example 2 4.35	**Example 4**	$\begin{array}{r} {\scriptstyle 1\ 2} \\ 4.62 \\ 27.9 \\ +\ \ 0.62054 \\ \hline 33.14054 \end{array}$

Example 6

$$\begin{array}{r} {\scriptstyle 16\ 9\ 9}\\ {\scriptstyle 2\ \ \cancel{6}\ \cancel{10}\ \cancel{10}\ 10}\\ \cancel{3}.\cancel{7}\ \cancel{0}\ \cancel{0}\ \cancel{0}\\ -1.9\ 7\ 1\ 5\\ \hline 1.7\ 2\ 8\ 5 \end{array}$$

Check:
$$\begin{array}{r} {\scriptstyle 1\ .111}\\ 1.9715\\ +1.7285\\ \hline 3.7000 \end{array}$$

Example 8

$$\begin{array}{r} 4.68\\ \times 6.03\\ \hline 1404\\ 28080\\ \hline 28.2204 \end{array}$$

Example 10 $6.9 \times 1000 = 6900$

Example 12 $4.0273 \times 10^2 = 402.73$

Example 14

$$\begin{array}{r} 2.7\\ 0.052\overline{)0.140.4}\\ -104\\ \hline 36\ 4\\ -36\ 4\\ \hline 0 \end{array}$$

Example 16

$$\begin{array}{r} 72.73 \approx 72.7\\ 5.09\overline{)370.20.00}\\ -356\ 3\\ \hline 13\ 90\\ -10\ 18\\ \hline 3\ 72\ 0\\ -3\ 56\ 3\\ \hline 15\ 70\\ -15\ 27\\ \hline \end{array}$$

Example 18 $309.21 \div 10{,}000 = 0.030921$

Example 20 $42.93 \div 10^4 = 0.004293$

Example 22

Strategy

To find the average monthly cost for gasoline:
▷ Find the sum of the costs.
▷ Divide the sum of the costs by the number of months (3).

Solution

$$\begin{array}{r} \$118.50\\ 130.50\\ +\ 109.50\\ \hline \$358.50 \end{array}$$

$$\begin{array}{r} \$119.50\\ 3\overline{)\$358.50} \end{array}$$

The average monthly cost for gasoline was $119.50.

Exercises   Pages 81–86

1. 7.4   **3.** 23.0   **5.** 22.68   **7.** 480.33   **9.** 1.039   **11.** 1946.375   **13.** 0.69   **15.** 16.305
17. 21.331   **19.** 37.612   **21.** 110.7666   **23.** 34.8779   **25.** 36.3647   **27.** 73.636   **29.** 88.591
31. 86.9097   **33.** 13.9282   **35.** 418.75593   **37.** 0.014   **39.** 4.088   **41.** 74.716   **43.** 8.666
45. 0.7727   **47.** 3.273   **49.** 791.247   **51.** 57.3685   **53.** 31.334   **55.** 342.9268   **57.** 6.719
59. 206.857   **61.** 4.5795   **63.** 423.175   **65.** 15.7865   **67.** 15.9696   **69.** 2.678   **71.** 6.93
73. 1.84   **75.** 39.5   **77.** 2.72   **79.** 0.603   **81.** 13.50   **83.** 79.80   **85.** 4.316   **87.** 1.794
89. 0.072   **91.** 0.1323   **93.** 0.03568   **95.** 0.0784   **97.** 0.076   **99.** 3.787   **101.** 34.48
103. 20.148   **105.** 0.04255   **107.** 0.17686   **109.** 0.19803   **111.** 195.168   **113.** 14.8657
115. 53.9961   **117.** 2.116   **119.** 2.331   **121.** 21.46   **123.** 69.3   **125.** 3.9   **127.** 3295.4
129. 35,700   **131.** 6.3   **133.** 3.9   **135.** 49,000   **137.** 0.53   **139.** 7.7   **141.** 132   **143.** 130
145. 0.04   **147.** 4.14   **149.** 9.69   **151.** 2.2   **153.** 0.24   **155.** 49.8   **157.** 6.1   **159.** 680
161. 290   **163.** 3.6   **165.** 4.7   **167.** 1.3   **169.** 6.5   **171.** 0.8   **173.** 0.81   **175.** 0.09
177. 12.73   **179.** 22.70   **181.** 0.249   **183.** 0.229   **185.** 0.104   **187.** 0.360   **189.** 1   **191.** 34
193. 3   **195.** 57   **197.** 4.267   **199.** 2.37835   **201.** 0.82537   **203.** 8.765   **205.** 0.02954
207. 0.0018932   **209.** $36.20   **211.** 270 hamburgers   **213.** $1256.25   **215.** 10.1 gal   **217.** $82.78
219. 18 in.

Section 5   Pages 87–88

Example 2 $\dfrac{0.56}{16\overline{)9.00}} \approx 0.6$

Example 4 $4\dfrac{1}{6} = \dfrac{25}{6}$ $\dfrac{4.166}{6\overline{)25.000}} \approx 4.17$

Example 6 $0.56 = \dfrac{56}{100} = \dfrac{14}{25}$

$5.35 = 5\dfrac{35}{100} = 5\dfrac{7}{20}$

Example 8

$0.12\dfrac{7}{8} = \dfrac{12\dfrac{7}{8}}{100} = 12\dfrac{7}{8} \div 100 =$

$\dfrac{103}{8} \times \dfrac{1}{100} = \dfrac{103}{800}$

Example 10 $64.009 < 64.99$

Example 12 $\dfrac{5}{8} = 0.625$

$0.63 > \dfrac{5}{8}$

Exercises   Pages 89–90

1. 0.625   **3.** 0.667   **5.** 0.167   **7.** 0.417   **9.** 1.75   **11.** 0.083   **13.** 2.25   **15.** 0.778   **17.** 2.333
19. 4   **21.** 0.5   **23.** 16.778   **25.** 87.5   **27.** 0.688   **29.** 0.16   **31.** 8.4   **33.** 3.083   **35.** 0.917
37. 1.438   **39.** 4.667   **41.** $\dfrac{4}{5}$ **43.** $\dfrac{8}{25}$ **45.** $\dfrac{1}{8}$ **47.** $1\dfrac{1}{4}$ **49.** $16\dfrac{9}{10}$ **51.** $8\dfrac{2}{5}$ **53.** $8\dfrac{437}{1000}$
55. $7\dfrac{3}{4}$ **57.** $8\dfrac{1}{200}$ **59.** $14\dfrac{3}{125}$ **61.** $1\dfrac{17}{25}$ **63.** $\dfrac{9}{200}$ **65.** $16\dfrac{18}{25}$ **67.** $\dfrac{33}{100}$ **69.** $6\dfrac{7}{200}$ **71.** $\dfrac{23}{150}$
73. $\dfrac{703}{800}$ **75.** $\dfrac{17}{160}$ **77.** $\dfrac{2}{3}$ **79.** $\dfrac{207}{700}$ **81.** $0.15 < 0.5$ **83.** $6.65 > 6.56$ **85.** $2.504 > 2.054$
87. $8.304 > 8.034$ **89.** $\dfrac{3}{8} > 0.365$ **91.** $\dfrac{2}{3} > 0.65$ **93.** $\dfrac{5}{9} > 0.55$ **95.** $0.62 > \dfrac{7}{15}$ **97.** $0.161 > \dfrac{1}{7}$
99. $\dfrac{7}{36} < 0.198$ **101.** $0.623 > 0.6023$ **103.** $0.87 > 0.087$ **105.** $0.033 < 0.3$ **107.** $8.881 > 8.818$
109. $0.835 > \dfrac{11}{16}$ **111.** $\dfrac{4}{9} < 0.445$

Review/Test   Page 93

1. $3\dfrac{3}{5}$ (2.1A)   **2.** $\dfrac{49}{5}$ (2.1A)   **3.** $\dfrac{45}{72}$ (2.1B)   **4.** $\dfrac{5}{8}$ (2.1C)   **5.** $\dfrac{3}{8} < \dfrac{5}{12}$ (2.1D)   **6.** $1\dfrac{61}{90}$ (2.2A)   **7.** $22\dfrac{4}{15}$ (2.2A)
8. $\dfrac{7}{48}$ (2.2B)   **9.** $13\dfrac{81}{88}$ (2.2B)   **10.** $\dfrac{4}{9}$ (2.3A)   **11.** 8 (2.3A)   **12.** $1\dfrac{3}{7}$ (2.3B)   **13.** $2\dfrac{2}{19}$ (2.3B)   **14.** 7.095 (2.4A)
15. 458.581 (2.4B)   **16.** 27.76626 (2.4B)   **17.** 2.4723 (2.4C)   **18.** 1.538 (2.4D)   **19.** 0.692 (2.5A)
20. $\dfrac{33}{40}$ (2.5A)   **21.** $0.66 < 0.666$ (2.5B)   **22.** $\dfrac{3}{8} > 0.35$ (2.5B)   **23.** $8\dfrac{1}{3}$ mi (2.3C)   **24.** $7.88 (2.4E)

Cumulative Review/Test   Page 94

1. $1\dfrac{7}{48}$ (2.2A)   **2.** 2.154 (2.4D)   **3.** $7\dfrac{1}{2}$ (2.3A)   **4.** $\dfrac{8}{9} < 0.98$ (2.5B)   **5.** 291,278 (1.2B)   **6.** $6\dfrac{1}{4}$ (2.1A)
7. 416.3997 (2.4B)   **8.** 0.733 (2.5A)   **9.** $2\dfrac{5}{8}$ (2.3B)   **10.** 73,154 (1.3A)   **11.** $\dfrac{23}{3}$ (2.1A)   **12.** 21.0764 (2.4B)
13. $\dfrac{1}{6}$ (2.5A)   **14.** 55.26066 (2.4C)   **15.** 1 (1.4D)   **16.** $\dfrac{15}{48}$ (2.1B)   **17.** 290,000 (1.1C)   **18.** $\dfrac{13}{24}$ (2.2B)
19. $\dfrac{2}{5}$ (2.1C)   **20.** $2 \cdot 2 \cdot 11$ (1.4A)   **21.** 0.06 (2.4A)   **22.** $\dfrac{7}{9} < \dfrac{5}{6}$ (2.1D)   **23.** 80 (2.4E)   **24.** $37.89 (2.4E)

Answers to Chapter 3

Section 1 Pages 96–104

Example 2 -232

Example 4

Example 6
a. $-12 < 7$
b. $-4.5 < 0$

Example 8
$|-7| = 7$
$|3.4| = 3.4$

Example 10
$\left|2\frac{1}{2}\right| = 2\frac{1}{2}$
$|-9| = 9$

Example 12
$-|-12| = -12$

Example 14
$-3 + (-6) = -9$

Example 16
$15.9 - 10.37 = 5.53$
$10.37 + (-15.9) = -5.53$

Example 18
$-5\frac{3}{8} + 9\frac{5}{12} = -5\frac{9}{24} + 9\frac{10}{24} =$
$4\frac{1}{24}$

Example 20
$-2 + 4 + (-8) + 7 =$
$2 + (-8) + 7 =$
$-6 + 7 =$
1

Example 22
$12 - 15 = 12 + (-15) = -3$

Example 24
$11.4 - 5.72 = 5.68$
$5.72 - 11.4 = 5.72 + (-11.4) =$
-5.68

Example 26
$8\frac{1}{2} - \left(-2\frac{3}{4}\right) = 8\frac{1}{2} + 2\frac{3}{4} =$
$8\frac{2}{4} + 2\frac{3}{4} = 10\frac{5}{4} = 11\frac{1}{4}$

Example 28
$-14.2 - (-7.3) - 7.89 =$
$-14.2 + 7.3 + (-7.89) =$
$-6.9 + (-7.89) = -14.79$

Example 30
$-3.5 \times 7 = -24.5$

Example 32
$-3 \times (-6) \times \left(-\frac{1}{2}\right) =$
$18 \times \left(-\frac{1}{2}\right) =$
-9

Example 34
$-15 \div 5 = -3$

Example 36
$18 \div (-4) = -4.5$

Example 38
$-6.25 \div (-1.49) \approx 4.19$

Example 40
$9 - 9 \div (-3) = 9 - (-3) =$
$9 + 3 = 12$

Example 42
$8 \div 4 \cdot 4 - (-2)^2 =$
$8 \div 4 \cdot 4 - 4 = 2 \cdot 4 - 4 =$
$8 - 4 = 8 + (-4) = 4$

Example 44
$8 - (-15) \div (2 - 7) =$
$8 - (-15) \div (-5) =$
$8 - 3 = 8 + (-3) = 5$

Example 46
$7 \div \left(\frac{1}{7} - \frac{3}{14}\right) - 9 =$
$7 \div \left(-\frac{1}{14}\right) - 9 = -98 - 9 =$
$-98 + (-9) = -107$

Exercises   Pages 105–110

1. -30 **3.** $+7\frac{1}{4}$ **5.** $+12,382$ **7.** (number line -4 to 4)   **9.** (number line -4 to 4)

11. (number line)   **13.** (number line)   **15.** (number line)

17. $3 < 5$ **19.** $-8 < -3$ **21.** $0 < 10$ **23.** $-12 < 3$ **25.** $9 > -1$ **27.** $0 < 5$ **29.** $6 > 4\frac{1}{2}$

31. $-10 < 40$ **33.** $-3\frac{1}{2} < 2\frac{1}{3}$ **35.** $5.3 > -6.9$ **37.** $-8.5 > -10.9$ **39.** $-3\frac{1}{3} < 2\frac{1}{8}$ **41.** 7

43. 8 **45.** 12 **47.** 4 **49.** 0.1 **51.** 4 **53.** -6 **55.** -8 **57.** $\frac{1}{2}$ **59.** 6.4 **61.** -1.7

63. 45.9 **65.** 3.4 **67.** $-1\frac{1}{2}$ **69.** 13.08 **71.** 1 **73.** -4 **75.** -13 **77.** -81 **79.** 167

81. 590 **83.** -4 **85.** 17 **87.** 35 **89.** -1.63 **91.** 3.5 **93.** 1.91 **95.** -1.22 **97.** -181.51

99. 94.626 **101.** 5.5 **103.** $-\frac{5}{24}$ **105.** $\frac{1}{10}$ **107.** $-\frac{13}{36}$ **109.** $-7\frac{5}{6}$ **111.** $\frac{13}{24}$ **113.** $2\frac{19}{45}$

115. -7 **117.** -16 **119.** 13 **121.** 18 **123.** 275 **125.** -178 **127.** -16 **129.** 13 **131.** 3

133. 22 **135.** -18.5 **137.** 1.68 **139.** 1.1 **141.** -3.37 **143.** -7.34 **145.** -17.97

147. -9.47 **149.** $\frac{7}{24}$ **151.** $-\frac{8}{15}$ **153.** $-\frac{1}{12}$ **155.** $\frac{37}{60}$ **157.** $-5\frac{3}{8}$ **159.** -56 **161.** 72 **163.** 0

165. -576 **167.** -72 **169.** 36 **171.** 0 **173.** -168 **175.** 28.14 **177.** -7.84 **179.** -112.97

181. $\frac{3}{20}$ **183.** $-\frac{5}{6}$ **185.** $-6\frac{3}{4}$ **187.** $-\frac{3}{7}$ **189.** $-\frac{1}{15}$ **191.** $-1\frac{1}{3}$ **193.** $\frac{45}{272}$ **195.** -3 **197.** 7

199. -1.78 **201.** 10.56 **203.** -18 **205.** -13.10 **207.** 13.57 **209.** 0 **211.** -0.53

213. -0.10 **215.** -3 **217.** 0 **219.** 2 **221.** 3 **223.** -2 **225.** 1 **227.** 2 **229.** 0

231. 10 **233.** 32 **235.** -6 **237.** -4 **239.** 13 **241.** -24 **243.** 33 **245.** -13 **247.** -19

249. -9.7 **251.** -8 **253.** -6.14 **255.** -14.7 **257.** -1 **259.** 0 **261.** $\frac{13}{70}$ **263.** $1\frac{11}{24}$

265. $3\frac{1}{2}$ **267.** 30 **269.** 6 **271.** -2

Section 2   Pages 111–118

Example 2 -4

Example 4
$2xy + y^2$
$2(-4)(2) + (2)^2$
$2(-4)(2) + 4$
$-8(2) + 4$
$-16 + 4$
-12

Example 6
$\dfrac{a^2 + b^2}{a + b}$
$\dfrac{(5)^2 + (-3)^2}{5 + (-3)}$
$\dfrac{25 + 9}{5 + (-3)}$
$\dfrac{34}{2} = 17$

Example 8
$x^3 - 2(x + y) + z^2$
$(2)^3 - 2[2 + (-4)] + (-3)^2$
$(2)^3 - 2(-2) + (-3)^2$
$8 - 2(-2) + 9$
$8 + 4 + 9$
$12 + 9$
21

Example 10
$3a - 2b - 5a + 6b$
$-2a + 4b$

Example 12
$-3y^2 + 7 + 8y^2 - 14$
$5y^2 - 7$

Example 14
$-5(4y^2)$
$-20y^2$

Example 16
$-7(-2a)$
$14a$

Example 18
$(-5x)(-2)$
$10x$

Example 20
$5(3 + 7b)$
$15 + 35b$

Example 22
$(3a - 1)5$
$15a - 5$

Example 24
$-8(-2a + 7b)$
$16a - 56b$

Example 26	$-(5x - 12)$ $-5x + 12$	**Example 28**	$3(-a^2 - 6a + 7)$ $-3a^2 - 18a + 21$
Example 30	$3y - 2(y - 7x)$ $3y - 2y + 14x$ $y + 14x$	**Example 32**	$-2(x - 2y) + 4(x - 3y)$ $-2x + 4y + 4x - 12y$ $2x - 8y$
Example 34	$-5(-2y - 3x) + 4y$ $10y + 15x + 4y$ $14y + 15x$	**Example 36**	$3y - 2[x - 4(2 - 3y)]$ $3y - 2[x - 8 + 12y]$ $3y - 2x + 16 - 24y$ $-21y - 2x + 16$

Exercises   Pages 119–122

1. $2x^2$; $5x$; $\underline{-8}$ **3.** $-a^4$; $\underline{6}$ **5.** $9b^2$; $-4\underline{ab}$; $\underline{a^2}$ **7.** $-8\underline{n}$; $-3n^2$ **9.** $1, -9$ **11.** $1, -4, -1$ **13.** 12
15. -4 **17.** 6 **19.** -2 **21.** -5 **23.** 25 **25.** -15 **27.** 10 **29.** 1 **31.** 5 **33.** 57
35. 5 **37.** 6 **39.** 10 **41.** 8 **43.** -3 **45.** -2 **47.** -22 **49.** 4 **51.** 20 **53.** $14x$
55. $5a$ **57.** $-6y$ **59.** $-3b - 7$ **61.** $5a$ **63.** $-2ab$ **65.** $5xy$ **67.** 0 **69.** $-\frac{5}{6}x$ **71.** $-\frac{1}{24}x^2$
73. $11x$ **75.** $7a$ **77.** $-2y^2$ **79.** $17x - 3y$ **81.** $-2a - 6b$ **83.** $-3x - 8y$ **85.** $-4x^2 - 2x$
87. $12x$ **89.** $-21a$ **91.** $6y$ **93.** $8x$ **95.** $-6a$ **97.** $12b$ **99.** $-15x^2$ **101.** x^2 **103.** a
105. x **107.** x **109.** y **111.** $3x$ **113.** $-2x$ **115.** $-8a^2$ **117.** $-2x$ **119.** $-x - 2$ **121.** $8x - 6$
123. $-2a - 14$ **125.** $-6y + 24$ **127.** $35 - 21b$ **129.** $-9 + 15x$ **131.** $15x^2 + 6x$ **133.** $2y - 18$
135. $-15x - 30$ **137.** $-6x^2 - 28$ **139.** $-6y^2 + 21$ **141.** $3x^2 - 3y^2$ **143.** $-2x^2 + 6y^2$ **145.** $-6a^2 + 7b^2$
147. $4x^2 - 12x + 20$ **149.** $-3y^2 + 9y + 21$ **151.** $-3a^2 - 5a + 4$ **153.** $-2x - 16$ **155.** $-9 - 12y$
157. $7n - 7$ **159.** $12x^2 - 9x + 12$ **161.** $10x^2 - 20xy - 5y^2$ **163.** $-2x - 16$ **165.** $18y - 51$
167. $6x + 28$ **169.** $5x - 75$ **171.** $4x - 4$ **173.** $38x - 63$ **175.** b **177.** $y + 20x$

Section 3   Pages 123–124

Example 2	the unknown number: n three eighths of the number: $\frac{3}{8}n$ five sixths of the number: $\frac{5}{6}n$ $\frac{3}{8}n - \frac{5}{6}n =$ $\frac{9}{24}n - \frac{20}{24}n =$ $-\frac{11}{24}n$	**Example 4**	the unknown number: n twice the number: $2n$ the sum of six and twice the number: $6 + 2n$ $4(6 + 2n) =$ $24 + 8n$

Exercises   Pages 125–126

1. $n + 3n$; $4n$ **3.** $(n + 6) + 5$; $n + 11$ **5.** $n - (n + 10)$; -10 **7.** $\frac{1}{6}n + \frac{4}{9}n$; $\frac{11}{18}n$ **9.** $\frac{n}{3} + n$; $\frac{4n}{3}$
11. $14\left(\frac{1}{7}n\right)$; $2n$ **13.** $10n - 2n$; $8n$ **15.** $(n - 6) + 16$; $n + 10$ **17.** $4n - n$; $3n$ **19.** $15n - 5n$; $10n$
21. $15(10 + n^3)$; $150 + 15n^3$ **23.** $6(n - 7)$; $6n - 42$ **25.** $8(n + 11)$; $8n + 88$ **27.** $9(n + 100)$; $9n + 900$
29. $10(n - 50)$; $10n - 500$ **31.** $4(n + 19)$; $4n + 76$ **33.** $\frac{2}{3}(n + 12)$; $\frac{2}{3}n + 8$ **35.** $(9 - n) - 12$; $-3 - n$
37. $10 - \left(\frac{2}{3}n + 4\right)$; $6 - \frac{2}{3}n$ **39.** $(n^2 + 3) + 2n^2$; $3n^2 + 3$ **41.** $(n + 7) + (2 - 2n)$; $-n + 9$
43. $(6 + n) + 2(n - 3)$; $3n$ **45.** $n + 4(n - 9)$; $5n - 36$

Review/Test   Page 129

1. $-4 > -6.5$ (3.1A)   **2.** $-3\frac{1}{2}$ (3.1B)   **3.** -4.46 (3.1C)   **4.** $-5\frac{11}{14}$ (3.1C)   **5.** 32 (3.1C)   **6.** $-1\frac{3}{8}$ (3.1C)

7. 1 (3.1C)   **8.** 26.32 (3.1D)   **9.** $-4\frac{3}{5}$ (3.1D)   **10.** 27 (3.1D)   **11.** $-\frac{5}{12}$ (3.1D)   **12.** -26 (3.1E)

13. -4 (3.1E)   **14.** 22 (3.2A)   **15.** $-9x - 7y$ (3.2B)   **16.** $-2x - 5y$ (3.2B)   **17.** $2x$ (3.2C)

18. $-36y$ (3.2C)   **19.** $-4x + 8$ (3.2D)   **20.** $-10x^2 + 15x - 30$ (3.2D)   **21.** $7x + 38$ (3.2D)

22. $2x + y$ (3.2D)   **23.** $10(n - 3)$; $10n - 30$ (3.3A)   **24.** $11 + 2(n + 4)$; $19 + 2n$ (3.3A)

Cumulative Review/Test   Page 130

1. $6a$ (3.2C)   **2.** 0 (3.1C)   **3.** 3.489 (3.1D)   **4.** $24 - 6x$ (3.2D)   **5.** 0 (1.4D)   **6.** $-3\frac{3}{8}$ (3.1C)

7. $-3x + 21y$ (3.2D)   **8.** -4 (3.1E)   **9.** $4\frac{13}{14}$ (2.2B)   **10.** -3 (3.1C)   **11.** $\frac{25}{42}$ (3.1D)   **12.** 16 (3.2A)

13. $30b$ (3.2C)   **14.** $2\frac{7}{12}$ (2.3B)   **15.** $-10\frac{13}{24}$ (3.1C)   **16.** $5x - 43$ (3.2D)   **17.** $-7a - 10b$ (3.2B)

18. 1.80939 (2.4B)   **19.** 432 (1.3B)   **20.** $31\frac{1}{2}$ (3.1D)   **21.** 1.25 (2.5A)   **22.** $5x^2$ (3.2B)

23. $-9y^2 + 9y + 21$ (3.2D)   **24.** $(3 + n)5 + 12$; $27 + 5n$ (3.3A)

Answers to Chapter 4

Section 1   Pages 132–136

Example 2

$$5 - 4x = 8x + 2$$

$$\begin{array}{c|c} 5 - 4\left(\frac{1}{4}\right) & 8\left(\frac{1}{4}\right) + 2 \\ 5 - 1 & 2 + 2 \\ 4 = 4 \end{array}$$

Yes, $\frac{1}{4}$ is a solution.

Example 4

$$10x - x^2 = 3x - 10$$

$$\begin{array}{c|c} 10(5) - (5)^2 & 3(5) - 10 \\ 50 - 25 & 15 - 10 \\ 25 \neq 5 \end{array}$$

No, 5 is not a solution.

Example 6

$$\frac{1}{2} = x - \frac{2}{3}$$

$$\frac{1}{2} + \frac{2}{3} = x - \frac{2}{3} + \frac{2}{3}$$

$$\frac{7}{6} = x$$

The solution is $\frac{7}{6}$.

Example 8

$$-\frac{2}{5}x = 6$$

$$\left(-\frac{5}{2}\right)\left(-\frac{2}{5}x\right) = \left(-\frac{5}{2}\right)(6)$$

$$x = -15$$

The solution is -15.

Example 10

$$4x - 8x = 16$$

$$-4x = 16$$

$$\left(-\frac{1}{4}\right)(-4x) = \left(-\frac{1}{4}\right)(16)$$

$$x = -4$$

The solution is -4.

Example 12

$$2 = 11 + 3x$$

$$2 + (-11) = 11 + (-11) + 3x$$

$$-9 = 3x$$

$$\frac{1}{3}(-9) = \frac{1}{3}(3x)$$

$$-3 = x$$

The solution is -3.

Example 14

$$x - 5 + 4x = 25$$

$$5x - 5 = 25$$

$$5x - 5 + 5 = 25 + 5$$

$$5x = 30$$

$$\frac{1}{5} \cdot 5x = \frac{1}{5} \cdot 30$$

$$x = 6$$

The solution is 6.

Exercises   Pages 137–140

1. Yes   **3.** No   **5.** Yes   **7.** Yes   **9.** Yes   **11.** No   **13.** Yes   **15.** No   **17.** Yes   **19.** No

21. 2   **23.** 15   **25.** 6   **27.** 0   **29.** -2 **31.** -7 **33.** -7 **35.** -12 **37.** 2   **39.** -5

41. 15   **43.** 14   **45.** -1 **47.** 1   **49.** $-\frac{2}{3}$ **51.** $-\frac{1}{2}$ **53.** 0.6529   **55.** -0.283 **57.** 9.257

59. 3   **61.** -4 **63.** -2 **65.** 9   **67.** 5   **69.** -4 **71.** 0   **73.** 6   **75.** -10 **77.** 12

79. -12 **81.** 3   **83.** -24 **85.** 9   **87.** $\frac{4}{5}$ **89.** $\frac{8}{7}$ **91.** 4   **93.** 3   **95.** 3   **97.** 6   **99.** -1

101. -3 **103.** 2   **105.** -2 **107.** 2   **109.** 5   **111.** -3 **113.** -1 **115.** 2   **117.** 2

119. -7 **121.** 0   **123.** $\frac{6}{7}$ **125.** $\frac{13}{9}$ **127.** -1 **129.** $\frac{3}{4}$ **131.** $\frac{4}{9}$ **133.** $\frac{1}{3}$ **135.** $-\frac{1}{3}$

137. $-\frac{1}{7}$ **139.** $\frac{1}{3}$ **141.** $-\frac{1}{6}$ **143.** 1   **145.** 1   **147.** $-\frac{4}{3}$ **149.** $-\frac{3}{2}$ **151.** 18   **153.** 8

155. -16 **157.** 25   **159.** 21   **161.** $\frac{8}{3}$ **163.** 2   **165.** 3   **167.** 1   **169.** -2

Section 2   Pages 141–144

Example 2

$$5x + 4 = 6 + 10x$$
$$5x + (-10x) + 4 = 6 + 10x + (-10x)$$
$$-5x + 4 = 6$$
$$-5x + 4 + (-4) = 6 + (-4)$$
$$-5x = 2$$
$$\left(-\frac{1}{5}\right)(-5x) = -\frac{1}{5} \cdot 2$$
$$x = -\frac{2}{5}$$

The solution is $-\frac{2}{5}$.

Example 6

$$5x - 4(3 - 2x) = 2(3x - 2) + 6$$
$$5x - 12 + 8x = 6x - 4 + 6$$
$$13x - 12 = 6x + 2$$
$$13x + (-6x) - 12 = 6x + (-6x) + 2$$
$$7x - 12 = 2$$
$$7x - 12 + 12 = 2 + 12$$
$$7x = 14$$
$$\frac{1}{7} \cdot 7x = \frac{1}{7} \cdot 14$$
$$x = 2$$

The solution is 2.

Example 4

$$5x - 10 - 3x = 6 - 4x$$
$$2x - 10 = 6 - 4x$$
$$2x + 4x - 10 = 6 - 4x + 4x$$
$$6x - 10 = 6$$
$$6x - 10 + 10 = 6 + 10$$
$$6x = 16$$
$$\frac{1}{6} \cdot 6x = \frac{1}{6} \cdot 16$$
$$x = \frac{8}{3}$$

The solution is $\frac{8}{3}$.

Example 8

$$-2[3x - 5(2x - 3)] = 3x - 8$$
$$-2[3x - 10x + 15] = 3x - 8$$
$$-2[-7x + 15] = 3x - 8$$
$$14x - 30 = 3x - 8$$
$$14x + (-3x) - 30 = 3x + (-3x) - 8$$
$$11x - 30 = -8$$
$$11x - 30 + 30 = -8 + 30$$
$$11x = 22$$
$$\frac{1}{11} \cdot 11x = \frac{1}{11} \cdot 22$$
$$x = 2$$

The solution is 2.

Example 10

Strategy

To find the location of the fulcrum when the system balances, replace the variables F_1, F_2, and d in the lever system equation by the given values and solve for x.

Solution

$$F_1 \cdot x = F_2 \cdot (d - x)$$
$$45x = 80(25 - x)$$
$$45x = 2000 - 80x$$
$$45x + 80x = 2000 - 80x + 80x$$
$$125x = 2000$$
$$\frac{1}{125} \cdot 125x = \frac{1}{125} \cdot 2000$$
$$x = 16$$

The fulcrum is 16 ft from the 45-pound force.

Exercises   Pages 145–146

1. $-\frac{1}{2}$ **3.** 3   **5.** 3   **7.** -1 **9.** -1 **11.** 2   **13.** -2 **15.** -3 **17.** -8 **19.** 0   **21.** -1

23. -3 **25.** -1 **27.** -2 **29.** -2 **31.** $\frac{2}{3}$ **33.** $\frac{5}{6}$ **35.** $-\frac{2}{3}$ **37.** 3   **39.** 4   **41.** 2

43. 3   **45.** 2   **47.** 2   **49.** -7 **51.** -2 **53.** $\frac{3}{8}$ **55.** $\frac{4}{7}$ **57.** $\frac{1}{2}$ **59.** 5   **61.** $\frac{20}{3}$ **63.** 2

65. 6 ft from the 40-pound force   **67.** 560 lb

Section 3   Pages 147–152

Example 2   The unknown number: n

four less than one third of a number	equals	five minus two thirds of the number

$$\frac{1}{3}n - 4 = 5 - \frac{2}{3}n$$
$$\frac{1}{3}n + \frac{2}{3}n - 4 = 5 - \frac{2}{3}n + \frac{2}{3}n$$
$$n - 4 = 5$$
$$n - 4 + 4 = 5 + 4$$
$$n = 9$$

The number is 9.

Example 4   The unknown number: n

two times the difference between a number and eight	is equal to	the sum of six times the number and eight

$$2(n - 8) = 6n + 8$$
$$2n - 16 = 6n + 8$$
$$2n + (-6n) - 16 = 6n + (-6n) + 8$$
$$-4n - 16 = 8$$
$$-4n - 16 + 16 = 8 + 16$$
$$-4n = 24$$
$$-\frac{1}{4}(-4n) = -\frac{1}{4}(24)$$
$$n = -6$$

The number is -6.

Example 6

Strategy

▷ First consecutive integer: n
  Second consecutive integer: $n + 1$
  Third consecutive integer: $n + 2$
▷ The sum of the three integers is -6.

Solution

$$n + (n + 1) + (n + 2) = -6$$
$$3n + 3 = -6$$
$$3n = -9$$
$$n = -3$$
$$n + 1 = -3 + 1 = -2$$
$$n + 2 = -3 + 2 = -1$$

The three consecutive integers are -3, -2, and -1.

Example 8

Strategy

▷ The number of years ago: x

	Present age	Past age
Half dollar	25	$25 - x$
Dime	15	$15 - x$

▷ At a past age, the half dollar was twice as old as the dime.

Solution

$$25 - x = 2(15 - x)$$
$$25 - x = 30 - 2x$$
$$25 + x = 30$$
$$x = 5$$

Five years ago the half dollar was twice as old as the dime.

Example 10

Strategy

▷ Rate of the first train: r
Rate of the second train: $2r$

	Rate	Time	Distance
1st train	r	3	$3r$
2nd train	$2r$	3	$3(2r)$

▷ The sum of the distances traveled by each train equals 288 mi.

Solution

$$3r + 3(2r) = 288$$
$$3r + 6r = 288$$
$$9r = 288$$
$$r = 32$$
$$2r = 2(32) = 64$$

The first train is traveling at 32 mph.
The second train is traveling at 64 mph.

Example 12

Strategy

▷ Time spent flying out: t
Time spent flying back: $5 - t$

	Rate	Time	Distance
Out	150	t	$150t$
Back	100	$5 - t$	$100(5 - t)$

▷ The distance out equals the distance back.

Solution

$$150t = 100(5 - t)$$
$$150t = 500 - 100t$$
$$250t = 500$$
$$t = 2 \text{ (The time out was 2 h.)}$$

The distance $= 150t = 150(2) = 300$ mi.
The parcel of land was 300 mi away.

Exercises   Pages 153–156

1. $x + 12 = 10$; $x = -2$ **3.** $\frac{2}{3}x = 6$; $x = 9$ **5.** $12 - 5x = 7$; $x = 1$ **7.** $3x + x = 12$; $x = 3$
9. $2x + (x + 3) = 15$; $x = 4$ **11.** $3(x + 2) = 15$; $x = 3$ **13.** $4x = 2x + 10$; $x = 5$ **15.** $x + 4 = 3x - 8$; $x = 6$ **17.** $4(3x - 1) = 2x + 6$; $x = 1$ **19.** 15, 16, 17   **21.** 20, 22, 24   **23.** 15, 17, 19   **25.** 4, 6
27. 3, 5   **29.** $-8, -7, -6$ **31.** 11, 13, 15   **33.** $-1, 1, 3$ **35.** 7 years   **37.** nickel: 16 years; dime: 40 years   **39.** 25 years   **41.** 65 years   **43.** replica: 2 years; antique: 47 years   **45.** watercolor: 3 years; oil painting: 17 years   **47.** 5¢ coin: 4 years; 10¢ coin: 8 years   **49.** 8 mph and 16 mph   **51.** 150 mi
53. 120 m   **55.** 48 mi   **57.** 3 hours at 45 mph; 2 hours at 30 mph   **59.** 32 mph

Section 4   Pages 157–160

Example 2   The solution set is the numbers greater than -2.

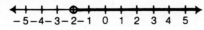

Example 4
$$x + 2 < -2$$
$$x + 2 + (-2) < -2 + (-2)$$
$$x < -4$$

Example 6
$$5x + 3 > 4x + 5$$
$$5x + (-4x) + 3 > 4x + (-4x) + 5$$
$$x + 3 > 5$$
$$x + 3 + (-3) > 5 + (-3)$$
$$x > 2$$

Example 8
$$-\frac{3}{4}x \geq 18$$
$$-\frac{4}{3}\left(-\frac{3}{4}x\right) \leq -\frac{4}{3}(18)$$
$$x \leq -24$$

Exercises   Pages 161–162

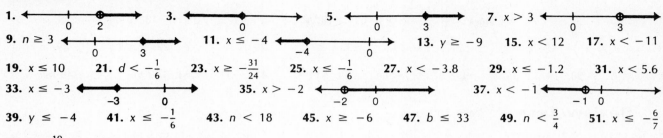

1. (number line, open circle at 2)   **3.** (number line, closed circle at 0)   **5.** (number line, closed circle at 3)   **7.** $x > 3$ (number line, open circle at 3)

9. $n \geq 3$ (number line, closed circle at 3)   **11.** $x \leq -4$ (number line, closed circle at -4)   **13.** $y \geq -9$ **15.** $x < 12$ **17.** $x < -11$

19. $x \leq 10$ **21.** $d < -\frac{1}{6}$ **23.** $x \geq -\frac{31}{24}$ **25.** $x \leq -\frac{1}{6}$ **27.** $x < -3.8$ **29.** $x \leq -1.2$ **31.** $x < 5.6$

33. $x \leq -3$ (number line, closed circle at -3)   **35.** $x > -2$ (number line, open circle at -2)   **37.** $x < -1$ (number line, open circle at -1)

39. $y \leq -4$ **41.** $x \leq -\frac{1}{6}$ **43.** $n < 18$ **45.** $x \geq -6$ **47.** $b \leq 33$ **49.** $n < \frac{3}{4}$ **51.** $x \leq -\frac{6}{7}$

53. $x > \frac{10}{7}$ **55.** $x \leq 4.2$ **57.** $m > -8$

Section 5   Pages 163–164

Example 2
$$5 - 4x > 9 - 8x$$
$$5 - 4x + 8x > 9 - 8x + 8x$$
$$5 + 4x > 9$$
$$5 + (-5) + 4x > 9 + (-5)$$
$$4x > 4$$
$$\tfrac{1}{4}(4x) > \tfrac{1}{4}(4)$$
$$x > 1$$

Example 4
$$8 - 4(3x + 5) \leq 6(x - 8)$$
$$8 - 12x - 20 \leq 6x - 48$$
$$-12 - 12x \leq 6x - 48$$
$$-12 - 12x + (-6x) \leq 6x + (-6x) - 48$$
$$-12 - 18x \leq -48$$
$$-12 + 12 - 18x \leq -48 + 12$$
$$-18x \leq -36$$
$$-\tfrac{1}{18}(-18x) \geq -\tfrac{1}{18}(-36)$$
$$x \geq 2$$

Example 6

Strategy   To find the maximum number of miles:
▷ Write an expression for the cost of each car, using x to represent the number of miles driven during the week.
▷ Write and solve an inequality.

Solution

Cost of a Company A car	is less than	Cost of a Company B car

$$8(7) + 0.10x < 10(7) + 0.08x$$
$$56 + 0.10x < 70 + 0.08x$$
$$56 + 0.10x + (-0.08x) < 70 + 0.08x + (-0.08x)$$
$$56 + 0.02x < 70$$
$$56 + (-56) + 0.02x < 70 + (-56)$$
$$0.02x < 14$$
$$\tfrac{1}{0.02}(0.02x) < \tfrac{1}{0.02}(14)$$
$$x < 700$$

The maximum number of miles is 699.

Exercises   Pages 165–166

1. $x < 4$ **3.** $x < -4$ **5.** $y < \frac{1}{2}$ **7.** $x \geq 1$ **9.** $x \leq 5$ **11.** $x < 0$ **13.** $x < \frac{2}{3}$ **15.** $x < 20$

17. $x > 500$ **19.** $x > 2$ **21.** $x \leq -5$ **23.** $y \leq \frac{5}{2}$ **25.** $x < \frac{25}{11}$ **27.** $x > 11$ **29.** $n \leq \frac{11}{18}$

31. $x \geq 6$ **33.** 19   **35.** $\frac{3}{2}$ **37.** 73 or better   **39.** $1190   **41.** -11 **43.** 149 mi   **45.** 349 mi

Review/Test   Page 169

1. No (4.1A)   **2.** Yes (4.1A)   **3.** -5 (4.1B)   **4.** -12 (4.1C)   **5.** -3 (4.1D)   **6.** 5 (4.1D)   **7.** -5 (4.2A)

8. $-\frac{1}{2}$ (4.2A)   **9.** $-\frac{1}{3}$ (4.2B)   **10.** $\frac{12}{11}$ (4.2B)   **11.** (4.4A)

12. $x < -3$ (4.4B)   **13.** $x > \frac{1}{8}$ (4.4B)   **14.** $x \geq 3$ (4.4C)

15. $x \geq -\frac{40}{3}$ (4.4C)   **16.** $x \leq -3$ (4.5A)   **17.** $x < -\frac{22}{7}$ (4.5A)   **18.** 20 ft from the 20-pound force (4.2C)

19. $3n - 15 = 27$; $n = 14$ (4.3A)   **20.** 5, 7, 9 (4.3B)   **21.** 10 years (4.3C)   **22.** first plane: 225 mph; second plane: 125 mph (4.3D)   **23.** -9 (4.5B)   **24.** -21 (4.5B)

Cumulative Review/Test   Page 170

1. $x \leq 9$ (4.4B)   **2.** -3 (4.2A)   **3.** $2 \cdot 2 \cdot 2 \cdot 2 \cdot 2 \cdot 5$ (1.4A)   **4.** (4.4C)   **5.** Yes (4.1A)

6. 36 (1.4B)   **7.** 1.990 (2.4D)   **8.** -5 (4.1B)   **9.** 6 (3.2A)   **10.** $x < -15$ (4.4C)   **11.** 2 (4.2B)   **12.** 14 (1.4C)

13. $\frac{8}{9}$ (4.1D)   **14.** $40a - 28$ (3.2D)   **15.** $5\frac{11}{18}$ (2.2B)   **16.** $x > 2$ (4.5A)   **17.** $-5a - 2b$ (3.2B)

18. -25 (4.1C)   **19.** $4\frac{2}{3}$ (2.3B)   **20.** $12 - 5x = -18$; $x = 6$ (4.3A)   **21.** 15 ft from the 25-pound force (4.2C)

22. 14 (4.3B)   **23.** 8 years (4.3C)   **24.** 359 mi (4.5B)

Answers to Chapter 5

Section 1 Pages 172–176

Example 2

$$\frac{20 \text{ lb}}{24 \text{ lb}} = \frac{20}{24} = \frac{5}{6}$$

Example 4

$$\frac{260 \text{ mi}}{8 \text{ hour}} \qquad 8\overline{)260.0}^{\,32.5}$$

32.5 mi/hour

Example 6

$x \cdot 7 = 14 \cdot 3$
$7x = 42$
$x = 6$

Check:

$$\frac{6}{14} \times \frac{3}{7} \Longrightarrow 14 \times 3 = 42$$
$$\qquad \Longrightarrow 6 \times 7 = 42$$

The solution is 6.

Example 8

$5 \cdot 20 = 8 \cdot x$
$100 = 8x$
$12.5 = x$

The solution is 12.5.

Example 10

$2(5x + 5) = (x + 3)6$
$10x + 10 = 6x + 18$
$4x + 10 = 18$
$4x = 8$
$x = 2$

The solution is 2.

Example 12

Strategy

To find the ratio, write the cost of radio advertising ($15,000) to the total cost ($17,000 + $20,000) in simplest form.

Solution

$$\frac{\$15,000}{\$15,000 + \$20,000} = \frac{15,000}{35,000} = \frac{3}{7}$$

The ratio is $\frac{3}{7}$.

Example 14

Strategy

To find the miles-per-hour rate, divide the number of miles (47) by the number of hours (3).

Solution

$$3\overline{)47.00}^{\,15.66} \approx 15.7$$

The rate is 15.7 mi per hour.

Example 16

Strategy

To find the number of tablespoons of fertilizer needed, write and solve a proportion using n to represent the number of tablespoons of fertilizer.

Solution

$$\frac{3 \text{ tablespoons}}{4 \text{ gal}} = \frac{n \text{ tablespoons}}{10 \text{ gal}}$$

$$\frac{3}{4} = \frac{n}{10}$$

$$3 \cdot 10 = 4 \cdot n$$

$$30 = 4n$$

$$7.5 = n$$

For 10 gal of water, 7.5 tablespoons of fertilizer are required.

Example 18

Strategy

To find the additional amount of medication required for a 200-pound adult, write and solve a proportion using x to represent the additional medication. Then $3 + x$ is the total amount required for a 200-pound adult.

Solution

$$\frac{150}{3} = \frac{200}{3 + x}$$

$$150(3 + x) = 3 \cdot 200$$

$$450 + 150x = 600$$

$$150x = 150$$

$$x = 1$$

One additional ounce is required for a 200-pound adult.

Exercises   Pages 177–180

1. $\frac{1}{5}$, 1:5, 1 TO 5   3. $\frac{2}{1}$, 2:1, 2 TO 1   5. $\frac{1}{1}$, 1:1, 1 TO 1   7. $\frac{7}{10}$, 7:10, 7 TO 10   9. $\frac{1}{2}$, 1:2, 1 TO 2

11. $\frac{2}{1}$, 2:1, 2 TO 1   13. $\frac{2}{3}$ 15. $\frac{1}{2}$ 17. $\frac{3}{2}$ 19. 2.5 ft/second   21. $325/week   23. 250 words/page

25. 52.4 mi/hour   27. 28 mi/gal   29. $1.65/lb   31. 9   33. 12   35. 5.7   37. 2.2   39. 88

41. 3.3   43. 23.1   45. 21.3   47. 7   49. 6   51. 1   53. −6   55. 4   57. 0.8   59. 2.7

61. $\frac{5}{6}$ 63. a. $36,000   b. $\frac{2}{5}$ 65. $12.50   67. $.96   69. $36   71. $.20   73. 10 lb   75. 10,000 people

77. 150 ft²   79. $90   81. 240 deer   83. 8 oz   85. 42 mi   87. 50 shares   89. $1\frac{1}{2}$ gal

Section 2   Pages 181–182

Example 2 $125\% = 125\left(\frac{1}{100}\right) = \frac{125}{100} = 1\frac{1}{4}$

$125\% = 125(0.01) = 1.25$

Example 4 $16\frac{2}{3}\% = 16\frac{2}{3}\left(\frac{1}{100}\right) = \frac{50}{3}\left(\frac{1}{100}\right) = \frac{1}{6}$

Example 6 $0.5\% = 0.5(0.01) = 0.005$

Example 8 $0.043 = 0.043(100\%) = 4.3\%$

Example 10 $2.57 = 2.57(100\%) = 257\%$

Example 12 $\frac{5}{9} = \frac{5}{9}(100\%) = \frac{500}{9}\% \approx 55.6\%$

Example 14 $\frac{9}{16} = \frac{9}{16}(100\%) = \frac{900}{16}\% = 56\frac{1}{4}\%$

Exercises Pages 183–184

1. $\frac{3}{4}$; 0.75   **3.** $\frac{1}{2}$; 0.50   **5.** $1\frac{1}{5}$; 1.20   **7.** $1\frac{1}{2}$; 1.50   **9.** $\frac{16}{25}$; 0.64   **11.** $1\frac{3}{5}$; 1.60   **13.** $\frac{7}{10}$; 0.70   **15.** $\frac{8}{25}$; 0.32

17. $\frac{87}{100}$; 0.87   **19.** $\frac{1}{50}$; 0.02   **21.** $3\frac{4}{5}$; 3.80   **23.** $\frac{1}{25}$; 0.04   **25.** $\frac{1}{9}$ **27.** $\frac{1}{8}$ **29.** $\frac{5}{16}$ **31.** $\frac{2}{3}$

33. $\frac{123}{800}$ **35.** $\frac{1}{15}$ **37.** $\frac{1}{200}$ **39.** $\frac{11}{16}$ **41.** $\frac{5}{6}$ **43.** 0.073   **45.** 0.158   **47.** 0.003   **49.** 0.0915

51. 0.1823   **53.** 0.0015   **55.** 0.065   **57.** 0.02   **59.** 0.0505   **61.** 15%   **63.** 5%   **65.** 17.5%

67. 115%   **69.** 62%   **71.** 316.5%   **73.** 0.8%   **75.** 6.5%   **77.** 73%   **79.** 70%   **81.** 103%

83. 101.2%   **85.** 54%   **87.** 33.3%   **89.** 45.5%   **91.** 87.5%   **93.** 166.7%   **95.** 128.6%   **97.** 37%

99. 12.5%   **101.** 17.5%   **103.** 34%   **105.** $37\frac{1}{2}$%   **107.** $35\frac{5}{7}$%   **109.** $18\frac{3}{4}$%   **111.** 125%

113. $155\frac{5}{9}$%   **115.** 30%   **117.** $23\frac{1}{3}$%   **119.** $27\frac{3}{11}$%

Section 3   Pages 185–188

Example 2

$P \times B = A$
$P(60) = 27$
$P = \frac{27}{60}$
$P = 0.45$

The percent is 45%.

Example 6

$\frac{16}{100} = \frac{n}{132}$
$16 \cdot 132 = 100 \cdot n$
$2112 = 100n$
$21.12 = n$

The number is 21.12.

Example 4

$\frac{26}{100} = \frac{22}{n}$
$26 \cdot n = 100 \cdot 22$
$26n = 2200$
$n \approx 84.62$

The number is 84.62.

Example 8

Strategy

To find the percent of defective wheel bearings, solve the basic percent equation using $A = 6$ and $B = 200$. The percent is unknown.

Solution

$P \times B = A$
$P(200) = 6$
$P = \frac{6}{200}$
$P = 0.03$

3% of the wheel bearings were defective.

Example 10

Strategy

To find the percent decrease, solve the basic percent equation using $B = 2500$ and $A = 500$. The percent is unknown.

Solution

$$P \times B = A$$
$$P(2500) = 500$$
$$P = \frac{500}{2500}$$
$$P = 0.2$$

The percent decrease is 20%.

Example 14

Strategy

To find the percent of pens which were not defective:
▷ Subtract to find the number of pens which were not defective $(200 - 5)$.
▷ Write and solve a proportion using n to represent the percent of pens which were not defective. The base is 200 and the amount is the number of pens not defective.

Solution

$200 - 5 = 195$ number of pens not defective

$$\frac{n}{100} = \frac{195}{200}$$
$$200 \cdot n = 195 \cdot 100$$
$$200n = 19{,}500$$
$$n = \frac{19{,}500}{200}$$
$$n = 97\frac{1}{2}\%$$

$97\frac{1}{2}\%$ of the pens were not defective.

Example 12

Strategy

To find the number of days it snowed, write and solve a proportion using n to represent the number of days (amount). The percent is 64%. The base is 150.

Solution

$$\frac{64}{100} = \frac{n}{150}$$
$$64 \cdot 150 = 100 \cdot n$$
$$9600 = 100n$$
$$\frac{9600}{100} = n$$
$$96 = n$$

It snowed 96 days.

Exercises   Pages 189–190

1. 65   **3.** 25%   **5.** 75   **7.** 12.5%   **9.** 400   **11.** 19.5   **13.** 9   **15.** 25%   **17.** 20   **19.** 24%
21. 7.2   **23.** 400   **25.** 14.8%   **27.** 222.87   **29.** 200%   **31.** 8.51   **33.** 200   **35.** 8   **37.** 74%
39. $2.30   **41.** 6.4 gal   **43.** $4000   **45.** 40%   **47.** 270,000 take-offs and landings   **49.** $99

Section 4   Pages 191–196

Example 2

Strategy

▷ Additional amount: x

Principal	Rate	Interest
5000	0.08	0.08(5000)
x	0.11	0.11x
5000 + x	0.09	0.09(5000 + x)

▷ The sum of the interest earned by the two investments equals 9% of the total investment.

Solution

$$0.08(5000) + 0.11x = 0.09(5000 + x)$$
$$400 + 0.11x = 450 + 0.09x$$
$$400 + 0.02x = 450$$
$$0.02x = 50$$
$$x = 2500$$

$2500 more must be invested at 11%.

Example 6

Strategy

▷ Liters of water: x

	Amount	Percent	Quantity
Water	x	0	0x
12%	5	0.12	5(0.12)
8%	x + 5	0.08	0.08(x + 5)

▷ The sum of the quantities before mixing is equal to the quantity after mixing.

Solution

$$0x + 5(0.12) = 0.08(x + 5)$$
$$0.60 = 0.08x + 0.40$$
$$0.20 = 0.08x$$
$$2.5 = x$$

The pharmacist adds 2.5 L of water to the 12% solution to get an 8% solution.

Example 4

Strategy

▷ Pounds of $.55 fertilizer: x

	Amount	Cost	Value
$.80 fertilizer	20	$.80	0.80(20)
$.55 fertilizer	x	$.55	0.55x
$.75 fertilizer	20 + x	$.75	0.75(20 + x)

▷ The sum of the values before mixing equals the value after mixing.

Solution

$$0.80(20) + 0.55x = 0.75(20 + x)$$
$$16 + 0.55x = 15 + 0.75x$$
$$16 - 0.20x = 15$$
$$-0.20x = -1$$
$$x = 5$$

5 lb of the $.55 fertilizer must be added.

Exercises   Pages 197–200

1. $2000 at 6% interest and $3000 at 9% interest   **3.** $2000   **5.** $1600 at 9% interest and $2400 at 6% interest   **7.** $2500   **9.** $8000   **11.** $15,000 at 7.5% interest and $10,000 at 9.25% interest   **13.** 60 lb at $2.50 per pound and 20 lb at $3.10 per pound   **15.** 16 oz   **17.** $2.75 per pound   **19.** 25 gal of cranberry juice and 75 gal of apple juice   **21.** 36 lb   **23.** $3.70 per pound   **25.** 17.25 lb   **27.** 1500 bushels of soybeans and 3500 bushels of corn   **29.** $3 per ounce   **31.** 1.5 L   **33.** 40 gal of 21% butterfat and 20 gal of 15% butterfat   **35.** 10 g   **37.** 20%   **39.** 40 L of 85% syrup and 110 L of pure syrup   **41.** 20 lb   **43.** 44%   **45.** 300 lb of 20% polyester and 300 lb of 50% polyester   **47.** 20 lb   **49.** 10%

Review/Test   Page 203

1. $\frac{1}{3}$ (5.1A)   **2.** $2250/month (5.1B)   **3.** -1 (5.1C)   **4.** $\frac{3}{5}$; 0.60 (5.2A)   **5.** $\frac{5}{8}$ (5.2A)   **6.** 0.182 (5.2A)

7. 37.5% (5.2B)   **8.** 80% (5.2B)   **9.** $87\frac{1}{2}$% (5.2B)   **10.** 125% (5.3A/5.3B)   **11.** 80 (5.3A/5.3B)

12. 28.3 (5.3A/5.3B)   **13.** $3\frac{1}{3}$ qt (5.1D)   **14.** 2 additional pounds (5.1D)   **15.** $30,000 (5.3C)   **16.** 91.3% (5.3C)

17. 3850 transistors (5.3C)   **18.** 184 hours (5.3C)   **19.** $1500 at 7% interest and $5500 at 9% interest (5.4A)   **20.** $10,000 (5.4A)   **21.** 8 lb at $7 per pound and 4 lb at $4 per pound (5.4B)   **22.** 80 g (5.4B)   **23.** 20 gal (5.4C)   **24.** 30 oz (5.4C)

Cumulative Review/Test   Page 204

1. $2^4 \cdot 3^3$ (1.3B)   **2.** 8% (5.2B)   **3.** $10\frac{11}{24}$ (2.2A)   **4.** 6 (3.1C)   **5.** 20 (5.3A/5.3B)   **6.** $133\frac{1}{3}$% (5.3A/5.3B)

7. $\frac{9}{5}$ (5.1C)   **8.** 7.5% (5.2B)   **9.** -21 (3.2A)   **10.** $\frac{5}{12}$ (2.1C)   **11.** 4 (1.4D)   **12.** $\frac{1}{6}$ (5.2A)

13. 40 (5.3A/5.3B)   **14.** $6x + 4y$ (3.2B)   **15.** 1.1196 (2.4B)   **16.** 22.9 (5.1C)   **17.** $\frac{4}{5}$ (5.2A)

18. $3x - 6$ (3.2D)   **19.** -16 (4.2B)   **20.** $64 (5.1D)   **21.** 20% (5.3C)   **22.** $6000 (5.4A)   **23.** 60 g (5.4B)   **24.** 30 oz (5.4C)

Answers to Chapter 6

Section 1   Pages 206–208

Example 2	$5x^3 + 6x^2 + x - 1$	**Example 4**	The degree of the polynomial $9x^4 - 3x^2 + 11$ is 4.

Example 6

$$2x^2 + 4x - 3$$
$$+\ 5x^2 - 6x$$
$$\overline{7x^2 - 2x - 3}$$

Example 8

$$(-3x^2 + 2y^2) + (-8x^2 + 9xy)$$
$$-11x^2 + 9xy + 2y^2$$

Example 10

$$8y^2 - 4xy + x^2$$
$$-\ 2y^2 - xy + 5x^2 \ =$$

$$8y^2 - 4xy + x^2$$
$$+\ -2y^2 + xy - 5x^2$$
$$\overline{6y^2 - 3xy - 4x^2}$$

Example 12

$$(-3a^2 - 4a + 2) - (5a^3 + 2a - 6)$$
$$(-3a^2 - 4a + 2) + (-5a^3 - 2a + 6)$$
$$-5a^3 - 3a^2 - 6a + 8$$

Exercises   Pages 209–210

1. $3x^3 + 8x^2 - 2x - 6$ **3.** $5a^3 - 3a^2 + 2a + 1$ **5.** $r^5 + r^3 - 6r^2 + 5$ **7.** $-y^4 + 1$ **9.** $-9a^2 + a + 3$
11. 4 **13.** 6 **15.** 1 **17.** $8y^2 + 4y$ **19.** $3x^2 + 15x - 24$ **21.** $4x^2 - 9x + 9$ **23.** $-y^3 + y^2 - 6y - 2$
25. $5r^3 - 5r^2 + r - 3$ **27.** $y^2 + 7y$ **29.** $8x^2 - 2xy$ **31.** $-3x^2 + 8x + 6$ **33.** $3y^3 + 2y^2 + 8y - 12$
35. $3y^3 - 4y^2 + 4y + 35$ **37.** $7x^3 + 2x^2 - 2x + 1$ **39.** $-6y$ **41.** $-7a^2 - 2a + 4$ **43.** $-2x^2 + 7x - 8$
45. $2y^3 + 5y^2 - 4y + 5$ **47.** $x^3 - 2x^2 - 4x + 6$ **49.** $3x^2 - 4xy$ **51.** $8y^2 - y + 3$
53. $-3x^3 + 2x^2 + 3x + 2$ **55.** $-4b^3 + b^2 - b + 15$ **57.** $-2x^3 + 5x^2 - 2x - 7$

Section 2   Pages 211–216

Example 2

$$(3x^2)(6x^3) =$$
$$(3 \cdot 6)(x^2 \cdot x^3) = 18x^5$$

Example 4

$$(-3xy^2)(-4x^2y^3) =$$
$$[(-3)(-4)](x \cdot x^2)(y^2 \cdot y^3) =$$
$$12x^3y^5$$

Example 6

$$(3x)(2x^2y)^3 =$$
$$(3x)(2^3x^6y^3) = (3x)(8x^6y^3) =$$
$$(3 \cdot 8)(x \cdot x^6)y^3 = 24x^7y^3$$

Example 8

$$(3x^2)^2(-2xy^2)^3 =$$
$$(3^2x^4)[(-2)^3x^3y^6] =$$
$$(9x^4)(-8x^3y^6) =$$
$$[9(-8)](x^4 \cdot x^3)y^6 =$$
$$-72x^7y^6$$

Example 10

$$(-2y + 3)(-4y) = 8y^2 - 12y$$

Example 12

$$-a^2(3a^2 + 2a - 7) =$$
$$-3a^4 - 2a^3 + 7a^2$$

Example 14

$$2y^3 + 2y^2 - 3$$
$$\times 3y - 1$$
$$\overline{-2y^3 - 2y^2 + 3}$$
$$6y^4 + 6y^3 - 9y$$
$$\overline{6y^4 + 4y^3 - 2y^2 - 9y + 3}$$

Example 16

$$a^3 - 2$$
$$\times a + 7$$
$$\overline{7a^3 - 14}$$
$$a^4 - 2a$$
$$\overline{a^4 + 7a^3 - 2a - 14}$$

Example 18	$(b - 5)(b + 8) =$ $b^2 + 8b - 5b - 40 =$ $b^2 + 3b - 40$	**Example 20**	$(4y - 5)(2y - 3) =$ $8y^2 - 12y - 10y + 15 =$ $8y^2 - 22y + 15$
Example 22	$(3b + 2)(3b - 5) =$ $9b^2 - 15b + 6b - 10 =$ $9b^2 - 9b - 10$	**Example 24**	$(4x - y)(2x + 3y) =$ $8x^2 + 12xy - 2xy - 3y^2 =$ $8x^2 + 10xy - 3y^2$
Example 26	$(2a + 5c)(2a - 5c) =$ $4a^2 - 25c^2$	**Example 28**	$(3x + 2y)^2 = 9x^2 + 12xy + 4y^2$

Exercises   Pages 217–220

1. $2x^2$ **3.** $12x^2$ **5.** $6a^7$ **7.** x^3y^5 **9.** $-10x^9y$ **11.** x^7y^8 **13.** $-6x^3y^5$ **15.** x^4y^5z **17.** $a^3b^5c^4$
19. $-a^5b^8$ **21.** $-6a^5b$ **23.** $40y^{10}z^6$ **25.** $x^3y^3z^2$ **27.** $30x^6y^8$ **29.** $-24a^3b^3c^3$ **31.** 64 **33.** 4
35. -64 **37.** x^9 **39.** x^{14} **41.** x^4 **43.** $4x^2$ **45.** $-8x^6$ **47.** x^4y^6 **49.** $9x^4y^2$ **51.** $27a^8$
53. $-8x^7$ **55.** x^8y^4 **57.** a^4b^6 **59.** $16x^{10}y^3$ **61.** $-8a^7b^5$ **63.** $-54a^9b^3$ **65.** $-72a^5b^5$ **67.** $x^2 - 2x$
69. $-x^2 - 7x$ **71.** $3a^3 - 6a^2$ **73.** $-5x^4 + 5x^3$ **75.** $12x^3 - 6x^2$ **77.** $6x^2 - 12x$ **79.** $3x^2 + 4x$
81. $-x^3y + xy^3$ **83.** $2x^4 - 3x^2 + 2x$ **85.** $2a^3 + 3a^2 + 2a$ **87.** $3x^6 - 3x^4 - 2x^2$ **89.** $-6y^4 - 12y^3 + 14y^2$
91. $-2a^3 - 6a^2 + 8a$ **93.** $6y^4 - 3y^3 + 6y^2$ **95.** $x^3y - 3x^2y^2 + xy^3$ **97.** $x^3 + 4x^2 + 5x + 2$
99. $a^3 - 6a^2 + 13a - 12$ **101.** $-2b^3 + 7b^2 + 19b - 20$ **103.** $-6x^3 + 31x^2 - 41x + 10$ **105.** $x^3 - 3x^2 + 5x - 15$
107. $x^4 - 4x^3 - 3x^2 + 14x - 8$ **109.** $15y^3 - 16y^2 - 70y + 16$ **111.** $5a^4 - 20a^3 - 5a^2 + 22a - 8$
113. $y^4 + 4y^3 + y^2 - 5y + 2$ **115.** $x^2 + 4x + 3$ **117.** $a^2 + a - 12$ **119.** $y^2 - 5y - 24$
121. $y^2 - 10y + 21$ **123.** $2x^2 + 15x + 7$ **125.** $3x^2 + 11x - 4$ **127.** $4x^2 - 31x + 21$ **129.** $3y^2 - 2y - 16$
131. $9x^2 + 54x + 77$ **133.** $21a^2 - 83a + 80$ **135.** $2x^2 + 3xy + y^2$ **137.** $3x^2 - 10xy + 8y^2$
139. $10a^2 + 14ab - 12b^2$ **141.** $9x^2 - 6xy - 35y^2$ **143.** $35x^2 + 31xy + 6y^2$ **145.** $35a^2 - 12ab + b^2$
147. $14a^2 + 31ab - 10b^2$ **149.** $36a^2 - 63ab + 20b^2$ **151.** $33x^2 + 83xy + 14y^2$ **153.** $10x^2 - 21xy - 10y^2$
155. $16x^2 - 78xy + 27y^2$ **157.** $y^2 - 36$ **159.** $16x^2 - 49$ **161.** $y^2 - 6y + 9$ **163.** $36x^2 - 60x + 25$
165. $81x^2 - 4$ **167.** $x^2 + 6xy + 9y^2$ **169.** $4x^2 - 12xy + 9y^2$ **171.** $4 - 25x^2$ **173.** $4a^2 - 36ab + 81b^2$
175. $4 + 28x + 49x^2$

Section 3   Pages 221–224

Example 2	$\dfrac{42y^{12}}{-14y^{17}} = -\dfrac{2 \cdot 3 \cdot \overset{1}{\cancel{7}} \overset{1}{\cancel{y^{12}}}}{\underset{1}{2} \cdot \underset{1}{\cancel{7}}y^{17}} = -\dfrac{3}{y^5}$	**Example 4**	$\dfrac{12r^4s^2}{-8r^3s} = -\dfrac{\overset{1}{2} \cdot \overset{1}{2} \cdot 3r^4s^2}{\underset{1}{2} \cdot \underset{1}{2} \cdot 2r^3s} = -\dfrac{3rs}{2}$
Example 6	$\dfrac{(2x^2y)^3}{-4xy^5} = -\dfrac{2^3x^6y^3}{4xy^5} =$ $-\dfrac{\overset{1}{2} \cdot \overset{1}{2} \cdot 2x^6y^3}{\underset{1}{2} \cdot \underset{1}{2}xy^5} = -\dfrac{2x^5}{y^2}$	**Example 8**	$\dfrac{4x^3y + 8x^2y^2 - 4xy^3}{2xy} =$ $\dfrac{4x^3y}{2xy} + \dfrac{8x^2y^2}{2xy} - \dfrac{4xy^3}{2xy} =$ $2x^2 + 4xy - 2y^2$

Example 10

$$\frac{24x^2y^2 - 18xy + 6y}{6xy} =$$

$$\frac{24x^2y^2}{6xy} - \frac{18xy}{6xy} + \frac{6y}{6xy} =$$

$$4xy - 3 + \frac{1}{x}$$

Example 12

$$\begin{array}{r} x^2 + 2x - 1 \\ 2x - 3\overline{)2x^3 + x^2 - 8x - 3} \\ \underline{2x^3 - 3x^2} \\ 4x^2 - 8x \\ \underline{4x^2 - 6x} \\ -2x - 3 \\ \underline{-2x + 3} \\ -6 \end{array}$$

$$(2x^3 + x^2 - 8x - 3) \div (2x - 3) =$$

$$x^2 + 2x - 1 - \frac{6}{2x - 3}$$

Exercises   Pages 225–226

1. $3x$ **3.** $-x$ **5.** $4x^3$ **7.** $-\frac{4}{x^2}$ **9.** $\frac{a}{b^4}$ **11.** y^3 **13.** $\frac{3}{5}$ **15.** $\frac{24}{b}$ **17.** $-\frac{3}{5ab^2}$ **19.** $-\frac{4b}{9}$

21. $-\frac{2x^2y^2}{11z^5}$ **23.** $-8a^3b^4$ **25.** $\frac{4a^2}{9b^3}$ **27.** $\frac{x^2y^2}{z^3}$ **29.** $\frac{a^2}{b}$ **31.** $x + 1$ **33.** $2a - 5$ **35.** $3a + 2$

37. $4b^2 - 3$ **39.** $x - 2$ **41.** $-x + 2$ **43.** $x^2 + 3x - 5$ **45.** $x^4 - 3x^2 - 1$ **47.** $xy + 2$ **49.** $-3y^3 + 5$

51. $3x - 2 + \frac{1}{x}$ **53.** $-3x + 7 - \frac{6}{x}$ **55.** $4a - 5 + 6b$ **57.** $9x + 6 - 3y$ **59.** $x + 5$ **61.** $b - 7$

63. $y - 5$ **65.** $2y - 7$ **67.** $2y + 6 + \frac{25}{y - 3}$ **69.** $x - 2 + \frac{8}{x + 2}$ **71.** $3y - 5 + \frac{10}{y + 2}$

73. $6x - 12 + \frac{19}{x + 2}$ **75.** $b - 5 - \frac{24}{b - 3}$ **77.** $x^2 - 3$ **79.** $4a + 1$ **81.** $x^2 + 2x + 3$

Section 4   Pages 227–230

Example 2

$$\frac{2^{-2}}{2^3} = 2^{-5} = \frac{1}{2^5} = \frac{1}{32}$$

Example 4

$$(-2x^2)(x^{-3}y^{-4})^{-2} =$$

$$(-2x^2)(x^6y^8) = -2x^8y^8$$

Example 6

$$\frac{(3x^{-2}y)^3}{9xy^0} = \frac{3^3x^{-6}y^3}{9xy^0} =$$

$$\frac{\overset{1}{\cancel{3}} \cdot \overset{1}{\cancel{3}} \cdot 3x^{-6}y^3}{\underset{1}{\cancel{3}} \cdot \underset{1}{\cancel{3}}xy^0} = 3x^{-7}y^3 = \frac{3y^3}{x^7}$$

Example 8

$$942{,}000{,}000 = 9.42 \times 10^8$$

Example 10

$$2.7 \times 10^{-5} = 0.000027$$

Example 12

$$\frac{5{,}600{,}000 \times 0.000000081}{900 \times 0.000000028} =$$

$$\frac{5.6 \times 10^6 \times 8.1 \times 10^{-8}}{9 \times 10^2 \times 2.8 \times 10^{-8}} =$$

$$\frac{(5.6)(8.1) \times 10^{6+(-8)-(2)-(-8)}}{(9)(2.8)} =$$

$$1.8 \times 10^4 = 18{,}000$$

Example 14

Strategy

To find the time, use the equation $d = rt$, where r is the speed of light and d is the distance of the sun from the earth.

Solution

$$d = rt$$
$$9.3 \times 10^7 = (1.86 \times 10^5)t$$
$$\frac{9.3 \times 10^7}{1.86 \times 10^5} = t$$
$$5 \times 10^2 = t$$

Light travels to the earth from the sun in 5×10^2 seconds.

Exercises   Pages 231–232

1. $\frac{1}{5^2} = \frac{1}{25}$ **3.** $\frac{1}{3^3} = \frac{1}{27}$ **5.** $\frac{1}{2^6} = \frac{1}{64}$ **7.** $\frac{1}{x^2}$ **9.** $\frac{1}{a^6}$ **11.** $\frac{x^2}{y^3}$ **13.** $\frac{1}{xy^2}$ **15.** x **17.** $\frac{1}{a^7}$ **19.** $\frac{1}{x^4}$

21. $\frac{1}{a^8}$ **23.** $\frac{y}{x^3}$ **25.** $\frac{b}{a^2}$ **27.** $\frac{1}{a^4}$ **29.** $\frac{1}{a^6}$ **31.** x^6 **33.** a^{18} **35.** 1 **37.** $\frac{y^4}{x^4}$ **39.** $\frac{x}{y^5}$ **41.** $\frac{y^4}{x^4}$

43. $\frac{y^2}{x^4}$ **45.** $-\frac{8x^3}{y^6}$ **47.** $\frac{16x^4}{y^6}$ **49.** $\frac{2}{x^4}$ **51.** $-\frac{5}{a^8}$ **53.** $\frac{3a^4}{8b^5}$ **55.** $\frac{1}{a^5b^6}$ **57.** $\frac{y^4}{4x^3}$ **59.** $\frac{1}{x^3}$

61. $\frac{1}{x^{12}y^{12}}$ **63.** 4.67×10^{-6} **65.** 4.3×10^6 **67.** 0.000000123 **69.** $634,000$ **71.** $20,800,000$

73. $150,000$ **75.** 0.000000015 **77.** $20,000,000,000$ **79.** 2.592×10^{10} km

81. 3.38983×10^5 times heavier   **83.** 5.785344×10^{12} mi

Review/Test   Page 235

1. $-8x^3 - 2x^2 + 5x + 3$ (6.1A)   **2.** 4 (6.1A)   **3.** $3x^3 + 6x^2 - 8x + 3$ (6.1A)   **4.** $-5a^3 + 3a^2 - 4a + 3$ (6.1B)
5. $-6x^3y^6$ (6.2A)   **6.** x^8y^{12} (6.2B)   **7.** $4x^3 - 6x^2$ (6.2C)   **8.** $6y^4 - 9y^3 + 18y^2$ (6.2C)
9. $x^3 - 7x^2 + 17x - 15$ (6.2C)   **10.** $-4x^4 + 8x^3 - 3x^2 - 14x + 21$ (6.2C)   **11.** $a^2 + 3ab - 10b^2$ (6.2D)

12. $10x^2 - 43xy + 28y^2$ (6.2D)   **13.** $16y^2 - 9$ (6.2E)   **14.** $4x^2 - 20x + 25$ (6.2E)   **15.** $-\frac{4}{x^6}$ (6.3A)

16. $\frac{9y^6}{x}$ (6.3A)   **17.** $4x^4 - 2x^2 + 5$ (6.3B)   **18.** $x + 7$ (6.3C)   **19.** $2x + 3 + \frac{2}{2x-3}$ (6.3C)   **20.** $\frac{a^4}{b^6}$ (6.4A)

21. $-\frac{6b}{a}$ (6.4A)   **22.** 5×10^{-8} (6.4B)   **23.** 0.039 (6.4B)   **24.** 1.2×10 hours (6.4C)

Cumulative Review/Test   Page 236

1. $15b^2 - 31b + 14$ (6.2D)   **2.** $3y^3 + 2y^2 - 10y$ (6.1B)   **3.** -16 (4.1C)   **4.** $6a - 4 + \frac{2}{a^2}$ (6.3B)   **5.** $4\frac{1}{5}$ (2.3A)

6. 22% (5.3A/5.3B)   **7.** $\frac{6y^2}{x^6}$ (6.4A)   **8.** $6y^4 + 8y^3 - 16y^2$ (6.2C)   **9.** $\frac{5}{9} > 0.5$ (2.5B)   **10.** $2\frac{3}{11}$ (3.1E)

11. $9b^2 + 12b + 4$ (6.2E)   **12.** 0.00081 (6.4B)   **13.** $-9x$ (3.2C)   **14.** $a - 7$ (6.3C)

15. $10a^3 - 39a^2 + 20a - 21$ (6.2C)   **16.** -6.8 (3.1B)   **17.** 0.0024 (6.4B)   **18.** -16 (4.2A)   **19.** $\frac{1}{2b^2}$ (6.3A)

20. a^9b^{15} (6.2B)   **21.** $4b^3 - 4b^2 - 8b - 4$ (6.1A)   **22.** $-8x^3y^6$ (6.2A)   **23.** $4[n + (n + 1)]$; $8n + 4$ (3.3A/4.3B)
24. 1.25 seconds (6.4C)

Answers to Chapter 7

Section 1   Pages 238–240

Example 2

$12x^3y^6 = 2 \cdot 2 \cdot 3 \cdot x^3y^6$

$15x^2y^3 = 3 \cdot 5 \cdot x^2 \cdot y^3$

The GCF is $3x^2y^3$.

Example 6

$14a^2 = 2 \cdot 7 \cdot a^2$

$21a^4b = 3 \cdot 7 \cdot a^4b$

The GCF is $7a^2$.

$14a^2 - 21a^4b =$

$7a^2(2) + 7a^2(-3a^2b) =$

$7a^2(2 - 3a^2b)$

Example 10

$6x^4y^2 = 2 \cdot 3 \cdot x^4 \cdot y^2$

$9x^3y^2 = 3 \cdot 3 \cdot x^3 \cdot y^2$

$12x^2y^4 = 2 \cdot 2 \cdot 3 \cdot x^2 \cdot y^4$

The GCF is $3x^2y^2$.

$6x^4y^2 - 9x^3y^2 + 12x^2y^4 =$

$3x^2y^2(2x^2) + 3x^2y^2(-3x) + 3x^2y^2(4y^2) =$

$3x^2y^2(2x^2 - 3x + 4y^2)$

Example 4

$8a^4bc = 2 \cdot 2 \cdot 2 \cdot a^4 \cdot b \cdot c$

$12ab^3 = 2 \cdot 2 \cdot 3 \cdot a \cdot b^3$

$20abc^2 = 2 \cdot 2 \cdot 5 \cdot a \cdot b \cdot c^2$

The GCF is $4abc$.

Example 8

$18a^4 = 2 \cdot 3 \cdot 3 \cdot a^4$

$27a^3 = 3 \cdot 3 \cdot 3 \cdot a^3$

$9a^2 = 3 \cdot 3 \cdot a^2$

The GCF is $9a^2$.

$18a^4 + 27a^3 - 9a^2 =$

$9a^2(2a^2) + 9a^2(3a) + 9a^2(-1) =$

$9a^2(2a^2 + 3a - 1)$

Exercises   Pages 241–242

1. x^3 **3.** xy^4 **5.** xy^4z^2 **7.** ab^2c^3 **9.** $3x^2$ **11.** $2a$ **13.** $7a^3$ **15.** 1 **17.** $3a^2b^2$ **19.** ab
21. ab **23.** $4x$ **25.** $4a$ **27.** $3m^2n^2$ **29.** $5(a + 1)$ **31.** $6(1 - 3x)$ **33.** $2(x^2 - 10)$ **35.** $8(2 - a^2)$
37. $4(2x + 3)$ **39.** $6(5a - 1)$ **41.** $x(7x - 3)$ **43.** $a^2(3 + 5a^3)$ **45.** $x(9 - 5x)$ **47.** $b^2(6b - 5)$
49. $3y(y^3 - 3)$ **51.** $4a^2(3a^3 - 8)$ **53.** $8y^4(2 - y^3)$ **55.** $ab(ab + 1)$ **57.** $m^2n^2(m^2 - n^2)$ **59.** $3ab(4ab^4 - 3)$
61. $a^2b(1 + a^2b)$ **63.** $5x^2y - 7ab^3$ **65.** $4x^2(2y^3 - 1)$ **67.** $b(b^2 - 5b - 7)$ **69.** $4(2y^2 - 3y + 8)$
71. $5y(y^2 - 4y + 2)$ **73.** $3y^2(y^2 - 3y - 2)$ **75.** $3y(y^2 - 3y + 8)$ **77.** $a^2(6a^3 - 3a - 2)$
79. $ab(2a - 5ab + 7b)$ **81.** $2b(2b^4 + 3b^2 - b)$ **83.** $x^2(8y^2 - 4y + 1)$

Section 2   Pages 243–246

Example 2

$(x - \blacksquare)(x - \blacksquare)$

	Factors	Sums
	$-1, -20$	-21
	$-2, -10$	-12
	$-4, -5$	-9

$(x - 4)(x - 5)$

$x^2 - 9x + 20 = (x - 4)(x - 5)$

Example 4

$(x + \blacksquare)(x - \blacksquare)$

	Factors	Sums
	$+1, -18$	-17
	$-1, +18$	17
	$+2, -9$	-7
	$-2, +9$	7
	$+3, -6$	-3
	$-3, +6$	3

$(x + 6)(x - 3)$

$x^2 + 3x - 18 = (x + 6)(x - 3)$

Example 6

The GCF is $3b$.

$3a^2b - 18ab - 81b = 3b(a^2 - 6a - 27)$

Factor the trinomial.

$3b(a + \blacksquare)(a - \blacksquare)$

Factors	Sums
$+1, -27$	-26
$-1, +27$	26
$+3, -9$	-6
$-3, +9$	6

$3b(a + 3)(a - 9)$

$3a^2b - 18ab - 81b = 3b(a + 3)(a - 9)$

Example 8

The GCF is 3.

$3x^2 - 9xy - 12y^2 = 3(x^2 - 3xy - 4y^2)$

Factor the trinomial.

$3(x + \blacksquare y)(x - \blacksquare y)$

Factors	Sums
$+1, -4$	-3
$-1, +4$	3
$+2, -2$	0

$3(x + y)(x - 4y)$

$3x^2 - 9xy - 12y^2 = 3(x + y)(x - 4y)$

Exercises   Pages 247–248

1. $(x + 1)(x + 2)$ **3.** $(x + 1)(x - 2)$ **5.** $(a + 4)(a - 3)$ **7.** $(a - 2)(a - 1)$ **9.** $(a + 2)(a - 1)$
11. $(b - 3)(b - 3)$ **13.** $(b + 8)(b - 1)$ **15.** $(y + 11)(y - 5)$ **17.** $(y - 2)(y - 3)$ **19.** $(z - 5)(z - 9)$
21. $(z + 8)(z - 20)$ **23.** $(p + 3)(p + 9)$ **25.** $(x + 10)(x + 10)$ **27.** $(b + 4)(b + 5)$ **29.** $(x + 3)(x - 14)$
31. $(b + 4)(b - 5)$ **33.** $(y + 3)(y - 17)$ **35.** $(p + 3)(p - 7)$ **37.** Nonfactorable over the integers.
39. $(x - 5)(x - 15)$ **41.** $(x - 7)(x - 8)$ **43.** $(x + 8)(x - 7)$ **45.** $(a + 3)(a - 24)$ **47.** $(a - 3)(a - 12)$
49. $(z + 8)(z - 17)$ **51.** $(c + 9)(c - 10)$ **53.** $2(x + 1)(x + 2)$ **55.** $3(a + 3)(a - 2)$ **57.** $a(b + 5)(b - 3)$
59. $x(y - 2)(y - 3)$ **61.** $z(z - 3)(z - 4)$ **63.** $3y(y - 2)(y - 3)$ **65.** $3(x + 4)(x - 3)$ **67.** $5(z + 4)(z - 7)$
69. $2a(a + 8)(a - 4)$ **71.** $(x - 2y)(x - 3y)$ **73.** $(a - 4b)(a - 5b)$ **75.** $(x + 4y)(x - 7y)$
77. Nonfactorable over the integers. **79.** $z^2(z - 5)(z - 7)$ **81.** $b^2(b - 10)(b - 12)$ **83.** $2y^2(y + 3)(y - 16)$
85. $3y^2(y + 3)(y + 15)$ **87.** $3y(x + 3)(x - 5)$ **89.** $4x(x + 3)(x - 2)$ **91.** $5(p + 12)(p - 7)$
93. $15a(b + 4)(b - 1)$ **95.** $3y(x + 15)(x - 3)$

Section 3   Pages 249–252

Example 2

$(\blacksquare x + \blacksquare)(\blacksquare x - \blacksquare)$ or
$(\blacksquare x - \blacksquare)(\blacksquare x + \blacksquare)$

Factors of 2: 1, 2   Factors of -3: $+1, -3$
$\qquad\qquad\qquad\qquad\qquad\qquad -1, +3$

Trial Factors	Middle Term
$(1x + 1)(2x - 3)$	$-3x + 2x = -x$
$(1x - 3)(2x + 1)$	$x - 6x = -5x$
$(1x - 1)(2x + 3)$	$3x - 2x = x$
$(1x + 3)(2x - 1)$	$-x + 6x = 5x$

$(x + 1)(2x - 3)$

$2x^2 - x - 3 = (x + 1)(2x - 3)$

Example 4

The GCF is $2a^2$.

$4a^2b^2 + 26a^2b - 14a^2 = 2a^2(2b^2 + 13b - 7)$

Factor the trinomial.

$2a^2(\blacksquare b + \blacksquare)(\blacksquare b - \blacksquare)$ or
$2a^2(\blacksquare b - \blacksquare)(\blacksquare b + \blacksquare)$

Factors of 2: 1, 2   Factors of -7: $+1, -7$
$\qquad\qquad\qquad\qquad\qquad\qquad -1, +7$

Trial Factors	Middle Term
$(1b + 1)(2b - 7)$	$-7b + 2b = -5b$
$(1b - 7)(2b + 1)$	$b - 14b = -13b$
$(1b - 1)(2b + 7)$	$7b - 2b = 5b$
$(1b + 7)(2b - 1)$	$-b + 14b = 13b$

$2a^2(b + 7)(2b - 1)$
$4a^2b^2 + 26a^2b - 14a^2 = 2a^2(b + 7)(2b - 1)$

Example 6

The GCF is $3y$.

$12y + 12y^2 - 45y^3 = 3y(4 + 4y - 15y^2)$

Factor the trinomial.

$3y(\blacksquare + \blacksquare y)(\blacksquare - \blacksquare y)$ or $3y(\blacksquare - \blacksquare y)(\blacksquare + \blacksquare y)$

Factors of 4: 1, 4   Factors of -15: $+1, -15$
              2, 2 $-1, +15$
                                        $+3, -5$
                                        $-3, +5$

Trial Factors	Middle Term
$(1 + 1y)(4 - 15y)$	$-15y + 4y = -11y$
$(1 - 15y)(4 + 1y)$	$y - 60y = -59y$
$(1 - 1y)(4 + 15y)$	$15y - 4y = 11y$
$(1 + 15y)(4 - 1y)$	$-y + 60y = 59y$
$(1 + 3y)(4 - 5y)$	$-5y + 12y = 7y$
$(1 - 5y)(4 + 3y)$	$3y - 20y = -17y$
$(1 - 3y)(4 + 5y)$	$5y - 12y = -7y$
$(1 + 5y)(4 - 3y)$	$-3y + 20y = 17y$
$(2 + 1y)(2 - 15y)$	$-30y + 2y = -28y$
$(2 - 1y)(2 + 15y)$	$30y - 2y = 28y$
$(2 + 3y)(2 - 5y)$	$-10y + 6y = -4y$
$(2 - 3y)(2 + 5y)$	$10y - 6y = 4y$

$3y(2 - 3y)(2 + 5y)$

$12y + 12y^2 - 45y^3 = 3y(2 - 3y)(2 + 5y)$

Exercises   Pages 253–256

1. $(x + 1)(2x + 1)$ **3.** $(y + 3)(2y + 1)$ **5.** $(a - 1)(2a - 1)$ **7.** $(b - 5)(2b - 1)$ **9.** $(x + 1)(2x - 1)$
11. $(x - 3)(2x + 1)$ **13.** $(t + 2)(2t - 5)$ **15.** $(p - 5)(3p - 1)$ **17.** $(3y - 1)(4y - 1)$ **19.** Nonfactorable over the integers.   **21.** $(2t - 1)(3t - 4)$ **23.** $(x + 4)(8x + 1)$ **25.** Nonfactorable over the integers.
27. $(3y + 1)(4y + 5)$ **29.** $(a + 7)(7a - 2)$ **31.** $(b - 4)(3b - 4)$ **33.** $(z - 14)(2z + 1)$
35. $(p + 8)(3p - 2)$ **37.** $(2x - 3)(3x - 4)$ **39.** $(b + 7)(5b - 2)$ **41.** $(2a - 3)(3a + 8)$
43. $(z + 2)(4z + 3)$ **45.** $(2p + 5)(11p - 2)$ **47.** $(y + 1)(8y + 9)$ **49.** $(3t + 1)(6t - 5)$
51. $(b + 12)(6b - 1)$ **53.** $(3x + 2)(3x + 2)$ **55.** $(2b - 3)(3b - 2)$ **57.** $(3b + 5)(11b - 7)$
59. $(3y - 4)(6y - 5)$ **61.** $(3a + 7)(5a - 3)$ **63.** $(2y - 5)(4y - 3)$ **65.** $(2z + 3)(4z - 5)$ **67.** Nonfactorable over the integers.   **69.** $(2z - 5)(5z - 2)$ **71.** $(6z + 5)(6z + 7)$ **73.** $2(x + 1)(2x + 1)$ **75.** $5(y - 1)(3y - 7)$
77. $x(x - 5)(2x - 1)$ **79.** $b(a - 4)(3a - 4)$ **81.** Nonfactorable over the integers.   **83.** $(x + y)(3x - 2y)$
85. $(a + 2b)(3a - b)$ **87.** $(y - 2z)(4y - 3z)$ **89.** $(3 - x)(4 + x)$ **91.** $(4 + z)(7 - z)$ **93.** $(8 + x)(1 - x)$
95. $3(x + 5)(3x - 4)$ **97.** $4(4y - 1)(5y - 1)$ **99.** $z(2z + 3)(4z + 1)$ **101.** $y(2x - 5)(3x + 2)$
103. $4(2x - 3)(3x - 2)$ **105.** $a^2(7a - 1)(5a + 2)$ **107.** $5(3b - 2)(b - 7)$ **109.** $(x - 7y)(3x - 5y)$
111. $3(8y - 1)(9y + 1)$ **113.** $(1 - x)(21 + x)$ **115.** $(3a - 2b)(5a + 7b)$ **117.** $z(3 - z)(11 + z)$
119. $2x(x + 1)(5x + 1)$ **121.** $5(t + 2)(2t - 5)$ **123.** $p(p - 5)(3p - 1)$ **125.** $2(z + 4)(13z - 3)$
127. $2y(y - 4)(5y - 2)$ **129.** $yz(z + 2)(4z - 3)$ **131.** $b^2(4b + 5)(5b + 4)$ **133.** $2a(2a - 3)(3a + 8)$
135. $p^2(3 - p)(12 + p)$ **137.** $y(2x - 7y)(4x - 5y)$ **139.** $xy(3x + 2)(3x + 2)$ **141.** $ab(2a - b)(a - 5b)$

Section 4   Pages 257–260

Example 2

$25a^2 - b^2 = (5a)^2 - b^2 = (5a + b)(5a - b)$

Example 4

$n^8 - 36 = (n^4)^2 - 6^2 = (n^4 + 6)(n^4 - 6)$

Example 6

$\sqrt{a^2} = a$

$\sqrt{100} = 10$ $2(10a) = 20a$

The trinomial is a perfect square.

$a^2 + 20a + 100 = (a + 10)^2$

Example 8

$\sqrt{25a^2} = 5a$

$\sqrt{9b^2} = 3b$ $2(5a \cdot 3b) = 30ab$

The trinomial is a perfect square.

$25a^2 - 30ab + 9b^2 = (5a - 3b)^2$

Example 10

$5x(2x + 3) - 4(2x + 3) = (2x + 3)(5x - 4)$

Example 12

$2y(5x - 2) - 3(2 - 5x) =$
$2y(5x - 2) + 3(5x - 2) = (5x - 2)(2y + 3)$

Example 14

The GCF is $3x$.

$12x^3 - 75x = 3x(4x^2 - 25)$

Factor the difference of two squares.

$3x(2x + 5)(2x - 5)$

Example 16

The common binomial factor is $b - 7$.

$a^2(b - 7) + (7 - b) =$
$a^2(b - 7) - (b - 7) = (b - 7)(a^2 - 1)$

Factor the difference of two squares.

$(b - 7)(a + 1)(a - 1)$

Example 18

The GCF is $4x$.

$4x^3 + 28x^2 - 120x = 4x(x^2 + 7x - 30)$

Factor the trinomial.

$4x(x + 10)(x - 3)$

Exercises   Pages 261–262

1. $(x + 2)(x - 2)$ **3.** $(a + 9)(a - 9)$ **5.** $(2x + 1)(2x - 1)$ **7.** $(x^3 + 3)(x^3 - 3)$ **9.** $(5x + 1)(5x - 1)$
11. $(1 + 7x)(1 - 7x)$ **13.** Nonfactorable over the integers.   **15.** $(x^2 + y)(x^2 - y)$ **17.** $(3x + 4y)(3x - 4y)$
19. $(xy + 2)(xy - 2)$ **21.** $(y + 1)^2$ **23.** $(a - 1)^2$ **25.** Nonfactorable over the integers.   **27.** $(x + y)^2$
29. $(2a + 1)^2$ **31.** $(8a - 1)^2$ **33.** $(4b + 1)^2$ **35.** $(2b + 7)^2$ **37.** $(5a + 3b)^2$ **39.** $(7x + 2y)^2$
41. $(a + b)(x + 2)$ **43.** $(b + 2)(x - y)$ **45.** $(x - 3)(z - 1)$ **47.** $(b - 2c)(x + y)$ **49.** $(x - 2)(a - 5)$
51. $(y - 2)(b - 2a)$ **53.** $(y - 3)(b - 3)$ **55.** $(x - y)(a + 2)$ **57.** $2(x + 3)(x - 3)$ **59.** $y(y - 5)^2$
61. $a^2(a - 3)(a - 8)$ **63.** $6(y - 2)(y - 6)$ **65.** Nonfactorable over the integers.   **67.** $3b(a + 9)(a - 2)$
69. $a^2(b + 11)(b - 8)$ **71.** $b^2(a + 3)^2$ **73.** $xy(x - 2y)(2x - 3y)$ **75.** $2a(3a + 2)^2$ **77.** $(a + 2)(a - 2)(a^2 + 4)$
79. $2(x - 3)(2a - b)$ **81.** $(a - b)(y + 1)(y - 1)$

Review/Test   Page 265

1. $4ab^3$ (7.1A)   **2.** $2x(3x^2 - 4x + 5)$ (7.1B)   **3.** $(p + 2)(p + 3)$ (7.2A)   **4.** $(a - 3)(a - 16)$ (7.2A)
5. $(x + 5)(x - 3)$ (7.2A)   **6.** $(x + 3)(x - 12)$ (7.2A)   **7.** $5(x^2 - 9x - 3)$ (7.2B)   **8.** $2y^2(y + 1)(y - 8)$ (7.2B)
9. Nonfactorable over the integers. (7.3A)   **10.** $(2x + 1)(3x + 8)$ (7.3A)   **11.** $(3x - 1)(4x + 1)$ (7.3A)
12. $4(x + 4)(2x - 3)$ (7.3B)   **13.** $3y^2(2x^2 + 3x + 4)$ (7.3B)   **14.** $(b + 4)(b - 4)$ (7.4A)   **15.** $(2x + 7y)(2x - 7y)$ (7.4A)
16. $(p + 6)^2$ (7.4B)   **17.** $(2a - 3b)^2$ (7.4B)   **18.** $(x - 2)(a + b)$ (7.4C)   **19.** $(p + 1)(x - 1)$ (7.4C)
20. $3(a + 5)(a - 5)$ (7.4D)   **21.** $3(x + 2y)^2$ (7.4D)   **22.** $y(y + 3)(y - 3)$ (7.4D)   **23.** $3(2a - 3)^2$ (7.4D)
24. $(a + b)(a - b)(x - y)$ (7.4D)

Cumulative Review/Test   Page 266

1. 12 (3.2D)

2. $(x - 3)(3y - 2)$ (7.4C)

3. $(p + 1)(p - 10)$ (7.2A)

4. 7 (3.1C)

5. 4 (3.1E)

6. $(x + 2y)(x - 7y)$ (7.2B)

7. -31 (3.2A)

8. $15x^2$ (3.2C)

9. $(3x - 2)(3x + 7)$ (7.3A)

10. $\frac{2}{3}$ (4.1C)

11. $6xy^2$ (7.1A)

12. $3a(2a + 5)(3a + 2)$ (7.3B)

13. $2(3x - 4y)^2$ (7.4D)

14. $\frac{7}{4}$ (4.2A)

15. $(2x + 7y)^2$ (7.4B)

16. 45 (5.3A/5.4B)

17. $\frac{y^6}{x^8}$ (6.4A)

18. $5xy^2(3 - 4y^2)$ (7.1B)

19. 3 (4.2B)

20. $9a^6b^4$ (6.2B)

21. $(6a + 7b)(6a - 7b)$ (7.4A)

22. $x^3 - 3x^2 - 6x + 8$ (6.2C)

23. 10, 12, and 14 (4.3B)

24. 168 mi (4.3D)

Answers to Chapter 8

Section 1   Pages 268–272

Example 2

$$\frac{6x^5y}{12x^2y^3} = \frac{\overset{1}{2}\cdot\overset{1}{3}\cdot x^5y}{\underset{1}{2}\cdot 2\cdot\underset{1}{3}\cdot x^2y^3} = \frac{x^3}{2y^2}$$

Example 4

$$\frac{x^2 + 2x - 24}{16 - x^2} = \frac{\overset{-1}{(x-4)}(x+6)}{\underset{1}{(4-x)}(4+x)} = -\frac{x+6}{x+4}$$

Example 6

$$\frac{x^2 + 4x - 12}{x^2 - 3x + 2} = \frac{\overset{1}{(x-2)}(x+6)}{(x-1)\underset{1}{(x-2)}} = \frac{x+6}{x-1}$$

Example 8

$$\frac{12x^2 + 3x}{10x - 15}\cdot\frac{8x - 12}{9x + 18} =$$

$$\frac{3x(4x+1)}{5(2x-3)}\cdot\frac{4(2x-3)}{9(x+2)} =$$

$$\frac{\overset{1}{3x}(4x+1)\cdot 2\cdot 2\overset{1}{(2x-3)}}{\underset{1}{5(2x-3)}\cdot\underset{1}{3}\cdot 3(x+2)} = \frac{4x(4x+1)}{15(x+2)}$$

Example 10

$$\frac{x^2 + 2x - 15}{9 - x^2}\cdot\frac{x^2 - 3x - 18}{x^2 - 7x + 6} =$$

$$\frac{(x-3)(x+5)}{(3-x)(3+x)}\cdot\frac{(x+3)(x-6)}{(x-1)(x-6)} =$$

$$\frac{\overset{-1}{(x-3)}(x+5)\cdot\overset{1}{(x+3)}\overset{1}{(x-6)}}{\underset{1}{(3-x)}\underset{1}{(3+x)}\cdot(x-1)\underset{1}{(x-6)}} = -\frac{x+5}{x-1}$$

Example 12

$$\frac{16x^4y^3}{3a^5b^2} \div \frac{2xy^3}{9a^6b^5} = \frac{16x^4y^3}{3a^5b^2}\cdot\frac{9a^6b^5}{2xy^3} =$$

$$\frac{16x^4y^3\cdot 9a^6b^5}{3a^5b^2\cdot 2xy^3} = 24ab^3x^3$$

Example 14

$$\frac{a^2}{4bc^2 - 2b^2c} \div \frac{a}{6bc - 3b^2} =$$

$$\frac{a^2}{4bc^2 - 2b^2c}\cdot\frac{6bc - 3b^2}{a} =$$

$$\frac{a^2\cdot 3\overset{1}{b}\overset{1}{(2c-b)}}{2\underset{1}{bc}\underset{1}{(2c-b)}\cdot a} = \frac{3a}{2c}$$

Example 16

$$\frac{3x^2 + 26x + 16}{3x^2 - 7x - 6} \div \frac{2x^2 + 9x - 5}{x^2 + 2x - 15} =$$

$$\frac{3x^2 + 26x + 16}{3x^2 - 7x - 6}\cdot\frac{x^2 + 2x - 15}{2x^2 + 9x - 5} =$$

$$\frac{\overset{1}{(3x+2)}(x+8)\cdot\overset{1}{(x+5)}\overset{1}{(x-3)}}{\underset{1}{(3x+2)}\underset{1}{(x-3)}\cdot(2x-1)\underset{1}{(x+5)}} = \frac{x+8}{2x-1}$$

Exercises   Pages 273–276

1. $\frac{3}{4x}$ **3.** $\frac{1}{x+3}$ **5.** -1 **7.** $\frac{2}{3y}$ **9.** $-\frac{3}{4x}$ **11.** -5 **13.** $\frac{a}{b}$ **15.** $-\frac{2}{x}$ **17.** $\frac{y-2}{y-3}$ **19.** $\frac{x+5}{x+4}$

21. $\frac{x+4}{x-3}$ **23.** $-\frac{x+2}{x+5}$ **25.** $\frac{2(x+2)}{x+3}$ **27.** $\frac{2x-1}{2x+3}$ **29.** $-\frac{x+7}{x+6}$ **31.** $-\frac{y+2}{y+5}$ **33.** $\frac{2}{3xy}$ **35.** $\frac{8xy^2ab}{3}$

37. $\frac{2}{9}$ **39.** $\frac{y^2}{x}$ **41.** $\frac{y(x+4)}{x(x+1)}$ **43.** $\frac{x^3(x-7)}{y^2(x-4)}$ **45.** $-\frac{y}{x}$ **47.** $\frac{x+3}{x+1}$ **49.** $\frac{x-5}{x+3}$ **51.** $-\frac{x+3}{x+5}$

53. $\frac{12x^4}{(x+1)(2x+1)}$ **55.** $-\frac{x+3}{x-12}$ **57.** $\frac{x+2}{x+4}$ **59.** $\frac{2x-5}{2x-1}$ **61.** $\frac{3x-4}{2x+3}$ **63.** $\frac{2xy^2ab^2}{9}$ **65.** $\frac{5}{12}$ **67.** $3x$

69. $\frac{y(x+3)}{x(x+1)}$ **71.** $\frac{x+7}{x-7}$ **73.** $-\frac{4ac}{y}$ **75.** $\frac{x-5}{x-6}$ **77.** 1 **79.** $-\frac{x+6}{x+5}$ **81.** $\frac{2x+3}{x-6}$ **83.** $\frac{4x+3}{2x-1}$

85. $\frac{(2x+5)(4x-1)}{(2x-1)(4x+5)}$

Section 2   Pages 277–282

Example 2

$8uv^2 = 2 \cdot 2 \cdot 2 \cdot u \cdot v \cdot v$ $12uw = 2 \cdot 2 \cdot 3 \cdot u \cdot w$

$\text{LCM} = 2 \cdot 2 \cdot 2 \cdot 3 \cdot u \cdot v \cdot v \cdot w = 24uv^2w$

Example 4

$m^2 - 6m + 9 = (m - 3)(m - 3)$

$m^2 - 2m - 3 = (m + 1)(m - 3)$

$\text{LCM} = (m - 3)(m - 3)(m + 1)$

Example 6

The LCM is $36xy^2z$.

$\dfrac{x - 3}{4xy^2} = \dfrac{x - 3}{4xy^2} \cdot \dfrac{9z}{9z} = \dfrac{9xz - 27z}{36xy^2z}$

$\dfrac{2x + 1}{9y^2z} = \dfrac{2x + 1}{9y^2z} \cdot \dfrac{4x}{4x} = \dfrac{8x^2 + 4x}{36xy^2z}$

Example 8

$\dfrac{2x}{25 - x^2} = \dfrac{2x}{-(x^2 - 25)} = -\dfrac{2x}{x^2 - 25}$

The LCM is $(x - 5)(x + 5)(x + 2)$.

$\dfrac{x + 4}{x^2 - 3x - 10} = \dfrac{x + 4}{(x + 2)(x - 5)} \cdot \dfrac{x + 5}{x + 5} =$

$\dfrac{x^2 + 9x + 20}{(x + 2)(x - 5)(x + 5)}$

$\dfrac{2x}{25 - x^2} = -\dfrac{2x}{(x - 5)(x + 5)} \cdot \dfrac{x + 2}{x + 2} =$

$-\dfrac{2x^2 + 4x}{(x + 2)(x - 5)(x + 5)}$

Example 10

$\dfrac{3}{xy} + \dfrac{12}{xy} = \dfrac{3 + 12}{xy} = \dfrac{15}{xy}$

Example 12

$\dfrac{2x^2}{x^2 - x - 12} - \dfrac{7x + 4}{x^2 - x - 12} = \dfrac{2x^2 - (7x + 4)}{x^2 - x - 12} =$

$\dfrac{2x^2 - 7x - 4}{x^2 - x - 12} = \dfrac{(2x + 1)\overset{1}{\cancel{(x - 4)}}}{(x + 3)\underset{1}{\cancel{(x - 4)}}} = \dfrac{2x + 1}{x + 3}$

Example 14

$\dfrac{x^2 - 1}{x^2 - 8x + 12} - \dfrac{2x + 1}{x^2 - 8x + 12} + \dfrac{x}{x^2 - 8x + 12} =$

$\dfrac{(x^2 - 1) - (2x + 1) + x}{x^2 - 8x + 12} = \dfrac{x^2 - 1 - 2x - 1 + x}{x^2 - 8x + 12} =$

$\dfrac{x^2 - x - 2}{x^2 - 8x + 12} = \dfrac{(x + 1)\overset{1}{\cancel{(x - 2)}}}{\underset{1}{\cancel{(x - 2)}}(x - 6)} = \dfrac{x + 1}{x - 6}$

Example 16

The LCM of the denominators is $24y$.

$\dfrac{z}{8y} = \dfrac{z}{8y} \cdot \dfrac{3}{3} = \dfrac{3z}{24y}$ $\dfrac{4z}{3y} = \dfrac{4z}{3y} \cdot \dfrac{8}{8} = \dfrac{32z}{24y}$

$\dfrac{5z}{4y} = \dfrac{5z}{4y} \cdot \dfrac{6}{6} = \dfrac{30z}{24y}$

$\dfrac{z}{8y} - \dfrac{4z}{3y} + \dfrac{5z}{4y} = \dfrac{3z}{24y} - \dfrac{32z}{24y} + \dfrac{30z}{24y} =$

$\dfrac{3z - 32z + 30z}{24y} = \dfrac{z}{24y}$

Example 18

The LCM is $x - 2$.

$\dfrac{5x}{x - 2} = \dfrac{5x}{x - 2} \cdot \dfrac{1}{1} = \dfrac{5x}{x - 2}$

$\dfrac{3}{2 - x} = \dfrac{3}{-(x - 2)} \cdot \dfrac{-1}{-1} = \dfrac{-3}{x - 2}$

$\dfrac{5x}{x - 2} - \dfrac{3}{2 - x} = \dfrac{5x}{x - 2} - \dfrac{-3}{x - 2} =$

$\dfrac{5x - (-3)}{x - 2} = \dfrac{5x + 3}{x - 2}$

Example 20

The LCM is $(3x - 1)(x + 4)$.

$\dfrac{4x}{3x - 1} = \dfrac{4x}{3x - 1} \cdot \dfrac{x + 4}{x + 4} = \dfrac{4x^2 + 16x}{(3x - 1)(x + 4)}$

$\dfrac{9}{x + 4} = \dfrac{9}{x + 4} \cdot \dfrac{3x - 1}{3x - 1} = \dfrac{27x - 9}{(3x - 1)(x + 4)}$

$\dfrac{4x}{3x - 1} - \dfrac{9}{x + 4} =$

$\dfrac{4x^2 + 16x}{(3x - 1)(x + 4)} - \dfrac{27x - 9}{(3x - 1)(x + 4)} =$

$\dfrac{4x^2 + 16x - (27x - 9)}{(3x - 1)(x + 4)} = \dfrac{4x^2 + 16x - 27x + 9}{(3x - 1)(x + 4)} =$

$\dfrac{4x^2 - 11x + 9}{(3x - 1)(x + 4)}$

Example 22

The LCM is $(x + 5)(x - 5)$.

$$\frac{2x - 1}{x^2 - 25} = \frac{2x - 1}{(x + 5)(x - 5)}$$

$$\frac{2}{5 - x} = \frac{2}{-(x - 5)} \cdot \frac{-1 \cdot (x + 5)}{-1 \cdot (x + 5)} = \frac{-2(x + 5)}{(x + 5)(x - 5)}$$

$$\frac{2x - 1}{x^2 - 25} + \frac{2}{5 - x} =$$

$$\frac{2x - 1}{(x + 5)(x - 5)} + \frac{-2(x + 5)}{(x + 5)(x - 5)} =$$

$$\frac{2x - 1 + (-2)(x + 5)}{(x + 5)(x - 5)} = \frac{2x - 1 - 2x - 10}{(x + 5)(x - 5)} =$$

$$\frac{-11}{(x + 5)(x - 5)} = -\frac{11}{(x + 5)(x - 5)}$$

Example 24

The LCM is $(3x + 2)(x - 1)$.

$$\frac{2x - 3}{3x^2 - x - 2} = \frac{2x - 3}{(3x + 2)(x - 1)}$$

$$\frac{5}{3x + 2} = \frac{5}{3x + 2} \cdot \frac{x - 1}{x - 1} = \frac{5x - 5}{(3x + 2)(x - 1)}$$

$$\frac{1}{x - 1} = \frac{1}{x - 1} \cdot \frac{3x + 2}{3x + 2} = \frac{3x + 2}{(3x + 2)(x - 1)}$$

$$\frac{2x - 3}{3x^2 - x - 2} + \frac{5}{3x + 2} - \frac{1}{x - 1} =$$

$$\frac{2x - 3}{(3x + 2)(x - 1)} + \frac{5x - 5}{(3x + 2)(x - 1)} - \frac{3x + 2}{(3x + 2)(x - 1)} =$$

$$\frac{(2x - 3) + (5x - 5) - (3x + 2)}{(3x + 2)(x - 1)} =$$

$$\frac{2x - 3 + 5x - 5 - 3x - 2}{(3x + 2)(x - 1)} =$$

$$\frac{4x - 10}{(3x + 2)(x - 1)} = \frac{2(2x - 5)}{(3x + 2)(x - 1)}$$

Exercises   Pages 283–288

1. $24x^3y^2$ **3.** $30x^4y^2$ **5.** $8x^2(x + 2)$ **7.** $6x^2y(x + 4)$ **9.** $36x(x + 2)^2$ **11.** $6(x + 1)^2$

13. $(x - 1)(x + 2)(x + 3)$ **15.** $(2x + 3)^2(x - 5)$ **17.** $(x - 1)(x - 2)$ **19.** $(x - 3)(x + 2)(x + 4)$

21. $(x + 4)(x + 1)(x - 7)$ **23.** $(x + 6)(x - 6)(x + 4)$ **25.** $(x - 10)(x - 8)(x + 3)$ **27.** $(3x - 2)(x - 3)(x + 2)$

29. $(x + 2)(x - 3)$ **31.** $(x + 6)(x - 3)$ **33.** $\frac{4x}{x^2}, \frac{3}{x^2}$ **35.** $\frac{4x}{12y^2}, \frac{3yz}{12y^2}$ **37.** $\frac{xy}{x^2(x - 3)}, \frac{6x - 18}{x^2(x - 3)}$

39. $\frac{9x}{x(x - 1)^2}, \frac{6x - 6}{x(x - 1)^2}$ **41.** $\frac{3x}{x(x - 3)}, -\frac{5}{x(x - 3)}$ **43.** $\frac{3}{(x - 5)^2}, -\frac{2x - 10}{(x - 5)^2}$ **45.** $\frac{3x}{x^2(x + 2)}, \frac{4x + 8}{x^2(x + 2)}$

47. $\frac{x^2 - 6x + 8}{(x + 3)(x - 4)}, \frac{x^2 + 3x}{(x + 3)(x - 4)}$ **49.** $\frac{3}{(x + 2)(x - 1)}, \frac{x^2 - x}{(x + 2)(x - 1)}$ **51.** $\frac{5}{(2x - 5)(x - 2)}, \frac{x^2 - 3x + 2}{(2x - 5)(x - 2)}$

53. $\frac{x^2 - 3x}{(x + 3)(x - 3)(x - 2)}, \frac{2x^2 - 4x}{(x + 3)(x - 3)(x - 2)}$ **55.** $\frac{x^2 - 3x}{(x - 3)^2(x + 3)}, \frac{x^2 + 2x - 3}{(x - 3)^2(x + 3)}$ **57.** $\frac{3x^2 + 12x}{(x - 5)(x + 4)}, \frac{x^2 - 5x}{(x - 5)(x + 4)}, -\frac{3}{(x - 5)(x + 4)}$

59. $\frac{11}{y^2}$ **61.** $-\frac{7}{x + 4}$ **63.** $\frac{8x}{2x + 3}$ **65.** $\frac{5x + 7}{x - 3}$ **67.** $\frac{2x - 5}{x + 9}$ **69.** $\frac{-3x - 4}{2x + 7}$ **71.** $\frac{1}{x + 5}$ **73.** $\frac{1}{x - 6}$

75. $\frac{3}{2y - 1}$ **77.** $\frac{1}{x - 5}$ **79.** $\frac{4y + 5x}{xy}$ **81.** $\frac{19}{2x}$ **83.** $\frac{5}{12x}$ **85.** $\frac{19x - 12}{6x^2}$ **87.** $\frac{52y - 35x}{20xy}$ **89.** $\frac{13x + 2}{15x}$

91. $\frac{7}{24}$ **93.** $\frac{x + 90}{45x}$ **95.** $\frac{x^2 + 2x + 2}{2x^2}$ **97.** $\frac{2x^2 + 3x - 10}{4x^2}$ **99.** $\frac{-3x^2 + 16x + 2}{12x^2}$ **101.** $\frac{x^2 - x + 2}{x^2y}$

103. $\frac{16xy - 12y + 6x^2 + 3}{12x^2y^2}$ **105.** $\frac{3xy - 6y - 2x^2 - 14x}{24x^2y}$ **107.** $\frac{9x + 2}{(x - 2)(x + 3)}$ **109.** $\frac{2(x + 23)}{(x - 7)(x + 3)}$ **111.** $\frac{2x^2 - 5x + 1}{(x + 1)(x - 3)}$

113. $\frac{4x^2 - 34x + 5}{(2x - 1)(x - 6)}$ **115.** $\frac{2a - 5}{a - 7}$ **117.** $\frac{4x + 9}{(x + 3)(x - 3)}$ **119.** $\frac{-x + 9}{(x - 3)(x + 2)}$ **121.** $\frac{14}{(x - 5)(x - 5)}$ **123.** $\frac{-2(x + 7)}{(x + 6)(x - 7)}$

125. $\frac{x - 4}{x - 6}$ **127.** $\frac{2x + 1}{x - 1}$ **129.** $\frac{-3(x^2 + 8x + 25)}{(x - 3)(x + 7)}$

Section 3 Pages 289–290

Example 2

The LCM of 3, x, 9, and x^2 is $9x^2$.

$$\frac{\frac{1}{3} - \frac{1}{x}}{\frac{1}{9} - \frac{1}{x^2}} = \frac{\frac{1}{3} - \frac{1}{x}}{\frac{1}{9} - \frac{1}{x^2}} \cdot \frac{9x^2}{9x^2} = \frac{\frac{1}{3} \cdot 9x^2 - \frac{1}{x} \cdot 9x^2}{\frac{1}{9} \cdot 9x^2 - \frac{1}{x^2} \cdot 9x^2} =$$

$$\frac{3x^2 - 9x}{x^2 - 9} = \frac{3x(\cancel{x - 3})^1}{(\cancel{x - 3})_1 (x + 3)} = \frac{3x}{x + 3}$$

Example 4

The LCM of x and x^2 is x^2.

$$\frac{1 + \frac{4}{x} + \frac{3}{x^2}}{1 + \frac{10}{x} + \frac{21}{x^2}} = \frac{1 + \frac{4}{x} + \frac{3}{x^2}}{1 + \frac{10}{x} + \frac{21}{x^2}} \cdot \frac{x^2}{x^2} =$$

$$\frac{1 \cdot x^2 + \frac{4}{x} \cdot x^2 + \frac{3}{x^2} \cdot x^2}{1 \cdot x^2 + \frac{10}{x} \cdot x^2 + \frac{21}{x^2} \cdot x^2} = \frac{x^2 + 4x + 3}{x^2 + 10x + 21} =$$

$$\frac{(x + 1)(\cancel{x + 3})^1}{(\cancel{x + 3})_1 (x + 7)} = \frac{x + 1}{x + 7}$$

Exercises Pages 291–292

1. x^2y^2z **3.** $\frac{mp}{n^2}$ **5.** $\frac{a^2 + 2}{a - 2}$ **7.** $\frac{b + 3}{b^2 - 3}$ **9.** $\frac{2x}{2x - 1}$ **11.** $\frac{4y}{4y - 1}$ **13.** $\frac{y - 2}{y}$ **15.** $\frac{x}{x - 3}$ **17.** $\frac{2 - a}{a}$

19. $-\frac{2x}{x + 2}$ **21.** $\frac{3y}{y + 3}$ **23.** $\frac{5x}{x + 2}$ **25.** $\frac{4x - 13}{2(3x - 10)}$ **27.** $\frac{5x - 37}{2x - 17}$ **29.** $\frac{x + 2}{x - 4}$ **31.** $\frac{a - 3}{a + 5}$ **33.** $-\frac{x + 6}{x + 7}$

35. $y - 1$ **37.** $\frac{1}{3x - 4}$ **39.** $\frac{4n + 1}{5n + 3}$ **41.** $\frac{13x + 3}{x + 1}$

Section 4 Pages 293–296

Example 2

$$\frac{2}{x + 6} = \frac{3}{x} \quad \text{The LCM is } x(x + 6).$$

$$\frac{x(\cancel{x + 6})^1}{1} \cdot \frac{2}{\cancel{x + 6}_1} = \frac{x(x + 6)}{1} \cdot \frac{3}{x}$$

$$2x = (x + 6)3$$
$$2x = 3x + 18$$
$$-x = 18$$
$$x = -18$$

-18 checks as a solution.
The solution is -18.

Example 4

$$\frac{5x}{x + 2} = 3 - \frac{10}{x + 2} \quad \text{The LCM is } x + 2.$$

$$\frac{(x + 2)}{1} \cdot \frac{5x}{x + 2} = \frac{(x + 2)}{1}\left(3 - \frac{10}{x + 2}\right)$$

$$\frac{\cancel{x + 2}^1}{1} \cdot \frac{5x}{\cancel{x + 2}_1} = \frac{x + 2}{1} \cdot 3 - \frac{\cancel{x + 2}^1}{1} \cdot \frac{10}{\cancel{x + 2}_1}$$

$$5x = (x + 2)3 - 10$$
$$5x = 3x + 6 - 10$$
$$5x = 3x - 4$$
$$2x = -4$$
$$x = -2$$

-2 does not check as a solution.
The equation has no solution.

Example 6

Strategy

To find the number of computers:
▷ Write the basic inverse variation equation, replace the variables by the given values, and solve for k.
▷ Write the inverse variation equation, replacing k by its value. Substitute 2000 for P and solve for s.

Solution

$$s = \frac{k}{P}$$

$$2000 = \frac{k}{2500}$$

$$5{,}000{,}000 = k$$

$$s = \frac{5{,}000{,}000}{P} = \frac{5{,}000{,}000}{2000} = 2500$$

At a price of $2000, 2500 computers can be sold.

Exercises   Pages 297–300

1. 3   **3.** 12   **5.** 10   **7.** 1   **9.** 9   **11.** -3 **13.** 2   **15.** $\frac{3}{5}$ **17.** 1   **19.** $\frac{1}{4}$ **21.** 3   **23.** $-\frac{3}{2}$

25. 1   **27.** -3 **29.** $\frac{1}{2}$ **31.** 8   **33.** No solution   **35.** 5   **37.** -1 **39.** 5   **41.** No solution

43. 0   **45.** No solution   **47.** 24   **49.** 10   **51.** 5   **53.** 8   **55.** 2   **57.** $\frac{16}{3}$ **59.** 12.56

61. $\frac{2}{9}$ **63.** 8 lb   **65.** 675 bushels   **67.** 224.8 ft   **69.** 400 ft   **71.** 30 revolutions per minute

73. 75 items   **75.** 48 lumens

Section 5   Pages 301–302

Example 2

$$5x - 2y = 10$$
$$5x + (-5x) - 2y = (-5x) + 10$$
$$-2y = -5x + 10$$
$$-\frac{1}{2}(-2y) = -\frac{1}{2}(-5x + 10)$$
$$y = \frac{5}{2}x - 5$$

Example 4

$$s = \frac{A + L}{2}$$
$$2 \cdot s = 2\left(\frac{A + L}{2}\right)$$
$$2s = A + L$$
$$2s + (-A) = A + (-A) + L$$
$$2s - A = L$$

Example 6

$$S = a + (n - 1)d$$
$$S = a + nd - d$$
$$S + (-a) = a + (-a) + nd - d$$
$$S - a = nd - d$$
$$S - a + d = nd - d + d$$
$$S - a + d = nd$$
$$\frac{1}{d}(S - a + d) = \frac{1}{d}(nd)$$
$$\frac{S - a + d}{d} = n$$

Example 8

$$S = C + rC$$
$$S = (1 + r)C$$
$$\frac{1}{1 + r} \cdot S = \frac{1}{1 + r}(1 + r)C$$
$$\frac{S}{1 + r} = C$$

Exercises   Pages 303–304

1. $y = -3x + 10$ **3.** $y = 4x - 3$ **5.** $y = -\frac{3}{2}x + 3$ **7.** $y = \frac{2}{5}x - 2$ **9.** $y = -\frac{2}{7}x + 2$

11. $y = -\frac{1}{3}x + 2$ **13.** $y = \frac{1}{4}x - 3$ **15.** $y = 3x + 7$ **17.** $x = -3y + 6$ **19.** $x = \frac{1}{3}y + 1$

21. $x = -\frac{5}{2}y + 5$ **23.** $x = 2y - 1$ **25.** $x = -\frac{4}{5}y - 4$ **27.** $x = \frac{2}{3}y + 5$ **29.** $x = \frac{2}{3a}$

31. $x = -\frac{1}{a}$ **33.** $x = \frac{2}{3a - 4}$ **35.** $x = -\frac{5}{6a}$ **37.** $x = -\frac{1}{4a}$ **39.** $x = -\frac{2}{6a + 1}$ **41.** $h = \frac{2A}{b}$

43. $t = \frac{d}{r}$ **45.** $T = \frac{PV}{nR}$ **47.** $L = \frac{P - 2W}{2}$ **49.** $b_1 = \frac{2A - hb_2}{h}$ **51.** $h = \frac{3V}{A}$ **53.** $S = C - Rt$

55. $P = \frac{A}{1 + rt}$ **57.** $w = \frac{A}{S + 1}$

Section 6   Pages 305–308

Example 2

Strategy

▷ Time for one printer to complete the job: t

	Rate	Time	Part
1st printer	$\frac{1}{t}$	2	$\frac{2}{t}$
2nd printer	$\frac{1}{t}$	5	$\frac{5}{t}$

▷ The sum of the parts of the task completed must equal 1.

Solution

$$\frac{2}{t} + \frac{5}{t} = 1$$
$$t\left(\frac{2}{t} + \frac{5}{t}\right) = t \cdot 1$$
$$2 + 5 = t$$
$$7 = t$$

Working alone, one printer takes 7 hours to print the payroll.

Example 4

Strategy

▷ Rate sailing across the lake: r
  Rate sailing back: $3r$

	Distance	Rate	Time
Across	6	r	$\frac{6}{r}$
Back	6	$3r$	$\frac{6}{3r}$

▷ The total time for the trip was 2 hours.

Solution

$$\frac{6}{r} + \frac{6}{3r} = 2$$
$$3r\left(\frac{6}{r} + \frac{6}{3r}\right) = 3r(2)$$
$$3r \cdot \frac{6}{r} + 3r \cdot \frac{6}{3r} = 6r$$
$$18 + 6 = 6r$$
$$24 = 6r$$
$$4 = r$$

The rate across the lake was 4 km/hour.

Exercises   Pages 309–310

1. 2 hours   **3.** 3 hours   **5.** 12 hours   **7.** 90 minutes   **9.** 3 hours   **11.** 2 hours
13. freight train: 30 mph; express train: 50 mph   **15.** 200 mph   **17.** prop plane: 150 mph; jet plane: 600 mph
19. 210 mph   **21.** 20 mph   **23.** 20 mph

Review/Test   Page 313

1. $\frac{2x^3}{3y^3}$ (8.1A)   **2.** $-\frac{x+5}{x+1}$ (8.1A)   **3.** $3(2x-1)(x+1)$ (8.2A)   **4.** $\frac{3x+6}{x(x+2)(x-2)}, \frac{x^2}{x(x+2)(x-2)}$ (8.2B)   **5.** $\frac{2}{x+5}$ (8.2C)

6. $\frac{3}{x+8}$ (8.2C)   **7.** $-\frac{3y}{4x}$ (8.2D)   **8.** $\frac{3}{(2x-1)(x+1)}$ (8.2D)   **9.** $\frac{4}{3x}$ (8.1B)   **10.** $\frac{x^3(x+3)}{y(x+2)}$ (8.1B)

11. $-\frac{bc}{2}$ (8.1C)   **12.** 1 (8.1C)   **13.** $\frac{x-3}{2x+3}$ (8.3A)   **14.** $\frac{x-3}{x-2}$ (8.3A)   **15.** 2 (8.4A)   **16.** $\frac{1}{3}$ (8.4A)

17. 35 (8.4B)   **18.** 4 (8.4B)   **19.** $y = \frac{3}{8}x - 2$ (8.5A)   **20.** $t = \frac{d-s}{r}$ (8.5A)   **21.** 6 minutes (8.6A)

22. 2 mph (8.6B)   **23.** 10 minutes (8.6A)   **24.** freight train: 30 mph; passenger train: 60 mph (8.6B)

Cumulative Review/Test   Page 314

1. $\frac{3}{(2x-1)(x+1)}$ (8.2D)   **2.** $(3x-1)(4x+1)$ (7.3A)   **3.** $3b^3 - b + 2$ (6.3B)   **4.** $\frac{x-1}{x-4}$ (8.1C)   **5.** 4 (8.4A)

6. $x^2 + 2x + 4$ (6.3C)   **7.** $a^2 + ab - 12b^2$ (6.2D)   **8.** $(y-6)(y-1)$ (7.2A)   **9.** $\frac{x+3}{x+5}$ (8.3A)   **10.** $\frac{2x^3}{3y^5}$ (8.1A)

11. -4 (5.1C)   **12.** a^3b^7 (6.2A)   **13.** $\frac{3}{x+3}$ (8.2C)   **14.** $a(2a-3)(a+5)$ (7.3B)   **15.** $-\frac{9}{2}$ (4.1D)

16. 21 (8.4B)   **17.** 10 (5.3A/5.3B)   **18.** $\frac{5}{3x+1}$ (8.1B)   **19.** $-\frac{x-2}{x+5}$ (8.1A)   **20.** $t = \frac{f-v}{a}$ (8.5A)

21. 70% (5.4C)   **22.** 180 minutes (8.6A)   **23.** 3 mph (8.6B)   **24.** 80 times per minute (8.4B)

Answers to Chapter 9

Section 1   Pages 316–322

Example 2

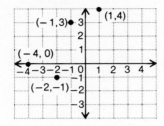

Example 4

$A(4, 2)$
$B(-3, 4)$
$C(-3, 0)$
$D(0, 0)$

Example 6

a) Abscissa of point A: 2
   Abscissa of point C: -3
b) Ordinate of point B: -2
   Ordinate of point D: 0

Example 8

$y = -\frac{1}{2}x - 3$

-4	$-\frac{1}{2}(2) - 3$
	$-1 - 3$
	-4

$-4 = -4$

Yes, $(2, -4)$ is a solution of
$y = -\frac{1}{2}x - 3$.

Example 10

$y = -\frac{1}{4}x + 1$

$ = -\frac{1}{4}(4) + 1$

$ = -1 + 1$

$ = 0$

The ordered pair solution is $(4, 0)$.

Example 12

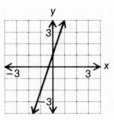

Example 14

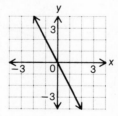

Example 16

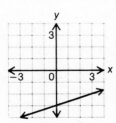

Example 18

$5x - 2y = 10$
$ -2y = -5x + 10$
$ y = \frac{5}{2}x - 5$

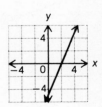

Example 20 $x - 3y = 9$
$-3y = -x + 9$
$y = \frac{1}{3}x - 3$

Example 22

Example 24

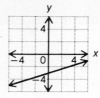

Exercises   Pages 323–328

1.

3.

5.

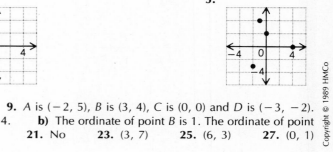

7. A is $(2, 3)$, B is $(4, 0)$, C is $(-4, 1)$ and D is $(-2, -2)$.   **9.** A is $(-2, 5)$, B is $(3, 4)$, C is $(0, 0)$ and D is $(-3, -2)$.
11. a) The abscissa of point A is 2. The abscissa of point C is -4.   **b)** The ordinate of point B is 1. The ordinate of point D is -3.   **13.** Yes   **15.** No   **17.** No   **19.** Yes   **21.** No   **23.** $(3, 7)$ **25.** $(6, 3)$ **27.** $(0, 1)$
29. $(-5, 0)$

31.

33.

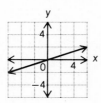

35.

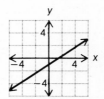

37.

39.

41.

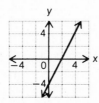

43.

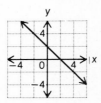

45.

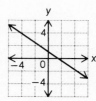

47.

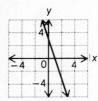

49.

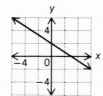

51.

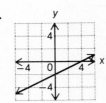

53.

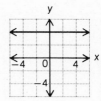

55.

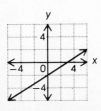

57.

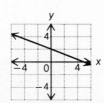

59.

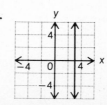

61.

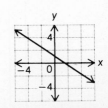

Copyright © 1989 HMCo

Section 2   Pages 329–334

Example 2 x-intercept: y-intercept:

$4x - y = 4$ $4x - y = 4$

$4x - 0 = 4$ $4(0) - y = 4$

$\quad\quad 4x = 4$ $\quad -y = 4$

$\quad\quad\quad x = 1$ $\quad\quad y = -4$

$(1, 0)$ $(0, -4)$

Example 4 x-intercept: y-intercept:

$y = 3x - 6$ $y = 3x - 6$

$0 = 3x - 6$ $b = -6$

$-3x = -6$ $(0, -6)$

$\quad\quad x = 2$

$(2, 0)$

Example 6   Let $P_1 = (-1, 2)$ and $P_2 = (1, 3)$.

$m = \dfrac{y_2 - y_1}{x_2 - x_1} = \dfrac{3 - 2}{1 - (-1)} = \dfrac{1}{2}$

The slope is $\dfrac{1}{2}$.

Example 8   Let $P_1 = (1, 2)$ and $P_2 = (4, -5)$.

$m = \dfrac{y_2 - y_1}{x_2 - x_1} = \dfrac{-5 - 2}{4 - 1} = \dfrac{-7}{3}$

The slope is $-\dfrac{7}{3}$.

Example 10   Let $P_1 = (2, 3)$ and $P_2 = (2, 7)$.

$m = \dfrac{y_2 - y_1}{x_2 - x_1} = \dfrac{7 - 3}{2 - 2} = \dfrac{4}{0}$

The line has no slope.

Example 12   Let $P_1 = (1, -3)$ and $P_2 = (-5, -3)$.

$m = \dfrac{y_2 - y_1}{x_2 - x_1} = \dfrac{-3 - (-3)}{-5 - 1} = \dfrac{0}{-6} = 0$

The line has zero slope.

Example 14 y-intercept $= (0, b) = (0, -1)$

$m = -\dfrac{1}{4}$

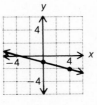

Example 16 y-intercept $= (0, b) = (0, 0)$

$m = -\dfrac{3}{5}$

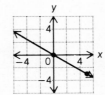

Example 18   Solve the equation for y.

$x - 2y = 4$

$\quad -2y = -x + 4$

$\quad\quad y = \dfrac{1}{2}x - 2$

y-intercept $= (0, b) = (0, -2)$

$m = \dfrac{1}{2}$

Exercises   Pages 335–338

1. The *x*-intercept is (3, 0), and the *y*-intercept is (0, −3).   **3.** The *x*-intercept is (2, 0), and the *y*-intercept is (0, −6).
5. The *x*-intercept is (10, 0), and the *y*-intercept is (0, −2).   **7.** The *x*-intercept is (−4, 0), and the *y*-intercept is (0, 12).
9. The *x*-intercept and the *y*-intercept are both (0, 0).   **11.** The *x*-intercept is (6, 0), and the *y*-intercept is (0, 3).

13. *x*-intercept: (2, 0)   **15.** *x*-intercept: (4, 0)
y-intercept: (0, 5)   y-intercept: (0, −3)

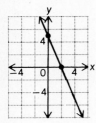

17. −2   **19.** $\frac{1}{3}$ **21.** $-\frac{5}{2}$ **23.** $-\frac{1}{2}$ **25.** −1   **27.** no slope   **29.** 0   **31.** $-\frac{1}{3}$ **33.** 0   **35.** −5

37. no slope   **39.** $-\frac{2}{3}$

41. 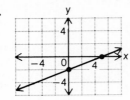   **43.** 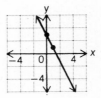   **45.** 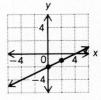   **47.**

49.   **51.** 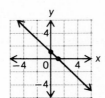   **53.** 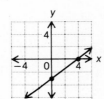   **55.**

Section 3   Pages 339–340

Example 2	$y = \frac{3}{2}x + b$	**Example 4**	$m = \frac{3}{4}$ $(x_1, y_1) = (4, -2)$
	$-2 = \frac{3}{2}(4) + b$		$y - y_1 = m(x - x_1)$
	$-2 = 6 + b$		$y - (-2) = \frac{3}{4}(x - 4)$
	$-8 = b$		$y + 2 = \frac{3}{4}x - 3$
	$y = \frac{3}{2}x - 8$		$y = \frac{3}{4}x - 5$
			The equation of the line is
			$y = \frac{3}{4}x - 5$.

Exercises   Pages 341–342

1. $y = 2x + 2$ **3.** $y = -3x - 1$ **5.** $y = \frac{1}{3}x$ **7.** $y = \frac{3}{4}x - 5$ **9.** $y = -\frac{3}{5}x$ **11.** $y = \frac{1}{4}x + \frac{5}{2}$

13. $y = -\frac{3}{4}x + \frac{1}{4}$ **15.** $y = -x$ **17.** $y = 2x - 3$ **19.** $y = -2x - 3$ **21.** $y = \frac{2}{3}x$ **23.** $y = \frac{1}{2}x + 2$

25. $y = -\frac{3}{4}x - 2$ **27.** $y = \frac{3}{4}x + \frac{5}{2}$ **29.** $y = -\frac{1}{2}x$ **31.** $y = x - 3$

Section 4   Pages 343–344

Example 2

$$\begin{array}{c|c} 2x - 5y = 8 \\ \hline 2(-1) - 5(-2) & 8 \\ -2 + 10 & 8 \\ 8 = 8 \end{array}$$

$$\begin{array}{c|c} -x + 3y = -5 \\ \hline -(-1) + 3(-2) & -5 \\ 1 + (-6) & -5 \\ -5 = -5 \end{array}$$

Yes, $(-1, -2)$ is a solution of the system of equations.

Example 4

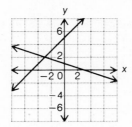

The solution is $(-3, 2)$.

Example 6

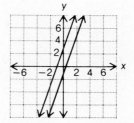

The lines are parallel and therefore do not intersect. The system of equations has no solution.

Exercises   Pages 345–348

1. Yes   **3.** Yes   **5.** No   **7.** No   **9.** No   **11.** Yes   **13.** Yes   **15.** Yes   **17.** No

19.

The solution is (4, 1).

21.

The solution is (4, 1).

23.
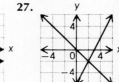
The solution is (4, 3).

25.
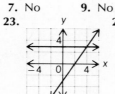
The solution is (3, −2).

27.

The solution is (2, −2).

29.
The system of equations has no solution.

31.

Any solution of one equation is also a solution of the other equation.

33.
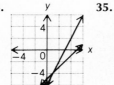
The solution is (1, −4).

35.

The solution is (0, 0).

37.

The system of equations has no solution.

39.
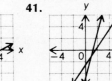
The solution is (0, −2).

41.
The solution is (1, −1).

Section 5   Pages 349–354

Example 2

(1) $7x - y = 4$

(2) $3x + 2y = 9$

Solve equation (1) for y.

$$7x - y = 4$$
$$-y = -7x + 4$$
$$y = 7x - 4$$

Substitute in equation (2).

$$3x + 2y = 9$$
$$3x + 2(7x - 4) = 9$$
$$3x + 14x - 8 = 9$$
$$17x - 8 = 9$$
$$17x = 17$$
$$x = 1$$

Substitute in equation (1).

$$7x - y = 4$$
$$7(1) - y = 4$$
$$7 - y = 4$$
$$-y = -3$$
$$y = 3$$

The solution is $(1, 3)$.

Example 6

(1) $y = -2x + 1$

(2) $6x + 3y = 3$

$$6x + 3y = 3$$
$$6x + 3(-2x + 1) = 3$$
$$6x - 6x + 3 = 3$$
$$3 = 3$$

The two equations represent the same line. Any ordered pair that is a solution of one equation is also a solution of the other equation.

Example 4

(1) $3x - y = 4$

(2) $y = 3x + 2$

$$3x - y = 4$$
$$3x - (3x + 2) = 4$$
$$3x - 3x - 2 = 4$$
$$-2 = 4$$

The lines are parallel. The system has no solution.

Example 8

(1) $x - 2y = 1$

(2) $2x + 4y = 0$

Eliminate y.

$$2(x - 2y) = 2 \cdot 1$$
$$2x + 4y = 0$$

$$2x - 4y = 2$$
$$2x + 4y = 0$$

Add the equations.

$$4x = 2$$
$$x = \frac{2}{4} = \frac{1}{2}$$

Replace x in equation (2).

$$2\left(\frac{1}{2}\right) + 4y = 0$$
$$1 + 4y = 0$$
$$4y = -1$$
$$y = -\frac{1}{4}$$

The solution is $\left(\frac{1}{2}, -\frac{1}{4}\right)$.

Example 10

(1) $2x - 3y = 4$
(2) $-4x + 6y = -8$

Eliminate y.

$$2(2x - 3y) = 2 \cdot 4$$
$$-4x + 6y = -8$$

$$4x - 6y = 8$$
$$-4x + 6y = -8$$

Add the equations.

$$0 + 0 = 0$$
$$0 = 0$$

The two equations represent the same line. Any ordered pair that is a solution of one equation is also a solution of the other equation.

Example 12

(1) $4x + 5y = 11$
(2) $3y = x + 10$

Write equation (2) in the form
$Ax + By = C$.

$$3y = x + 10$$
$$-x + 3y = 10$$

Eliminate x.

$$4x + 5y = 11$$
$$4(-x + 3y) = 4 \cdot 10$$

$$4x + 5y = 11$$
$$-4x + 12y = 40$$

Add the equations.

$$17y = 51$$
$$y = 3$$

Replace y in equation (1).

$$4x + 5y = 11$$
$$4x + 5 \cdot 3 = 11$$
$$4x + 15 = 11$$
$$4x = -4$$
$$x = -1$$

The solution is $(-1, 3)$.

Exercises   Pages 355–358

1. $(2, 1)$ **3.** $(4, 1)$ **5.** $(-1, 1)$ **7.** $(3, 1)$ **9.** $(1, 1)$ **11.** $(-1, 1)$ **13.** no solution   **15.** no solution
17. $\left(-\frac{3}{4}, -\frac{3}{4}\right)$ **19.** $(5, 7)$ **21.** $(1, 7)$ **23.** $\left(\frac{17}{5}, -\frac{7}{5}\right)$ **25.** $\left(-\frac{6}{11}, \frac{31}{11}\right)$ **27.** $(2, 3)$ **29.** $(0, 0)$
31. The two equations represent the same line. Any ordered pair that is a solution of one equation is also a solution of the other equation.   **33.** $\left(\frac{20}{17}, -\frac{15}{17}\right)$ **35.** $(5, 2)$ **37.** $(-17, -8)$ **39.** $\left(-\frac{5}{7}, \frac{13}{7}\right)$ **41.** $(3, -2)$
43. $(5, -1)$ **45.** $(1, 3)$ **47.** $(1, 1)$ **49.** $(3, -2)$ **51.** The two equations represent the same line. Any ordered pair that is a solution of one equation is also a solution of the other equation.   **53.** $(3, 1)$ **55.** The two equations represent the same line. Any ordered pair that is a solution of one equation is also a solution of the other equation.
57. $\left(-\frac{13}{17}, -\frac{24}{17}\right)$ **59.** $(2, 0)$ **61.** $(0, 0)$ **63.** $(5, -2)$ **65.** $\left(\frac{32}{19}, -\frac{9}{19}\right)$ **67.** $(3, 4)$ **69.** $(1, -1)$
71. The two equations represent the same line. Any ordered pair that is a solution of one equation is also a solution of the other equation.   **73.** $(3, 1)$ **75.** $(-1, 2)$ **77.** $(1, 1)$ **79.** $\left(\frac{1}{2}, -\frac{1}{2}\right)$ **81.** $\left(\frac{2}{3}, \frac{1}{9}\right)$ **83.** $\left(\frac{7}{25}, -\frac{1}{25}\right)$

Review/Test   Page 361

1.   (9.1A)
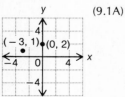
2. $(3, 0)$ (9.1B)   **3.**   (9.1C)
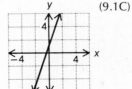
4.   (9.1D)
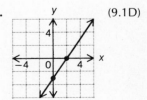

5. $(2, 0)$ and $(0, -3)$ (9.2A)   **6.** 2 (9.2B)   **7.** $y = 3x - 1$ (9.3A/9.3B)   **8.** $y = \frac{1}{2}x + 2$ (9.3A/9.3B)

9.   (9.2C)   **10.** 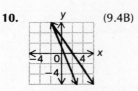   (9.4B)   **11.** Yes (9.4A)   **12.** (2, −1) (9.5A)   **13.** $\left(\frac{1}{2}, -1\right)$ (9.5B)

The solution is (−2, 6).

14. (1, −2) (9.5B)

Cumulative Review/Test   Page 362

1. −17x + 28 (3.2D)   **2.** 5(x + 2)(x + 1) (7.2B)   **3.** 4000 (6.4B)   **4.** Yes (9.4A)   **5.** 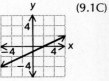   (9.1C)

6.   (9.2C)   **7.** $\frac{1}{15}$ (5.2A)   **8.** $\frac{3}{2}$ (4.1D)   **9.** (−6, 1) (9.5A)   **10.** (−2, −5) (9.1B)   **11.** −12 (3.1E)

12. (4, −3) (9.5B)   **13.** x-intercept: (6, 0); y-intercept: (0, −4) (9.2A)   **14.** $-\frac{5}{8}$ (3.2A)   **15.** $y = \frac{1}{2}x - 2$ (9.3A/9.3B)

16. −3x² (6.3A)   **17.** 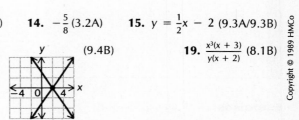   (9.1D)   **18.**   (9.4B)   **19.** $\frac{x^3(x + 3)}{y(x + 2)}$ (8.1B)

The solution is (2, 0).

20. 0 (9.2B)   **21.** −32x⁸y⁷ (6.2B)   **22.** x < −28 (4.4C)

Answers to Chapter 10

Section 1   Pages 364–370

Example 2

$\sqrt{28} = \sqrt{2^2 \cdot 7} = \sqrt{2^2}\sqrt{7} = 2\sqrt{7}$

Example 4

$-5\sqrt{32} = -5\sqrt{2^5} = -5\sqrt{2^4 \cdot 2} = -5\sqrt{2^4}\sqrt{2} = -5 \cdot 2^2\sqrt{2} = -20\sqrt{2}$

Example 6

$\sqrt{216} = \sqrt{2^3 \cdot 3^3} = \sqrt{2^2 \cdot 3^2(2 \cdot 3)} = \sqrt{2^2 \cdot 3^2}\sqrt{2 \cdot 3} = 2 \cdot 3\sqrt{2 \cdot 3} = 6\sqrt{6} \approx 6(2.499) \approx 14.694$

Example 8

$\sqrt{y^{19}} = \sqrt{y^{18} \cdot y} = \sqrt{y^{18}}\sqrt{y} = y^9\sqrt{y}$

Example 10

$\sqrt{45b^7} = \sqrt{3^2 \cdot 5 \cdot b^7} = \sqrt{3^2 b^6(5 \cdot b)} = \sqrt{3^2 b^6}\sqrt{5b} = 3b^3\sqrt{5b}$

Example 12

$3a\sqrt{28a^9 b^{18}} = 3a\sqrt{2^2 \cdot 7 \cdot a^9 \cdot b^{18}}$
$3a\sqrt{2^2 a^8 b^{18}(7a)} = 3a\sqrt{2^2 a^8 b^{18}}\sqrt{7a} = 3a \cdot 2 \cdot a^4 \cdot b^9\sqrt{7a} = 6a^5 b^9\sqrt{7a}$

Example 14

$\sqrt{25(a + 3)^2} = \sqrt{5^2(a + 3)^2} = 5(a + 3) = 5a + 15$

Example 16

$\sqrt{x^2 + 14x + 49} = \sqrt{(x + 7)^2} = x + 7$

Example 18

$9\sqrt{3} + 3\sqrt{3} - 18\sqrt{3} = -6\sqrt{3}$

Example 20

$\sqrt{27b} - 2\sqrt{12b} + 7\sqrt{3b} =$
$\sqrt{3^3 b} - 2\sqrt{2^2 \cdot 3b} + 7\sqrt{3b} =$
$\sqrt{3^2}\sqrt{3b} - 2\sqrt{2^2}\sqrt{3b} + 7\sqrt{3b} =$
$3\sqrt{3b} - 2 \cdot 2\sqrt{3b} + 7\sqrt{3b} =$
$3\sqrt{3b} - 4\sqrt{3b} + 7\sqrt{3b} = 6\sqrt{3b}$

Example 22

$2\sqrt{50} - 5\sqrt{32} = 2\sqrt{2 \cdot 5^2} - 5\sqrt{2^5} =$
$2\sqrt{5^2}\sqrt{2} - 5\sqrt{2^4}\sqrt{2} = 2 \cdot 5\sqrt{2} - 5 \cdot 2^2\sqrt{2} =$
$10\sqrt{2} - 20\sqrt{2} = -10\sqrt{2}$

Example 24

$y\sqrt{28y} + 7\sqrt{63y^3} = y\sqrt{2^2 \cdot 7y} + 7\sqrt{3^2 \cdot 7 \cdot y^3} =$
$y\sqrt{2^2}\sqrt{7y} + 7\sqrt{3^2 \cdot y^2}\sqrt{7y} =$
$y \cdot 2\sqrt{7y} + 7 \cdot 3 \cdot y\sqrt{7y} = 2y\sqrt{7y} + 21y\sqrt{7y} =$
$23y\sqrt{7y}$

Example 26

$2\sqrt{27a^5} - 4a\sqrt{12a^3} + a^2\sqrt{75a} =$
$2\sqrt{3^3 \cdot a^5} - 4a\sqrt{2^2 \cdot 3 \cdot a^3} + a^2\sqrt{3 \cdot 5^2 \cdot a} =$
$2\sqrt{3^2 \cdot a^4}\sqrt{3a} - 4a\sqrt{2^2 \cdot a^2}\sqrt{3a} + a^2\sqrt{5^2}\sqrt{3a} =$
$2 \cdot 3 \cdot a^2\sqrt{3a} - 4a \cdot 2 \cdot a\sqrt{3a} + a^2 \cdot 5\sqrt{3a} =$
$6a^2\sqrt{3a} - 8a^2\sqrt{3a} + 5a^2\sqrt{3a} = 3a^2\sqrt{3a}$

Exercises   Pages 371–374

1. 4   **3.** 7   **5.** $4\sqrt{2}$ **7.** $2\sqrt{2}$ **9.** $18\sqrt{2}$ **11.** $10\sqrt{10}$ **13.** $\sqrt{15}$ **15.** $\sqrt{29}$ **17.** $-54\sqrt{2}$
19. $3\sqrt{5}$ **21.** 0   **23.** $48\sqrt{2}$ **25.** $\sqrt{105}$ **27.** 30   **29.** $30\sqrt{5}$ **31.** $5\sqrt{10}$ **33.** $4\sqrt{6}$ **35.** 18
37. 15.492   **39.** 16.968   **41.** 16   **43.** 16.585   **45.** 15.652   **47.** 18.76   **49.** x^3 **51.** $y^7\sqrt{y}$
53. a^{10} **55.** $x^2 y^2$ **57.** $2x^2$ **59.** $2x\sqrt{6}$ **61.** $xy^3\sqrt{xy}$ **63.** $ab^5\sqrt{ab}$ **65.** $2x^2\sqrt{15x}$ **67.** $7a^2 b^4$
69. $3x^2 y^3\sqrt{2xy}$ **71.** $2x^5 y^3\sqrt{10xy}$ **73.** $4a^4 b^5\sqrt{5a}$ **75.** $8ab\sqrt{b}$ **77.** $x^3 y$ **79.** $8a^2 b^3\sqrt{5b}$

81. $6x^2y^3\sqrt{3y}$ **83.** $4x^3y\sqrt{2y}$ **85.** $5a + 20$ **87.** $2x^2 + 8x + 8$ **89.** $x + 2$ **91.** $y + 1$ **93.** $3\sqrt{2}$
95. $-\sqrt{7}$ **97.** $-11\sqrt{11}$ **99.** $10\sqrt{x}$ **101.** $-2\sqrt{y}$ **103.** $-11\sqrt{3b}$ **105.** $2x\sqrt{2}$ **107.** $-3a\sqrt{3a}$
109. $-5\sqrt{xy}$ **111.** $8\sqrt{5}$ **113.** $8\sqrt{2}$ **115.** $15\sqrt{2} - 10\sqrt{3}$ **117.** $\sqrt{x}$ **119.** $-12x\sqrt{3}$
121. $2xy\sqrt{x} - 3xy\sqrt{y}$ **123.** $-9x\sqrt{3x}$ **125.** $-13y^2\sqrt{2y}$ **127.** $4a^2b^2\sqrt{ab}$ **129.** $7\sqrt{2}$ **131.** $6\sqrt{x}$
133. $-3\sqrt{y}$ **135.** $-45\sqrt{2}$ **137.** $13\sqrt{3} - 12\sqrt{5}$ **139.** $32\sqrt{3} - 3\sqrt{11}$ **141.** $6\sqrt{x}$ **143.** $-34\sqrt{3x}$
145. $10a\sqrt{3b} + 10a\sqrt{5b}$ **147.** $-2xy\sqrt{3}$ **149.** $-7b\sqrt{ab} + 4a\sqrt{ab}$ **151.** $3ab\sqrt{2a} - ab + 4ab\sqrt{3b}$

Section 2   Pages 375–378

Example 2

$\sqrt{5a}\sqrt{15a^3b^4}\sqrt{3b^5} = \sqrt{225a^4b^9} = \sqrt{3^25^2a^4b^9} =$
$\sqrt{3^25^2a^4b^8}\sqrt{b} = 3 \cdot 5a^2b^4\sqrt{b} = 15a^2b^4\sqrt{b}$

Example 4

$\sqrt{5x}(\sqrt{5x} - \sqrt{25y}) = \sqrt{5^2x^2} - \sqrt{5^3xy} =$
$\sqrt{5^2x^2} - \sqrt{5^2}\sqrt{5xy} = 5x - 5\sqrt{5xy}$

Example 6

$(2\sqrt{x} + 7)(2\sqrt{x} - 7) = 4\sqrt{x^2} - 7^2 = 4x - 49$

Example 8

$(3\sqrt{x} - \sqrt{y})(5\sqrt{x} - 2\sqrt{y}) =$
$15\sqrt{x^2} - 6\sqrt{xy} - 5\sqrt{xy} + 2\sqrt{y^2} =$
$15\sqrt{x^2} - 11\sqrt{xy} + 2\sqrt{y^2} =$
$15x - 11\sqrt{xy} + 2y$

Example 10

$\dfrac{\sqrt{15x^6y^7}}{\sqrt{3x^7y^9}} = \sqrt{\dfrac{15x^6y^7}{3x^7y^9}} = \sqrt{\dfrac{5}{xy^2}} =$
$\dfrac{\sqrt{5}}{y\sqrt{x}} = \dfrac{\sqrt{5}}{y\sqrt{x}} \cdot \dfrac{\sqrt{x}}{\sqrt{x}} = \dfrac{\sqrt{5x}}{xy}$

Example 12

$\dfrac{\sqrt{y}}{\sqrt{y} + 3} = \dfrac{\sqrt{y}}{\sqrt{y} + 3} \cdot \dfrac{\sqrt{y} - 3}{\sqrt{y} - 3} = \dfrac{y - 3\sqrt{y}}{y - 9}$

Example 14

$\dfrac{\sqrt{27x^3} - 3\sqrt{12x}}{\sqrt{3x}} = \dfrac{\sqrt{27x^3}}{\sqrt{3x}} - \dfrac{3\sqrt{12x}}{\sqrt{3x}} = \sqrt{\dfrac{27x^3}{3x}} - 3\sqrt{\dfrac{12x}{3x}} =$
$\sqrt{9x^2} - 3\sqrt{4} = \sqrt{3^2x^2} - 3\sqrt{2^2} =$
$3x - 3 \cdot 2 = 3x - 6$

Exercises   Pages 379–380

1. 5 **3.** 6 **5.** x **7.** x^3y^2 **9.** $3ab^6\sqrt{2a}$ **11.** $12a^4b\sqrt{b}$ **13.** $2 - \sqrt{6}$ **15.** $x - \sqrt{xy}$
17. $5\sqrt{2} - \sqrt{5x}$ **19.** $4 - 2\sqrt{10}$ **21.** $x - 6\sqrt{x} + 9$ **23.** $3a - 3\sqrt{ab}$ **25.** $10abc$
27. $15x - 22y\sqrt{x} + 8y^2$ **29.** $x - y$ **31.** $10x + 13\sqrt{xy} + 4y$ **33.** 4 **35.** 7 **37.** 3 **39.** $x\sqrt{5}$
41. $\dfrac{a^2}{7}$ **43.** $\dfrac{\sqrt{3}}{3}$ **45.** $\dfrac{3\sqrt{x}}{x}$ **47.** $\dfrac{2\sqrt{y}}{xy}$ **49.** $\dfrac{2\sqrt{3x}}{3y}$ **51.** $-\dfrac{\sqrt{2} + 3}{7}$ **53.** $\dfrac{15 - 3\sqrt{5}}{20}$ **55.** $\dfrac{x\sqrt{y} + y\sqrt{x}}{x - y}$
57. -5 **59.** $\dfrac{7}{4}$ **61.** $-x^2$

Section 3   Pages 381–382

Example 2

$\sqrt{4x} + 3 = 7$ Check: $\sqrt{4x} + 3 = 7$
$\sqrt{4x} = 4$ $\sqrt{4 \cdot 4} + 3 = 7$
$(\sqrt{4x})^2 = 4^2$ $\sqrt{4^2} + 3 = 7$
$4x = 16$ $4 + 3 = 7$
$x = 4$ $7 = 7$

The solution is 4.

Example 4

$\sqrt{3x - 2} - 5 = 0$ Check: $\sqrt{3x - 2} - 5 = 0$
$\sqrt{3x - 2} = 5$ $\sqrt{3 \cdot 9 - 2} - 5 = 0$
$(\sqrt{3x - 2})^2 = 5^2$ $\sqrt{27 - 2} - 5 = 0$
$3x - 2 = 25$ $\sqrt{25} - 5 = 0$
$3x = 27$ $\sqrt{5^2} - 5 = 0$
$x = 9$ $5 - 5 = 0$

The solution is 9. $0 = 0$

Example 6

$\sqrt{4x + 3} = \sqrt{x + 12}$

$(\sqrt{4x + 3})^2 = (\sqrt{x + 12})^2$

$4x + 3 = x + 12$

$4x = x + 9$

$3x = 9$

$x = 3$

Check:

$\sqrt{4x + 3} = \sqrt{x + 12}$

$\sqrt{4 \cdot 3 + 3} = \sqrt{3 + 12}$

$\sqrt{12 + 3} = \sqrt{15}$

$\sqrt{15} = \sqrt{15}$

The solution is 3.

Exercises   Pages 383–384

1. 25   **3.** 144   **5.** No solution   **7.** 5   **9.** 16   **11.** 8   **13.** No solution   **15.** 12   **17.** $\frac{1}{2}$ **19.** 6

21. 24   **23.** 2   **25.** −4   **27.** −1   **29.** 2   **31.** $-\frac{2}{5}$ **33.** $-\frac{9}{4}$ **35.** $\frac{4}{3}$ **37.** 25   **39.** No solution

41. 5   **43.** 15   **45.** 4   **47.** 5   **49.** 1   **51.** 5   **53.** $\frac{1}{3}$ **55.** 6   **57.** 4   **59.** 1   **61.** $\frac{5}{4}$

Review/Test   Page 387

1. $3\sqrt{5}$ (10.1A)   **2.** $5\sqrt{3}$ (10.1A)   **3.** $-8\sqrt{5}$ (10.1A)   **4.** 13.230 (10.1A)   **5.** $11x^4y$ (10.1B)
6. $6x^3y\sqrt{2x}$ (10.1B)   **7.** $4a^2b^5\sqrt{2ab}$ (10.1B)   **8.** $x + 2$ (10.1B)   **9.** $5\sqrt{y}$ (10.1C)   **10.** $-5\sqrt{2}$ (10.1C)
11. $21\sqrt{2y} - 12\sqrt{2x}$ (10.1C)   **12.** $-2xy\sqrt{3xy} - 3xy\sqrt{xy}$ (10.1C)   **13.** $4x^2y^2\sqrt{5y}$ (10.2A)   **14.** $6x^2y\sqrt{y}$ (10.2A)
15. $a - \sqrt{ab}$ (10.2A)   **16.** $y + 2\sqrt{y} - 15$ (10.2A)   **17.** 9 (10.2B)   **18.** $7ab\sqrt{a}$ (10.2B)
19. $\sqrt{3} + 1$ (10.2B)   **20.** $x - 4$ (10.2B)   **21.** 11 (10.3A)   **22.** 25 (10.3A)   **23.** 3 (10.3A)   **24.** 2 (10.3A)

Cumulative Review/Test   Page 388

1. $x \leq -\frac{9}{2}$ (4.5A)   **2.** 8 (10.2B)   **3.** $4ab\sqrt{2ab} - 5ab\sqrt{ab}$ (10.1C)   **4.** (1, 1) (9.5A)

5. $y = \frac{1}{2}x - 2$ (9.3A/9.3B)   **6.** $-\frac{1}{12}$ (3.1E)   **7.** $-6 - 3\sqrt{5}$ (10.2B)   **8.** $6\sqrt{3}$ (10.1A)

9. $2a(a - 5)(a - 3)$ (7.2B)   **10.** 6 (10.3A)   **11.** $\frac{1}{4(x + 1)}$ (8.1B)   **12.** $\frac{x + 3}{x - 3}$ (8.2D)   **13.** $-4\sqrt{2}$ (10.1C)

14. $\frac{5}{3}$ (8.4A)   **15.** $6x^5y^5$ (6.2A)   **16.** $3\sqrt{2} - x\sqrt{3}$ (10.2A)   **17.** $3x^2y^2(4x - 3y)$ (7.1B)   **18.** $\frac{1}{13}$ (4.2B)

19. $14a^5b^2\sqrt{2a}$ (10.2A)   **20.** 750 (5.3A/5.3B)   **21.** 5000 fish (5.1D)   **22.** −26 (4.5B)

23. 48 hours (8.6A)   **24.** 56 oz (5.4C)

Answers to Chapter 11

Section 1   Pages 390–392

Example 2

$x^2 + 2x - 8 = 0$
$(x + 4)(x - 2) = 0$

$x + 4 = 0 \qquad\qquad x - 2 = 0$
$\qquad x = -4 \qquad\qquad\qquad x = 2$

The solutions are -4 and 2.

Example 4

$$2x^2 = (x + 2)(x + 3)$$
$$2x^2 = x^2 + 5x + 6$$
$$x^2 - 5x - 6 = 0$$
$$(x + 1)(x - 6) = 0$$

$x + 1 = 0 \qquad\qquad x - 6 = 0$
$\qquad x = -1 \qquad\qquad\qquad x = 6$

The solutions are -1 and 6.

Example 6

$x^2 + 81 = 0$
$\qquad x^2 = -81$
$\qquad \sqrt{x^2} = \sqrt{-81}$
$\sqrt{-81}$ is not a real number.
The equation has no real number solution.

Example 8

$$4(x + 2)^2 = 9$$
$$(x + 2)^2 = \frac{9}{4}$$
$$\sqrt{(x + 2)^2} = \sqrt{\frac{9}{4}}$$
$$x + 2 = \pm\sqrt{\frac{9}{4}} = \pm\frac{3}{2}$$

$x + 2 = \frac{3}{2} \qquad\qquad\qquad x + 2 = -\frac{3}{2}$
$\qquad x = -\frac{1}{2} \qquad\qquad\qquad\qquad x = -\frac{7}{2}$

The solutions are $-\frac{1}{2}$ and $-\frac{7}{2}$.

Exercises   Pages 393–394

1. 5 and -3 **3.** -7 and 8   **5.** $-\frac{5}{3}$ and 4   **7.** -5 and 3   **9.** 1 and 3   **11.** -1 and -2 **13.** 3

15. 0 and $-\frac{2}{3}$ **17.** -2 and 5   **19.** $\frac{2}{3}$ and 1   **21.** $\frac{1}{3}$ and -3 **23.** $\frac{2}{3}$ **25.** $-\frac{1}{2}$ and $\frac{3}{2}$ **27.** $\frac{1}{2}$

29. -3 and 3   **31.** $-\frac{1}{2}$ and $\frac{1}{2}$ **33.** -3 and 5   **35.** 1 and 5   **37.** -1 and $\frac{13}{2}$ **39.** -7 and 7

41. -8 and 8   **43.** $-\frac{8}{3}$ and $\frac{8}{3}$ **45.** $-\frac{5}{2}$ and $\frac{5}{2}$ **47.** $-\frac{8}{5}$ and $\frac{8}{5}$ **49.** No real number solution

51. $-4\sqrt{3}$ and $4\sqrt{3}$ **53.** -9 and 5   **55.** -2 and 8   **57.** $-\frac{15}{2}$ and $\frac{3}{2}$ **59.** $\frac{26}{9}$ and $\frac{10}{9}$

61. $-5 + 5\sqrt{2}$ and $-5 - 5\sqrt{2}$ **63.** No real number solution   **65.** $-\frac{3}{4} + 2\sqrt{3}$ and $-\frac{3}{4} - 2\sqrt{3}$

Section 2   Pages 395–398

Example 2

$3x^2 - 6x - 2 = 0$

$\qquad 3x^2 - 6x = 2$

$\dfrac{1}{3}(3x^2 - 6x) = \dfrac{1}{3} \cdot 2$

$\qquad x^2 - 2x = \dfrac{2}{3}$

Complete the square.

$x^2 - 2x + 1 = \dfrac{2}{3} + 1$

$\qquad (x - 1)^2 = \dfrac{5}{3}$

$\qquad \sqrt{(x - 1)^2} = \sqrt{\dfrac{5}{3}}$

$\qquad x - 1 = \pm\sqrt{\dfrac{5}{3}} = \pm\dfrac{\sqrt{15}}{3}$

$x - 1 = \dfrac{\sqrt{15}}{3} \qquad\qquad x - 1 = -\dfrac{\sqrt{15}}{3}$

$\qquad x = 1 + \dfrac{\sqrt{15}}{3} \qquad\qquad x = 1 - \dfrac{\sqrt{15}}{3}$

$\qquad\quad = \dfrac{3 + \sqrt{15}}{3} \qquad\qquad\quad = \dfrac{3 - \sqrt{15}}{3}$

The solutions are $\dfrac{3 + \sqrt{15}}{3}$ and $\dfrac{3 - \sqrt{15}}{3}$.

Example 6

$\quad x^2 + 8x + 8 = 0$

$\qquad x^2 + 8x = -8$

$x^2 + 8x + 16 = -8 + 16$

$\qquad (x + 4)^2 = 8$

$\quad \sqrt{(x + 4)^2} = \sqrt{8}$

$\qquad x + 4 = \pm\sqrt{8} = \pm2\sqrt{2}$

$x + 4 = 2\sqrt{2} \qquad\qquad x + 4 = -2\sqrt{2}$

$\quad x = -4 + 2\sqrt{2} \qquad\qquad x = -4 - 2\sqrt{2}$

$\qquad = -4 + 2(1.414) \qquad\qquad = -4 - 2(1.414)$

$\qquad = -4 + 2.828 \qquad\qquad\quad = -4 - 2.828$

$\qquad = -1.172 \qquad\qquad\qquad = -6.828$

The solutions are approximately -1.172 and -6.828.

Example 4

$x^2 + 6x + 12 = 0$

$\quad x^2 + 6x = -12$

$x^2 + 6x + 9 = -12 + 9$

$\quad (x + 3)^2 = -3$

$\sqrt{(x + 3)^2} = \sqrt{-3}$

$\sqrt{-3}$ is not a real number.

The quadratic equation has no real number solution.

Exercises   Pages 399–400

1. 1 and -3 **3.** 8 and -2 **5.** 2   **7.** no real number solution   **9.** -1 and -4 **11.** -8 and 1

13. $-2 + \sqrt{3}$ and $-2 - \sqrt{3}$ **15.** $-3 + \sqrt{14}$ and $-3 - \sqrt{14}$ **17.** $1 + \sqrt{2}$ and $1 - \sqrt{2}$

19. $\dfrac{-3 + \sqrt{13}}{2}$ and $\dfrac{-3 - \sqrt{13}}{2}$ **21.** 2 and 1   **23.** $\dfrac{-1 + \sqrt{13}}{2}$ and $\dfrac{-1 - \sqrt{13}}{2}$ **25.** $-5 + 4\sqrt{2}$ and $-5 - 4\sqrt{2}$

27. $\dfrac{3 + \sqrt{29}}{2}$ and $\dfrac{3 - \sqrt{29}}{2}$ **29.** $\dfrac{1 + \sqrt{17}}{2}$ and $\dfrac{1 - \sqrt{17}}{2}$ **31.** no real number solution   **33.** 1 and $\dfrac{1}{2}$

35. -3 and $\dfrac{1}{2}$ **37.** 2 and $\dfrac{3}{2}$ **39.** 1 and $-\dfrac{1}{2}$ **41.** -2 and $\dfrac{1}{3}$ **43.** -2 and $-\dfrac{2}{3}$ **45.** $\dfrac{1}{2}$ and $-\dfrac{3}{2}$

47. $\dfrac{1}{3}$ and $-\dfrac{3}{2}$ **49.** $-\dfrac{1}{2}$ and $\dfrac{4}{3}$ **51.** $\dfrac{1 + \sqrt{2}}{2}$ and $\dfrac{1 - \sqrt{2}}{2}$ **53.** $\dfrac{2 + \sqrt{5}}{2}$ and $\dfrac{2 - \sqrt{5}}{2}$ **55.** 2 and 4

57. $1 + \sqrt{6}$ and $1 - \sqrt{6}$ **59.** -4.193 and 1.193 **61.** 2.766 and -1.266 **63.** -1.652 and 0.152

Section 3   Pages 401–402

Example 2
$$3x^2 + 4x - 4 = 0$$
$$a = 3, b = 4, c = -4$$
$$x = \frac{-(4) \pm \sqrt{(4)^2 - 4(3)(-4)}}{2 \cdot 3}$$
$$= \frac{-4 \pm \sqrt{16 + 48}}{6}$$
$$= \frac{-4 \pm \sqrt{64}}{6} = \frac{-4 \pm 8}{6}$$
$$x = \frac{-4 + 8}{6} \qquad x = \frac{-4 - 8}{6}$$
$$= \frac{4}{6} = \frac{2}{3} \qquad = \frac{-12}{6} = -2$$

The solutions are $\frac{2}{3}$ and -2.

Example 4
$$x^2 + 2x = 1$$
$$x + 2x - 1 = 0$$
$$a = 1, b = 2, c = -1$$
$$x = \frac{-(2) \pm \sqrt{(2)^2 - 4(1)(-1)}}{2 \cdot 1}$$
$$= \frac{-2 \pm \sqrt{4 + 4}}{2} = \frac{-2 \pm \sqrt{8}}{2}$$
$$= \frac{-2 \pm 2\sqrt{2}}{2} = -1 \pm \sqrt{2}$$

The solutions are $-1 + \sqrt{2}$ and $-1 - \sqrt{2}$.

Exercises   Pages 403–404

1. 5 and -1 **3.** -3 and 5   **5.** -7 and 1   **7.** 2 and -3 **9.** 3 and -1 **11.** -5 and 1   **13.** $-\frac{1}{2}$ and 1

15. no real number solution   **17.** 0 and 1   **19.** $\frac{3}{2}$ and $-\frac{3}{2}$ **21.** $\frac{3}{2}$ and $-\frac{5}{2}$ **23.** 3 and $-\frac{2}{3}$

25. -3 and $\frac{4}{5}$ **27.** $-\frac{1}{2}$ and $\frac{2}{3}$ **29.** no real number solution   **31.** $1 + \sqrt{6}$ and $1 - \sqrt{6}$

33. $-3 + \sqrt{10}$ and $-3 - \sqrt{10}$ **35.** $2 + \sqrt{13}$ and $2 - \sqrt{13}$ **37.** $\frac{1 + \sqrt{2}}{2}$ and $\frac{1 - \sqrt{2}}{2}$

39. $-3 + 2\sqrt{2}$ and $-3 - 2\sqrt{2}$ **41.** $\frac{3 + 2\sqrt{6}}{2}$ and $\frac{3 - 2\sqrt{6}}{2}$ **43.** $\frac{-1 + \sqrt{2}}{3}$ and $\frac{-1 - \sqrt{2}}{3}$ **45.** $-\frac{1}{2}$

47. no real solution   **49.** $\frac{-4 + \sqrt{5}}{2}$ and $\frac{-4 - \sqrt{5}}{2}$ **51.** $\frac{1 + 2\sqrt{3}}{2}$ and $\frac{1 - 2\sqrt{3}}{2}$ **53.** $\frac{-5 + \sqrt{2}}{3}$ and $\frac{-5 - \sqrt{2}}{3}$

55. 5.690 and -3.690 **57.** 7.690 and -1.690 **59.** 4.590 and -1.090 **61.** -2.118 and 0.118
63. 1.105 and -0.905

Review/Test   Page 407

1. 5 and -6 (11.1A)   **2.** $-\frac{1}{3}$ and 8 (11.1A)   **3.** $-\frac{3}{2}$ and 4 (11.1A)   **4.** -4 and $\frac{5}{3}$ (11.1A)   **5.** $\frac{5}{2}$ and $\frac{1}{3}$ (11.1A)

6. -4 and 5 (11.1A)   **7.** -9 and 9 (11.1B)   **8.** $-\frac{5}{4}$ and $\frac{5}{4}$ (11.1B)   **9.** -2 and 2 (11.1B)

10. -3 and 15 (11.1B)   **11.** $5 + 3\sqrt{2}$ and $5 - 3\sqrt{2}$ (11.1B)   **12.** $-4 + 2\sqrt{5}$ and $-4 - 2\sqrt{5}$ (11.1B)

13. $-2 + 2\sqrt{5}$ and $-2 - 2\sqrt{5}$ (11.2A)   **14.** $3 + \sqrt{14}$ and $3 - \sqrt{14}$ (11.2A)   **15.** $\frac{5 + \sqrt{33}}{2}$ and $\frac{5 - \sqrt{33}}{2}$ (11.2A)

16. $\frac{-3 + \sqrt{41}}{2}$ and $\frac{-3 - \sqrt{41}}{2}$ (11.2A)   **17.** $\frac{3 + \sqrt{7}}{2}$ and $\frac{3 - \sqrt{7}}{2}$ (11.2A)   **18.** $\frac{-4 + \sqrt{22}}{2}$ and $\frac{-4 - \sqrt{22}}{2}$ (11.2A)

19. $-2 + \sqrt{2}$ and $-2 - \sqrt{2}$ (11.3A)   **20.** $\frac{-3 + \sqrt{37}}{2}$ and $\frac{-3 - \sqrt{37}}{2}$ (11.3A)   **21.** $\frac{3 + \sqrt{33}}{2}$ and $\frac{3 - \sqrt{33}}{2}$ (11.3A)

22. $\frac{5 + \sqrt{29}}{2}$ and $\frac{5 - \sqrt{29}}{2}$ (11.3A)   **23.** $-\frac{1}{2}$ and 3 (11.3A)   **24.** $\frac{1 + \sqrt{13}}{6}$ and $\frac{1 - \sqrt{13}}{6}$ (11.3A)

Cumulative Review/Test   Page 408

1. $\frac{x + 2}{2(x + 1)}$ (8.2D)   **2.** $y = -\frac{4}{3}x - 2$ (9.3A/9.3B)   **3.** $x(3x - 4)(x + 2)$ (7.3B)   **4.** 2 and $-\frac{1}{2}$ (11.3A)

5. $(2, -2)$ (9.5B)   **6.** $a - 2$ (10.2A)   **7.** $-12a^8b^4$ (6.2B)   **8.** $-28x + 27$ (3.2D)   **9.** $\frac{1}{2}$ and $-\frac{2}{3}$ (11.1A)

10. $\frac{3}{2}$ (4.1C)   **11.** $x + 2 - \frac{4}{x - 2}$ (6.3C)   **12.** $\frac{9x^2(x - 2)^2}{(2x - 3)^2}$ (8.1C)   **13.** $\frac{x - 4}{2x + 5}$ (8.3A)   **14.** $6ab\sqrt{a}$ (10.2B)

15. $\frac{21}{13}$ (4.2B)   **16.** $5 + 3\sqrt{2}$ and $5 - 3\sqrt{2}$ (11.1B)   **17.** $x > \frac{1}{9}$ (4.5A)   **18.** x-intercept: $(3, 0)$;

y-intercept: $(0, -4)$ (9.2A)   **19.** $\frac{-7 + \sqrt{13}}{6}$ and $\frac{-7 - \sqrt{13}}{6}$ (11.2A)   **20.** $2x - 3$ (10.2B)   **21.** \$2.25 per pound (5.4B)

22. 250 additional shares (5.1D)   **23.** 77 or better (4.5B)   **24.** 30 mph (8.6B)

Answers to Chapter 12

Section 1   Pages 410–418

Example 2

$$QR + RS + ST = QT$$
$$24 + RS + 17 = 62$$
$$41 + RS = 62$$
$$RS = 21$$

Example 4

$$AB + BC = AC$$
$$\tfrac{1}{4}(BC) + BC = AC$$
$$\tfrac{1}{4}(16) + 16 = AC$$
$$4 + 16 = AC$$
$$20 = AC$$

Example 6

Strategy

To find the larger angle, write and solve a system of equations using x to represent one angle and y to represent the other angle.

Solution

$$x + y = 180°$$
$$x - y = 40°$$
$$2x = 220°$$
$$x = 110°$$

The larger of the two angles is 110°.

Example 8

$$a + 68° = 118°$$
$$a = 50°$$

$$\angle a = 50°$$

Example 10

$$(x + 15°) + 2x = 180°$$
$$3x + 15° = 180°$$
$$3x = 165°$$
$$x = 55°$$

Example 12

$$3x + (x + 40°) = 180°$$
$$4x + 40° = 180°$$
$$4x = 140°$$
$$x = 35°$$

Example 14

$$\angle x + \angle b = 180°$$
$$100° + \angle b = 180°$$
$$\angle b = 80°$$

$$\angle a + \angle b + \angle c = 180°$$
$$45° + 80° + \angle c = 180°$$
$$125° + \angle c = 180°$$
$$\angle c = 55°$$

$$\angle y = \angle c = 55°$$

Example 16

Strategy

To find the measure of each angle:
▷ Let x = the measure of the smallest angle. Then $2x - 3$ = the measure of the second angle. The right angle equals 90°. The sum of the angles of a triangle is 180°.
▷ Substitute the value of x into the variable expression for the second angle.

Solution

$$x + (2x - 3) + 90 = 180$$
$$3x + 87 = 180$$
$$3x = 93$$
$$x = 31$$

$$2x - 3 = 2(31) - 3 = 62 - 3 = 59$$

The angles measure 31°, 59°, and 90°.

Exercises   Pages 419–424

1. 28°   **3.** 18°   **5.** 40° and 50°   **7.** 80° and 100°   **9.** 14   **11.** 28   **13.** 30   **15.** 71°   **17.** 86°
19. 30°   **21.** 36°   **23.** 127°   **25.** 116°   **27.** 20°   **29.** 20°   **31.** 20°   **33.** 141°   **35.** 106°
37. 68°   **39.** $\angle a = 38°$; $\angle b = 142°$ **41.** $\angle a = 47°$; $\angle b = 133°$ **43.** 20°   **45.** 47°   **47.** $\angle x = 155°$;
$\angle y = 70°$ **49.** $\angle a = 45°$; $\angle b = 135°$ **51.** $\angle BOC = 90° - x$ **53.** 60°   **55.** 35°   **57.** 102°   **59.** 45°
61. 14°   **63.** 30°, 60°, 90°   **65.** 32°, 37°, 111°   **67.** 38°, 66°, 76°   **69.** 25° and 65°   **71.** 47° and 85°
73. 30°   **75.** 40°

Section 2   Pages 425–432

Example 2

Strategy

To find the length of each side, use the equation for the perimeter of a triangle. Let x = the length of one of the two equal sides. Then $0.50x$ = the length of the third side of the triangle.

Solution

$$P = a + b + c$$
$$125 = x + x + 0.50x$$
$$125 = 2.50x$$
$$50 = x$$

$$0.50x = 0.50(50) = 25$$

The lengths of the sides of the triangle are 50 ft, 50 ft, and 25 ft.

Example 4

Strategy

To find the perimeter, find the sum of the lengths of the four sides.

Solution

$$P = (3x + 1) + (3x + 1) + (2x - 5) + (2x - 5)$$
$$P = 3x + 1 + 3x + 1 + 2x - 5 + 2x - 5$$
$$P = 10x - 8$$

The perimeter is $10x - 8$.

Example 6

Strategy

To find the perimeter of square *ABCD*:
▷ Solve the equation for the circumference of a
circle for *d*.
▷ Use the equation for the perimeter of a square.
The length of a side of the square equals the
diameter of the circle.

Solution

$$C = \pi d$$
$$6\pi = \pi d$$
$$6 = d$$

$$P = 4s = 4(6) = 24$$

The perimeter of square *ABCD* is 24 cm.

Example 10

Strategy

To find the area:
▷ Use the equation for the perimeter of a rectangle to
find the length of the rectangle.
▷ Use the equation for the area of a rectangle.

Solution

$$P = 2L + 2W$$
$$54 = 2L + 2(6)$$
$$54 = 2L + 12$$
$$42 = 2L$$
$$21 = L$$

$$A = LW$$
$$A = 21 \cdot 6$$
$$A = 126$$

The area is 126 in².

Example 8

Strategy

To find the area, use the equation for the area of a
rectangle.

Solution

$$A = LW$$
$$A = (x + 4)(2x - 1)$$
$$A = 2x^2 + 7x - 4$$

The area is $2x^2 + 7x - 4$.

Example 12

Strategy

To find the area, subtract the area of the triangle from
the area of the rectangle.

Solution

$$A = LW - \frac{1}{2}bh$$
$$A = 10(6) - \frac{1}{2}(6)(4)$$
$$A = 60 - 12$$
$$A = 48$$

The area is 48 in².

Exercises   Pages 433–438

1. 17.4 cm   **3.** 16 m   **5.** 204 yd   **7.** 48.8 cm   **9.** 9 in.   **11.** 4.71 in.   **13.** $12x + 8$ **15.** $10x - 8$
17. $6x + 8$ **19.** $6x + 7$ **21.** length: 120 ft; width: 100 ft   **23.** length: 15 m; width: 10 m   **25.** 4 ft, 7 ft, 9 ft
27. 2.55 cm   **29.** 3.18 m   **31.** 8 in.   **33.** 31.4 ft   **35.** 40.26 cm   **37.** 50.56 m   **39.** 30.99 cm
41. 4.2 cm²   **43.** 0.32 m²   **45.** $12\frac{1}{4}$ in²   **47.** 1728 yd²   **49.** 226.87 cm²   **51.** $x^2 + 3x - 28$
53. $x^2 + 4x + 4$ **55.** $6x^2 - 8x$ **57.** $\pi x^2 + 6\pi x + 9\pi$ **59.** base: 20 ft; height: 5 ft   **61.** length: 30 in.;
width: 10 in.   **63.** base: 3 m; height: 12 m   **65.** length: 15 in.; width: 5 in.   **67.** 10 in.   **69.** 113.04 in²
71. 14 ft   **73.** 10 square units   **75.** 16 in²   **77.** 100 cm²   **79.** 19,024 ft²

Section 3   Pages 439–444

Example 2

Strategy

To find the perimeter:
▷ Use the Pythagorean Theorem to find the length of the hypotenuse.
▷ Use the equation for the perimeter of a triangle.

Solution

$$c^2 = a^2 + b^2$$
$$c^2 = 4^2 + 8^2$$
$$c^2 = 16 + 64$$
$$c^2 = 80$$
$$\sqrt{c^2} = \sqrt{80}$$
$$c = 4\sqrt{5} \approx 8.9$$

$$P = a + b + c$$
$$P = 4 + 8 + 8.9$$
$$P = 20.9$$

The perimeter is 20.9 in.

Example 4

Strategy

The diagonal of a square separates the square into two isosceles right triangles. To find the length of the diagonal of the square, find the hypotenuse of an isosceles right triangle with a leg of length 5 cm.

Solution

$$c = \sqrt{2}(\text{length of a leg})$$
$$c = \sqrt{2}(5) \approx (1.414)5 = 7.07$$

The length of a diagonal is 7.1 cm.

Example 6

Strategy

To find FG, solve a proportion to find the height.

Solution

$$\frac{AC}{DF} = \frac{CH}{FG}$$
$$\frac{10}{15} = \frac{7}{FG}$$
$$10(FG) = 15(7)$$
$$10(FG) = 105$$
$$FG = 10.5$$

The height FG of triangle DEF is 10.5 m.

Example 8

Strategy

To find the perimeter of triangle ABC:
▷ Solve a proportion to find the length of side AC.
▷ Solve a proportion to find the length of side BC.
▷ Use the equation for the perimeter of a triangle.

Solution

$$\frac{AC}{DF} = \frac{AB}{DE}$$
$$\frac{AC}{6} = \frac{4}{8}$$

$$(AC)8 = 6(4)$$
$$8(AC) = 24$$
$$AC = 3$$

$$\frac{BC}{EF} = \frac{AB}{DE}$$
$$\frac{BC}{10} = \frac{4}{8}$$

$$(BC)8 = 10(4)$$
$$8(BC) = 40$$
$$BC = 5$$

$$P = a + b + c$$
$$P = 3 + 4 + 5$$
$$P = 12$$

The perimeter of triangle ABC is 12 in.

Exercises   Pages 445–448

1. 5 in.   **3.** 8.6 cm   **5.** 11.2 ft   **7.** 4.5 cm   **9.** 12.7 yd   **11.** 6 ft and 10.4 ft   **13.** 21.2 cm   **15.** 8 m
17. 11.3 yd   **19.** 7.4 m   **21.** 24.3 cm   **23.** 28.4 m   **25.** 10.2 cm   **27.** 40 in²   **29.** 16 m²

31. 11.3 m   **33.** 16.4 m   **35.** 35°   **37.** 7.2 cm   **39.** 3.3 m   **41.** 18 ft   **43.** 16 m   **45.** 12 m
47. 12 in.   **49.** 56.3 cm²   **51.** 6.3   **53.** 6   **55.** 30

Section 4   Pages 449–452

Example 2

Strategy

To find the width, use the equation for the volume of a rectangular solid.

Solution

$V = LWH$
$111 = (2.1)(W)(5.5)$
$111 = 11.55W$
$9.6 \approx W$

The width is 9.6 m.

Example 6

Strategy

To find the volume:
▷ Find the diameter of the globe.
▷ Use the equation for the volume of a rectangular solid. The length, width, and height are equal to the length of the diameter of the globe.

Solution

$d = 2r = 2(5) = 10$

$V = LWH$
$V = 10(10)(10)$
$V = 1000$

The volume of the box is 1000 in³.

Example 4

Strategy

To find the volume, add the volume of the rectangular solid and the volume of the cylinder.

Solution

$V = LWH + \pi r^2 h$
$V = 8(8)(2) + 3.14(1)^2(2)$
$V = 128 + 6.28$
$V = 134.28$

The volume is 134.28 cm³.

Exercises   Pages 453–454

1. 164.85 in³   **3.** 904.32 cm³   **5.** $(x^3 + 6x^2 + 12x + 8)$ cm³   **7.** $(\pi x^3 + \pi x^2 - 16\pi x + 20\pi)$ cm³   **9.** 2.5 ft
11. 4 in.   **13.** length: 5 in.; width: 5 in.   **15.** 461.92 m³   **17.** 155.44 cm³   **19.** 395.64 ft³   **21.** 75.36 m³
23. The volume is quadrupled (multiplied by 4).   **25.** 5832 in³   **27.** 48 blocks

Review/Test   Page 457

1. 75° and 105° (12.1A)   **2.** 19° (12.1A)   **3.** 127° (12.1B)   **4.** $\angle a = 138°$; $\angle b = 42°$ (12.1B)   **5.** $\angle x = 22°$; $\angle y = 158°$ (12.1C)   **6.** 35° and 55° (12.1C)   **7.** 12 cm, 12 cm, and 8 cm (12.2A)   **8.** 0.96 m (12.2A)
9. length: 13 ft; width: 9 ft (12.2B)   **10.** 9.14 cm (12.2A)   **11.** 40 m² (12.2B)   **12.** $AB = 8$ ft, $AC = 6.93$ ft (12.3A)
13. 29.21 cm (12.3A)   **14.** 24 in. (12.3B)   **15.** 10 in. (12.4A)   **16.** 117.23 m³ (12.4A)

Cumulative Review/Test   Page 458

1. $3460 (2.4E)   **2.** $(x^3 + 12x^2 + 48x + 64)$ cm³ (12.4A)   **3.** 8 (4.2A)   **4.** 6.8% (5.2B)   **5.** 90° and 37° (12.1C)
6. 20.6 in. (12.3A)   **7.** $-\dfrac{1}{b^4}$ (6.3A)   **8.** $(2x + 1)(3x - 4)$ (7.3A)   **9.** 37° and 53° (12.1A)   **10.** 10.5 m (12.3B)
11. $x \geq 2$ (4.4B)   **12.** 20 m (12.2A)   **13.** 1.91 in. (12.2A)   **14.** 20 m (12.2B)   **15.** 1.32 (3.1E)
16. $-13x + 33$ (3.2D)   **17.** $C = Rt + S$ (8.5A)   **18.** $-\dfrac{5}{9}$ (8.4A)   **19.** $a = 43°$, $b = 137°$ (12.1B)
20. 29° (12.1A)   **21.** $\dfrac{1}{x^5 y^5}$ (6.4A)   **22.** $-\dfrac{7}{3}$ (9.2B)   **23.** 14 (10.3A)   **24.** $\dfrac{2 + \sqrt{14}}{2}$ and $\dfrac{2 - \sqrt{14}}{2}$ (11.2A/11.3A)

Answers to Cumulative Review/Final Exam

Cumulative Review/Final Exam   Pages 459–462

1. 144 (1.3B)   **2.** 25 (1.4D)   **3.** $2\frac{5}{8}$ (2.2B)   **4.** 60.205 (2.4B)   **5.** 0.69 (2.4D)   **6.** -3.8 (3.1B)   **7.** $-\frac{1}{2}$ (3.1D)

8. $-\frac{1}{5}$ (3.2A)   **9.** $-3x + 11$ (3.2D)   **10.** 5 (4.1D)   **11.** $\frac{1}{3}$ (4.2B)   **12.** $x > \frac{2}{3}$ (4.4C)   **13.** $y < \frac{1}{3}$ (4.5A)

14. 24.5 mi/gal (5.1B)   **15.** $\frac{45}{2}$ (5.1C)   **16.** 37.5% (5.2B)   **17.** 45 (5.3A/5.3B)   **18.** $-2x^2 + 2x + 12$ (6.1B)

19. $-32x^{10}y^5$ (6.2B)   **20.** $-2x^3 + 8x^2 - 7x + 3$ (6.2C)   **21.** $\frac{3y^5}{4x}$ (6.3A)   **22.** $x^2 + 3x - 4$ (6.3C)   **23.** $-18y^2$ (6.4A)

24. 4.73×10^{-6} (6.4B)   **25.** $-3y^2(y^2 - 2y + 7)$ (7.1B)   **26.** $(x - 9)(x + 1)$ (7.2A)   **27.** $(3x + 4)(2x - 3)$ (7.3A)

28. $-3x(2x + 3)(x + 2)$ (7.3B)   **29.** $(7y + 1)(7y - 1)$ (7.4A)   **30.** $(y - 1)(x - 2)$ (7.4C)

31. $3x^2(2 - 3y)(2 + 3y)$ (7.4D)   **32.** $-\frac{3}{x}$ (8.1A)   **33.** 1 (8.1C)   **34.** 3 (8.2C)   **35.** $\frac{10x + 32}{(x + 5)(x - 1)}$ (8.2D)

36. $\frac{2a}{a - 2}$ (8.3A)   **37.** 2 (8.4A)   **38.** 4 (8.4B)   **39.** $t = \frac{L - a}{ac}$ (8.5A)   **40.** 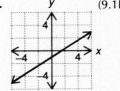 (9.1D)

41. -3 (9.2B)   **42.** $y = -\frac{3}{4}x - 1$ (9.3A/9.3B)   **43.** $(2, -1)$ (9.5A/9.5B)   **44.** $16\sqrt{2}$ (10.1A)   **45.** $9a^3$ (10.1B)

46. $38\sqrt{3y}$ (10.1C)   **47.** $3x\sqrt{2} - x\sqrt{3}$ (10.2A)   **48.** $3\sqrt{2} + 3$ (10.2B)   **49.** 3 (10.3A)   **50.** $\frac{3}{2}$ and -1 (11.1A)

51. $1 + \sqrt{3}$ and $1 - \sqrt{3}$ (11.1B)   **52.** $\frac{1 + \sqrt{10}}{3}$ and $\frac{1 - \sqrt{10}}{3}$ (11.2A/11.3A)   **53.** 30° (12.1B)   **54.** 15 (12.3B)

55. 30°, 60°, 90° (12.1C)   **56.** 12 m (12.2A)   **57.** 8 cm (12.2B)   **58.** 22.4 in. (12.3A)   **59.** 12 in. (12.4A)

60. 129 mi (2.3C)   **61.** \$81.71 (2.4E)   **62.** 33, 35, and 37 (4.3B)   **63.** 64 years (4.3C)   **64.** 76,000 people (5.1D)

65. 40,000 people (5.3C)   **66.** \$3000 (5.4A)   **67.** \$4.50/lb (5.4B)   **68.** 25% (5.4C)   **69.** 6 hours (8.6A)

70. 17 mph (8.6B)

Index